GENETICS OF THE FOWL

NORTON CREEK CLASSICS

Older books about agriculture often have special significance to today's small-scale farmers, who find themselves facing problems similar to those surmounted by our grandparents and great-grandparents. Many books published between 1900 and 1960 have crucial information that is unavailable elsewhere. However, these books have been out of print for decades. They are hard to find and almost entirely forgotten.

The Norton Creek Classics represent a few carefully selected volumes from the treasure trove of our agricultural heritage.

GENETICS OF THE FOWL

by

F. B. HUTT, Ph.D., (Edin.)

Professor of Animal Genetics
New York State College of Agriculture, Cornell University

First Edition, 1949

A Norton Creek Classic

Norton Creek Press
36475 Norton Creek Road
Blodgett, Oregon 97326

https://www.nortoncreekpress.html

Genetics of the Fowl.

Published by Norton Creek Press, 2003.

Originally published: New York: McGraw-Hill Book Company, 1949.

ISBN 0-9721770-3-5

2 4 6 8 10 9 7 5 3

TO MY MOTHER

*in gratitude for her help over many a
rough spot along the path*

PREFACE

The purpose of this book is to survey our present knowledge of heredity and variation in the domestic fowl. A great amount of information on this subject has accumulated since the day when Bateson's pioneering studies of simple breed characteristics were announced to the Royal Society in 1901. Much of it is scattered through the scientific journals of the world, and some of it is unknown or inaccessible to geneticists and poultrymen who want to know what is inherited and how. An attempt has been made in this book to meet that need. The last chapter tells how our present knowledge may best be utilized in the breeding of better fowls.

In reviewing the many different contributions, some "culling" has been inevitable, particularly with respect to the earlier literature, in which a valiant attempt was evident to fit most inherited characters into simple Mendelian ratios. Elsewhere, interpretations have been made to reconcile results of different workers who were not in agreement. In addition, as the reader of Chaps. 10 and 12 will discover, the author has ventured to express his own unorthodox ideas on some subjects, even though they are the direct antitheses of some of the fundamenal tenets of the poultryman's current faith. This is done, not with any hope of ousting those same tenets from the poultryman's creed, but merely to stimulate some little thought about them.

No attempt is made in this book to teach simple principles of genetics, and hence the familiar diagrams of segregating single combs and barred feathers are omitted. This is merely because the material in the book is used as a text and reference book for students in poultry genetics, all of whom have had an introductory course in genetics before undertaking to study inheritance and breeding in this one species. Nevertheless, sufficient explanation has been given so that the poultryman or hatcheryman who has not been exposed to a full course in genetics need not feel lost in any chapter of the book. In fact, it has been no more necessary to write the geneticists' jargon in terms that any poultryman can understand than to use the poultryman's everyday vocabulary in terms intelligible to some laboratory geneticist who does not know a wattle from a side sprig.

Domestic birds other than the fowl have been considered whenever they show some type of mutation that may yet be encountered in the fowl or serve to illustrate some important principle. Thus, the turkeys with pendulous crops provide an excellent demonstration of the interaction of genetic and environmental influences. Nevertheless, the systematic review of inheritance in domestic birds other than the fowl is left for the writers of other books.

The author is indebted to many investigators who have provided illustrative material and to the various journals that have kindly given permission to use pictures originally published in their pages. An acknowledgement both to the man and to the journal is made in each case. The *Journal of Heredity, Journal of Genetics, Physiological Zoology, Poultry Science,* and *Anatomical Record* have been most helpful. Special thanks are due to colleagues who read various chapters and made helpful suggestions. These include Dr. W. F. Lamoreux, who read the first seven chapters, Dr. L. W. Sharp (Chap. 2), Dr. G. O. Hall (Chap. 7), and Dr. R. K. Cole (Chaps. 10 and 12).

The last chapter is written primarily for the good, practical poultry breeder. In that part of it dealing with the progeny test, the author has reviewed some of the principles and practices found helpful in his own experience. The reader is reminded that other breeders may have other methods equally good. If the author's fellow geneticists do not see eye to eye with him in this chapter, it is to be hoped that they will appreciate better the Appendix, in which a system of genetic symbols is given for all the mutations known to date in the fowl.

F. B. HUTT

ITHACA, N.Y.
August, 1949

CONTENTS

CONTENTS

III, and IV, respectively, the latter being numbered from the inside to the outside of the foot.

6. The eggs are *polylecithal* (with much yolk) and *telolecithal* (with the nucleus and active cytoplasm at one pole). As such they undergo *meroblastic* cleavage following fertilization. This means that division of the cytoplasm is confined to a very shallow portion of the surface of the egg, in contrast to the situation in *isolecithal* eggs, in which cleavage is *holoblastic* and the whole egg divides.

7. The embryo has both an amnion and an allantois, the latter serving as an organ of respiration.

8. Products of the digestive, excretory, and reproductive systems are voided through a cloaca. This applies also to amphibians but to few mammals.

9. The females are *heterogametic* since they produce eggs of two sorts, one giving rise to males, the other to females. There is both genetic and cytological evidence for this in birds, and cytological studies of 28 species of reptiles by Matthey (1931) showed all males to be *homogametic,* thus indicating the females as the heterogametic sex in that class.

Differences between Birds and Reptiles. With so many things in common it is necessary to remember that birds differ from reptiles in having a coat of feathers, in adaptation of the forelimb for flight, and (except in flightless birds) in having a keel on the sternum for attachment of the large muscles which make flight possible. Other adaptations for flight include the air sacs, which not only lessen the density of the body but also permit more complete oxygenation of the blood in the lungs than would be possible without them. Birds differ from all lower vertebrates in having some mechanism for controlling body temperature. They are able to maintain temperatures much higher than those of mammals. The ovary and oviduct are usually suppressed on the right side. Birds as a class are oviparous; some reptiles are viviparous, and others oviparous. The pelvic girdle and hind limbs of birds are adapted so that all the weight of the body is carried on two limbs, instead of four as in most other vertebrates. Existing birds lack true teeth.

Compared with reptiles, birds have a greatly improved circulatory system. In most reptiles arterial and venous blood are not completely separated in the heart, though there is a partially formed septum in the ventricle. In crocodiles this septum is complete, so that these animals have a four-chambered heart just as birds do. However, the crocodiles are not able to make as good use of it as birds can because in the former the left aortic arch still carries to the dorsal aorta some venous blood which it receives (through the foramen Panizzae) from the right aortic arch. This left arch is present in the avian embryo, but it degenerates. As a result, in birds the exhausted venous blood of the right ventricle is all forced out through the pulmonary arteries to the lungs, and none of it goes to the dorsal aorta. That great duct, which carries blood to the whole arterial system, is supplied only with oxygenated blood, which comes through the right aortic arch from the left ventricle. This improvement in the facilities for getting oxygen to the tissues of the body was probably the chief means by which birds were enabled to maintain higher metabolism and higher temperatures than their reptilian ancestors. It may well have been a contributory factor in making flight possible.

GENERAL CLASSIFICATION OF BIRDS

The phylum Chordata includes some rather primitive forms (Hemichorda, Urochorda) and the Euchorda, animals with a true notochord and gill slits. This latter group contains the lancelets, of which the embryologists' Amphioxus is the familiar type, and the true vertebrates, which comprise the group Craniata (or Vertebrata). These are characterized by the possession of a skull, a heart of three or four chambers, a complex brain, and red blood corpuscles. The Craniata in turn may be subdivided into at least six classes, of which the Aves is one.

The birds may be classified in several different ways according to the particular ideas of the zoologist who does the classifying. The following scheme from Parker and Haswell (1921) is simple and is adequate for our purposes. Only a few of the characteristics are given for each group.

I. ARCHAEORNITHES
   Includes thus far only Archaeopteryx and Archaeornis, described earlier.
II. NEORNITHES
   Includes all other birds. There are no teeth except in a few extinct species. The tail is short and ends in a pygostyle. The metacarpals and some carpal bones are fused in a carpo-metacarpus. Claws are absent except in Opisthocomus.
   A. RATITAE. Flightless; the breastbone lacks a keel or has only a vestigial one; barbules of the feathers lack hooklets.
      Extinct examples: Dinornithes (moas), Aepyornithes.
      Living examples: Casuarius (cassowary), Apteryx (kiwi), Struthio (ostrich).
   B. CARINATAE. The sternum has a carina, or keel; barbules have hooklets. This group can be divided into 20 to 25 different orders according to the method of classification used and the viewpoint of the taxonomist.
      Orders of the Carinatae containing domestic birds are:
         Anseriformes: ducks, geese, and swans.
         Galliformes: the fowl, turkey, guinea fowl, peafowl, and pheasants.
         Columbiformes: pigeons and doves.
         Passeriformes: canary.

The Galliformes. This order, which contains more domesticated species than any other, is subdivided by Peters (1934) as shown on page 5.

Undoubtedly the general body conformation which makes them valuable sources of meat has been responsible in three separate regions for the domestication of the fowl, the turkey, and the guinea fowl. In their na-

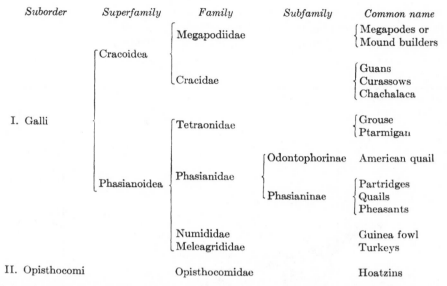

Suborder	Superfamily	Family	Subfamily	Common name
	Cracoidea	Megapodiidae		Megapodes or Mound builders
		Cracidae		Guans Curassows Chachalaca
I. Galli		Tetraonidae		Grouse Ptarmigan
	Phasianoidea	Phasianidae	Odontophorinae	American quail
			Phasianinae	Partridges Quails Pheasants
		Numididae		Guinea fowl
		Meleagrididae		Turkeys
II. Opisthocomi		Opisthocomidae		Hoatzins

tive habitats the Phasianidae are confined to the Orient, the Numididae to Africa, and the Meleagrididae to America.

THE GENUS GALLUS

The domestic fowl belongs to the genus Gallus of the subfamily Phasianinae. Characteristics of this genus are generally said to include a short, stout, and curved beak, one or two wattles, a large comb, and feet particularly fitted for scratching. The tail is laterally compressed and includes seven or eight pairs of rectrices. As in all Phasianinae, the tail feathers are moulted centripetally, *i.e.*, beginning with the outer feathers and progressing inward. The outer and inner primaries are shorter than the middle ones, and the outer secondaries are somewhat shorter than the inner ones. As a result the outspread wing has a somewhat bilobed appearance. However, Beebe (1918–1922, Vol. II) points out that the only characteristic really distinguishing the genus is the comb, all the rest being found in other genera of pheasants.

The genus includes four species, the distribution of which is shown in Fig. 2. Three of these are alike in body conformation and in having 14 tail feathers, a serrated comb, and two wattles. The fourth, *G. varius*, differs from these in having 16 tail feathers, an unserrated comb, and a single median wattle.

1. *Gallus gallus* (Linné). This species, at various times known as *G. bankiva* and *G. ferrugineus*, is called the Red Jungle Fowl and is often

declared to be the ancestor of all domestic fowls. It is widely distributed through north central and eastern India, Burma, Siam, Cochin China, the Malay Peninsula, the Philippines, and Sumatra. The males and females resemble very much those of Black-breasted Red Games and Brown Leg-

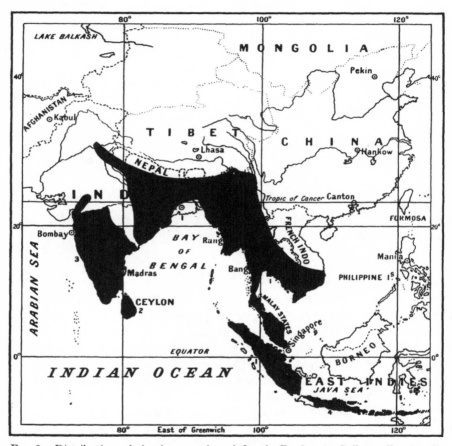

FIG. 2. Distribution of the four species of Jungle Fowls. 1, *Gallus gallus*; 2, *G. lafayettii*; 3, *G. sonneratii*; 4, *G. varius*. (*From Beebe, courtesy of H. F. and G. Witherby*.)

horns. The males have orange-red lanceolate feathers in the hackle, wing-bow, and saddle regions, and the lower plumage, including the breast, is black (Fig. 4). The females have reddish-brown feathers stippled with black (Fig. 3). The legs are slate-colored, but it is not clear from the various descriptions whether they may be willow (indicating the presence of the gene *w* for yellow skin) or not. The eggs are buff in color.

dominantly black, but there is such a green sheen that the bird is commonly known as either the Black or the Green Jungle Fowl. Feathers of the neck are quite short and rounded, lacking the lacy appearance of the hackles in the other species. In the females the under parts are buff, and the rest of the plumage is greenish black and brown.

From the geneticist's viewpoint none of the descriptions thus far given of the four species of Gallus is very satisfactory, since, with very few exceptions, the ornithologists' general accounts of plumage color and shank color do not reveal which of the many characters now genetically identified in the domestic fowl are to be found in any of these four possible ancestors. Extensive accounts of the life of these four species of Gallus in their natural habitats are given by Beebe (1918–1922) and in abridged form by the same author (1931).

ORIGIN OF THE FOWL

The close resemblance of *Gallus gallus* to two varieties of domestic fowls is probably responsible in part for the opinion of some writers that all domestic fowls are descended from that wild species. On the other hand the Asiatic breeds—Cochins, Langshans, and Brahmas—and their descendants differ sufficiently from the Mediterranean breeds to justify the opinion of other writers that some ancestor other than *G. gallus* must have contributed to the formation of these heavy breeds. The theories of *monophyletic* origin (from one species) and of *polyphyletic* origin (from more than one species) both have their advocates.

Monophyletic Origin. Supporters of this theory take their cue from Darwin (1868), who considered *Gallus gallus* the sole ancestor of domestic fowls for the following reasons:

1. Domestic fowls mated freely with *G. gallus,* rarely with others.

2. Progeny from this cross were fertile, but the evidence available to Darwin indicated that hybrids of domestic fowls with the three other species were rarely fertile. It has since been shown that all four species of Gallus produce fertile hybrids with the domestic fowl, but the data available are not on an accurate quantitative basis. It is therefore difficult as yet to say that one species is any less fertile than another in crosses with domestic varieties, except for *G. varius,* the hybrids from which are apparently subnormal in fertility.

3. The voice of *G. sonneratii* and of its hybrids differs from that of the fowl.

4. Black-breasted Red Games resemble *G. gallus* in color and in other respects. Similarly colored birds are found in other breeds.

5. In Darwin's own experiments crosses of various breeds occasionally produced fowls resembling *G. gallus*. This he considered a reversion to the ancestral type. It was natural that the importance of reversion was overemphasized, for Darwin could not know that most cases of so-called "reversion" result merely from the interaction of complementary genes, which, when brought together, produce in the offspring an appearance unlike that of either parent.

Polyphyletic Origin. Supporters of this theory may choose between two possibilities. Either (1) all fowls are descended from two or more of the four existing wild species of Gallus; or (2) the Mediterranean breeds may have had such an origin, but some other ancestor now extinct gave rise to the Asiatic breeds.

The second theory is prompted by the differences between the Mediterranean breeds and the Asiatic ones. The latter, including Cochins, Brahmas, Langshans, and the Aseel fowl of Malay, differ from the former in having short wings, poor capacity for flight, large size, a wide drooping tail, and a rather stolid temperament. Their eggs are brown or tinted, while those of Mediterranean breeds are white. Darwin found that in Cochins the long axis of the occipital foramen in the skull was vertical, whereas in *G. gallus* it was horizontal. These characteristics of Asiatic fowls are not found in *G. gallus*, *G. lafayettii*, or *G. sonneratii*. Ghigi (1922) has pointed out that some of them are incompatible with survival in nature and that the Asiatic fowls might have been maintained under domestication while their ill-adapted ancestor became extinct under natural conditions. Whether the present-day Cochin shows the characteristics of some extinct ancestor or merely extremes of variation resulting from artificial selection starting with the Red Jungle Fowl is unknown. It is certain, however, that in nature the Cochin and any ancestors like it would have no more chance of survival than the similarly large, flightless, and disproportioned dodo, which became extinct in comparatively recent times.

Apart from the more obvious differences between Mediterranean and Asiatic breeds with respect to form and temperament, descendants of these two groups differ in important physiological characters (Hutt, 1941). These are discussed more fully in other chapters. In comparison with the so-called "heavy" breeds, White Leghorns are

1. Less subject to broodiness.
2. More resistant to a deficiency of vitamin B_1 (Lamoreux and Hutt, 1939).
3. Less subject to "slipped tendon," a condition indicating an abnormally high requirement of manganese (Serfontein and Payne, 1934).
4. Better able to withstand extreme heat (Hutt, 1938).

5. More resistant to *Salmonella pullorum* (Hutt and Scholes, 1941).
6. More susceptible to the nematode, *Ascaridia lineata* (Ackert *et al.,* 1935).

With the exception of broodiness, none of these differences could possibly have resulted from deliberate artificial selection since domestication of the fowl. They may possibly indicate lines of descent from different ancestors, but most of them may equally well have resulted from natural selection under exposures to different environments of two geographic races derived from a single ancestral species. Since White Leghorns have been the sole representative of the Mediterranean breeds in most of the comparisons listed above, these physiological differences should not yet be considered as differentiating the entire group of Mediterranean breeds from the descendants of the Asiatic breeds, though it seems probable that they may be associated in some way with the distinctive nervous temperament of fowls in the former group.

Apart from the possibility that some extinct ancestor may have given rise to the Asiatic breeds, there is good evidence that all four of the existing species of jungle fowls may have contributed to the domesticated population. Hybrids between any wild species of Gallus and the domestic fowl are fertile. In some of these cases fertility may not be so high as in matings of domestic fowls, but that would not prevent a contribution to the common stock from any species.

Attempts have been made by some writers to ascribe certain characteristics of domestic fowls to the various wild species from which they might have come. While both golden and silver varieties are found in several domestic breeds, *G. gallus* apparently occurs only in the reddish-golden form and silver variants have not been described. It is easy, therefore, to conclude that the silver gene of domestic breeds came, not from *G. gallus,* but from *G. sonneratii,* in which no golden variants are found, all specimens being undoubtedly grey or silver. Similarly, the extended black plumage (solid black) can be attributed to *G. varius* and yellow shanks to *G. sonneratii.* Unfortunately the descriptions thus far available of the different wild species and of their offspring following crosses with domestic fowls are in terms which permit recognition of only a few of the genes known to occur in the domestic fowl. Apart from this, the fact remains that pea comb, rose comb, dominant white, polydactyly, crest, and many other genetic characters of domestic breeds have arisen by mutation since fowls were domesticated, since they do not occur in any of the wild species. Presumably, those which are found in existing wild relatives of *G. gallus* could also have occurred by mutation in descendants of that species since its domestication.

Summary. Little or no real evidence to support the theory of monophyletic origin has been advanced since Darwin discussed the problem.

That scientist did not consider the evidence for such an origin as good for the fowl as for the pigeon. However, constant repetition of the familiar statement that all domestic fowls are descended from the Red Jungle Fowl of India has apparently led some writers to consider the question settled. The statement of Beebe (1918–1922, Vol. II) that "there can be no doubt that the Red Jungle Fowl alone is the direct ancestor of all our domestic poultry, so this question is removed from the discussion" would be difficult to prove. Punnett (1923) suggested that systematic crossing of the four wild species with one another and with domestic breeds is desirable and that "until this has been done there can be no certainty as to the manner in which our various races of poultry have arisen, and any further discussion as to their origin is merely waste of time." This is as pertinent now as when it was first written.

ZOOLOGICAL NAMES OF DOMESTIC BIRDS

Concerning the origin of other domestic birds there has been less discussion than about that of the fowl. Polyphyletic origins have been suggested for the duck, pigeon, and turkey, but adequate evidence to support these claims has not yet been advanced. Assuming that the domestic birds are the same as the wild species which they resemble most closely, their names are as follows:

Family	Genus	Species	Common name
	Phasianus	colchicus	Ring-necked pheasant
Phasianidae	Gallus	domesticus	Fowl
	Pavo	cristatus	Peafowl
Numididae	Numida	meleagris	Guinea fowl
Meleagrididae	Meleagris	gallopavo	Turkey
Columbidae	Columba	livia	Pigeon
	Anser	anser	Goose
Anatidae	Cairina	moschata	Muscovy duck
	Anas	platyrhynchos	Duck

Those who like trinomial nomenclature better than the author may repeat the specific name in the case of the guinea fowl, turkey, pigeon, and duck, thus assigning subspecific rank to these domestic birds. It seems doubtful, however, that if one geographic race could be domesticated others could not or would not. It is also doubtful that a widely diffused domestic stock could be kept free from intermixture with other subspecies. For example, the ring-necked pheasants now abundant in a half-wild, half-domesticated state in Europe and American are apparently an admixture of three subspecies of *Phasianus colchicus*, these being *P. c. colchicus*, *P. c. torquatus*, and *P. c. mongolicus*. In such a case it seems safer not to attempt to assign subspecific rank to the mixed population.

The correct zoological name of the domestic fowl must, for the present at least, depend somewhat upon the particular faith of the writer who uses it. There is no provision in the International Code of Zoological Nomenclature whereby mere domestication of a wild species justifies changing its name. Those who believe that all domestic fowls are descended from the Red Jungle Fowl should therefore stick to *Gallus gallus*. On the other hand, if several distinct wild species produce by hybridization a new animal sufficiently different from any of them to justify its being considered a separate species, a new name is in order. The use of the familiar term *Gallus domesticus* is therefore probably permissible, but only to those who believe in a polyphyletic origin of domestic fowls.

ORIGIN OF BREEDS

Mutations. Many persons have some difficulty in understanding how the different breeds within a domestic species came to be differentiated. Some clarification of this point may be helpful, and for that purpose the fowl provides excellent material. Since the domestication of the jungle fowls, many mutations have occurred. These changes in the germ plasm cause alterations in the *phenotype*, or appearance, of the birds. Most mutations are *recessive* to the wild type. This means that a change in a single gene will not produce a visible effect until two birds are mated both of which carry the same mutation. The effects of the mutation in *homozygous* form are then evident in a certain proportion of the progeny. If it is a simple mutation with full expression of the character, approximately one-quarter of the offspring of such a mating will show the new character resulting from the mutation. If the mutation be a *dominant* one with complete expression of its effects, the latter will be visible at once in the progeny of any bird carrying such a mutation. One difference between a dominant and a recessive mutation is that the latter will not be manifest until two birds that carry it happen to mate, whereas the dominant mutation is recognizable in the next generation after its occurrence.

Selection. Such visible changes, or "sports," are often interesting variations in the structure of the plumage, color of feathers, pattern of feathers, shape of comb, color of skin, and other features of the bird. These are preserved by the breeder as interesting curiosities. Some of them, such as the silky and frizzled plumage, are such as to lessen the ability of a bird to survive in nature, but when they are interesting modifications, as are these two, the breeder makes a special effort to preserve them.   One can imagine the satisfaction caused to some early fancier by the first appearance of a topknot, or crest, in his fowls and the years of selection through which small mutations enhancing its expression were accumulated until the whole process resulted in the beautifully crested Polish and Houdan fowls of today.   Somewhere a mutation occurred which shortened the legs of fowls and which was preserved to produce the Creepers, or Scots Dumpies, of today.   The general interest of breeders in such a curiosity is shown by the fact that similar mutations shortening the legs were also preserved in Dexter cattle, the Ancon sheep, and the Dachshund.

In addition to the mutations which cause conspicuous changes, many others exert almost imperceptible effects by themselves but occur in such numbers that many of them together induce very marked changes.   Such are the genes affecting body size, capacity for egg production, ability to resist disease, and most other characters of economic importance.   Continuous accumulation of genes for large body size can result in a 5,000-gm. Jersey Black Giant, and, at the other extreme, constant selection of the smaller birds can produce a bantam weighing only one-tenth of that amount.

As a result of such mutations and of the breeders' desire to perpetuate the unusual things, there is much more variation in any domestic species than in its wild progenitor.   Mutations that occur frequently might be preserved in several different localities.   Others occurring rarely might be found only in one district unless the fowls were transported elsewhere. In this way, birds of one area would gradually acquire certain characteristics not found in fowls elsewhere.   This process, which would by itself eventually give rise to different breeds, has undoubtedly been accelerated by the differing preferences of the breeders in various parts of the world. These depend upon individual whims, prevailing opinions, market requirements, climatic conditions, and other factors, all of which vary greatly in different parts of the globe.

Differentiation of breeds has gone on for centuries and is still in progress.   Within recent years Black-tailed Red Leghorns have been produced in the United States because fanciers wanted something different from existing varieties of Leghorns.   Chantecler fowls with small cushion (walnut) combs were put together in Canada with the belief that a breed different from existing ones was desirable in the cold winter climate of that country.   Climatic conditions in Russia make the large comb of the Leghorn particularly susceptible to frost, and, to overcome that handicap in an otherwise desirable breed, Petrov (1935) bred Leghorns having the small comb of the Orloffs, which is less affected by frost.   These Leghorns might be labelled as a new breed.   Poultrymen supplying the New York

CHAPTER 2

CYTOLOGY

Knowledge of the chromosomes in domestic birds and of the nature of the germ cells is important to the poultry geneticist for a number of reasons, among which are the following:

1. The chromosomes apparently carry most of the inheritance and possibly all of it.

2. The number of linkage groups is as large as the haploid number of chromosomes, so that the latter figure gives some idea of the success or failure to be expected in studies of linkage and in attempts to map the chromosomes.

3. It is desirable to have cytological confirmation of the genetic evidence that in birds the female sex is the heterogametic one.

4. Cases of aberrant inheritance, such as the exceptions to the rule occasionally encountered in sex-linked crosses and in gynandromorphs, result from abnormal behavior of the chromosomes and are more readily interpreted by one familiar with the normal behavior of those structures.

5. Incompatibility of chromosomes is a factor in the sterility and subnormal fertility of hybrids, and even within a species aberrant behavior of chromosomes may be a factor affecting the efficiency of reproduction.

GAMETOGENESIS

Formation of the Gonads. The history of the *primordial germ cells,* which give rise to the gonads, has been carefully studied by Swift (1914). They are first seen in the embryo during the primitive streak stage at about 18 hours of incubation and are found up to the three-somite stage. They originate from the entoderm of the germ wall, anterior and anterolateral to the embryo, near the margin of the area pellucida. These cells are several times as large as somatic cells and contain many globules of yolk. The nucleus is large and somewhat clearer than in somatic cells. It usually lies to one side of the cell, and associated with it is a large, dense, cytoplasmic mass, the attraction sphere. When the mesoderm is extended out toward the area pellucida, the primordial germ cells become included in it and pass by amoeboid movement into the blood vessels that are forming in the mesoderm. After being carried in the blood stream

19

to all parts of the body, they become concentrated at the site of the future gonads after 4 days of incubation. Regardless of sex, the primordial germ cells are much more numerous at the site of the left gonad than on the right side (Firket, 1914; Swift, 1915).

By this time (4 days of incubation) the epithelial cells lining the body cavity have become differentiated at the site of the gonads and, together with the primordial germ cells, form what is called the *germinal epithelium*. This becomes somewhat thickened, and the gonads are visible as whitish ridges in the body cavity. At 6 and 7 days of incubation there is in males a single proliferation of *sex chords* from the germinal epithelium. These are chains, or strands, of cells including ordinary epithelial cells and primordial germ cells. They give rise eventually to the seminiferous tubules of the testis. In females this first proliferation of sex chords occurs, as it does in males, at 6 and 7 days of incubation, but the primordial germ cells in them do not develop very far. These sex chords eventually form the medulla of the ovary. According to Swift (1915) the sex of the embryo is evident (in sections) immediately after the first proliferation of sex chords, at about 6½ days. In females the number of primordial germ cells in the germinal epithelium does not seem much reduced, but in males the number of such cells left behind after the first proliferation of sex chords is small. At 7 days the left gonad is much larger than the right in females, whereas in males the two are of nearly equal size. From 8 to 11 days the germ cells in females multiply rapidly in the germinal epithelium, producing as a result somewhat smaller cells called *oögonia*. These, along with cells of epithelial origin, form a second series of sex chords that give rise to the cortex of the ovary, in which the definitive oöcytes are developed. Detailed accounts of the formation of the gonads are given by Firket (1914) and Swift (1915, ovary; 1916, testis).

The general history of the germ cells during and after formation of the gonad is that they undergo a period of rapid multiplication, then a resting period in which there is an increase in size in the female cells. This is followed by two *meiotic* divisions (maturation divisions) in which the number of chromosomes is reduced to half that in the somatic cells. Since these processes differ in the two sexes, they are considered separately here.

Oögenesis. The changes in the nucleus of the fowl's oöcyte from 10 days of incubation to shortly after hatching were studied in detail by D'Hollander (1904), and those from hatching to maturity by Sonnenbrodt (1908) and Van Durme (1914). Following the rapid multiplication of the oögonia in the embryo of 8 to 11 days and their transport to the ovary in the second proliferation of sex chords, these cells undergo the first stages of the reduction division. At this stage they are known as "primary" oöcytes. In the 14-day embryo the chromatin in the nuclei of these cells appears as a network of thin threads in the centre of which there is an aggregation of chromatinic granules. By 17 days, cells appear in which the chromatin appears in the form of threads oriented with their ends toward the attraction sphere. In this stage homologous chromosomes of maternal and paternal origin undergo pairing, or *synapsis*. By hatching time these paired threads have shortened and become bivalent chromosomes. However, the two parts of these chromosomes do not separate till ovulation occurs in the mature fowl. Shortly after hatching most of the oöcytes go into a resting stage during which there are no major visible changes in the nucleus.

Growth and Maturation. After the chick hatches, the oöcytes increase in size by the accumulation of yolk. This process is almost imperceptible, but Brambell (1926) found by measuring oöcytes at different ages that they varied from 10 to 20 microns in diameter at 4 days and from 38 to 380 microns at 6 weeks. Fauré-Frémiet and Kaufman (1928) reported that the number of oöcytes in the ovarian cortex decreased in the first 15 days after hatching. They considered the larger oöcytes, over 80 microns in diameter, in the 15-day chick to be the "privileged oöcytes," capable of further development. However, in Brambell's chicks of 6 weeks, oöcytes over 75 microns in diameter were abnormal and showed signs of atresia. This suggests that those which grow most rapidly subsequently degenerate.

During growth of the oöcyte, the nucleus is comparatively inactive. The maturation divisions have been studied in the pigeon by Harper (1904), in the fowl and other birds by Van Durme (1914), in the fowl by Olsen (1942), and in the turkey by Olsen and Fraps (1944). The first maturation division and extrusion of the first polar body occur just before the follicle ruptures to release the ovum. According to Olsen, the spindle for the second maturation division is also formed prior to ovulation. Normally, the egg is fertilized in the infundibulum of the oviduct within 15 minutes after ovulation. After the second maturation division the female pronucleus contains the haploid number of chromosomes (probably 39 or 40), but the full diploid number is quickly restored by fusion with the male pronucleus. Extrusion of the second polar body coincides with that fusion or precedes it.

Spermatogenesis. A rapid multiplication of primordial germ cells results in the formation of great numbers of spermatogonia in the embryo between 13 and 15 days of age (Swift, 1916). After the chick hatches, the spermatogonia remain quiescent till sexual maturity, at which time the primary spermatocytes undergo the characteristic maturation divisions. These processes have been studied in the fowl by Guyer (1916) and Miller (1938). In the latter's preparations the successive changes in the nucleus preceding the division of the cell into two secondary spermatocytes were clearly seen (Fig. 5). These are identical with those seen earlier in the oöcyte by D'Hollander except that in spermatogenesis the process is a continuous one without the long delay that occurs in the oöcyte between synapsis and the first division of the nucleus. As the knot of coiled threads becomes unravelled after synapsis, all the chromatin appears to be in a single thick thread, in the pachytene stage (Fig. 5, number 17). This strand eventually lengthens, becomes thinner, and breaks up into shorter threads which appear to be split longitudinally. These gradually become the tetrads, or groups of quadruple chromosomes. Each tetrad comprises two homologous chromosomes, each of which is split longitudinally in anticipation of the second meiotic division that follows separation of the homologous chromosomes in the first division.[1] The tetrads become shortened and thickened before coming to the equatorial plate in the metaphase.

Each of the two secondary spermatocytes resulting from division of the primary spermatocyte in turn divides, giving rise to two *spermatids*. In the spermatid the nucleus gradually lengthens out, a tail is formed, and the cell is found in the lumen of the tubule as a fully formed spermatozoon. All the spermatozoa carry the haploid number of chromosomes, which is apparently either 39 or 40 in the fowl.

Heterogamety. There are a number of important differences between males and females in the formation of avian germ cells. As was noted above, the maturation divisions in the male make a fairly continuous process which is initiated at sexual maturity. In females the process begins in the 14-day embryo and ends months later after the entrance of spermatozoa into the egg. In the male, products of the two maturation divisions are equal in form and in function, whereas in the female the first and second polar bodies are very small and both are non-functional. Thus a primary spermatocyte produces eventually four spermatozoa, but a primary oöcyte gives rise to only one egg.

Moreover, in birds the males are *homogametic*, producing spermatozoa which are identically alike in their complement of sex chromosomes, each carrying one, whereas females are *heterogametic*, producing in equal numbers ova of two different sorts. One kind of egg carries a sex chromosome and when fertilized gives rise to a male chick. The other kind lacks a sex chromosome and when fertilized produces a female chick. Whether the ovum resulting from any given maturation division is to

[1] For details see Sharp (1934).

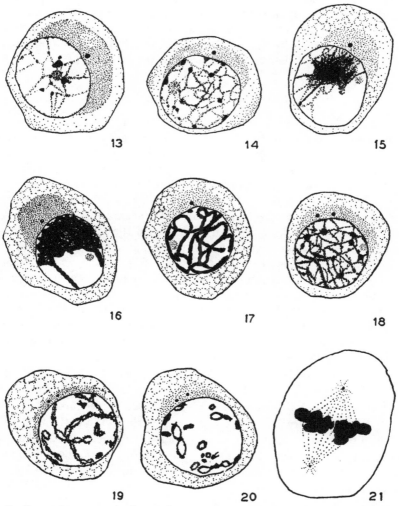

FIG. 5. Successive stages in the nucleus of primary spermatocytes of the fowl prior to their division. 13, resting spermatocyte; 14, early spireme; 15, synaptene stage; 16, bouquet stage; 17, pachytene stage; 18, diffuse stage; 19, strepsinema breaking up into tetrads; 20, diakinesis; 21, division of primary spermatocyte, side view. (*From Miller in Anat. Record.*)

have a sex chromosome or not depends upon how the sex chromosome is lined up on the spindle of the first (reduction) division, and that apparently usually depends upon chance alone. By chance it is extruded in the polar body in one-half of such divisions and retained in the egg in the remainder of the divisions. As a result approximately half the eggs are male-determining, and the remainder produce the other sex.

THE CHROMOSOMES

Chromosomes are studied to best advantage in rapidly growing tissues of the embryo or in the active testis, where many cells are in the process of division. Counts of chromosomes are most easily made in sections across the equatorial plate of cells in the metaphase of nuclear division. In somatic cells the diploid number is seen, but in the division of primary spermatocytes and oöcytes, where the homologous chromosomes are closely paired, it is somewhat easier to make accurate counts because only the haploid number should then be seen. In the large eggs of birds it is very difficult to cut any sections with assurance that they will be at the right time and plane to catch the single egg nucleus in reduction division. On the other hand, in the testis of mature active males there are usually hundreds of cells in various stages of division, so that the chances of finding suitable cells for study are infinitely greater in that organ. For that reason the testis is favored for studies of avian chromosomes, though cells of the amnion, of the embryonic soma, and of tumors are also useful for studies of somatic cell division.

For purposes of study, tissues of this sort are first fixed in one of the standard fixing solutions. Allen's modification of Bouin's fluid has proved very useful for this purpose. After the usual procedures of dehydration, clearing, infiltration with paraffin, embedding, and cutting in sections 4 to 6 microns in thickness, the sections are stained. Heidenhain's haematoxylin is a favorite for this purpose. Other stains used include polychrome blue (Sokolow and Trofimow, 1933), Mallory's and Delafield's haematoxylin counterstained with Congo Red (Miller, 1938), and Feulgen's stain.

Difficulties. In comparison with those of some other species the chromosomes of birds are rather difficult to study.

1. Fixation is useless if not instantaneous (White, 1932). With slow fixation the smaller chromosomes clump in the metaphase plates, and it is impossible to make accurate counts. White found that smears from the testis provided some of his best preparations, probably because of the more rapid fixation possible in thin films of cells.

2. The shortest chromosomes are almost at the limit of microscopic vision, which is a little below 0.2 micron. In the material of Sokolow and Trofimow the largest chromosomes were 6 to 6.5 microns in length and 0.5 micron in diameter, but from there they graded down to barely visible dots.

3. In prophase stages the chromomeres of smaller chromosomes appear disconnected so that one chromosome may appear to be two or three. Thus Hance (1926) found that counts of the fowl's chromosomes

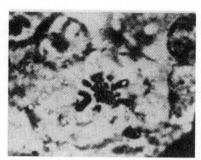

FIG. 6. Photomicrographs of polar view (*left*) and side view (*right*) of dividing primary spermatocytes. In the cell in side view, the black dot above the equatorial plate and apparently outside of the spindle is the sex chromosome. Details of this cell are better seen in Fig. 7, which shows a camera lucida drawing of it (No. 22). (*From Miller in Anat. Record.*)

made in prophases varied from 60 to 70, while those made in metaphases varied from 29 to 42, with an average for 78 cells of 33 chromosomes.

4. In sections it is difficult to find cells cut to show all the chromosomes in a polar view of the equatorial plate. Sections at other than a right angle to the long axis of the spindle cannot ordinarily show all the chromosomes.

5. The general practice is to overstain the sections and then destain to the stage of maximum differentiation. The many small chromosomes destain more rapidly than the comparatively few large ones, and this may cause errors in counting. Thus, Sokolow and Trofimow (1933) found 71 chromosomes in one dark preparation before destaining but only 53 afterward.

6. Much searching of sections and smears is necessary to find cells in active division, and among these only a fraction may be suitable for study (Fig. 6). Miller (1938) overcame this difficulty (*a*) by inducing excessive spermatogenesis with gonadotropic hormones prior to taking tissues for study and (*b*) by taking tissue at night rather than in the daytime. It was shown by Riley (1937) that spermatogenesis in spar-

rows is more active between midnight and dawn than at other periods of the day or night.

Chromosome Numbers. One of the earliest determinations of the number of chromosomes in the domestic fowl was that of Sonnenbrodt

TABLE 1. CHROMOSOME NUMBERS IN DOMESTIC BIRDS

Species	Investigator	Date	Observed chromosome number	
			Haploid	Diploid
Gallus domesticus....	Sonnenbrodt	1908	♀ 12	
	Guyer	1916	♂ 9	18
	Shiwago	1924	.....	32
	Hance	1926	.....	35–40
	Akkeringa	1927	.....	32–44
	Suzuki	1930	♂ 37	♂ 74, ♀ 73
	White	1932	♂ 33	♂ 66 ± 2, ♀ 65 ± 2
	Sokolow and Trofimow	1933	.....	32–71
	Unger	1936	.....	44–61
	Miller	1938	40	51–60
	Yamashina	1944	39	♂ 78, ♀ 77
Meleagris gallopavo..	Shiwago	1929	.....	46
	Werner	1931	♂ 38	♂ 76, ♀ 77
	Sokolov, Tiniakov, and Trofimov	1934	38	—
Phasianus colchicus..	Trofimov and Tiniakov	1933	.....	41–63
Phasianus torquatus.	Unger	1936	.....	52–61
Pavo cristatus........	Tiniakov	1934	.....	36–58
Columba livia........	Oguma	1927	♂ 31	♂ 62, ♀ 61
Anas platyrhyncha...	Werner	1927	♂ 38	♂ 76, ♀ 77
	Crew and Koller	1936	.....	48–69
	Alikhanjan	1936	.....	43–49
	Sokolovskaja	1935	.....	36–56
Cairina moschata....	Crew and Koller	1936	.....	Max. 72
	Sokolovskaja	1935	.....	34–62

(1908), who concluded that there were 12 pairs of chromosomes in the primary oöcytes, indicating a diploid number of 24. A year later Guyer (1909) concluded that the correct diploid number was probably 17. From then on, as techniques improved, the number of chromosomes as determined by various observers has steadily increased. Miller (1938) found that in primary spermatocytes, where counting was somewhat more accurate than in other cells, the number of bivalent paired chromosomes varied from 38 to 40, with the latter found most frequently. This would mean that in somatic cells the (diploid) number is 80 in males. From similar studies Yamashina (1944) concluded that the diploid number is 78 in males and 77 in females. A selection of representative counts of chromosomes in the fowl and in other domestic birds is given in Table 1. No recent count has been reported for the guinea fowl. It is evident that the chromosome numbers for birds are comparatively high. For a more extensive list the reader is referred to Oguma and Makino (1937).

Sex Chromosomes. Genetic evidence that in the fowl the female is heterogametic dated back to Spillman's explanation in 1908 of the behavior of barring in reciprocal crosses between barred and non-barred fowls. It was to be expected, therefore, that the male should have two

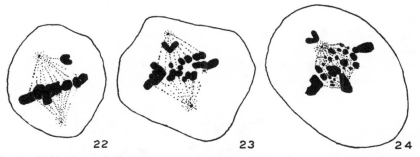

FIG. 7. Side views of dividing primary spermatocytes of an ovariotomized female, showing the characteristic appearance of the V-shaped, unpaired sex chromosome as it passes to one pole of the spindle in advance of the autosomes. Camera lucida drawings. (*From Miller in Anat. Record.*)

sex chromosomes and the female only one. There is food for sober reflection and a warning against dogmatic interpretation in the cold fact that up to 1933 at least eight different cytologists found the largest chromosome to be paired in males, single in females and, *ipso facto*, the sex chromosome. Suzuki (1930) was the first to point out that the largest chromosome is paired in both males and females and that the smallest V-shaped chromosome is the sex chromosome. This was independently determined by Sokolow and Trofimow (1933), who pointed out that it is fifth of all of the chromosomes in size, and confirmed by Unger (1936), Miller (1938), and Yamashina (1944).

Miller obtained conclusive proof of the identity of the sex chromosome in an extremely interesting manner. The history of their study showed that mere attempts to match up the fowl's chromosomes in pairs and so to determine which one was unpaired in females could lead to serious errors.

However, the identity of the sex chromosome could be determined with accuracy from the study of primary oöcytes or spermatocytes in the heterogametic sex. In such cells the unpaired sex chromosome should pass in the anaphase to one pole or the other and should therefore be easily identifiable. Since maturation divisions of the oöcytes are difficult to find in the fowl, it was desirable to have one of the heterogametic sex (*i.e.*, a female) undergo spermatogenesis. This was accomplished by removing the left ovary of a female chick at 4 days of age, with resultant formation on the right side of a testis-like organ in which active spermatogenesis occurred. In the primary spermatocytes, it was clearly evident that the fifth, V-shaped chromosome was unpaired at the equatorial plate and passed undivided, and somewhat ahead of the remainder, to one pole of the spindle (Fig. 7). There can no longer be any doubt that it is the sex chromosome.

Individuality of the Chromosomes. It was shown by Sokolow and Trofimow (1933) that there are certain characteristics by which the seven largest chromosomes of the fowl may be identified (Fig. 8). The figures in parentheses give the mean relative lengths of these seven.

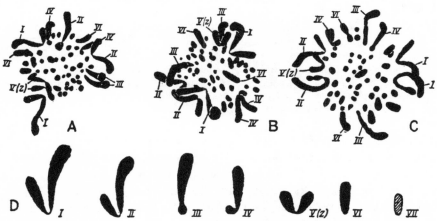

Fig. 8. Chromosomes of the fowl. *A*, from an embryonic testis, showing two V-shaped sex chromosomes, Z. *B*, from an embryonic ovary, showing only one sex chromosome. *C*, from a somatic cell, evidently female because it has only one sex chromosome. The smallest chromosomes are not shown in these diagrams. *D*, the seven largest chromosomes, showing their distinguishing characteristics as outlined in the context. (*From Sokolow and Trofimow in Z. ind. Abst. Vererb.*)

First Pair (28). Largest chromosome with unequal arms and subterminal attachment of the spindle fibre; the shorter arm is usually a little longer than half the long arm. The closed end is toward the equatorial plate in metaphase, toward the pole of the spindle in anaphase.

Second Pair (21.6). Total length is three-quarters that of the first chromosome. The small arm is shorter than half the larger. A subterminal constriction shows the point of attachment of the spindle fibre.

Third Pair (16.2). Rod-shaped; length is between those of the long arms of the first and second chromosomes. One end is thinner and has a terminal knob, which in metaphase is toward the centre, in anaphase toward the pole. The spindle fibre is attached terminally.

Fourth Pair (12.8). Hook-shaped; about half the length of the largest chromosome. One end is thinner than the other, and the spindle fibre has a subterminal attachment.

Fifth Pair (12.4). V-shaped or U-shaped, with median attachment of the spindle fibre.

Sixth Pair (8). A straight rod; one end thinner than the other, but no constrictions evident.

Seventh Pair (5). A short rod.

The remaining chromosomes vary from short rods down to spheres and dots.

Comparative Cytology. Sokolov, Tiniakov, and Trofimov (1936) compared the largest chromosomes in seven different species of Galliformes and found in all of them chromosomes almost identical with the first, third, fifth, sixth, and seventh of the fowl, described above (Fig. 8). In the peafowl and guinea fowl there is a hook-shaped chromosome like the second largest in the fowl. This was not recognizable in *Tetrao tetrix* (black grouse), *Phasianus colchicus* (ring-necked pheasant), *Meleagris gallopavo* (turkey), and *Nycthemerus argentatus* (silver pheasant), but there were some indications that in these four species the hook-shaped chromosome had broken up into a long rod and a short one. The sex chromosomes were almost identical in all seven species. These investigators concluded that the marked variation in phenotype found in these seven species had resulted, not from any great changes in the form of the chromosomes, but rather from the occurrence of different mutations in chromosomes morphologically almost identical.

It is characteristic of avian and reptilian cells that in polar views of metaphase plates the large chromosomes are arranged radially around a central area through which the smaller chromosomes are dispersed.

Literature Cited

Akkeringa, L. J. 1927. Die Chromosomen bei einigen Hühnerrassen. *Z. mikroskop.-anat. Forsch.*, **8**:325–342.

Alikhanjan, S. I. 1936. The karyotype of the mallard (trans. title). *Zool. J. (Moscow)*, **15**:74–81.

Brambell, F. W. R. 1926. The oogenesis of the fowl (*Gallus bankiva*). *Phil. Trans. Roy. Soc. (London)*, B, **214**:113–151.

Crew, F. A. E., and P. C. Koller. 1936. Genetical and cytological studies of the intergeneric hybrid of *Cairina moschata* and *Anas platyrhyncha platyrhyncha*. *Proc. Roy. Soc. Edinburgh*, **56**:210–241.

D'Hollander, F. 1904–1905. Recherches sur l'oogenèse et sur la structure et la signification du noyau vitellin de Balbiani chez les oiseaux. *Arch. anat. micr.*, **7**:117–180.

Fauré-Frémiet, E., and L. Kaufman. 1928. La loi de décroissance progressive du taux de la ponte chez la poule. *Ann. physiol. physicochim. biol.*, **4**:64–122.

Firket, J. 1914. Recherches sur l'organogenèse des glandes sexuelles chez les oiseaux. *Arch. biol.*, **29**:201–351.

Guyer, M. F. 1909. The spermatogenesis of the domestic chicken (*Gallus gallus dom.*). *Anat. Anz.*, **34**:573–580.

———. 1916. Studies on the chromosomes of the common fowl as seen in testes and in embryos. *Biol. Bull.*, **31**:221–269.

Hance, R. T. 1926. Sex and the chromosomes in the domestic fowl (*Gallus domesticus*). *J. Morphol. Physiol.*, **43**:119–145.

Harper, E. H. 1904. The fertilization and early development of the pigeon's egg. *Am. J. Anat.*, **3**:349–386.

Miller, R. A. 1938. Spermatogenesis in a sex-reversed female and in normal males of the domestic fowl, *Gallus domesticus*. *Anat. Record*, **70**:155–189.

Oguma, K. 1927. Studies on the sauropsid chromosomes. I. The sexual difference of chromosomes in the pigeon. *J. Coll. Agr., Hokkaido Imp. Univ.*, **16**:203–227.

——— and S. Makino. 1937. A new list of the chromosome numbers in Vertebrata. *J. Faculty Sci., Hokkaido Imp. Univ.*, **5**:297–356.

Olsen, M. W. 1942. Maturation, fertilization, and early cleavage in the hen's egg. *J. Morphol.*, **70**:513–533.

——— and R. M. Fraps. 1944. Maturation, fertilization, and early cleavage of the egg of the domestic turkey. *J. Morphol.*, **74**:297–309.

Riley, G. M. 1937. Experimental studies on spermatogenesis in the house sparrow, *Passer domesticus* (Linnaeus). *Anat. Record*, **67**:327–351.

Sharp, L. W. 1934. "Introduction to Cytology," 3d ed. New York: McGraw-Hill Book Company, Inc.

Shiwago, P. J. 1924. The chromosome complexes in the somatic cells of male and female of the domestic chicken. *Science*, **60**:45–46.

———. 1929. Über den Chromosomenkomplex der Truthennen. *Z. Zellforsch. mikroskop. Anat.*, **9**:106–115.

Sokolov, N. N., G. G. Tiniakov, and I. E. Trofimov. 1934. On the chromosomes of the domestic turkey (trans. title). *Biol. Zhur.* (Russian), **3**:648–654.

———, ———, and ———. 1936. On the morphology of the chromosomes in Gallinaceae, *Cytologia*, **7**:466–489.

——— and I. E. Trofimow. 1933. Individualität der Chromosomen und Geschlechtsbestimmung beim Haushuhn (*Gallus domesticus*). *Z. ind. Abst. Vererb.*, **65**:327–352.

Sokolovskaja, I. I. 1935. A comparative study of the karyotype of *C. moschata*, *A. platyrhyncha* and their hybrid (trans. title). *Biol. Zhur.* (Russian), **4**:893–905.

Sonnenbrodt. 1908. Die Wachstumsperiode der Oocyte des Huhnes. *Arch. mikroskop. Anat. Entwicklungsmech.*, **72**:415–480.

Suzuki, K. 1930. On the chromosomes of the domestic fowl (trans. title). *Zool. Mag.* (Japan), **42**:358.

Swift, C. H. 1914. Origin and early history of the primordial germ-cells in the chick. *Am. J. Anat.*, **15**:483–516.

———. 1915. Origin of the definitive sex cells in the female chick and their relation to the primordial germ-cells. *Am. J. Anat.*, **18**:441–470.

———. 1916. Origin of the sex-chords and definitive spermatogonia in the male chick. *Am. J. Anat.*, **20**:375–410.

Tiniakov, G. 1934. Peacock and hen hybrids and a comparative analysis of the caryotype of their parents (trans. title). *Biol. Zhur.* (Russian), **3**:41–63.

Trofimov, I. E., and G. G. Tiniakov. 1933. The karyotype of the pheasant, *Phasianus colchicus,* and its comparison with the karyotype of the domestic fowl, *Gallus domesticus* (trans. title). *Biol. Zhur.* (Russian), **2**:33–43.

Unger, H. 1936. Beitrag zur Chromosomenforschung der Vögel. *Z. Zellforsch. mikroskop. Anat.*, **25**:476–500.

Van Durme, M. 1914. Nouvelles recherches sur la vitellogenèse des oeufs d'oiseaux aux stades d'accroissement, de maturation, de fécondation et du début de la segmentation. *Arch. biol.*, **29**:71–200.

Werner, O. S. 1927. The chromosomes of the India Runner duck. *Biol. Bull.*, **52**: 330–373.

———. 1931. The chromosomes of the domestic turkey. *Biol. Bull.*, **61**:157–164.

White, M. J. D. 1932. The chromosomes of the domestic fowl. *J. Genetics*, **26**:345–350.

Yamashina, Y. 1944. Karyotype studies in birds. I. Comparative morphology of chromosomes in seventeen races of domestic fowl. *Cytologia*, **13**:270–296.

CHAPTER 3

VARIATIONS IN THE SKELETON

It is sometimes difficult to say with certainty upon inspection of a hereditary variation in structure just what parts are affected. For example, most poultrymen probably consider the large crest found in several breeds as a change in the plumage. Actually the crest results from an abnormality of the brain which affects the skeleton and incidentally causes the erection of the feathers forming the crest. However, in attempting to arrange the known mutations in some kind of systematic way, it is necessary to classify them. In so doing, the author has based his classification upon the structures first affected in the development of the chick and those showing the major modification. It is fully recognized that most mutations have had inadequate embryological study and that the manifold effects of some genes make any classification difficult.

NORMAL VARIABILITY IN THE SKELETON

Measurements of the cranium and of the humerus, ulna, femur, and tibia of related White Leghorn fowls analyzed by Schneider and Dunn (1924) showed that variability in the skeleton of the fowl is of about the same order as in bones of other animals. Coefficients of variability for these bones fell between 2.9 and 4.4 per cent. In somewhat more heterogeneous Leghorn material, Hutt (1929) found slightly more variability, but for none of 13 bones in the limbs did the coefficient of variability in either males or females exceed 6.47 per cent. In comparison with these figures for the bones, body weight of the fowl shows three to five times as much variability. In the Leghorn skeletons of Schneider and Dunn the correlations between the lengths of different bones in the same skeleton were high, ranging from .57 for that between the length of cranium and femur to .94 for the correlation between humerus and ulna. High correlations like these indicate that some underlying conditions, genetic and environmental, are affecting the size of several (probably all) parts of the body. As might be expected, the correlation is highest between two contiguous bones in one limb and lower between bones farther apart.

Although size of all parts is affected somewhat alike by genetic and environmental conditions determining size as a whole, some bones are more variable than others. In both male and female skeletons studied by Hutt (1929) the tarso-metatarsus was more variable than any other bone in the wing or leg (phalanges were measured only in digit III). This applied both to absolute lengths and to length in proportion to the proximal bone of the limb. Such a condition is unusual because in general the variability increases with increasing size of the object being measured. In this case the tarso-metatarsus is much smaller than the tibio-tarsus, though exceeding the latter bone in variability. There was a greater difference between males and females in length of this bone than in any other measured in the limbs, and in dwarfed fowls it was reduced in proportionate length more than others. The data of Latimer (1927) indicate that in comparison with other bones of similar size ossification in the tarso-metatarsus is completed relatively early in females and relatively late in males.

VARIATIONS IN THE AXIAL SKELETON

Dominant Rumplessness, *Rp*

This character has been known for centuries. A rumpless bird illustrated by Aldrovandus (1600) was labelled as a Persian fowl. Rumpless bantams have been considered by some writers as a separate breed but are now seldom seen. Brown (1906) quoted a correspondent's statement that near Liége, in Belgium, there was a breed called Rumpless, or Hedge Fowls, which were valued because, having no tails, they escaped easily from the foxes. Peculiarly enough, Castello (1924) while investigating the origin of the rumpless Araucana fowls of Chile found that for the very same reason the Indians of Araucana preferred the rumpless fowls to normal ones. These identical but quite independent reports from two continents suggest how easily poultrymen the world over have been able to find reasons for preserving certain mutations.

Morphology. The anatomy of rumpless fowls has been given in detail by Du Toit (1913) and by Landauer and Dunn (1925). The differences between hereditary rumplessness and the non-genetic but congenital type which occurs sporadically were reported by Landauer (1928), who also described the intermediate rumplessness resulting from the action of modifying genes upon the hereditary type. No difference between complete genetic rumplessness and the accidental type can be seen in living birds, and even in dissected specimens it is difficult to distinguish the two.

Normal Tail. There are 16 synsacral vertebrae (fused with the synsacrum, or pelvis), 5 free caudals, and the pygostyle. It is in the last 5
of the synsacral vertebrae, known as *synsacro-caudals*, that the chief
difference between genetic and accidental rumplessness is found. Normal
fowls have a uropygial gland, known also as the "oil gland" and "preen
gland." There are 14 or 16 rectrices, or tail feathers.

Accidental Rumplessness. This is the non-genetic type. Affected
birds lack the pygostyle, all free caudal vertebrae, the uropygial gland,

FIG. 9. A rumpless White Leghorn hen from normal parents. Such cases are most
likely to be of the non-genetic accidental type.

and all rectrices. They also lack the *last two* (rarely only one) of the
synsacro-caudals. As is to be expected with such changes in the skeleton,
the musculature of the region is not the same as in normal fowls. One
of these birds is shown in Fig. 9.

Complete Genetic Rumplessness. This differs from the previous type
in that one or two vertebrae are missing from the *centre* of the five synsacro-caudals, rather than from the posterior end of that series as in the
accidental type. The difference is not easy to detect, since the identity
of the missing vertebrae can be determined only by careful comparison
of the lateral processes of the remaining vertebrae in the two types.
There is a small bony knob on the end of the last vertebra, which is not
found in the accidental type. It is considered by Landauer as homologous with the last two vertebrae of the pygostyle. Deviations of the two
types of rumplessness from the normal are shown in Fig. 10.

Intermediate Genetic Rumplessness. This condition is more variable than the others. According to Dunn and Landauer (1934) the uropygial gland is absent in about 75 per cent or more of the birds with intermediate rumplessness but may be present in rudimentary form in 25 per cent or less and functional in less than 2 per cent. The number of tail feathers varies from 2 to 17, being fewest in birds with greatest reduction of the rump. The average number was 8.7 in males and 9.8 in females.

In the skeleton there is the same excalation of one or two vertebrae

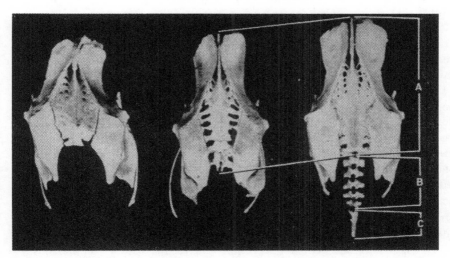

FIG. 10. From left to right, accidental rumplessness, hereditary dominant rumplessness, and normal. Differences are explained in the context. The normal specimen shows the three divisions of the synsacro-caudal vertebrae: *A*, synsacral; *B*, five free caudal vertebrae; *C*, pygostyle. (*From Landauer and Dunn in J. Heredity.*)

from the centre of the five synsacro-caudals as in the complete type. A bony protuberance representing the two distal vertebrae of the pygostyle is present, as before, on the caudal end of the vertebral column. The distinguishing feature of intermediate rumplessness is that all five free caudal vertebrae are usually present though fused together irregularly.

Classification. Rumplessness is evident in the 4-day embryo (Du Toit), and apparently those over 14 days of incubation can be distinguished from normals with reasonable accuracy. Dunn and Landauer found that at any time after hatching the rumpless condition could be distinguished from the normal one with complete accuracy and from intermediates with an accuracy of more than 92 per cent. Intermediates were separated from normals at hatching with 98 per cent accuracy before the accumulation of modifying genes that lessened the degree of rumplessness, but in later years 10 per cent of the intermediates were indistinguishable from normal chicks at hatching, though the distinction was apparent during growth or upon dissection.

In living birds accidental rumplessness can be distinguished from genetic rumplessness only by a breeding test. Any rumpless birds coming from parents with normal tails are more likely to be non-genetic than to have arisen by mutation.

Genetics. In the seventeenth century Nathaniel Highmore (1651) wrote,

"Myself also have seen a kinde of Poultry without rumps: which breeding with their own kinde, still brought forth Chicken wanting that part: If with others, sometimes they had rumps, sometimes but part of a rump."

In other words, rumplessness is a dominant character, and when heterozygotes are mated with normal fowls some of the progeny have normal tails, others an intermediate rumplessness. This early evidence and similar indications in the writings of Darwin and of Tegetmeier have been amply confirmed in later times by Davenport (1909) and by Dunn and Landauer (1934). The accidentally rumpless fowls do not transmit the abnormality to their progeny. This non-genetic type is caused by accidents during development of the embryo, and its frequency, which is ordinarily less than 1 per 1,000 birds, can be increased by altering the environmental conditions in the early stages of incubation.

A single dominant gene, Rp, is responsible for hereditary rumplessness, and the intermediate condition is caused by an unknown number of modifying genes preventing in various degrees the full expression of the character. Dunn and Landauer found that in unselected populations all intermediates were heterozygous for Rp and when mated together such birds yielded rumpless and normal fowls in a ratio of 3:1.

Modifiers. Some of these rumpless progeny were intermediates, but while the proportion of heterozygotes among the rumpless was two-thirds, a much smaller proportion showed intermediate rumplessness. Evidently some of the heterozygotes were unaffected by the modifiers. However, by continuous outcrossing of intermediate rumpless stock to normal fowls and selection of breeders showing the least effects of the gene, the number of modifiers in the stock was increased to the point where they were apparently affecting not only all heterozygotes but homozygotes as well. Table 2, adapted from Dunn and Landauer (1936), shows the increase in the proportion of intermediates among the rumpless progeny from matings of intermediate rumpless parents.

TABLE 2. INCREASE OF INTERMEDIATE RUMPLESS BY SELECTION

Year	Rumpless birds,* number	Intermediate, per cent
1927–1932	347	42.4
1933	214	71.0
1934	174	78.1
1935	141	88.0

* Including both complete and intermediate types.

In these populations the proportion of intermediates could not deviate much from 66⅔ per cent if only heterozygotes were subject to modification. The high proportion of intermediates in the last 2 years of selection indicates that enough modifiers had been accumulated to affect also some of the $Rp\ Rp$ birds. It is evident from the consistent increase of intermediates that among the populations of normal fowls to which the intermediate rumpless birds were outcrossed there must have been a considerable number of genes capable of preventing complete manifestation of the rumpless condition.

Nature of Modifiers. It is not easy to explain with finality why this should be so. Two different interpretations have been offered.

1. As will be seen in the next two sections the gene Rp is an undesirable one tending to promote the extinction of the race rather than its survival. A number of mutations with similar deleterious effects are known in all species that have been adequately studied, but most of them are recessives. Fisher (1930) has suggested that whenever an undesirable dominant mutation occurs, the individuals carrying any genes suppressing it have the best chance of survival and such genes are preserved. If in the history of the species the mutation recurs frequently, the accumulation of modifying genes may be carried to the point where they prevent the complete manifestation of the once dominant mutation in the heterozygote. It is thus gradually changed toward the normal condition and, when enough modifiers are present, may even become recessive. In the rumpless fowls of Dunn and Landauer the modification through the intermediate types toward the normal fully tailed condition has been accelerated by artificial selection. It is Fisher's idea that over a few million years the same situation could be brought about by recurring mutation and natural selection.

2. On the other hand there must be a considerable number of genes promoting normal development of the vertebrae in the tail region. Any

such forces conducive to normal development are antagonistic to abnormal development. Consequently the gradual accumulation by selective breeding of genes promoting normal development in the tail region may array a set of forces sufficient to prevent an expression of the gene *Rp* as complete as that found in unselected stock. Both of these theories are plausible. Neither is proved.

Effects of *Rp* on Viability. In the experiments described, mortality during the last few days of incubation fell a little more heavily on the rumpless chicks than on the normal ones. Among the hatched birds absence or incomplete development of the oil gland prevents the plumage from having its normal oily sheen. As a result it fails to shed water, and the birds are probably more susceptible to chilling in wet weather than are normal fowls. This may account for the fact that in the birds of Dunn and Landauer mortality during the first 2 months after hatching was significantly higher in the rumpless and intermediate birds than in normals of the same stock. In this respect the rumpless ones did not differ from the intermediates.

Effects of *Rp* on Fertility. In these same experiments the rumpless condition was found to be incompatible with normal fertility [1] (Table 3).

TABLE 3. FERTILITY OF RUMPLESS AND INTERMEDIATE RUMPLESS FOWLS *

Mating	Rumpless birds tested	Fertile eggs, per cent
1. Normal ♀ × intermediate rumpless ♂...	21	71
2. Normal ♀ × rumpless ♂..............	6	65
3. Intermediate rumpless ♀ × intermediate rumpless ♂.......................	44	43
4. Rumpless ♀ × normal ♂..............	53	31
5. Rumpless ♀ × intermediate rumpless ♂.	21+	21
6. Rumpless ♀ × rumpless ♂.............	?	17

* After Dunn and Landauer.

It is quite evident that the highest fertility was obtained when the female was normal and the male showed only partial rumplessness. With

[1] Throughout this book the term "fertility" refers only to fertilization of the eggs and *not* to the number of living offspring produced per breeding animal or per flock. It is sometimes used in the latter sense in animal husbandry. The efficiency of reproduction depends upon the numbers of eggs fertilized and the subsequent mortality of embryos. In the fowl these two factors can be separated, and since they appear to be entirely unrelated in that species, it is better to keep them so.

increasing manifestation of the character in either sex, or both, fertility steadily declined, reaching its lowest point when both parents were completely rumpless. A large number of eggs was tested in each mating, and the results are quite significant. Matings 2 and 4, which are reciprocal, show clearly that the gene lowers fertility in the female (31 per cent) much more than in the male (65 per cent) when both are mated with normal fowls of the opposite sex. Among intermediate rumpless birds the males have nearly normal fertility, but less than half of the females do as well, and 10 per cent of them are totally infertile. There is considerable variation among individuals in any one group. Thus when 53 rumpless females were mated with normal males, half of them produced no fertile eggs whatever, but about one-tenth had more than 80 per cent of their eggs fertile.

These facts are especially interesting because, though infertility is a perennial source of economic loss to the poultry industry, factual knowledge of the conditions responsible is very scant. It is true that rumpless fowls have no important place in economic poultry production, but the conditions obviously contributing to infertility in rumpless birds may also be operating, though to a lesser and unrecognized degree, in what appear to be completely normal fowls. These are (1) the presence of saddle feathers and fluff feathers over the cloaca in both sexes; (2) absence of tail feathers, which normally serve as a balancing organ during copulation; (3) modifications of the musculature and in the relation of the cloaca to the rump.

Experimental Induction of Rumplessness. Danforth (1932) has shown that by changing the environmental temperature rather abruptly during the first week of incubation the rumpless condition can be induced in genetically normal embryos. About 7.5 per cent of the chicks became rumpless, a frequency far in excess of the normal incidence of accidental rumplessness. By injecting insulin into the yolks of eggs prior to incubation, Landauer (1945) induced rumplessness in 42 per cent of Leghorn embryos that survived to 17 days of incubation. Various other chemicals had similar but less extreme capacity to cause rumplessness. In other experiments, Landauer and Baumann (1943) induced rumplessness in about 7 per cent of embryos by mechanical shaking prior to incubation.

The bearing of these results on the embryological basis for genetic rumplessness has yet to be determined, but it seems possible that an arrest of development at a stage critical for development of the caudal vertebrae may be the underlying cause.

Recessive Rumplessness, *rp 2*

Landauer (1945a) studied a type of rumplessness that outwardly resembles both the dominant and the accidental types but differs in many ways. It is apparently the abnormality commonly known to poultrymen as "roachback."

Morphology. The pygostyle and free caudal vertebrae may be absent but more commonly are fused into a bony knot. The uropygial gland may be absent or rudimentary, with corresponding reduction in tail feathers. Intermediate forms may have almost normal tails. None of these points would differentiate recessive rumplessness from the other types.

One difference is that the fused caudal vertebrae are commonly bent downward, and appear to be laterally compressed in the recessive type. Some of the birds (up to 55 per cent in females and 36 per cent in males) show kypho-scoliosis, or curvature of the spine and humping of the back. In these cases the acetabula are at different levels, and the femur is distorted, by way of compensation, for locomotion. Some of the birds (up to 17 per cent in males, 8 per cent in females) have supernumerary ribs, mostly rudimentary, on one or both sides.

Genetics. This mutation is not only completely recessive but has such a low penetrance that from matings of rumpless birds *inter se* only 33 to 38 per cent of the progeny showed the condition. It is apparently much influenced by modifying genes, but the main gene, which Landauer has designated *rp 2*, is autosomal.

This mutation may be identical with that studied by Czaja (1939) in Polish Greenlegs, which in the extreme forms prevented locomotion. As in Landauer's material, the penetrance of the character was very low, only 9 per cent being obtained from backcrosses.

Number of Vertebrae

Variations in the number of vertebrae in the dorsosacrum have been studied by Promptoff (1928). The dorsosacral region begins with the most posterior of the seven dorsal vertebrae, which is the last vertebra with ribs and the first within the sacrum. It is called the synsacro-thoracic and, if the vertebrae be numbered from the skull backward, is V 21. In addition, the region includes two, three, or four synsacro-thoracico-lumbar vertebrae behind this first one.

Morphology. In dissecting about 4,000 specimens, Promptoff found the three main types of dorsosacrum listed below.

Four Dorsosacral Vertebrae (*V* 21–*V* 24). The last of these and sometimes the last two have broad transverse processes. This type was found in all breeds of fowls and in about 75 per cent of the birds examined. It is somewhat variable.

Five Dorsosacral Vertebrae (*V* 21–*V* 25). In this type there are always broad transverse processes on the last two. Dorsosacra of this kind were more frequent among the larger birds and occurred in about 25 per cent of the skeletons.

Three Dorsosacral Vertebrae (*V* 21–*V* 23). This type was more frequent in bantams and varied little. In synsacra of such birds the acetabulum is moved forward, frequently to the level of V 28, whereas in fowls with five dorsosacrals it is shifted backward to the level of V 31.

Genetics. Genetic analysis of variations like these is difficult. Since the number of vertebrae were determined only by dissection, neither phenotypes nor genotypes of the breeders were known with certainty when crosses were made. It was therefore difficult to make critical matings to verify hypotheses, and although a great number of birds was examined and the hereditary nature of the variations was evident, an exact genetic basis for them was not conclusively established. Promptoff found indications that three pairs of genes were involved. One of these induced the bantam type (three dorsosacrals) and was apparently epistatic to the other two.

Schmidt (1922) found that the total number of vertebrae in fowls varied from 39 to 44 and that there was a consistent difference between two males in their influence upon the number of vertebrae in their offspring.

It is doubtful that a simple genetic basis should be expected for variations like these in the number of vertebrae. Tuff and Berge (1936) used X-ray photography to determine at an early age the number of vertebrae in live pigs and showed that it was subject to considerable variation of genetic origin, but no simple genetic basis was evident for it. Sawin (1937) found similar hereditary variations in the number of vertebrae in the rabbit, but the number of genes involved could not be determined.

Short Spine in Turkeys

Morphology. Asmundson (1942) has described a peculiar abnormality, lethal to turkey embryos, in which the neck and body are markedly shortened (Fig. 11). In some cases the head is normal, but in others the skull, eyes, and upper beak are reduced in size. Shortening of the spine is caused by a crowding together of the vertebrae, and not, apparently, by the elimination of any of them. The cervical vertebrae are all present, though crowded. Bones of the limbs are normal in length and in ash content, but in the scapula, ilium, and ischium the proportion of ash is subnormal.

Genetics. This abnormality is a simple recessive autosomal character. Matings of carriers yielded 59 normal:14 short spine. Since none of the affected embryos hatch, it is a fully lethal mutation. From the standpoint of comparative genetics, it is of interest that a mutation with almost

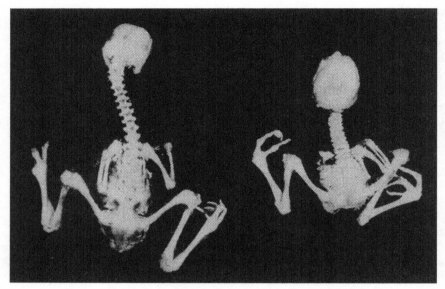

FIG. 11. Skeleton of short-spined turkey (*right*) at 29 days of incubation; normal specimen of same age on left. (*From Asmundson in Proc. S. Exptl. Biol. Med.*)

identical effects upon the axial skeleton, and with none at all on the appendicular skeleton, occurs in cattle (Mohr and Wriedt, 1930).

Crooked Beaks

Fowls with various abnormalities of the beak are seen in many different breeds and have been reported from several countries. The most common of these is probably the non-genetic condition associated with unilateral microphthalmia or anophthalmia in chick embryos, but the majority of these are never seen because they die during the later stages of incubation. A few hatch. This abnormality probably results, as do other teratological conditions, from an accident in development, sometimes induced by an unfavorable environment.

The most common kind of crooked beak in older chickens is probably that which develops between 3 and 8 weeks of age in chicks which were normal at hatching (Fig. 12). The lower beak is unaffected except that, since it is not used for pecking, the end is not worn down as much as in normal fowls and one side is worn more than the other. At maturity the tip of the upper beak tends to curl downward. In the skulls of affected birds there is a marked asymmetry of the maxillae, nasals, and premaxillae, which is probably responsible for the condition of the beak.

Fig. 12. Hereditary crooked beak in a young cockerel.

Birds with the upper beak straight but much shortened are sometimes found in families showing crooked beaks, and the two forms are probably genetically identical.

Genetics. This type of crooked beak is hereditary, but the manifestation of the character is so irregular that a definite genetic basis for it is as yet unknown. In extensive studies by Landauer (1938) the condition was clearly recessive to the normal, but no Mendelian ratios were observed. Some matings of normal parents produced only a single crossbeak in 21, 30, and 48 chicks. From four matings of cross-beaked birds *inter se* the ratio in the progeny was 91 normal:53 cross-beaked. Apparently only a small proportion of the birds homozygous for crooked beak are visibly affected. On the other hand, some of the results of

Mercier and Poisson (1925) suggest that in their stock the character was even manifested by heterozygotes.

Birds with crooked beaks survive, especially if the beaks are trimmed and if the feed is supplied in a deep hopper. The variation in which the upper beak is straight but shortened is more likely to be fatal before maturity, because of the difficulty in feeding.

Other Types. In some birds the upper beak is normal, but the lower one is twisted. Little is known of this condition or its causes. In the author's experience it reduces viability more than the hereditary type just described. Mercier and Poisson (1927) found that in such birds the cornified region at the tip of the tongue is extended and somewhat up-curved. Cornification increases with age and use, till fragments at the end fall off and the tongue is eventually so shortened that birds 2 to 3 years old can no longer feed even from dishes. Another kind of crooked beak, reported by Landauer (1938), is a hereditary condition in which the beaks are crossed at hatching, some becoming normal later on. This was found only in White Leghorns. Its manifestation was just as irregular as that of the type discussed above. Seven matings of cross-beaked fowls yielded 113 normal:155 affected. One mating of normal parents produced a single cross-beaked chick of this type among 59 offspring. Although the genetic basis for both these types of crooked beak is unknown, they are apparently different. Apart from the difference in the ages at which the defect appears, Landauer found that crosses of the two types yielded only normal progeny.

Abnormal or Missing Maxillae, *mx*

A defect of the skeleton that is lethal to homozygotes was found by Asmundson (1936) in a flock of inbred Single-comb White Leghorns (Fig. 13).

Morphology. The character is recessive, and heterozygotes are normal. In homozygous embryos the maxillae in the upper beak are either absent or much reduced. The premaxillae are normal in many cases but smaller than usual in some embryos. The nasals are present but sometimes reduced in size, and other bones of the face are sometimes affected. The upper beak is frequently bent to one side, and in some cases the eyes appear to be slightly smaller than normal.

Affected embryos can be distinguished easily from normals by the twelfth day of incubation. The condition appears to have little or no effect on the viability of the embryo up to the time of hatching, but of 53 such embryos observed by Asmundson only 1 was able to hatch unaided. The defect of the beak apparently prevents most of the chicks from pipping the shell. Seven that were helped out of their shells all died within 1 week.

Genetics. A ratio of 173 normal:58 abnormal in matings of heterozygotes showed clearly that a single recessive gene in homozygous condi-

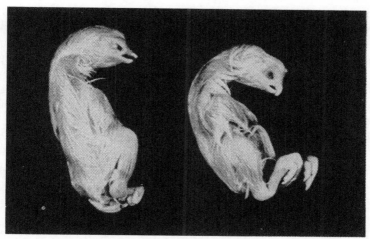

Fig. 13. Chick embryos showing abnormal maxillae, a lethal mutation. (*Courtesy of V. S. Asmundson.*)

tion was responsible for the abnormality. Since short names are desirable in linkage studies, and elsewhere, this character, which Asmundson called "abnormal upper mandible," might be known as "amaxilla." The symbol *mx* is proposed.

Short Upper Beak, *su*

Another mutation affecting the beak, in this case semi-lethal, was studied by Landauer (1941).

Morphology. The upper beak is shortened by amounts varying from about a millimeter up to half its normal length. The lower beak is apparently unaffected. This defect was evident in some embryos as early as the ninth day of incubation. In some of those which hatched, the beak became normal during growth. In others it twisted to one side, more frequently to the right than to the left. The mutation also reduces the length of the long bones in the wing and leg, particularly in the latter. Embryos of 18 and 20 days with short upper beaks were somewhat smaller than normal ones.

Genetics. Embryos thus affected are homozygous for an autosomal, recessive gene for which the symbol *su* (short upper) is proposed. In an

F_2 population of 652 embryos at least 18 days old and in 250 progeny from the backcross of heterozygotes to a homozygote, the ratios of normal to abnormal were very close to those of 3:1 and 1:1 expected for a simple recessive character. This not only confirmed the genetic basis for short upper beak but also showed that, prior to 18 days of incubation, mortality among the defective embryos was no higher than in normal ones. About two thirds of the embryos with short upper beak apparently died on the twenty-first and twenty-second days of incubation, but one third were still alive at the end of the latter day. Although about 13 per cent of the embryos with short upper beak that were alive on the eighteenth day eventually hatched, mortality among these was high, presumably because of difficulties in eating. In 5 years of selection against these lethal effects of the mutation, Landauer (1946) raised hatchability of homozygotes practically to normal (77 per cent), and among those hatched the proportion with normal beaks was raised from zero in 1941 to 71 per cent in 1945. Those still abnormal at hatching usually became normal before maturity.

Missing Mandible, *md*

Morphology. This abnormality differs from the two previous ones in that the mandible, or lower beak, is reduced to a mere vestige. The upper beak is also reduced but remains from one-quarter to two-thirds of normal size. It is frequently pointed upward or even curved over the front part of the head. There is always some degree of cerebral hernia. The abnormality is recognizable in young embryos as soon as the beak begins to form.

Genetics. This mutation was found by Marble *et al.* (1944) in White Leghorns and shown to be a simple, recessive autosomal character. It was lethal to all homozygotes, but some of them were still alive at 21 days of incubation.

Genetic tests yielded 378 normal:134 lethal from heterozygotes mated *inter se*. The expected ratio of carriers to non-carriers among normal chicks from such matings is 2:1. In tests of 31 females the actual numbers found were 22 carriers and 9 lacking the gene, a close fit to expectation. The symbol *md* is proposed.

Short Mandible, *sm*

Morphology. Somewhat similar to the missing mandible just described is the short lower beak studied by McGibbon (1946) in White Leghorns. In affected chicks and embryos the lower beak is seldom more than half the normal length; in extreme cases the rami are buckled up or down, almost at right angles to the normal plane, and sometimes cause the mouth to be propped open. Other parts of the skeleton are apparently normal. In extreme cases the tip of the tongue is curled under.

Only half the affected embryos hatch, and few of the chicks survive. In those still alive at 5 to 6 months of age, the lower beak is about normal in length, but unless the upper beak be trimmed, the bird cannot close its mouth because of the downward curvature of the upper beak.

Genetics. This abnormality segregated in F_2 and backcross populations as a simple recessive autosomal character. When birds that had survived were mated together, they produced 2 normal offspring and 37 with the defect. The 2 exceptions suggest that some birds may not show the character though homozygous for it. Short mandible must be classified as a semi-lethal mutation.

VARIATIONS IN THE APPENDICULAR SKELETON

Polydactyly, *Po*

The so-called "fifth toe" is a variation fairly widely spread among domestic fowls and is a breed characteristic in Dorkings, Houdans, Silkies, and Antokolkas. Columella, writing in the first century, described the best hens for breeding and stated "those are believed to be the best bred that have five toes."

Morphology. The extra toe is not at all homologous with the fifth toe commonly found in other vertebrates. A cartilaginous rudiment of the fifth toe is found in the embryo on the outer side of the foot, but it does not develop. The extra digit of polydactylous fowls arises from the metatarsal of the first toe, or hallux, on the *inner* side of the foot (Fig. 14). Actually the fifth toe is not an extra digit but rather a duplication of the hallux and more comparable to the teratological dichotomy, or reduplication, occasionally found in other parts of the body and in double monsters. The first toe normally consists of one metatarsal and two phalanges, the distal one of which bears a claw. The following variations are found in polydactylous birds:

1. A single toe, longer than the normal hallux, made up of 1 metatarsal and 3 phalanges; it was designated by Warren (1944) as "polyphalangism."
2. Single at the base but bifurcated at the distal end, with 1 metatarsal, but 2 phalanges in each branch.
3. Two separate digits, arising from 2 parallel metatarsals, one of which contains 3 or 4 phalanges, the other 2 or 3. This is the most common type. Sometimes the 2 metatarsals are fused.
4. Division of the claw only.
5. Hallux replaced by 3 digits. More frequent in Silkies but found also in Houdans and Dorkings.

Fisher (1935) found that, in 50 feet of birds heterozygous for poly-dactyly, 28 were type 3, 14 were type 2, 1 was type 1, and 7 were normal. Variations found in 6 of his birds are shown in Fig. 15. There was some evidence in his stocks that in homozygotes the total number of bones in the region of the hallux (counting both feet) was 12 to 14, compared with only 7 or 8 in heterozygotes and 6 in normal birds. However, some hetero-

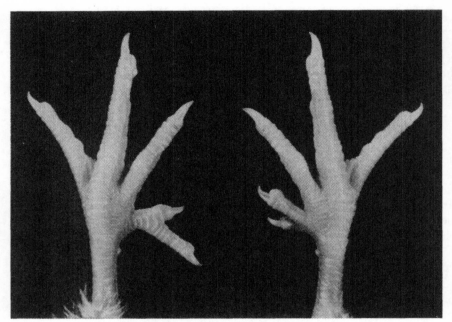

Fig. 14. Bilateral polydactyly of a common type.

zygotes are phenotypically normal and can be detected only by a breed-ing test.

Polydactyly is recognizable at hatching. According to Kaufmann-Wolf (1908) it is apparent as early as the fifth day of incubation. In some animals, including man, polydactyly occurs on all four limbs. Bar-furth (1911a) discovered that in polydactylous embryos a small rudi-mentary extra digit is often seen on the anterior edge of one or both wings, near the ala spuria, at 8 to 10 days of incubation. After 10 days of incubation, none of Barfurth's embryos showed this extra digit, but Baumann and Landauer (1944) found that it persists in some cases, be-ing present at hatching and throughout life. This expression of poly-dactyly in the wing was observed in homozygotes, 59 per cent of which showed it at hatching in one mating. Landauer (1948) has since stated that it is found only in homozygotes with bilateral polydactyly on the feet.

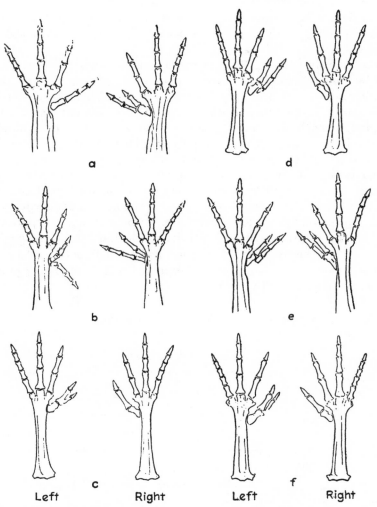

Left   Right   Left   Right

Fig. 15. Diagrams showing various forms of polydactyly seen in feet of six birds, *a* to *f*. [*From Fisher in Phil. Trans. Roy. Soc. (London).*]

Polydactyly has been suppressed by subjecting the embryos to low temperatures at 1 to 4 days of incubation (Sturkie, 1943; Warren, 1944). This effect was obtained more readily with heterozygotes than with homozygotes.

Genetics. Polydactyly results from the action of a single dominant gene, *Po,* but its expression is extremely irregular. (It is fully recognized that most dominant genes are only incompletely dominant in heterozygotes and that, while a single major gene is primarily responsible for the effect, undoubtedly many other genes contribute to the development of the affected part.)

In the extensive data of Bateson and Punnett, summarized and augmented by Punnett and Pease (1929), some matings gave a normal 3:1 segregation in F_2 and 1:1 in backcross, and individual homozygous males produced only polydactylous chicks in progenies of 55 and 65. On the other hand, some birds evidently homozygous still had 1 or 2 normal four-toed chicks among 60 or more polydactylous offspring. These investigators and others have also found that what appear to be normal four-toed fowls from polydactylous parents may produce five-toed offspring and thus prove to be heterozygous for the character. Landauer (1948) even found some homozygotes that showed no sign of polydactyly.

It is evident that some fowls carry genes which entirely or partially prevent the manifestation of polydactyly, particularly in heterozygotes. This is nicely shown by some matings in the data of Punnett and Pease, where the same polydactylous birds were mated both to White Leghorns and to Brown Leghorns (Table 4).

TABLE 4. SUPPRESSION OF POLYDACTYLY BY GENETIC MODIFIERS *

Progeny	Polydactylous parent			
	♀ W. D. 121		♂ W. D. (K.)	
	Four-toed parents			
	White Leghorn	Brown Leghorn	White Leghorns	Brown Leghorns
Number............	12	22	167	197
Bilateral polydactyly, per cent..........	100	72.7	96.4	77.1
Unilateral polydactyly, per cent..........	0	18.2	1.8	12.2
Four-toed, per cent....	0	9.1	1.8	10.7

* Data of Punnett and Pease, rearranged.

The matings with White Leghorns show that both polydactylous parents were evidently homozygous, but when they were crossed with Brown Leghorns about 10 per cent of the progeny failed to show the character, and still more showed it on one foot only. Obviously, the strain of Brown Leghorns used carried genes which prevented the complete expression of *Po*. Similar suppression of the character has been noticed in other investigations. The number of inhibiting or modifying genes involved is unknown.

Such a partial or complete suppression of a genetic character is not an uncommon phenomenon. The manifestation of a character or its suppression apparently depends upon a considerable number of genes which interact among themselves and with the environment. When two genes are necessary to overcome any conflicting forces and thus cause the character to appear, it is considered a recessive mutation. When only one such determining gene is necessary, the character is designated as a dominant one. However, in both cases the balance between determining and opposing forces may be so delicate that exceptions to the rule occur. Thus what is generally considered a recessive mutation may occasionally show in a heterozygote, and, similarly, a single dominant gene may be suppressed, in which case the supposedly dominant character does not show in the heterozygote.

Sometimes single inhibiting genes suppress a character, as is done in dominant white fowls, but usually there is an undetermined number of modifiers. These can be accumulated by selection to the point where they cause partial suppression of the character in most birds, as was done with the rumpless fowls. In the Brown Leghorns of Table 4, there were evidently more genes antagonistic to polydactyly than in the White Leghorns. These had presumably accumulated by chance rather than by artificial selection. Conversely, the expression of a character can be enhanced by selective breeding as is done by fanciers who wish maximum development of crest, frizzling, or plumage patterns. In selecting among the modifying genes either for suppression or enhancement of a character there is no certainty whether the end result is brought about by the elimination of genes antagonistic to the character desired or by accumulation of genes promoting its more complete expression.

The important thing to remember is that dominance and recessivity are relative terms and that the expression of most characters varies because of modifying genes, the number of which is usually unknown. In the case of polydactyly it is clear that in heterozygotes the character may be suppressed completely, may show on one foot only, or may be manifested to such a slight degree that only the claw is divided. Its expression is apparently equally good in both sexes (Punnett and Pease).

Asymmetry. Unilateral polydactyly, or heterodactyly, is most frequent in progenies, like those from the White Dorking × Brown Leghorn crosses shown in Table 4, in which a considerable proportion of the birds do not show the five-toed condition. It is obviously one degree of suppression of the character. There is as yet no explanation of the curious fact pointed out by Bond (1920, 1926) that in such cases the left foot is more often polydactylous than the right one. Table 5 shows that the data of different investigators are in agreement on this point.

TABLE 5.   ASYMMETRICAL EXPRESSION OF POLYDACTYLY

Observer	Poly-dactylous number	Uni-lateral, per cent	On left foot, number	On right foot, number
Bond (1920).....................	230	16.5	34	4
Bond (1926).....................	89	15.7	9	5
Barfurth (1911)..................	475	13.7	35	30
Barfurth (1911a).................	40	20.0	6	2
Punnett and Pease (1929), old data....	1,119	11.2	69	56
Punnett and Pease (1929), new data...	218	23.4	40	11
Total or average.................	2,171	13.9	193	108

The left foot is not the most affected in all matings, for Punnett and Pease reported one male with 12 heterodactylous offspring, 11 of which had polydactyly on the right foot only. By selection during 7 years, Landauer (1948) raised the proportion of polydactylous birds showing sinistral heterodactyly from 13 to 33 per cent. This was done at the expense of the long-toe form (polyphalangism), which practically disappeared from that stock. This form, in turn, was increased by selection in another line. Other evidence of the influence of modifying genes was provided by a third strain in which the proportion of polydactylous chicks having more than five toes on each foot was raised from 6 to 76 per cent by four generations of selection. Selection for dextral heterodactyly was less effective.

Duplicate Polydactyly, *Po^d*. This extreme type of polydactyly differs from the usual form in having the first digit split into two or replaced by three toes (Warren, 1941). In some variants there is even a doubling of the tarso-metatarsus and of almost the entire foot (Fig. 16). The extra toes are sometimes located proximally to the usual position, even as high as the inter-tarsal ("hock") joint. The frequency of these various manifestations in birds with duplicate polydactyly was studied by Harman and Nelson (1941). The wing is frequently affected as well as the feet.

This form of polydactyly is dominant and caused by an allele of the gene *Po*. The symbol *Po^d* is suggested. Warren (1941, 1944) was able

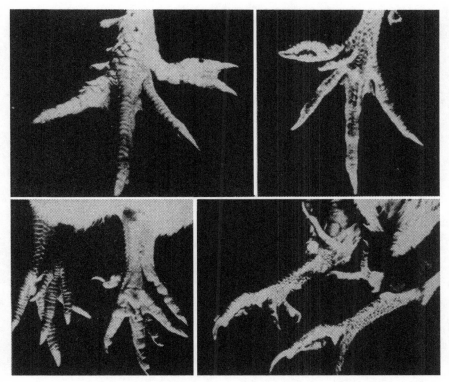

Fig. 16. Various forms of duplicate polydactyly, all caused by the same gene. (*From Warren in J. Heredity, 1941.*)

to prove its genetic nature (1) by crossing *Po po* × *Po^d po* stock and getting in the offspring approximately 3 polydactylous:1 normal and also (2) by linkage tests which showed that *Po^d* occupied the same position in the chromosome as *Po*.

This discovery established the first series of multiple alleles to be demonstrated in the fowl. It is not clear which of the two dominant mutations is dominant in birds of the genotype *Po Po^d* or whether or not these fowls are indistinguishable from those with either ordinary or duplicate polydactyly.

Diplopodia, *dp*

An abnormality studied by Taylor and Gunns (1947) is designated as "diplopodia" because it is characterized by partial doubling of structures in the foot (Fig. 17).

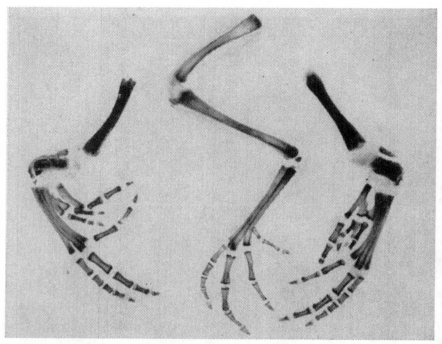

Fig. 17. Legs of two embryos showing the lethal mutation, diplopodia, and a normal leg in the centre for comparison. All are cleared and stained with alizarin. The one on the left shows three extra metatarsals and three extra digits. The leg on the right has two metatarsals, one of which is bifurcated, and four small supernumerary digits. (*From Taylor and Gunns in J. Heredity.*)

Morphology. Over three-quarters of the affected chicks have six toes per leg, which are arranged in two sets of three each. One set consists of digits II, III, and IV, as in normal feet. The other three replace the hallux and are usually smaller than normal and variable in size. There are one to four extra metatarsal bones as well as extra digits. In this respect diplopodia is distinctly different from both polydactyly and its allele, duplicate.

Variant forms of the mutation show two or four extra toes instead of three. Some lack supernumerary metatarsals, and a few retain the hallux in addition to an extra set of one to three toes. Asymmetry is common. The femur, tibio-tarsus, and tarso-metatarsus are shortened in embryos with typical diplopodia. About 97 per cent of the chicks have extra digits in the wing, usually consisting of one phalanx only, and in about 80 per cent the maxilla is shortened.

Genetics. This remarkable abnormality is inherited as a simple, recessive autosomal character. Heterozygotes mated *inter se* produced 1,531 embryos, of which 22.7 per cent showed the mutation. The fact that some of these matings yielded fewer diplopod embryos than the 25 per cent expected was attributed to its suppression by modifying genes or environmental influences. The symbol *dp* is suggested.

Diplopodia is lethal to about 98 per cent of the homozygotes, most of which apparently die during the last week of incubation. Out of 423 diplopods, only 9 were hatched. One of these was raised but proved too abnormal for reproduction.

Brachydactyly, *By*

This is a variation in the outer toe. If the digits of the foot be numbered from the inner to the outermost one as D I, II, III, and IV, the corresponding numbers of phalanges are normally two, three, four, and five.

Morphology. In normal fowls D IV is about 10 per cent longer than D II or a little more, but in brachydactylous ones D IV is as short as D II or shorter. Four degrees of the condition were recognized by Danforth (1919).

1. All five phalanges are present, but the fourth and sometimes the third are shortened.

2. The third and fourth are replaced by a single phalanx, like the fourth, but larger.

3. The third and fourth are fused; all are reduced. The claw is only a small flat scale and the fifth phalanx a nodule into which is inserted the terminal slip of the flexor profundis tendon.

4. There are only two bones; no nail.

Brachydactyly is recognizable in some embryos at 9 days, in nearly all by 10, but some cases may be overlooked even in later embryos.

Genetics. The extensive data of Warren (1940) show that brachydactyly is caused by an incompletely dominant autosomal gene, *By*. Most of the birds homozygous for this lack the nail and some of the phalanges of D IV, *i.e.*, they are Danforth's grade 4. Heterozygotes are affected somewhat less severely but are recognizable by shortening of the toe. In one of Warren's matings 6 per cent of the homozygotes showed the phenotype characteristic of heterozygotes.

Association with Feathered Feet. Danforth (1919*a*) found brachydactyly most common in birds with feathered shanks, and fowls showing one of these characters, but lacking the other, reproduced the missing one as readily as did birds showing it. From various matings, each yielding both normal and brachydactylous chicks, the progeny when classified showed a very marked association of brachydactyly with feathered shanks (Table 6).

TABLE 6. ASSOCIATION OF BRACHYDACTYLY WITH FEATHERED SHANKS
(FROM DANFORTH)

Type of D IV	Birds, number	Shanks feathered, per cent	Shanks not feathered, per cent
Brachydactylous....	217	73.7	26.3
Normal...........	290	3.5	96.5

Because of this association of the two characters any genetic interpretation of one must consider the other. Much has been written about the genetics of shank feathering, but the number of genes involved is still unknown. Since many of those studying the feathering did not notice the brachydactyly, there is still less information about the latter character. That the very marked association of the two conditions was not a peculiarity of Danforth's strains is certain because the same thing has been observed by Schmalhausen (1934), Fisher (1938), Jaap (1939), and Warren (1940) in entirely unrelated stocks in three different countries. It is still possible that brachydactyly may be associated more with some types of shank feathering than with others.

Embryology. It seems probable from the interesting investigations of Schmalhausen that the association of these conditions is dependent not upon linkage of separate genes for each but rather upon certain processes common to both in embryonic development. The feathers of the shank develop on the outer side of the foot, and so does the fourth digit. What is commonly called "shank feathering" is really foot feathering, since the feathers are on the tarso-metatarsus. At an early stage in development there is an active movement of skeletogenous mesenchyme toward the posterior and outer side of the limb. This material is used in normal fowls to form bones, but, according to Schmalhausen, in embryos of birds with feathered shanks it is used largely for the mesodermal rudiments of the feathers. Since the period for formation of feather rudiments coincides with that for development of the distal phalanges of D IV, there is an interaction of conflicting forces. In birds with genes promoting shank feathering, most of the available material goes for feathers (Table 6) with brachydactyly as an accompaniment. The conflict is evidently not a decisive one in all cases. The varying degrees of brachydactyly suggest that the outcome may depend in part upon the action of modifying genes and probably also upon environmental influ-

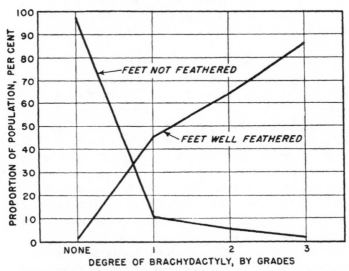

Fɪɢ. 18. Graphs showing that the shorter the outer toe, the higher the proportion of birds with well-feathered feet and the lower the proportion without feathers at all. The intermediates are omitted. Grade 3 represents the greatest reduction of the outer toe. (*From data of Warren, 1940.*)

ences. This may explain why a few of Danforth's birds had feathered feet but normal toes. His 26 per cent of non-feathered birds among the brachydactylous suggests that in some birds there may be so little of the requisite mesenchymatous material available at the right time and place that feather rudiments cannot be formed and phalanges of D IV are defective also.

Schmalhausen's interpretation is supported by the fact that in Warren's brachydactylous birds the degree of shortening of the fourth toe was proportional to the extent of the feathering on the shanks. This is shown by the graphs in Fig. 18, which are drawn from the data for Warren's males and females combined. Grades 1, 2, and 3 represent increasingly severe stages in the shortening of the outer toe. In grade 1, D II and D IV are of equal length; in grade 3, the nail is missing, or some of the phalanges are. While the difference between normality and brachy-dactyly is not strictly comparable with the difference between any two grades of brachydactyly, it is clear that the proportion of birds with no feathers on the feet decreases, and the proportion well feathered in-creases, as the fourth toe becomes shorter.

Because of this relationship it seems more likely that the two condi-tions are caused by one and the same gene than that they arise from the action of two or more linked genes, one affecting the toe and the other the feathers. In the latter case, the amount of change in the toe would not necessarily be proportional to the degree of feathering.

Ungual Osteodystrophy

This abnormality, which affects only a small part of the skeleton, the ungual phalanx of the toes, was studied by Warren *et al.* (1944).

Morphology. In three-quarters of the affected birds the claw of the middle toe (digit III) is absent, shortened, or distorted on one or both feet. Sometimes the nail merely deviates from the median line. In the most extreme cases, all digits were abnormal, with some of the claws misplaced and attached at the side of the toe. Among 112 birds, 78 had abnormalities on one foot only, the remainder on both feet. In 168 affected toes, 65 per cent lacked the nail, and 35 per cent had it shortened or distorted. The defect is not in the keratinous nails that normally cover the ungual phalanges but in the bones themselves.

Genetics. The exact genetic basis for this character is not clear, al-though it is obviously hereditary. Affected × normal yields a preponder-ance of normal offspring but a few that show the defect. When affected birds are mated *inter se*, only about half the offspring show the character. The same degree of variation in manifestation of the character and the same irregular genetic behavior were observed independently by Warren at Kansas and by Mueller and Hutt at Cornell.

Creeper, *Cp*

The short-legged condition is known to occur in many different parts of the world. It is the distinguishing characteristic of several breeds, among which are the Courtes Pattes of France, the Scots Dumpies, the Japanese Bantams, and the Creepers of the United States and other countries. By poultrymen who fancy these varieties, they are commonly supposed to be superior to other fowls in brooding chicks because the fluff feathers are so close to the ground (Fig. 19) ; but, whether this be so or not, the undesirability of the mutation in any breed has been amply demonstrated.

Morphology. All the long bones of the limbs are shortened. The tibia appears more affected than others because the diaphysis of that bone is usually bent in the distal half and thickened. The fibula, which in normal fowls is thin and tapers to a point a little more than halfway

Fig. 19. A Creeper hen. (*From Cutler in J. Heredity.*)

down the tibia, is thicker in creepers,[2] extends the whole length of the tibia, and is firmly ankylosed to the latter bone at its distal end. Some birds have the toes permanently curled, suggesting abnormally short tendons. Some are unable to stand because of torsion in the shaft of the tibia.

The long bones of the limbs of male creepers were found by Landauer (1934) to be shorter than those of normal siblings by 18 to 31 per cent, with greatest proportionate reduction in the tarso-metatarsus. The same bones in creeper females were 13.4 to 24.4 per cent shorter than in normal siblings, with the tarso-metatarsus again most affected. Since growth

[2] The general rule followed in this book is to use capitals for breeds but not for mutations or for birds considered merely as showing some mutation whether or not they conform otherwise to breed standards. Thus, the fancier's Silky is white, but the geneticist's silky may be white, red, or black.

in females is normally retarded at an earlier age than in males, it is natural that the creeper females should be less abnormal than the males. Growth in creepers is apparently continued longer than in normal siblings.

Osteogenesis. The abnormalities of bone formation responsible for these deviations from normality in the bones of adults have been studied in detail in embryos, growing chicks, and adults by Landauer (1931). *Endochondral* ossification, the formation of bone in cartilage at the juncture of the cartilaginous epiphyses of the long bones with the shaft, or diaphysis, is deficient and goes little further than the first stages. Since this is the process by which growth in length of these bones is normally accomplished, this abnormality explains the general shortening of the long bones. On the other hand, *periosteal* ossification, the formation of bone in the layer of connective tissues surrounding the cartilage of both the epiphyses and the diaphysis, is normal or even more active than normal. Invasion of the underlying cartilage by the periosteal bone thus formed causes an increase in the diameter of the bone, a process which is apparently normal in creepers. The bending of the tibia apparently results from the unusually active formation of periosteal bone which Landauer found to occur at the site of the bend.

Classification. According to Landauer (1932) heterozygotes cannot be distinguished from normal embryos until they are about 6 days old. This presumably applies to microscopical examination of living embryos. Among those dying during the last week of the incubation period the two types can be differentiated by the short legs of the heterozygotes, and classification of such embryos is as easy as in hatched chicks, or more so (Landauer and Dunn, 1930).

Genetics. The original suggestion of Cutler (1925) that all adult creeper fowls are heterozygotes was confirmed by the extensive investigations of Landauer and Dunn (1930), who found that a dominant mutation, *Cp*, produced the condition in heterozygotes and is lethal to the homozygote. The latter die, not, as Cutler thought, after hatching, but usually early in the fourth day of incubation.

Matings of creeper × normal yielded these same types in the ratio of 1:1, but when both parents were creepers the ratio, when both hatched chicks and embryos dying late were counted, was 2 creepers:1 normal (Table 7).

Creepers from the United States, Germany, Scotland, and the Marquesas Islands are genetically identical, and Landauer (1942) has found that the same mutation is responsible for the short legs of Japanese Bantams.

Although the creeper mutation is undesirable in most poultry populations, it has proved of some importance to students of poultry genetics

TABLE 7. SEGREGATION OF THE Cp GENE *

Parental types	Number of chicks		Chicks and dead in shell	
	Cp	cp	Cp	cp
Creeper × normal.......	910	1,122	1,676	1,661
Expected, 1:1........	1,016	1,016	1,668.5	1,668.5
Creeper × Creeper......	412	227	775	388
Expected, 2:1........	426	213	775.3	387.7

* Landauer and Dunn.

because the demonstration by Serebrovsky and Petrov (1928) that creeper is closely linked with the gene for single comb provided the first case of autosomal linkage known in the fowl.

Studies of homozygous and heterozygous creepers have shown that the abnormality is the same as the achondroplasia, or chondrodystrophy, of man. A similar mutation has given rise to the short-legged Dexter cattle, in which it is also lethal to homozygotes.

Effects on Homozygous Embryos. Landauer (1932) concluded that the lethal effect of the $Cp\,Cp$ condition results from a general retardation of growth and its eventual cessation. However, Rudnick and Hamburger (1940) and Cairns (1941) obtained evidence that early death of homozygous embryos may result from the gene's preventing formation of the vascular system.

Most of them die during the first 6 days. Embryonic mortality in that period was found by Landauer and Dunn to be only 6.9 per cent in creeper normal matings (which could yield no homozygotes) but 28.5 and 23.3 per cent in different kinds of matings in which both parents were creepers.

A few of the homozygotes escape early death only to die during the last week of incubation. These are subnormal in size and show striking abnormalities (Landauer, 1933, 1939). All the extremities are short, but the reduction of the legs is proportionately greater than that in the wings. In some cases the humerus and femur are represented only by cartilaginous rudiments. The radius and ulna are usually fused in one bone, and the tibia and fibula are similarly fused in nearly every case. In the skull and shoulder girdle the bones laid down in cartilage have faulty ossification, while the membrane bones formed in connective tissue are little affected, if at all. Thus the scapula and coracoid are abnormal, but the clavicle is normal. The eyelids are rudimentary; both eyes are smaller than normal, and the sclerotic coat lacks cartilage. In general these embryos present the syndrome known as *phokomelia*.

The mean proportion of phokomelic embryos was found by Landauer and Dunn (1930) to be only 1.6 per cent in matings of creepers within one line and 2 per cent in crosses of different lines, but in crosses of creepers with Japanese Bantams the proportion of such survivors was much higher (Landauer, 1942). Presumably the hybrid vigor associated with outcrosses tends to prevent early death, but this does not account for the high proportion of homozygotes surviving in pure Japanese Bantams. Even in matings within that breed there were more such survivors than among the creepers, and in one case 93 per cent of the expected number of homozygotes were recovered as phokomelic embryos late in incubation.

Oddly enough, the proportion of homozygotes surviving to later stages is almost tripled when the eggs are incubated during the first 24 hours at 96°F. instead of the usual 99 to 100°F. (Landauer, 1944). This suggests that ordinarily the $Cp\,Cp$ genotype is influencing development even at that stage and that the bad effects are lessened by retardation of development.

Effects on Heterozygotes. The Cp gene is lethal not only to homozygotes but apparently also to about 5 per cent of the heterozygotes. This is shown (Table 7) by the deficiency of creepers among chicks hatched from creeper $\times$ normal matings. Since the ratio is restored to the expected 1:1 when the dead in shell are added to the hatched chicks, it is evident that more creepers than normal chicks die during the last few days of incubation.

Another peculiar effect is that hens carrying the gene lay eggs that are subject to about 5 per cent higher embryonic mortality than eggs from their non-creeper sisters, when both types of females are mated to the same males (Landauer and Bliss, 1943). This effect is associated with greater variability in the relative weight of the shell in eggs laid by creepers. Landauer (1935) also found in matings involving creepers some embryos with peculiar abnormalities not found in other stocks. These included lack of various parts of the legs or of the wings, misplaced bones in the limbs, and missing vertebrae.

Susceptibility to Nutritional Disorders. On diets deficient in vitamin D, creeper chicks were found by Landauer (1934a) to show the onset of rickets at an earlier age than non-creepers and, as judged by their difficulty in walking, more pronounced symptoms of that disorder. Histologically the rachitic creepers had fewer osteoblasts, a greater porosity of bone, and less of the osteoid tissue, which is formed in excessive amounts by rachitic non-creepers. These and other differences indicate that the creepers have less defence against rickets than non-creepers.

Similarly, the progeny of creeper females were more susceptible than the progeny of their normal siblings to the toxic effects of selenium, when that substance was supplied in seleniferous grain. Embryonic mortality at early stages was higher in the embryos from creepers. At later stages the usual teratological effects of selenium were found in both groups but were exaggerated in the embryos from the creeper dams (Landauer, 1946).

These cases are especially interesting because they show that a mutation appearing at first sight to be expressed only in a structural modification may include among its manifold effects a lowered defence against nutritional disease. Conversely, it emphasizes a point overlooked by many investigators in nutrition, namely, that the expression of a nutritional disorder varies considerably according to the genetic constitution of the animal affected.

Lethal in Short-Legged Cornish Indian Games, *Cl*

In proportion to the weight of their bodies, Cornish (Indian Game) fowls have comparatively short, thick legs which, in typical specimens, are set wide apart. The head is very broad and comparatively short. Among those with the shortest legs Landauer (1935*a*) found a lethal factor the effects of which are somewhat like those of the creeper gene.

Morphology. In short-legged Cornish fowls the tibio-tarsus and tarso-metatarsus are markedly shortened. The fibula is well developed and, just as in creepers, is fused at its distal end with the epiphysis of the tibia. It is probable that not all birds showing this condition are affected by the same gene, since some Cornish carried a lethal factor and others did not. Those heterozygous for the lethal gene did not differ phenotypically from those lacking it, and the two genotypes had to be distinguished by breeding tests.

Embryos homozygous for the lethal die during the last few days of incubation or are still alive at 22 days but unable to hatch. They have very short legs and wings and a short, broad head with bulging eyes and a very short beak. The legs are not shortened as much as in the phokomelic homozygous creepers but more so than in heterozygous creepers. Measurements of the bones (Landauer, 1939*a*) showed that the proportional reduction of the long bones of the limbs increased with increasing distance of any bone from the body. Even the toes are reduced in length.

Genetics. It is clear from Landauer's studies that a single gene in the homozygous condition is responsible for the lethal effect but that other genes, not lethal, may cause the short-legged condition in Cornish.

Reciprocal crosses between Cornish fowls carrying the lethal and heterozygous creepers yielded no deformed embryos and hatches of 81 and 88 per cent of the fertile egs. It is evident from this that the *Cp* mutation is quite distinct from the Cornish lethal. The symbol *Cl* is proposed for the latter.

Crosses between short-legged Cornish and other breeds produced birds in which the long bones of the legs were uniformly intermediate between the extremes in the parents. The gene or genes shortening the legs in Cornish may therefore be considered as incompletely dominant to the normal condition.

Chondrodystrophy, *ch*

Strictly speaking *chondrodystrophy* means an abnormal nourishment of cartilage. The term has been applied to various conditions in which the skeleton develops abnormally. These include (1) achondroplasia (as in creeper fowls); (2) a sporadic form of chondrodystrophy, not yet proved genetic, in which the tibiae are bent and the lower beak shortened (Dunn, 1927; Hutt and Greenwood, 1929, and others); and (3) a micromelia caused by deficiency of manganese and characterized by shortening of the long bones without bending of the tibiae (Lyons and Insko, 1937).

A fourth type of chondrodystrophy that was proved hereditary by Lamoreux (1942) is considered in this section.

Morphology. The abnormal embryos of this kind resemble very closely the sporadic type referred to above. Most of them die during the last few days of incubation, but many are still alive on the twenty-first and twenty-second days. These are usually unable to hatch without assistance. Abnormalities of the skeleton (Fig. 20) include extreme shortening of the lower beak, with corresponding overgrowth of the upper one to give a "parrot-beak" appearance. The long bones of the limbs are shortened, particularly the tibia, which is nearly always bent, sometimes almost at an angle of 90 degrees. Bones of the legs are shortened more than bones of the wing. One chick with an extreme form of this mutation was helped out of the egg but was quite unable to stand. At the other end of the range of variability, some of these chondrodystrophic chicks are almost normal, and one was reared to maturity.

Genetics. Lamoreux found the abnormality to be caused by an autosomal recessive gene, *ch*, in the homozygous condition. During 5 years, matings of heterozygotes together yielded 1,713 embryos over 10 days of age, and 22.5 per cent of these were chondrodystrophic. Evidence that some of the homozygotes were sufficiently normal to hatch and to escape recognition was found in the fact that in matings producing only modified types, and no extreme cases, the proportion of recognizably chondrodystrophic embryos was only 13.8 per cent. One such "normal overlap" was a male which, when mated with proven carriers, yielded a 1:1 ratio of normal and chondrodystrophic embryos, as would be expected if he were homozygous.

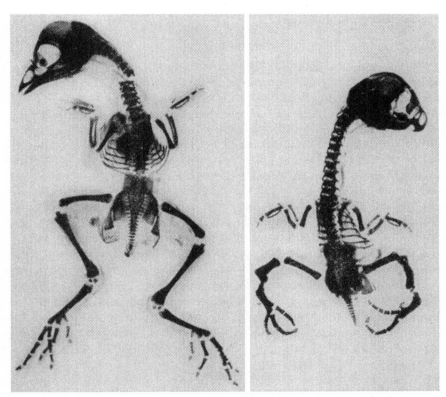

Fig. 20. Recessive chondrodystrophy in a chick that lived to 21 days of incubation (*right*) and a normal chick of the same age (*left*); both skeletons cleared and stained with alizarin. Shortening of the lower beak, marked reduction of the limbs, and bending of the tibiae and tarso-metatarsi are typical of this lethal character. (*From Lamoreux in J. Heredity.*)

This unifactorial type of chondrodystrophy differs from the sporadic type in that it affects females as much as males, and its frequency does not decline during the summer matings. Further evidence that the two conditions are genetically quite distinct was provided by five hens which had produced an unusually high proportion (21 per cent) of chondrodystrophic embryos of the sporadic type in matings quite *apart* from Lamoreux's inherited type. When these same hens were then mated to a male of the genotype, *Ch ch,* the proportion of chondrodystrophic embryos in their progeny dropped to 6.7 per cent. Had the sporadic and hereditary types been related in any way, this second mating should have increased still further the proportion of chondrodystrophic embryos from these five hens, whereas it actually decreased their number, even though half of the embryos must have gotten the *ch* gene from their sire. The two types are evidently quite different.

Wingless, *wg*

The remarkable abnormalities of this mutation, studied by Waters and Bywaters (1943), are not confined to the skeleton, but it is appropriate to discuss the condition under that heading.

Morphology. Most of the affected embryos lack wings completely, but a few may show various degrees of development between rudimentary humeri and normal wings. They are recognizable at 4 days of incubation by the absence of wing buds. When the legs have the third and fourth toes, these are always syndactylous. Toes are frequently missing or duplicated; the hallux may be misplaced, and down feathers are found on the feet. The lungs are missing or represented only by vestiges, and air sacs are apparently lacking, also. The metanephros, or definitive kidney, is not developed, but the mesonephros is present at 21 days of incubation. As in many other abnormalities of chick embryos some of the down is "clubbed," *i.e.*, in the form of little spherical granules.

Genetics. All these abnormalities result from homozygosity for an autosomal recessive gene. The symbol *wg* is proposed. Heterozygotes are apparently recognizable only by breeding tests. Five such females, all full sisters, when mated with a full brother yielded 111 normal:30 wingless, but six other full sisters produced none at all.

Micromelia

A lethal abnormality that superficially resembles Landauer's lethal in Cornish fowls is called *micromelia* by Asmundson (1942*a*), who found it in White Leghorns.

Morphology. As the name signifies, the limbs of the affected embryos are small. The femur, tibia, and tarso-metatarsus are less than half of the normal length, but much thicker. For example, the tibia, which is most affected, was in Asmundson's material only 41 per cent of normal length but 178 per cent of normal thickness. The amount of ash in the abnormal bones was about the same as in normal controls, but their dry weight was less. Consequently, the proportion of ash was higher in bones of the micromelic embryos.

Genetics. This abnormality apparently results from the simultaneous action of two pairs of autosomal recessive genes. The ratio of normal to micromelic embryos in families that contained any of the latter was 716:47. This is a very close fit to the 15:1 ratio expected if duplicate dominant genes resulted in normal development and if micromelic embryos are double recessives. The sex ratio in 40 of these was 22 ♂ ♂ :18 ♀ ♀.

None of these micromelic chicks hatched. Among 47 of them, 42 were alive at 14 days of incubation and many even at 22 days; hence the lethal effect must be exerted chiefly in the later stages of incubation.

Short Long Bones

This paradoxical name best describes a semi-lethal mutation in Bronze turkeys studied by Asmundson (1944).

Morphology. In homozygous affected poults the long bones of the limbs are subnormal in length but are not reduced as much as in the micromelic ones. These bones are thicker than normal. The femur is reduced less than the tibia and the humerus less than the radius and ulna. About 80 per cent of these birds die during the later stages of incubation, and only about 3 per cent reach maturity. The few that do so have shanks that are about 80 per cent of the normal length. Three such males weighed about 2,000 gm. less than normal ones of the same strain. They walked awkwardly and were unable to mate.

Genetics. This is a simple autosomal mutation. Heterozygotes mated *inter se* yielded ratios of 590 normal:184 short, the deviation from 3:1 being less than 10 in each class. It is not completely recessive, for heterozygotes can be detected by measuring the shank at 24 weeks of age, and even (with less accuracy) at hatching. In mature heterozygotes the shank is reduced, but length of the keel is not.

Similar Mutation in the Fowl. The abnormal chicks found by Hays (1944) in Rhode Island Reds resembled closely the condition in Asmundson's short-legged turkeys. Bones of the limbs were shortened and thickened, but not bent as in the various degrees of chondrodystrophy described by different investigators. The ratio of normal to abnormal chicks (172:54) from parents that produced any with this abnormality indicated that a unifactorial recessive mutation was responsible. About 30 per cent of the abnormal chicks hatched, but they were unable to walk, and all died within a week. The fact that the apparently normal siblings of these chicks experienced higher mortality to 6 months of age than controls suggests that the gene is lethal to some of the heterozygotes.

Lethal Dwarfs in the Pigeon

An abnormality found by Hollander (1945) in pigeons that died during later stages of incubation was designated as achondroplasia but would appear from the illustrations of his specimens to be considerably different from achondroplasia as it is manifested in the fowl and in other animals (Fig. 21). Moreover, it is different from any other hereditary ab-

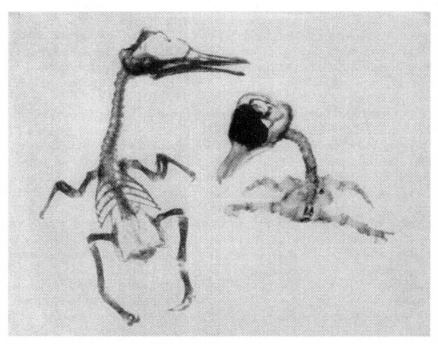

Fig. 21. Hereditary lethal dwarfing in the pigeon (*right*) compared with a normal embryo of the same age (with eyes removed). Both skeletons were cleared and stained with alizarin. Although a similar mutation has not yet been found in the fowl, it should be watched for in that species. (*From Hollander in J. Heredity.*)

normality thus far recognized in birds. Not only are the limbs greatly reduced, but so is the whole vertebral column. Even the bones of the head are reduced in size. There is no distortion of the cranium as in typical achondroplasia, and no "parrot beak." This extreme abnormality is apparently an autosomal recessive character, lethal to all homozygotes.

CROOKED BREASTBONE

The Carinatae, or Neognathae, that group of the Neornithes to which the majority of existing birds belong, is characterized by the presence on the lower aspect of the sternum of a projecting blade to which are attached the muscles operating the wings. This part of the sternum, known as the "carina," "crista sterni," or "keel," is normally straight but in fowls and turkeys is often found to be crooked. The abnormality is a source of considerable loss to poultrymen, particularly to turkey raisers, because dressed birds with badly crooked keels are unattractive in appearance, difficult to carve, and usually salable only at a discount that may run as much as 10 cents per pound.

Niemann (1931) found that 3.3 per cent of 50,613 turkeys shipped from Nevada had crooked keels, the incidence in different flocks being as shown in Table 8. Although experimental investigation of this abnormal-

TABLE 8. PROPORTIONS OF CROOKED KEELS IN 293 NEVADA TURKEY FLOCKS

Crooked keels per hundred birds	Flocks affected per hundred flocks
Less than 1	43
1–3	20
3–5	12
5–10	11
10–20	10
More than 20	4

ity has thus far been confined almost entirely to fowls, it seems probable that conclusions reached with that species are equally applicable to turkeys.

Poultrymen have for a long time argued about the causes of crooked breastbones, with roosting conditions, climatic conditions, heredity, and diet all considered more or less responsible. It is now clear that the abnormality results from hereditary susceptibility to faulty ossification in the sternum but that environmental influences are very important in determining the extent to which the hereditary weakness is expressed.

Morphology. The keel may be bent to the right or left, may show various degrees of concavity, or may be both concave and bent. These different forms and the different degrees of abnormality apparently all result from the same underlying condition. Bending to the right side is more common than bending to the left. Among 1,755 birds with crooked keels Warren (1937) found that 62 per cent were bent to the right, the proportion varying in different groups from 50 to 68 per cent.

Genetics. This character is so variable in its expression and so subject to environmental modification that in some matings no hereditary susceptibility may be apparent. Thus Biegert (1937) found that, when normal males were mated with females having keels (1) markedly crooked, (2) slightly curved, and (3) straight, the proportion of crooked breasts among the offspring was not significantly different in the three groups. However, when breeders were selected on the basis of the incidence of crooked keels in the whole family, Warren (1937) found the influence of heredity immediately apparent in the first generation from previously unselected stock. Crooked-keeled parents from families with many affected birds produced offspring of which 80 per cent developed the defect. Straight-keeled parents from families with few crooked keels produced at the same time progeny of which only 4 per cent had crooked keels. Further selection through six generations did not significantly decrease the incidence of crooked keels but did produce a strain in which only 3 per cent of the males showed the defect even under roosting conditions conducive to maximum development of crooked keels. At the same time and under the same conditions the incidence of the defect in males of the susceptible strain was 88 per cent.

Multiple factors are apparently responsible for differences in susceptibility to crooked keel. Warren found the F_1 generation from a cross of resistant $\times$ susceptible strains to be intermediate. In backcrosses to the crooked-keel strain, 67 per cent of the male progeny had crooked keels, whereas in backcrosses to the straight-keel strain only 32 per cent of the male progeny were affected. In reciprocal crosses there was no evidence of sex-linked genes with major effects.

TABLE 9. BACKCROSSES TO MALES FROM EACH OF THE PARENTAL STRAINS
(FROM WARREN)

| Phenotype of F_1 ♀ ♀ | Crooked-keel progeny, per cent | | | |
| | From ♂ ♂ of crooked-keel strain | | From ♂ ♂ of straight-keel strain | |
	♀ ♀	♂ ♂	♀ ♀	♂ ♂
Straight keel...........	62	65	15	26
Crooked keel...........	54.5	72	31	39

In Warren's backcrosses (Table 9) F_1 females with crooked keels had a higher proportion of affected progeny than did F_1 females with straight breastbones when both were mated to the same males. It is evident, since these F_1 birds were not genetically identical, that six generations of selection had failed to make the resistant and susceptible parent strains homozygous for the genes affecting development of the keel.

Reduction of the frequency of this defect is most likely to be accomplished, as with other multiple-factor conditions, by consistent use of the progeny test and the selection of breeders on the basis of the family record rather than on the appearance or performance of the individual. Mass selection, *i.e.*, the elimination from the breeding pen of all birds with crooked breasts, is important but is not enough. It is quite possible that the exceptional straight-keeled bird from a family in which the majority have crooked breasts may transmit more genetic susceptibility to the defect than the occasional bird with a crooked keel from a family in which all the rest are normal. Elimination of crooked breastbones will be easier in some strains than in others, since Warren found that unselected strains of Leghorns differed in susceptibility to the defect.

Physiological Basis. Since crooked keels may be considered as indicating softer bone and faulty ossification, a similarity to rickets is evident. However, the independence of the two conditions is shown by the fact that in 8-week-old birds with crooked keels the ash content of the leg bones is normal at 47 to 49 per cent (Platt, 1932; Warren, 1937), whereas in rachitic chickens the ash content of the bones is reduced below 40 per cent. There is no difference between crooked- and straight-keeled, adult laying females with respect to blood calcium and phosphorus or between males of susceptible and straight-keeled strains with respect to non-diffusible calcium (Warren, 1937). Crooked keel is obviously not the same as rickets. Warren's experiments, reported below, show clearly that the abnormality results from a specific weakness in the sternum.

Chicks from crooked-keel and straight-keel strains were reared on a rachitogenic diet containing enough vitamin D to induce a borderline condition but not severe rickets. Controls of both strains were reared on a normal diet.

TABLE 10. ASH CONTENT OF BONES OF 8-WEEK-OLD CHICKS PER CENT (FROM WARREN)

Strain	Condition of keel	Rachitogenic diet.		Normal diet	
		Leg bone	Sternum	Leg bone	Sternum
Straight keel............	Straight	39.7	27.8	51.5	37.8
Crooked keel............	Straight	38.5	24.7	50.0	38.6
Straight keel............	Crooked	37.9	19.9	No birds	No birds
Crooked keel............	Crooked	38.9	16.8	48.6	32.9

The figures for bone ash at 8 weeks (Table 10) show clearly the following points:

1. The percentage of ash in the sternum of normal birds on normal diets is less than in the leg bone (specific bone not stated, probably the femur).

2. Birds with crooked keels on normal diets have abnormal ossification in the sternum. This is aggravated and bone ash is still lower on a rachitogenic diet.

3. Birds with crooked keel are no more susceptible to rickets than those with normal keel since the leg bones of the two groups on a rachitogenic diet do not differ in ash content.

4. Birds of the crooked-keel strain are more susceptible to abnormal ossification of the sternum than those of the other strain, since in both comparisons on the rachitogenic diet the ash of the sternum is 3.1 per cent less for the crooked-keel strain than for the other.

5. Crooked keel results from a specific weakness in the sternum, not from faulty metabolism of calcium or from generally defective ossification throughout the body.

From the evolutionary point of view it would be of interest to know whether or not this defect of the sternum is confined to the carina or whether all parts of that rather complex bone are affected. The carina is a modification which makes flight possible, but we do not know for certain whether birds that fly do so because they have a carina or whether birds have developed a carina because they fly. The fact that carinate birds which have lost the power of flight have vestigial keels does not tell which is cause and which effect. The discovery of a hereditary condition preventing full development of the carina is of interest even though it does not answer this problem.

Factors Affecting Manifestation of Crooked Keel. *Sex.* In Warren's experiments more males were affected than females in three out of four groups, and among birds with crooked keel the ratio of very crooked to slightly crooked was 3:1 in males but only 2:1 in females. A similar higher incidence in males was observed by Carstens *et al.* (1936). The difference probably results from the fact that the rapid growth of chicks slows down sooner in females than in males and ossification is completed earlier in the former sex. The ash content of the tibia is higher in females than in males at 9 or 10 weeks (Holmes *et al.*, 1932; Schroeder, 1933). A similar difference probably prevails in other parts of the skeleton. Since most of the crooked keels appear after that age, it is natural that more males should be affected than females.

This difference between the sexes is not evident in all populations, and in some flocks it disappears entirely. In Warren's birds (Table 11) there were even more females affected than males in one of the largest groups. If his four populations be arranged in order of decreasing incidence of

TABLE 11. SEX DIFFERENCE IN THE INCIDENCE OF CROOKED KEELS (FROM WARREN)

| Population | Total birds both sexes | Crooked keels, per cent | | Difference |
		♀♀	♂♂	♂♂ − ♀♀
1. Selected strains...........	1,380	65.7	63.1	−2.6
2. Strain crosses.............	1,531	25.8	33.3	7.5 *
3. F₁ generation.............	1,010	45.3	50.5	5.2 *
4. Backcrosses..............	890	44.1	50.9	6.8 *

* Statistically significant difference.

crooked keels (1, 3, 4, 2), the sex differences increase in the same order. In other words, the difference between the sexes was greatest in the flock with fewest crooked keels and was insignificant in the selected strains in which about 65 per cent of the birds were affected. Presumably, when the environment and the genetic constitution of the population are such that a majority of the birds become affected, the differential susceptibility of the sexes is not an important factor in determining whether a bird will have a crooked keel or a straight one. Thus Platt (1932) found that, when environmental conditions were extremely bad, two-thirds of his birds had crooked keels at 8 weeks of age, long before sex differences in the time of completion of ossification could be an important influence. Conversely, when conditions are such that the majority are unaffected, the fact that growth of the skeleton ceases later in males than in females is likely to cause larger differences between the proportions of males and females that develop crooked breasts.

Roosts. Manifestation of an inherent susceptibility to crooked keel is markedly enhanced in chickens allowed to roost. Platt found that in White Leghorn cockerels on a normal diet the incidence of crooked keels at 8 weeks of age was 64 and 44 per cent in two lots that had been allowed to roost at 3 weeks. Non-roosting controls all had straight keels. Similarly, the proportion of females with crooked breastbones at 28 weeks was found by Carstens *et al.* (1936) to be three to five times as great (60 to 64 per cent) in birds with roosts as in those not allowed to roost. This does not mean that the best way to prevent crooked keels is to keep the birds from roosting, for any advantage in this direction is likely to be more than offset by the risks associated with crowding on the floor. Platt (1933) has shown that the degree of curvature is much less with roosts 3 inches wide than with those 1 inch wide.

Obviously, wide perches are desirable, but the data of Warren (1937) show that the incidence of the defect is more likely to be lessened by breeding than by modifications in the roosting conditions. When chicks of his crooked-keel strain were provided at 2 weeks of age with roosts 1 inch wide, 70 per cent of them had crooked keels at 24 weeks. In controls of the same strain not given roosts at all, 60 per cent were affected even under these favorable conditions. In contrast to this, among birds of the strain bred for straight keels and reared under the same conditions, none whatever had crooked keels, even in the group using the narrow roosts. It is evident from this that improvement of the genetic constitution of the bird provides a means of eliminating crooked keels that is much more effective than any attempt at control by removal of roosts.

Age at Roosting. Where the poultryman is raising chicks or poults purchased from hatcheries or breeders, he is unable to control the breeding except by exercising care in the choice of his stock and giving preference to poultrymen doing the right kind of breeding. In such an enterprise, the owner of the growing birds, particularly the turkey raiser, must use every means at his disposal to reduce the incidence of crooked keels. One of these is the provision of wide perches. Another is the withholding of roosts till a comparatively late age. Warren found that in chickens genetically susceptible to crooked keel the frequency of the defect at 24 weeks among birds provided with 1-inch roosts at different ages declined consistently from 92 per cent in those given perches at 4 weeks to only 11 per cent in those not given roosts till 12 weeks of age. This suggests a means of partial control for the poultryman able to avoid worse losses from crowding on the floor.

Other Conditions. Warren's data show a tendency for the earlier hatched birds to be affected more than April chicks. A similar trend was noted by Carstens *et al.* and Biegert (1937). The latter investigators found no relation between the degree of inbreeding and the occurrence of crooked keels in unselected stock. Biegert was unable to prevent or cure the defect by changing the amount of calcium, phosphorus, vitamin D, or protein in the diet. In his experiments the incidence of crooked keels in the progeny was not related to the hatchability of the eggs from which they came. In each of four different strains studied by Warren, the females which later developed crooked keels were heavier at 8 weeks than those which did not. This suggests that birds growing most rapidly are most subject to the deformity.

Relation to Economic Characters. All the investigators named in the previous paragraph and Asmundson (1921) agree that curvature of the keel has no deleterious effect on egg production. Carstens *et al.* and Biegert found that the eggs laid by birds with crooked keels hatched just as well as those from hens with straight ones. Apparently the economic loss caused by the deformity is no greater than that caused by the reduction in the market value of the dressed bird.

NON-GENETIC CONGENITAL VARIATIONS

In addition to the hereditary deviations from normality described in the foregoing pages there are a number of peculiar abnormalities of the skeleton that are not hereditary. They recur at rare intervals and apparently result from accidents in development. Most kinds of teratological development are fatal to the embryo before termination of the incubation period. The variations listed below are occasionally found in hatched chicks.

Sternum without Carina. The membranous primordia of the sternum originate on both sides of the body as expansions from the lower ends of the ribs. When these two primordia meet in the median line, their concrescence is followed shortly after by projection of the carina (Lillie, 1919). Failure of the two halves of the sternum to come together is probably responsible for the occasional appearance of a fowl in which the keel of the sternum is entirely lacking. In such birds the pericardial cavity is unprotected, and the beating of the heart is easily noted by palpation where the anterior end of the carina would normally be. A breeding test by Dunn (1924) showed that the condition was not hereditary in the one keelless cockerel tested.

Missing Limbs. A White Wyandotte that lacked both wings at hatching attained normal size and laid well (Terry, 1919). It learned to leap 2½ feet to its perch. Its offspring were normal, but only one generation was reported. A similar bird, the anatomy of which was studied by Kirkham and Haggard (1915), had a complete shoulder girdle but entirely lacked the bones of the wing. A Leghorn lacking the left wing at hatching was observed by the author. Prior to its death at about 8 weeks it was unable to balance or to stand up. The left clavicle and coracoid were much shortened, making an asymmetrical furcula.

Chicks lacking one leg occasionally hatch, but it is difficult to account for the appearance of 11 such birds from one setting of 13 eggs reported by Maas (1935). In these one limb was normal, but only the femur was present on the other side. In some birds the right limb was defective, in others the left. Seven of the birds were still alive at 5 months. Earlier progeny of the parent birds were normal.

Duplicity. Chicks with four legs and four wings occasionally hatch but do not survive. A more common abnormality is the persistence of one or two extra legs, usually attached to the synsacrum and showing various degrees of completeness. A number of these were illustrated by Aldrovandus in 1600, and they have been described many times in the literature on teratological development. The many different types of

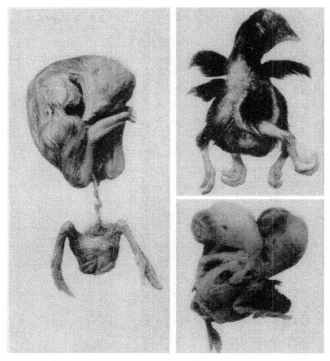

FIG. 22. Three kinds of non-genetic abnormalities of chick embryos. *Left,* omphalomelus; *right above,* ischiopagus, with four wings and four legs; *right below,* anadidymus, with two heads and a single body. (*From Hutt and Greenwood in Proc. Roy. Soc. Edinburgh.*)

duplicity found in chicks and ducklings are classified and illustrated by Komai and Nakamura (1938). Three of these found among other monsters by Hutt and Greenwood (1929a) are shown in Fig. 22. These include *omphalomelus,* in which the acardiacus, or parasite, consists only of a pelvic girdle and legs attached by a strand in the umbilical region; *anadidymus,* with duplication of anterior parts of the body; and *ischiopagus,* with a single head, but four wings and four legs. None of these types of duplicity has yet been shown to have any genetic basis.

Literature Cited

Aldrovandus, U. 1600. "Ornithologiae." Tomus Alter.

Asmundson, V. S. 1921. The relation of the keel bone to egg production. *Sci. Agr.*, 1:30–33; 63–67.

———. 1936. Abnormal upper mandible, a new lethal mutation in the domestic fowl. *J. Heredity*, 27:401–404.

———. 1942. Skeletal abnormalities of short-spined turkeys. *Proc. Soc. Exptl. Biol. Med.*, 50:120–123.

———. 1942a. An inherited micromelia in the domestic fowl. *J. Heredity*, 33:328–330.

———. 1944. Inherited shortening of the long bones in the turkey. *J. Heredity*, 35:295–299.

Barfurth, D. 1911. Experimentelle Untersuchung über die Vererbung der Hyperdactylie bei Hühnern. III. Mitteilung. Kontrollversuche und Versuche am Landhuhn. *Arch. Entwicklungsmech. Organ*, 31:479–511.

———. 1911a. Experimentelle Untersuchung über die Vererbung der Hyperdactylie bei Hühnern. IV. Mitteilung. Der Flügelhöcker des Hühnchens, eine rudimentäre Hyperdactylie. *Arch. Entwicklungsmech. Organ.*, 33:255–273.

Baumann, L., and W. Landauer. 1944. On the expression of polydactylism in the wings of fowl. *Anat. Record*, 90:225–233.

Biegert, H. 1937. Untersuchungen über Brustbeinverkrümmungen bei weissen Leghorn und rebhuhnfarbigen Italienern. *Arch. Geflügelk.*, 11:209–248.

Bond, C. J. 1920. On the left-sided incidence of the supernumerary digit in heterodactylous fowls. *J. Genetics*, 10:87–91.

———. 1926. Further observations on polydactyly and heterodactyly in fowls. *J. Genetics*, 14:253–256.

Brown, E. 1906. "Races of Domestic Poultry." London: Edward Arnold & Co.

Cairns, J. M. 1941. The "early lethal" action of the homozygous Creeper factor in the chick. *J. Exptl. Zoöl.*, 88:481–503.

Carstens, P., G. Wenzler, and J. Prüfer. 1936. Untersuchungen über die Verkrümmungen des Brustbeins beim Huhn. *Arch. Geflügelk.*, 10:97–129.

Castello, S. 1924. The *Gallus inauris* and the hen which lays blue eggs. *Book World's Poultry Congr., 2d Congr., Barcelona:* 113–118.

Cutler, I. E. 1925. Reptilian fowls. *J. Heredity*, 16:352–356.

Czaja, M. 1939. Ein semiletaler Faktor bei Hühnern, der Missbildungen der Wirbelsäule und des Beckens verursacht. *Proc. World's Poultry Congr., 7th Congr., Cleveland:* 55.

Danforth, C. H. 1919. The developmental relations of brachydactyly in the domestic fowl. *Am. J. Anat.*, 25:97–115.

———. 1919a. An hereditary complex in the domestic fowl. *Genetics*, 4:587–596.

———. 1932. Artificial and hereditary suppression of sacral vertebrae in the fowl. *Proc. Soc. Exptl. Biol. Med.*, 30:143–145.

Davenport, C. B. 1909. Inheritance of characteristics in domestic fowl. *Carnegie Inst. Wash. Pub.* 121.

Du Toit, P. J. 1913. Untersuchungen über das Synsacrum und den Schwanz von *Gallus domesticus* nebst Beobachtungen über Schwanzlosigkeit bei Kaulhühnern. *Jena. Z. Naturw.*, 49:149–312.

Dunn, L. C. 1924. A keelless cockerel. *J. Heredity*, 15:307–308.

Dunn, L. C. 1927. The occurrence of chondrodystrophy in chick embryos. II. The genetic evidence. *Arch. Entwicklungsmech. Organ.*, 110:341–365.

—— and W. Landauer. 1934. The genetics of the rumpless fowl with evidence of a case of changing dominance. *J. Genetics*, 29:217–243.

—— and ——. 1936. Further data on genetic modification of rumplessness in the fowl. *J. Genetics*, 33:401–405.

Fisher, R. A. 1930. "The Genetical Theory of Natural Selection." Oxford: Clarendon Press.

——. 1935. Dominance in poultry. *Phil. Trans. Roy. Soc. (London)* B, 225:195–226.

——. 1938. Dominance in poultry. Feathered feet, rose comb, internal pigment, and pile. *Proc. Roy. Soc. (London)* B, 125:25–48.

Harman, M. T., and F. Nelson. 1941. Polydactyl feet of two strains of chicks. *Am. Naturalist*, 75:540–549.

Hays, F. A. 1944. Chondrodystrophy in Rhode Island Reds. *Am. Naturalist*, 78:54–58.

Highmore, N. 1651. "The History of Generation." London: Printed by R. N., for John Martin.

Hollander, W. F. 1945. A lethal achondroplasia in the pigeon. *J. Heredity*, 36:297–300.

Holmes, A. D., M. G. Piggott, and W. B. Moore. 1932. The influence of sex on the size and composition of tibiae of growing chicks. *Poultry Sci.*, 11:243–249.

Hutt, F. B. 1929. Sex dimorphism and variability in the appendicular skeleton of the Leghorn fowl. *Poultry Sci.*, 8:202–218.

—— and A. W. Greenwood. 1929. Studies in embryonic mortality in the fowl. II. Chondrodystrophy in the chick. *Proc. Roy. Soc. Edinburgh*, 49:131–144.

—— and ——. 1929a. Studies in embryonic mortality in the fowl. III. Chick monsters in relation to embryonic mortality. *Proc. Roy. Soc. Edinburgh*, 49:145–155.

Jaap, R. G. 1939. Brachydactyly and syndactyly in ptilopod domestic fowl, *Gallus domesticus*. *Proc. Oklahoma Acad. Sci.*, 29:27–29.

Kaufmann-Wolf, M. 1908. Embryologische und anatomische Beiträge zur Hyperdactylie (Houdanhuhn). *Morph. Jahrb.*, 38:471–531.

Kirkham, W. B., and H. W. Haggard. 1915. A comparative study of the shoulder region of the normal and of a wingless fowl. *Anat. Record*, 9:159–180.

Komai, T., and K. Nakamura. 1938. Types of duplicity found in chicks and ducklings. *Mem. Coll. Sci., Kyoto Imp. Univ.*, B, 14:193–242.

Lamoreux, W. F. 1942. Hereditary chondrodystrophy in the fowl. *J. Heredity*, 33:275–283.

Landauer, W. 1928. The morphology of intermediate rumplessness in the fowl. *J. Heredity*, 19:453–467.

——. 1931. Untersuchungen über das Krüperhuhn. II. Morphologie und Histologie des Skelets, insbesondere des Skelets der langen Extremitätenknochen. *Z. mikroskop.-anat. Forsch.*, 25:115–180.

——. 1932. Studies on the Creeper fowl. III. The early development, and lethal expression of homozygous Creeper embryos. *J. Genetics*, 25:367–394.

——. 1933. Untersuchungen über das Krüperhuhn. IV. Die Missbildungen homozygoter Krüperembryonen auf späteren Entwicklungsstadien. *Z. mikroskop.-anat. Forsch.*, 32:359–412.

Landauer, W. 1934. Studies on the Creeper fowl. VI. Skeletal growth of Creeper chickens. *Storrs (Conn.) Agr. Expt. Sta..Bull.* 193.

———. 1934a. Studies on the Creeper fowl. VII. The expression of vitamin D deficiency (rickets) in Creeper chicks as compared with normal chicks. *Am. J. Anat.,* **55**:229–252.

———. 1935. Studies on the Creeper fowl. IX. Malformations occurring in the Creeper stock. *J. Genetics,* **30**:303–320.

———. 1935a. A lethal mutation in Dark Cornish fowl. *J. Genetics,* **31**:237–242.

———. 1938. Notes on cross-beak in fowl. *J. Genetics,* **37**:51–68.

———. 1939. Studies on the Creeper fowl. XII. Size of body, organs, and long bones of late homozygous Creeper embryos. *Storrs (Conn.) Agr. Expt. Sta. Bull.* 232.

———. 1939a. Studies on the lethal mutation of Cornish fowl. Growth in length of long bones and increase in weight of the body and of some organs. *Storrs (Conn.) Agr. Expt. Sta. Bull.* 233.

———. 1940. Studies on the Creeper fowl. XIII. The effect of selenium and the asymmetry of selenium-induced malformations. *J. Exptl. Zoöl.,* **83**:431–443.

———. 1941. A semi-lethal mutation in fowl affecting length of the upper beak and of the long bones. *Genetics,* **26**:426–439.

———. 1942. Studies on the Creeper fowl. XIV. The Japanese Bantam fowl. *Am. Naturalist,* **76**:308–317.

———. 1944. Length of survival of homozygous Creeper fowl embryos. *Science,* **100**:553–554.

———. 1945. Rumplessness of chicken embryos produced by the injection of insulin and other chemicals. *J. Exptl. Zoöl.,* **98**:65–77.

———. 1945a. Recessive rumplessness of fowl with kypho-scoliosis and supernumerary ribs. *Genetics,* **30**:403–428.

———. 1946. The results of selection against expression of the "short upper beak" mutation in fowl. *Am. Naturalist,* **80**:490–494.

———. 1948. The phenotypic modification of hereditary polydactylism of fowl by selection and by insulin. *Genetics,* **33**:133–157.

——— and L. Baumann. 1943. Rumplessness of chicken embryos produced by mechanical shaking of eggs prior to incubation. *J. Exptl. Zoöl.,* **93**:51–74.

——— and C. I. Bliss. 1943. Studies on the Creeper fowl. XV. Maternal inheritance in survival of embryos from reciprocal crosses involving the Creeper factor. *Genetics,* **28**:218–226.

——— and L. C. Dunn. 1925. Two types of rumplessness in domestic fowls. *J. Heredity,* **16**:152–160.

——— and ———. 1930. Studies on the Creeper fowl. I. Genetics. *J. Genetics,* **23**:397–413.

Latimer, H. B. 1927. Postnatal growth of the chicken skeleton. *Am. J. Anat.,* **40**:1–57.

Lillie, F. R. 1919. "The Development of the Chick," 2d ed. New York: Henry Holt and Company, Inc.

Lyons, M., and W. M. Insko, Jr. 1937. Chondrodystrophy in the chick embryo produced by manganese deficiency in the diet of the hen. *Kentucky Agr. Expt. Sta. Bull.* 371:62–75.

Maas, W. 1935. Einbeinige Hühner. *Arch. Geflügelk.,* **9**:321–323.

McGibbon, W. H. 1946. The inheritance of short lower mandible in the fowl. *Poultry Sci.,* **25**:406.

Marble, D. R., J. A. Harper, and E. V. Hammers. 1944. Inheritance in the domestic fowl of a lethal condition affecting both mandibles. *Poultry Sci.*, **23**:114–117.

Mercier, L., and R. Poisson. 1925. Nouvelles observations sur les poules à becs croisés. Hérédité de la dystrophie. *Compt. rend. soc. biol.*, **93**:1214–1216.

―――― and ――――. 1927. Adaptation de la langue chez les poules à becs croisés. *Bull. biol. France Belg.*, **61**:326–332.

Mohr, O. L., and C. Wriedt. 1930. Short spine, a new recessive lethal in cattle; with a comparison of the skeletal deformities in short spine and in amputated calves. *J. Genetics*, **22**:279–297.

Niemann, K. W. 1931. Crooked breasts in turkeys. *Nevada Agr. Expt. Sta. Bull.* 122.

Platt, C. S. 1932. Early roosting as a cause of crooked keels in S. C. White Leghorn cockerels. *Poultry Sci.*, **11**:362.

――――. 1933. Crooked keels in relation to width of perch. *Poultry Sci.*, **12**:333–334.

Promptoff, A. W. 1928. Inheritance of structural types in the dorso-sacrum of domestic poultry. *J. Genetics*, **20**:29–51.

Punnett, R. C., and M. S. Pease. 1929. Genetic studies in poultry. VII. Notes on polydactyly. *J. Genetics*, **21**:341–366.

Rudnick, D., and V. Hamburger. 1940. On the identification of segregated phenotypes in progeny from Creeper fowl matings. *Genetics*, **25**:215–224.

Sawin, P. B. 1937. Preliminary studies of hereditary variation in the axial skeleton of the rabbit. *Anat. Record*, **69**:407–428.

Schmalhausen, I. I. 1934. The phenogenetics of some morphological characters in the domestic fowl (trans. title). *Compt. rend. acad. sci. U.R.S.S.* (n.s.), **2**:331–336.

Schmidt, J. 1922. Diallel crossings with the domestic fowl. *J. Genetics*, **12**:241–245.

Schneider, M., and L. C. Dunn. 1924. On the length and variability of the bones of the White Leghorn fowl. *Anat. Record*, **27**:229–239.

Schroeder, C. H. 1933. Sexual differences in calcification of chicks and the effect on assays. *Poultry Sci.*, **12**:256–260.

Serebrovsky, A. S., and S. G. Petrov. 1928. A case of close autosomal linkage in the fowl. *J. Heredity*, **19**:305–306.

Sturkie, P. D. 1943. Suppression of polydactyly in the domestic fowl by low temperature. *J. Exptl. Zoöl.*, **93**:325–346.

Taylor, L. W., and C. A. Gunns. 1947. Diplopodia: A lethal form of polydactyly in chickens. *J. Heredity*, **38**:66–76.

Terry, J. R. 1919. A wingless Wyandotte. *J. Heredity*, **10**:175.

Tuff, P., and S. Berge. 1936. Vererbung der Wirbelanzahl und der Körperlänge beim Schwein. *Z. Zücht.: Reihe B. Z. Tierzücht. Züchtgsbiol.*, **35**:214–238.

Warren, D. C. 1937. Physiologic and genetic studies of crooked keels in chickens. *Kansas State Agr. Expt. Sta. Tech. Bull.* 44.

――――. 1940. Brachydactyly in the fowl. *J. Heredity*, **31**:141–144.

――――. 1941. A new type of polydactyly in the fowl. *J. Heredity*, **32**:2–5.

――――. 1944. Inheritance of polydactylism in the fowl. *Genetics*, **29**:217–231.

――――, C. D. Mueller, and F. B. Hutt. 1944. Inheritance of ungual osteodystrophy in the fowl. *J. Heredity*, **35**:354–358.

Waters, N. F., and J. H. Bywaters. 1943. A lethal embryonic wing mutation in the domestic fowl. *J. Heredity*, **34**:213–217.

CHAPTER 4

STRUCTURAL VARIATIONS IN THE SKIN

Apart from mutations affecting the comb, which are conspicuous and have therefore been adopted as breed characteristics, our knowledge of variations in the skin of the fowl is meagre if it be compared with the long list of genetic mutations known to affect the skin of man. For convenience, the available information is arranged according to modifications of (1) the comb, (2) the spurs, and (3) other variations.

COMBS

It will be remembered that the comb is really the distinguishing character of the genus Gallus. Most of our domestic breeds have single combs, as have *G. gallus*, *G. sonneratii*, and *G. lafayettii*. None have the upright but unserrated comb of the Javan Jungle Fowl. It is evident that since domestication of the ancestors of our modern domestic fowls there have been a number of mutations affecting the combs. These have produced the rose, pea, walnut, and trifid combs, an apparently combless type, a duplex, or V, comb, and side sprigs. Within each of these types there are variations.

Historical Interest. The first report of William Bateson (1902) to the Evolution Committee of the Royal Society of London included among other interesting studies reports of F_1 and F_2 generations from crosses of Indian Games (pea comb), Dorkings (rose comb), and Wyandottes (rose comb) with single-combed White Leghorn fowls. The 3:1 segregations of these characters in the F_2 generation showed clearly that pea comb and rose comb were both dominant to single comb and depended for their expression upon single genes. This provided the first proof that Mendel's laws applied to the animal kingdom as well as to the plants with which their discoverer had carried out his experiments.

Bateson's report was presented on Dec. 17, 1901, but his experiments were begun in 1898. Unaware of Mendel's work till its discovery by De Vries, Correns, and von Tschermak in 1900, Bateson was working out the laws of inheritance in the same way as Mendel. The domestic fowl has not since lost the prominent role it then played as a suitable animal for genetic studies.

Single Comb. *Genetic Variation.* Since crosses of single-combed Plymouth Rocks, Rhode Island Reds and other heavy breeds with single-combed Leghorns and other Mediterranean breeds produce only single-combed offspring, it is evident that the same gene is responsible for the condition in both groups. However, its expression is affected differently by the other genes differentiating these two groups. In the heavy breeds the comb is comparatively small and usually does not lop over in females.

Fig. 23. William Bateson, whose studies with the fowl provided the first evidence that Mendel's laws apply to animals. (*Courtesy of Professor Punnett.*)

In the Mediterranean breeds it is much larger and lops over in nearly all females and even in some males. Axelsson (1933) found the mean area of the comb in square millimetres to be 1,321 in White Leghorns, 389 in Rhode Island Reds, and 561 in Barnevelders. According to him and to Pearl and Pearl (1909), the area of the comb is about three times as variable as its length.

Size of the comb is best measured by its weight, but since it is usually impractical with living birds to weigh the comb alone, some other measure is desirable. Jones and Lamoreux (1943) found that the product of length × height was more closely correlated with weight than were other measures tried by them, the correlations ranging in different groups from +.85 to +.96.

Modification by Hormones. The shrunken combs of Leghorn capons respond so readily with rapid growth to injections of male hormones that assay of preparations containing these substances by means of comb growth in Leghorn capons is now a standard procedure in endocrinology. Combs of Rhode Island Red and Barred Rock capons do not grow so rapidly as those of Leghorns and do not attain equal development with equal dosages. According to Hardesty (1931) the comb of the Leghorn male is composed of (1) a central core of stout bundles of connective tissue, (2) an intermediate layer of looser connective tissue, the fibres of which are spread apart by a matrix of mucoid, and (3) an outer layer of dense connective tissue containing a network of blood capillaries. In capons the mucoid is not produced, the intermediate layer is not distended, and the comb is flaccid and thin. The lack of pressure in the intermediate layer lessens the blood pressure in the capillaries of the peripheral layer, and the result is a pale comb instead of a bright red one.

Number of Points. In Axelsson's birds the mean number of points on the comb was 5.06 in White Leghorns, 4.55 in Rhode Island Reds, and 6 in Barnevelders. Evidence that genetic modifiers determine to some extent the number of points was found in the following relationships:

NUMBER OF POINTS ON THE COMB

Sire	Daughters, average
3	4.83
4	5.19
5	5.26
6	5.51

From Axelsson's studies it would seem that variations in the number of points depend upon multiple factors.

Response to Light. In addition to the afore-mentioned modifications of the single comb induced by the different internal environments resulting from different genetic constitutions and from hormones, there is at least one part of the external environment which affects the size of the single comb and that is light. It is not uncommon for the combs of confined males of Mediterranean breeds to grow large and flop over to one side. Noting that the combs and wattles varied in size inversely with the amount of light reaching the birds, Domm (1930) considered that such fowls received their biologically active rays of light only through these appendages and that increased growth of the comb and wattles helped to compensate for a decrease in sunlight.

In the experiments of Buckner *et al.* (1932), Leghorn cockerels raised in confinement to 24 weeks of age then had combs with an average weight of 79 gm., while in controls of the same age reared outdoors the average comb weight was only 30 gm. While growth and development of the upright comb in males are related to the activity of the testis, the extensive development of the comb in confined males is not caused by male hormones. Though large, the combs are flabby, soft, dark red, and comparatively thin, in contrast to the upright, turgid, bright red, and thick comb of the normal male. In Buckner's cockerels the confined birds with large combs had smaller testes than the males with the small combs raised outdoors.

Evidence that growth of the comb in juvenile males is affected less by the amount of light than by the temperature was found by Lamoreux (1943). At 10½ weeks of age, cockerels getting less than 4 hours of light daily had combs practically as big as those getting 14 hours of light. In birds maintained at 36°F. combs were only one-third the size of others held at 85°F.

Heterogonic Growth. Occasionally the comb in a Leghorn or Minorca male increases in size out of all proportion to the body. Such heterogonic growth may prove fatal when the comb is so large that the muscles of the neck become fatigued and the bird cannot hold up its head. In one such case (Hutt, 1928) that had persisted for 4 days, after the bird was reduced to the point of death from fatigue and inability to take in food and water, a large part of the comb, weighing 58.7 gm., was removed, and recovery quickly followed.

Direction of the Lop. In 6,625 Single-comb White Leghorn pullets that had lopped combs, Mueller and Hutt (1942) found 73 per cent to have combs lopping over on the right side of the head. This proportion was fairly consistent in different strains and years, although in one year the proportion of right-lopping combs ranged in four strains from 62 to 82 per cent. The direction of the lop in adults is independent of the direction in which the comb may be bent in newly hatched chicks. With respect to egg production, age at first egg, body weight at that time, and viability, there was no difference between left loppers and right loppers. About 5 per cent of the pullets had combs that were still upright, not lopped to either side, in December, and these tended to be inferior to their full sisters of the same age that then had lopping combs.

No influence of heredity on the direction of the lop could be detected in several different kinds of matings that should have revealed such an influence had it existed.

Rose Comb, *R*. This condition is caused by a dominant gene, *R*. As with the single comb, its appearance is usually somewhat different in Mediterranean breeds from the typical, small, low rose comb of Wyandottes and Rhode Island Reds. In birds of the Leghorn type the comb is larger and usually covered with more small papillae, or tubercles, than are found in Wyandottes. In males these are quite large. According to

Fisher (1938), the gene R affects the skeleton as well as the skin, making the frontal bones between the orbits about 25 per cent wider than in comparable males with single combs.

Although it was demonstrated by Bateson in 1902 that single comb is a simple recessive to rose comb, poultrymen have been very slow to realize the ease with which birds heterozygous for rose comb can be detected. To the breeder of any rose-combed breed, such heterozygotes are undesirable in the breeding pen because, whenever two of them are mated together, some of the unwanted single-combed birds are sure to be found in their progeny. The common appearance of these offtype birds has given rise to some misconceptions, the persistence of which for many years after elucidation of the basis for rose and single combs is almost incomprehensible. The following are typical:

1. Wyandotte females "throw" single combs in the first year, but not in the second. This erroneous idea resulted from the use of an Rr male in one year and an RR sire the next.

2. Single-combed segregates from Rose-comb Rhode Island Red parents should not be used in matings of Single-comb Reds lest they produce rose-combed progeny. Actually such single-combed segregates are no more likely to produce rose-combed progeny than are any other single-combed birds.

Tests for Homozygosity. It happens that rose comb comes closer to being completely dominant than almost any other character in the fowl, and consequently the RR and Rr genotypes cannot be distinguished except by a breeding test. This is the routine genetic test for homozygosity for a dominent autosomal gene, *i.e.*, mating the suspect to the recessive form. If a rose-combed bird be mated with a single-combed one, 12 or 15 chicks will reveal whether the rose-combed parent is RR or Rr. One single-combed chick or embryo from such a mating is proof of heterozygosity in the bird tested, but up to 8 or more progeny, all rose-combed, are necessary to prove homozygosity. In such a test (backcross to recessive) the probability of a heterozygous male producing no single-combed chicks in 5 offspring is 3.1 per 100, but the probability of his having none among 10 offspring is only 1 per 1,000.

The use in the breeding pen of a male proved homozygous for R will ensure that all his progeny are rose-combed, but half of those from any heterozygous dam will be heterozygous and can cause the reappearance of single combs in succeeding generations. If in addition to the sire the females in the breeding pen are also tested and proved homozygous, then all progeny must be homozygous and no further testing is necessary in succeeding generations except that of any new stock introduced.

Pea Comb, P. An incompletely dominant gene, P, causes this type of comb (Bateson, 1902). It is a breed characteristic in Cornish Indian Games, Brahmas, Sumatra Games, and other breeds. In homozygotes it is small and marked with three longitudinal rows of papillae, or points, the centre row being the most conspicuous. In heterozygotes from a single-combed parent, dominance is only partial, and the central blade is well developed, thickened, and irregular, while the lateral ridges may be quite inconspicuous and appear as knobs resembling side sprigs. This is particularly so when the single-combed parent is a Minorca or Leghorn. In such stock, classifications should be made in adults rather than in chicks. Bateson and Punnett (1908) found "certain types of pea comb in which so little of the pea character was evident that in young chicks they were easily mistaken for singles."

It was noticed by Munro and Kosin (1940) that in pea-combed birds a ridge of thickened skin runs lengthwise of the body in a mid-ventral line just under the keel of the breastbone. This "breast ridge" was found in several pea-combed breeds, and in crossbreds, but never except in birds with pea combs. It may be caused by some gene very closely linked with P but is more likely another manifestation of the latter.

Walnut Comb. This comb is found in Malays, Chanteclers, and Orloffs. In the last breed it is more often designated as a "cushion comb," and in Malays it is sometimes referred to as a "strawberry comb." These three terms give an idea of its conformation and variations. It is smaller than any of the combs previously described, and the surface is somewhat uneven, presenting irregular furrows. In adults there are occasionally small feathers in the comb, and in chicks there are small hair-like feathers. According to Punnett (1923) these are usually found in a transverse furrow near the back of the comb, and by them the walnut comb may be distinguished from others when the chicks are hatched.

The first interpretation of the genetic basis for this comb was made by Bateson and Punnett (1905a) and confirmed in their later studies (1906, 1908). It now provides in many texts on genetics a familiar example of the interaction of complementary genes. The walnut comb results from the presence of both P and R and is obviously the outcome of two different forces attempting to produce rose and pea combs.

Since birds with walnut combs may be *PP RR, Pp RR, PP Rr,* or *Pp Rr,* attainment of homozygosity for the two genes by mass selection (elimination of rose, pea, and single combs) is likely to be a slow process. Nevertheless, Bateson and Punnett found only 4 of 20 Malays tested by them to be heterozygous for P. In comparatively recent years the walnut comb has been incorporated as a breed characteristic in the Canadian Chantecler (Wilfrid, 1927) and in Leghorns in Russia (Petrov, 1935) because it is less susceptible to freezing in cold weather. In such work, use of the progeny test to detect breeders homozygous for P and R would greatly accelerate fixation of the desired type of comb.

Duplex Comb, D. In Houdans, Crèvecoeurs, La Flèche, Polish, Buttercups, and Pavloffs the comb is single at the anterior end but bifurcated in the posterior part. The whole comb may be single except for a slight split at the posterior of the blade (Fig. 24). In other cases it is V-shaped.

Fig. 24. Duplex comb. One of the lesser manifestations of this mutation, affecting only the posterior part of the blade.

In Breda males two small papillae on each side of the median line back from the upper beak indicate the duplex condition, although the birds appear practically combless. In most breeds with duplex combs the two branches of homozygotes are single spikes or short leaf-like structures, but in Buttercups the diverging halves form a cup ringed with points like those on single combs.

From the experiments of Bateson and Punnett (1905, 1908) with Buttercups and Bredas, Hurst (1905) with Houdans and Davenport (1906) with Polish and Houdans it seems probable that the same dominant autosomal gene, D, is responsible for the duplex comb wherever it appears. The variations described above may be attributed to

1. Incomplete dominance of D in heterozygotes.
2. Interaction of D with rose, single, or pea combs of different types.

3. Modifying genes accumulated in different breeds by artificial selection.
4. Possible modification of the comb by the crest in crested breeds.

Breda Comb, *bd*. Since the single comb is recessive to both pea and rose combs, the question naturally arises, Is single merely the absence of the other two, or is there a gene for the upright, pointed single comb? This question was answered by the experiments of Bateson and Punnett (1908) with the Dutch Bredas. In these birds the females appear to be combless, but two small papillae represent the comb in males. When crossed with singles, Bredas produced bifurcated single combs. It is clear, therefore, that birds with single combs possess a gene for upright development of the comb and that in Bredas this gene is represented by its recessive allele. Punnett (1923) suggests for this gene the symbol *s*, but since that had previously been preempted for the sex-linked character gold, the use of *bd* is proposed. Bateson and Punnett also raised a small F_2 generation from the cross Breda $\times$ rose comb. In it there appeared combs of the Breda type, as well as both normal and duplex single combs, which showed that the gene *Bd* was contributed by the rose-combed parent. Since this gene is presumably present in all combs except the peculiar type found in the Breda, it can be omitted from comb genotypes except in crosses where the Breda is concerned. The familiar diagram showing the F_2 genotypes from the rose $\times$ pea cross and omitting *Bd* does not give the complete genotypes for these combs. However, it simplifies the demonstration to omit the gene for single upright comb, and this does no harm so long as the student mentally adds *Bd Bd* to all the combinations of *P*, *R*, and their alleles in that diagram.

Epistasis. Since *P* and *R* are both dominant to single comb, one might consider whether or not these three types of comb could be multiple alleles. This possibility is ruled out because it would require all walnut combs to be *P R* in genotype and it is clear that they can be any one of four different genotypes. Moreover, *P* and *R* have been shown to belong in different chromosomes. Strictly speaking, pea and rose are not dominant to single comb but rather are *epistatic* to it. Single comb is *hypostatic* to these two but *epistatic* to the combless type of the Breda. It should interest the poultry geneticist to know that the terms epistatic and hypostatic, now in common use, were added to the geneticist's vocabulary by Bateson and Punnett (1908), who first used them to explain the relationships between rose, single, and Breda combs.

Trifid and Bifid Combs. In Silkies the comb is like a short rose comb broken up at the posterior end into two, three, or more points. From the fact that in F_2 generations from crosses of Silkies $\times$ single combs there appear normal rose combs, as well as trifids (Bonhote, 1914; Cunningham, 1919; Punnett, 1923), it is clear that the Silkie comb is rose. Punnett sugested that the shortening of the comb may be caused by the crest but that the trifidity probably resulted from another gene. However, in progeny from Silkie crosses the trifid comb is usually found in crested birds, and the normal rose comb in non-crested ones (Cunningham, 1912). Among 545 descendants from Silkies, Jull (1930) found only 12 exceptions to this rule. He concluded that crest modifies a rose comb to the trifid condition and that his 12 exceptions were errors in classification. It must be recognized, however, that crest is not always associated with trifid comb in such matings, for the exceptions of Cunningham (1919) showed that the normal pointed rose comb could occur in birds with small crests.

Independence of Duplex. The multiple-point, or trifid, comb differs from the bifurcated combs caused by the duplex gene in being less deeply forked and in having more than one division. Since posterior splitting of the comb occurs in Buttercups, Bredas, and La Flèche, all breeds lacking crests, it is clear that action of *D* is entirely independent of any tendency toward splitting exerted by the crest.

Side Sprigs. These lateral projections near the posterior end of single combs vary from small tubercles to an almost complete splitting of the blade. They are considered as disqualifications by fanciers, and accordingly selection has been against this variation rather than toward its preservation.

Relation to Trifid. Punnett (1923) observed that side sprigs were more common than usual in single-combed birds from parents with trifid rose combs. This and the fact that such sprigs are usually located at the back of the comb suggest that in single combs they may be homologous with the trifid condition in rose combs. If so, there should be an association of crest with side sprigs. Among single-combed birds descended from Silkies the following segregations were observed by Jull (1930):

	Single combs, number	Proportion with side sprigs, per cent
Crested..............	99	19.2
Non-crested..........	124	1.6

There is evidently a definite association between crest and side sprigs. Since the latter are found frequently in Leghorns and other non-crested breeds, their occurrence cannot always be attributed to the gene for crest, although, where that gene is present, the incidence of side sprigs is higher in the crested birds.

Genetic Basis. The data of Asmundson (1926) eliminated any possibility that side sprigs in Leghorns might be caused by a single gene, either dominant or recessive, and indicated strongly that side sprigs result when two complementary dominant genes are present. This would explain why many offspring with side sprigs may be produced by parents lacking the defect. One such mating in Barred Rocks yielded progeny 80 per cent of which had side sprigs. However, on this basis, when birds with side sprigs are mated together, they should produce progeny among which at least 56 per cent (9 in 16) would have side sprigs and more than that if any of the parent birds were homozygous for one or both of the complementary genes. Since in one such mating Petrov (1935a) found only 9 per cent of the offspring with side sprigs, it would seem that complementary genes do not fully account for this extremely variable character.

Further evidence that the genes causing side sprigs interact with others in modifying the comb was adduced by Taylor (1946). By selection from families showing side sprigs he developed a stock with so-called "multiplex" combs, some of which had three rows of points almost as in pea-combed birds. Others had split combs, and many points, resembling a poorly shaped Buttercup comb. Crosses of multiplex × single yielded about half multiplex, a quarter with side sprigs, and a quarter single.

Spike Blade. This name was given by Warren (1939) to a variation of the single comb in which the posterior end terminates in a single spike, rather than in the usual broad oblong blade. It is not distinguishable from the normal comb until the birds are nearly mature.

Genetic Basis. This peculiarity was found to be inherited, but manifested somewhat irregularly. Matings of affected birds *inter se* yielded females that all had spike-bladed combs except 3 per cent, which were intermediate, but about 10 per cent of the male progeny had normal combs. Similarly, in other matings the mutation was always manifested better in females than in males. That this difference did not depend on sex-linked genes was shown by the similar segregations observed in reciprocal crosses between spike-bladed birds and normal ones. The character is recessive, but not completely so. In the reciprocal crosses just mentioned, the proportion of spike-bladed birds and intermediate birds in the F_1 generation was 18 per cent in the male progeny and 46 per cent in the female progeny. Backcrosses of normal F_1 birds to spike-bladed ones yielded the two types in approximately a 1:1 ratio, except for a shortage of spike-bladed males.

If the character is caused by one pair of genes, as seems possible, it can be manifested in some heterozygotes and suppressed in some homozygotes, particularly when the latter are males.

SPURS

It is probable that spurs have been evolved by natural selection as useful weapons of offence and defence. Since domestication of the fowl the general interest in cock-fighting in all parts of the world has probably caused considerable artificial selection for maximum development of spurs. The fact that selection of both kinds would be confined almost entirely to males may account for the fact that in present-day fowls spurs develop in all normal males, but not commonly in females. However, spurs do develop in some females, and Goodale (1925) has shown that with selection for only a comparatively short time the proportion of spurred females may be increased to 50 per cent. This suggests that lack of selection for spurs in that sex, together with a few thousand years of natural and artificial selection for good spurs in males, may be responsible for the sex dimorphism in this respect characterizing modern domestic fowls.

Morphology and Development. The spurs of adults are elongated conical structures consisting of a bony core surrounded by softer spongy tissue and covered on the outside by a cornified layer. The latter wears off, as a claw does, and is replaced from below. Length of the spurs increases with age in both males and females.

By the tenth day of incubation the site of the spur is indicated by a small papilla, which is confined to the epidermal layer (Louvier, 1932). When the spurs develop in the maturing bird, a growth of bone inward from the epidermis meets a bony outgrowth from the shank and the two fuse to form the spur. The outgrowth from the tarso-metatarsus is apparently induced by something in the epidermal centre, for, according to Kozelka (1933), removal of the spur papilla in male chicks prevents development of the bony projection from the shank. In contrast to this, the outgrowth from the shank is not necessary for development of the epidermal part into a full-sized spur. Graf (1926) and Kozelka (1929, 1932) have shown that when the spur papillae of young chicks are transplanted to other parts of the body they develop normally to full size, even though never attached to the skeleton (Fig. 25).

Control. Long spurs are undesirable in breeding males because they may injure the backs of the females during mating. They may also cause damage among bellicose males in the "bull pen" when the cocks are thrown together after the breeding season. Such spurs may be sawn off, but Smith (1932) has shown that their development may be prevented with caustic potash in the same way as development of horns in cattle is arrested. In cockerels 8 to 12 weeks old the cap of the spur is removed, and, when the blood flows, a small quantity of caustic potash (KOH) is rubbed in the wound. Regeneration occurred in 10 per cent of those treated by Smith, but a second application in these birds was effective.

Spurs in Females. Spurred females are found more frequently in Leghorns and other Mediterranean breeds than in the heavier fowls. Spurs

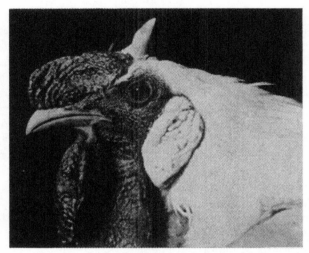

Fig. 25. A spur growing on the head after transplantation of the spur papilla when the bird was a chick. It is not attached to the skull. (*From Kozelka in J. Heredity.*)

are most common in old birds but may develop in the first year. It is commonly believed that spur-bearing females are partially masculinized and that they do not lay as well as normal hens. This idea is quite erroneous. Bauer (1931) could find no abnormalities of the ovary or of other endocrine glands in spurred females. Histological examination of the ovaries of such birds revealed no testicular tissue and only normal structure. Moreover, 48 spur-bearing females laid as well as normal controls, reproduced normally, and did not differ in conformation from females with undeveloped spurs.

Genetic Basis. By selection Goodale (1925) established a strain in which half of the females had well-developed spurs. When these were crossed with Cornish Indian Games, the F_1 females lacked spurs but in the F_2 generation and backcrosses spurred females reappeared. Apparently there is a genetic basis for the development of spurs in females, but its exact nature is not yet clear.

Are Spurs Secondary Sex Characters? A secondary sex character is one in which the sexes differ, the two forms, or conditions, resulting from the different effects of ovarian and testicular hormones. Spurs have been so classified by some investigators because their development is apparently inhibited in most females by ovarian hormones. When the ovary is removed, the resulting poulardes all grow spurs. On the other hand, spurs develop just as well in capons as in normal males. Whatever happens to the spurs after gonadectomy in either sex, that operation cannot reveal the whole mechanism affecting their development. This is because in such experiments the balance between endocrine secretions is disturbed by removal of the gonad, and there is always the possibility that effects attributed to removal of the ovary or testis may really have resulted from such secondary effects as hypertrophy of the hypophysis and changes in metabolism. This source of error is eliminated when spurs are transplanted from one sex to the other, without any operation that might affect the normal physiology of the host.

Spur Grafts. In Kozelka's experiments with Leghorns, 90 per cent of the autoplastic grafts (from one place to another in the same animal) persisted, but of 593 homoioplastic transplants (from one animal to another within the species) only 34 per cent grew successfully. These revealed the peculiarities and differences between male and female spurs listed below:

Male spurs

1. Grew in all parts of the body as well as in the normal site, except on the abdomen, where they remained undeveloped. A spur transplanted elsewhere than on the shank or comb became more slender than the normal control spur left on the shank.

2. Grafts to a region of the shank other than the original position often grew larger than normal controls.

3. Attachment to the bone was found only on the tarso-metatarsus.

4. Transplants developed into typical male spurs on both males and females.

Female spurs

1. Developed normally only on the scaly tissue of the shank. Elsewhere they were smaller than normal and immature in appearance.

2. On female hosts remained typically undeveloped as is normal in females.

3. Of persisting transplants of female spurs to male hosts only about 50 per cent enlarged to assume the size and structure typical of normal male spurs.

In the autoplastic transplants of spurs to the comb by Graf (1926) there was a steady growth of spurs in capons, but in males growth of the transplanted spur continued for only about 9 weeks after the operation and then ceased for half a year, to be followed by a remarkably rapid growth in the spring when sexual activity of the males was increased. This probably resulted from increased vascularity of the comb rather than from direct hormonal influences.

From the experiments in transplantation and in gonadectomy and from Goodale's breeding experiments, the following facts emerge:

1. Male and female spurs differ genetically, the former having much the greater potentialities for growth.

2. In some females the genetic capacity for spur growth is as great as in males, and the proportion of such birds in a flock can be increased by selection.

3. Male hormones are not necessary for development of spurs but provide a more favorable milieu than do female hormones.

4. Female hormones inhibit development of spurs in most females but are unable to overcome the greater capacity for growth inherent in the spurs of males.

5. These facts are in turn accommodated by the assumption that a definite threshold of genetic forces promoting spur growth must be reached before the antagonistic influence of the female hormone can be overcome. The author suggests that in males this threshold has been reached by natural and artificial selection and that by similar selection in females modifying genes can be accumulated in sufficient quantity to pass the limiting threshold and cause growth of spurs in most birds of that sex.

Spurs in Turkeys. According to the review by van Oordt (1936) of secondary sex characters in the turkey, the relation between gonadal hormones and development of spurs is quite different in that species from the situation in the fowl. Complete ovariotomy is not followed by spur growth in females. Castration in males prevents growth of spurs in some cases, but not in all. It seems probable from van Oordt's report that different breeds or strains may differ in the response of the spur to male hormones.

Double Spurs. Occasionally a male is found with a double spur on one leg or on both. One of these spurs is directly below the other, and both point in the same direction (Fig. 26). The upper spur is usually longer, but sometimes both are of the same length, and in some cases the lower may be the longer. Each spur has its own bony core and attachment to the rather large bony outgrowth of the tarso-metatarsus, from which both arise. Double spurs occur in females but, like normal ones, are usually incapable of development except after ovariotomy. Three

TABLE 12. INFLUENCE OF SEX ON MANIFESTATION OF DOUBLE SPURS

Parents	Offspring			
	Females		Males	
	Double	Single	Double	Single
Double × normal........	8	81	0	116
F₁ × double............	101	69	80	124
Double × double.......	71	19	59	47

such cases in ovariotomized females have been described by Domm (1931).

Warren (1946) found that the double spur is recognizable at hatching as a bipartite rudiment, markedly different from the normal single papilla. At that stage the double spurs of male and female chicks are identical

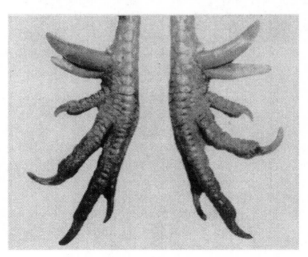

FIG. 26. Double spurs in an adult male.

in appearance. From a number of matings with double-spurred birds, he concluded that the abnormality is hereditary but does not segregate in clearly defined ratios. It is in general recessive, but in crosses with single spur about 10 per cent of the F_1 females had double spurs, and double × double yielded a high proportion of single spurs, especially in males.

A peculiar fact brought out in Warren's studies is that double spurs (*i.e.,* double papillae) are manifested more often in female chicks than in their full brothers (Table 12).

Multiple Spurs, *M*. *Morphology.* In Sumatra Games the males have a peculiar multiple spur consisting usually of a large central spur with a smaller one immediately above it and another below (Fig. 27). While a triple spur is usual, in some birds there are as many as five, three of which

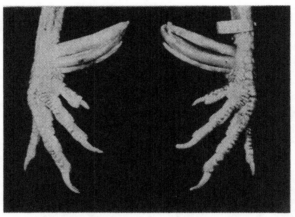

Fig. 27. Multiple spurs, a dominant mutation that is a breed characteristic in Sumatra Games.

are below the longest spur. All spurs point in one direction, and each has a bony central part. The upper two spurs are attached firmly to the tarso-metatarsus, but the lower ones terminate in a bony projection running downward from the normal site of attachment of the spur (Fig. 28). This projection is posterior to the hallux and may even project below the first phalanx of that digit.

The character shows clearly in females as three flattened and enlarged scales, one of which may be somewhat raised, but none of which resembles the rudimentary spur normally found in females. Chicks of both sexes show the multiple-spur condition clearly as enlarged scales and may be classified at hatching with accuracy of 95 per cent or better (Fig. 29).

Genetics. Investigations by the author (1941) show that this character results from a single dominant mutation, *M*, which usually segregates clearly in the F_2 and backcross generations. Over a 5-year period, various backcrosses yielded 750 multiple:792 normal. In some matings, the proportion of offspring with multiple spurs is below expectation.

Thus, one *Mm* male mated with four *mm* hens yielded a ratio of 30 multiple:81 normal. Since the expectation was 55.5 in each class, the character was evidently suppressed in about 46 per cent of the heterozygous progeny. Since the same four females yielded a ratio of 34:38 by another

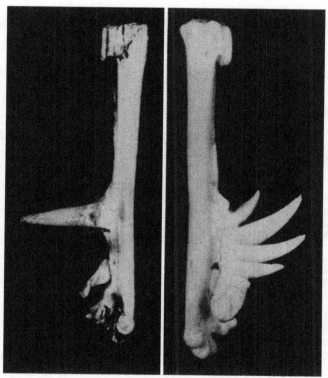

Fig. 28. Tarso-metatarsi showing (*left*) the bony core of a normal single spur and (*right*) the corresponding four points and downward projecting "flange" of a multiple-spurred shank.

male, it would seem that the first one carried modifying genes which inhibited formation of multiple spurs. Heterozygotes usually do not show the character fully, most of them having only two spurs.

The gene *M* is linked with the genes *D* and *Po* for duplex comb and polydactyly, respectively. Details are given in Chap. 14 on Linkage.

Supplementary Spurs. In a crossbred capon Caridroit and Regnier (1933) found peculiar extra spurs developing in the second year. On the right shank a double spur 0.5 cm. above the base of the normal spur, but on the front of the shank, was directed anteriorly and to the right, completely opposite to the direction of the normal spur. On the left foot a triple spur, also on the front of the shank but 2 cm. above the normal spur, was directed anteriorly and to the left. At 4 years both the supplementary spurs were found upon examination to be fully ossified and attached to the tarso-metatarsus. No explanation for this anomaly is available.

Spurlessness, *sl*. In this condition, studied by Kozelka (1933) in White Leghorns, the spur is absent at hatching or represented only by an

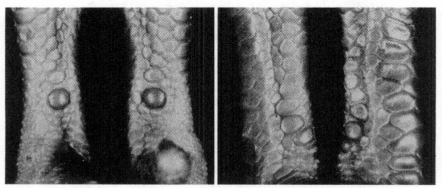

FIG. 29. Multiple-spur papillae (*right*) in the chick at hatching, in contrast with the normal single papilla (*left*). Mutations, like this one, that can be recognized at early stages are particularly useful for studies of linkage. (*From Hutt in J. Heredity.*)

enlarged scale. There may be no scales on the inner surface of the shank. At sexual maturity slight protuberances appear in males at the site of the normal spur. Some of these break through as the birds get older, and resemble short deformed spurs. These are always outgrowths from the tarso-metatarsus and lack that portion of the spur which normally develops from the epidermis. There is considerable variation in the degree of spurlessness in males, and 9 of 28 such birds showed vestiges of spurs on one shank or both. In females the spur region remains without any trace of a spur in nearly every case.

Genetics. Spurless is caused by a single recessive gene, *sl**. It is autosomal, but because its effects are much more apparent in males than in females, it is partially sex limited.

* Substituted for Kozelka's *s*, which had previously been preempted for gold.

OTHER VARIATIONS IN THE SKIN

Uropygial, *U*. The uropygial gland (oil, or preen, gland) is embedded in the skin overlying the last free caudal vertebrae. It consists of two lobes, each about the size of a pea. In numerous tubules in each lobe there is produced an oily secretion which is released through two small ducts (one from each lobe) in the single uropygial papilla. This secretion is used to preen the feathers.

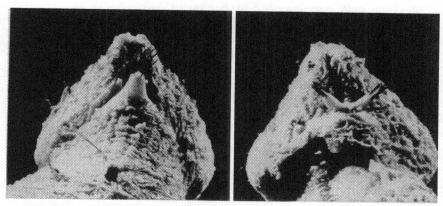

Fɪɢ. 30. Bifurcation of the uropygial papilla caused by a dominant gene. A heterozygote (*right*) in contrast with a normal papilla (*left*).

Morphology. A mutation designated as "uropygial" causing bifurcation of the papilla has been studied by Hutt (1932). In heterozygotes the gland itself is unaffected, but the papilla shows degrees of bifurcation varying from a condition in which there is an almost imperceptible groove in the tip of it, up to complete separation of two papillae by a gap of about 5 mm. at the surface of the skin (Fig. 30). In all these grades the oil gland functions normally, and one duct is found in each branch of the papilla. The character is recognizable in embryos at 14 days of incubation and at any time thereafter.

Among the offspring of birds with uropygial are found some chicks in which at hatching there are two tiny vestigial atrophic papillae. These are subsequently lost, and at maturity such birds have neither papillae nor oil gland.

Genetics. Breeding tests to date show that a single incompletely dominant gene, *U*, causes the double, or bifurcated, papilla but that many heterozygotes do not show any sign of the character. Most homozygotes show the two vestigial papillae at hatching but lack the uropygial gland

and have no uropygial papilla at maturity. However, some homozygotes have a functioning oil gland and a double papilla, *i.e.,* the phenotype of most heterozygotes. Obviously, action of the gene U is subject to considerable modification by other genes.

Linkage tests have shown that uropygial is linked with rose comb, there being about 30 per cent crossing over between the two genes (Hutt, 1936).

Dactylolysis. This peculiar mutation, which causes scleroderma and lesions in the feet resembling those attributed to deficiency of biotin or of pantothenic acid, was described by Shoffner (1945).

Description. At about 1 week of age, chicks that are normal up to that time show a "hard glassy" appearance on the sole of the foot and slight swelling. Within a day or two, cracks appear in the epidermis on the lower surface of the joints, and these become filled with bloody exudate. The distal portion of the toe becomes atrophied and dark in color and may eventually slough off. In some cases the scleroderma is slight, and recovery is effected without injury in a week or two. Others lose the distal portion of one or more toes, and some have such large cracks on the lower surface of the toes that recovery may require up to 12 weeks. Histological studies showed thickening of the layer of cornified epidermis.

Although data on viability were not given, it would appear that most of the chicks with this mutation die under the usual conditions of brooding and rearing. Those which do recover are apparently normal in other respects.

Genetics. So far as one can tell from the ratio of 228 normal:70 abnormal in an F_2 generation, dactylolysis is a simple recessive mutation. However, matings of dactylolytic birds with others presumed to be heterozygotes yielded 31 normal:10 abnormal, which is a significant deviation from the equal numbers expected for segregation of a unifactorial character with complete penetrance. The condition is clearly hereditary and not attributable to malnutrition, for several thousand unrelated chicks reared on the same diet as those with dacytylolysis did not show similar lesions.

Literature Cited

Asmundson, V. S. 1926. The inheritance of side sprigs. *J. Heredity,* **17**:280–284.

Axelsson, J. 1933. Heredity of size and form of the single comb in White Leghorns, Rhode Island Reds and Barnevelders. *Atti congr. mondiale di pollicoltura. 5th Congr.,* **2**:273–296.

Bateson, W. 1902. Experiments with poultry. *Repts. Evol. Comm. Roy. Soc.,* **I**: 87–124.

―――― and R. C. Punnett. 1905. Experimental studies in the physiology of heredity. Poultry. *Repts. Evol. Comm. Roy. Soc.,* **II**:99–119.

Bateson, W., and R. C. Punnett. 1905a. A suggestion as to the nature of the "walnut" comb in fowls. *Proc. Cambridge Phil. Soc.,* **13**:165–168.

—— and ——. 1906. Experimental studies in the physiology of heredity. Poultry. *Repts. Evol. Comm. Roy. Soc.,* **III**:11–30.

—— and ——. 1908. Experimental studies in the physiology of heredity. Poultry. *Repts. Evol. Comm. Roy. Soc.,* **IV**:18–35.

Bauer, H. R. 1931. Untersuchungen an sporentragenden Hennen. *Arch. Geflügelk.,* **5**:341–363.

Bonhote, J. L. 1914. Preliminary notes on the heredity of certain characters in a cross between Silky and Yokohama fowls. *Cairo Sci. J.,* **8**:83–90.

Buckner, G. D., W. M. Insko, and J. H. Martin. 1932. Effect of confinement on the growth of chicken combs and testes. *Am. J. Physiol.,* **102**:271–275.

Caridroit, F., and V. Regnier. 1933. Ergots supplémentaires chez le coq domestique. *Compt. rend. soc. biol.,* **114**:1079–1080.

Cunningham, J. T. 1912. Mendelian experiments on fowls. *Proc. Zool. Soc. London:* 241–259.

——. 1919. Results of a Mendelian experiment on fowls including the production of a pile breed. *Proc. Zool. Soc. London,* 173–202.

Davenport, C. B. 1906. Inheritance in poultry. *Carnegie Inst. Wash. Pub. 52.*

Domm, L. V. 1930. A factor modifying growth of head furnishings in Leghorn fowl. *Anat. Record,* **47**:314.

——. 1931. Spur dichotomy in the ovariotomized Brown Leghorn. *Anat. Record,* **48**:257–265.

Fisher, R. A. 1938. Dominance in poultry. Feathered feet, rose comb, internal pigment, and pile. *Proc. Roy. Soc. (London),* B, **125**:25–48.

Goodale, H. D. 1925. Data on the inheritance of spurs in the female of domestic poultry. *Anat. Record,* **31**:343.

Graf, H. 1926. Über transplantionen des Hahnensporns auf den Kamm. *Münch. tierärztl. Wochschr.,* **77**:571–575.

Hardesty, M. 1931. The structural basis for the response of the comb of the Brown Leghorn fowl to the sex hormones. *Am. J. Anat.,* **47**:277–323.

Hurst, C. C. 1905. Experiments with poultry. *Repts. Evol. Comm. Roy. Soc.,* **II**: 131–154.

Hutt, F. B. 1928. Potentially fatal fatigue of cervical muscles of the fowl resulting from an excessively large comb. *Vet. J.,* **84**:579–584.

——. 1932. Eight new mutations in the domestic fowl. *Proc. Intern. Genetic Congr. 6th Congr.,* **2**:96–97.

——. 1936. Genetics of the fowl. VI. A tentative chromosome map. Neue Forschungen in Tierzucht und Abstammungslehre (Duerst Festschrift) Bern: Verbandsdruckerei AG: 105–112.

——. 1941. Genetics of the fowl. 15. Multiple spurs, a mutation linked with duplex comb. *J. Heredity,* **32**:356–364.

Jones, D. G., and W. F. Lamoreux. 1943. Estimation of the size of comb on live fowl. *Endocrinology,* **32**:356–360.

Jull, M. A. 1930. The association of comb and crest characters in the domestic fowl. *J. Heredity,* **21**:21–28.

Kozelka, A. W. 1929. Integumental grafting in the domestic fowl. *J. Heredity,* **20**:2–14.

——. 1932. Integumental grafting as a means of analyzing the factors determining the secondary sexual characters of the Leghorn fowl. *J. Exptl. Zoöl.,* **61**:431–495.

Kozelka, A. W. 1933. Spurlessness of the White Leghorn. *J. Heredity,* **24**:71–78.

Lamoreux, W. F. 1943. Effect of differences in light and temperature upon the size of combs on White Leghorns. *Endocrinology,* **32**:497–504.

Louvier, R. 1932. L'ergot de *Gallus domesticus* chez l'embryon et chez le poussin. *Compt. rend. soc. biol.,* **109**:1116–1117.

Mueller, C. D., and F. B. Hutt. 1942. On the lopping of combs in White Leghorn females. *Poultry Sci.,* **21**:430–436.

Munro, S. S., and I. L. Kosin. 1940. Breast ridge in domestic fowl, a new dominant character linked with pea comb or another expression of the pea comb gene? *Am. Naturalist,* **74**:382–384.

Pearl, R., and M. D. Pearl. 1909. Data on variation in the comb of the domestic fowl. *Biometrika,* **6**:420–432.

Petrov, S. G. 1935. Breeding Leghorns resistant to frost with the Orloff type of comb (trans. title). *Collection Mem. 1935, Inst. Sci. Research Poultry Husbandry, Moscow.*

———. 1935a. The genetic nature of various comb forms in the domestic fowl (trans. title). *Genetika Selekcija seljsk.-hoz. Zivotn.,* **1**:337–350. Cited from *Animal Breeding Abstracts,* **5**:184.

Punnett, R. C. 1923. "Heredity in Poultry." London: Macmillan & Co., Ltd.

Shoffner, R. N. 1945. A dactylolysis mutation in the fowl. *J. Heredity,* **36**:375–378.

Smith, L. W. 1932. Preventing spur development on male birds. *Poultry Sci.,* **11**:241–242.

Taylor, L. W. 1946. Multiplex combs. *Poultry Sci.,* **25**:610–615.

van Oordt, G. J. 1936. The effect of gonadectomy on the secondary sexual characters of the turkey. *Arch. portugaises sci. biol.,* **5**:205–211.

Warren, D. C. 1939. Spike blade—A heritable single comb variation in the fowl. *J. Heredity,* **30**:257–260.

———. 1946. Double spur inheritance in the fowl. *J. Heredity,* **37**:323–324.

Wilfrid, M. 1927. The origin of the Canadian "Chantecler" fowl. *Proc. World's Poultry Congr. 3d Congr., Ottawa:*55–57.

CHAPTER 5

VARIATIONS IN THE PLUMAGE

Under this heading are included all inherited modifications of the plumage other than differences in color and pattern. These fall naturally into five different classifications, and, after a brief consideration of (1) the structure of normal feathers, they are presented as variations in (2) structure, (3) distribution, (4) length, (5) rate of growth, and (6) hen feathering.

STRUCTURE OF NORMAL FEATHERS

Morphology of Normal Feathers. In general, the many different kinds of feathers may be divided into two classes. The *neossoptiles* include the down and nestling feathers of newly hatched birds, while the *teleoptiles* include adult feathers of all kinds and the intermediate chick and juvenile feathers which in the fowl replace the down. The following three types of teleoptiles are found in the fowl:

1. *Plumules,* downy feathers such as those of the abdominal region (Fig. 31).
2. *Filoplumes,* long feathers apparently resembling hairs because they lack barbules except at the tip.
3. *Pennae,* or contour feathers, including the *remiges* (primaries and secondaries of the wing), the *rectrices* (tail feathers), and all others with a well-developed central shaft and not included in the other two classes.

The normal contour feather of the fowl (Fig. 31A) consists of the central quill, or shaft, and the *vane,* which includes both webs. The lower part of the shaft lacking barbs is termed the *calamus;* the rest of the shaft is the *rachis.* At the junction of these two parts there is on the ventral surface a small depression called the *superior umbilicus,* and at the base of the calamus is the *inferior umbilicus,* a small opening through which pulp from the follicle enters the calamus. An accessory feather, the *aftershaft,* arises on the ventral surface near the superior umbilicus (Fig. 31). This is rather inconspicuous and often entirely overlooked in feathers of the fowl. In rectrices and remiges it consists of only a few strands without any central shaft, but in some of the smaller feathers it is more apparent. In some birds the aftershaft is nearly as long as the main feather.

F<small>IG</small>. 31. Different feathers of the fowl. *A*, a penna, or contour, feather, in this case a remex with barely recognizable aftershaft arising from the superior umbilicus; *B*, a contour feather with long aftershaft; *C*, a plumule from an adult; *D*, first contour feathers of a chick showing at their tips the plumules of the chick's downy plumage, which they replace.

The web of the feather is formed by many *barbs,* which project from the rachis on both sides but in one plane. Each barb carries *proximal barbules* directed toward the base of the feather and *distal barbules* directed toward its tip. These are so arranged that the proximal barbules of one barb cross obliquely the distal barbules of the adjacent barb (Fig.

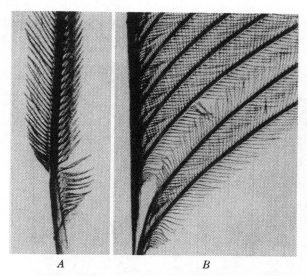

A   B

Fig. 32. Structure of the web of a feather. *A,* a single barb showing hooklets on the distal barbules (on the left) and the different structure of the proximal barbules; *B,* several barbs showing how the distal barbules of one interlock with the proximal barbules of the next. (*From Lillie and Wang in Physiol. Zoöl.*)

32). Normally, the barbules carry little projections or modifications of structure known as *barbicels.* On the proximal barbules these are like flanges, or scrolls, and on the distal barbules they are *hamuli,* or hooklets. The compact web of the feather is possible only because the hamuli of one barb interlock with the flanges of the next and thus hold the barbs together.

A detailed account of the development of feathers is beyond the scope of this book. For information on that subject the reader is referred to the series of studies by Lillie and Juhn (1932, 1938), Lillie (1940), and Lillie and Wang (1940, 1941) and to those of Hosker (1936) and Kuhn (1932).

VARIATIONS IN THE STRUCTURE OF FEATHERS

Silkiness, *h*

Fowls with the kind of plumage now designated as silky were seen by Marco Polo in China in the thirteenth century. The variety was known to Gesner, who described and illustrated it in his "History of Birds," published about 1555, as *Gallina lanigera,* the woolly fowl. A similar description is given by Aldrovandus (1600), whose artist made so certain

FIG. 33. A Silky hen.

that his illustration should show the lack of tail feathers that the bird appears rumpless. However, the silky fowls were apparently unknown in England as late as 1676, for in his ornithology published at that time Willoughby declares "The wool-bearing hen I take to be altogether fabulous and its figure in Aldrovandus fictitious" (Tegetmeier, 1867).

In modern times the mutation causing "silky" plumage has a world-wide distribution. In various localities it has given rise to breeds designated as Silkies (Fig. 33), Kiwis, Missouri Fluffs, and otherwise.

Description. The contour feathers have delicate shafts and unusually long barbs. These are frequently bifurcated, sometimes twice or more. The barbules are elongated, quite visible, and arranged irregularly, not all in one plane as in normal feathers. These barbules lack hamuli and scrolls, so that the proximal and distal barbules are identical, and there is nothing to hold the barbules together. This, along with the irregular arrangement of the barbules, accounts for the absence of a flat web in the feather and resultant silky appearance. The remiges (large wing feathers) and rectrices (tail feathers) are usually modified only in the distal part of the feather, but the rectrices are affected more than the wing feathers. The wing coverts are sometimes little affected.

Genetics. This character is caused by the autosomal recessive gene, h (hookless). Its recessive nature was shown long ago in matings of Silkies made by Darwin and Tegetmeier, and the unifactorial basis was proved in the F_2 and backcross generations raised by Bateson and Punnett (1908). The silkiness appearing sporadically in breeds that should have normal plumage was shown by Jones (1921) to be genetically identical with that in pure Silkies. Her collected records included reports of the mutation in nine different breeds.

Comparative Genetics. Lack of hamuli on the barbules is a characteristic of the ratite birds but ordinarily is not found in the teleoptiles of the Carinatae. A type of silkiness occurs as a simple dominant mutation in domestic pigeons, but in this species the barbules do not lack hooks (Cole and Hollander, 1939). The same mutation has been reported in the moor hen, *Gallinula*, by Bateson (1894). Although the character is associated in the Silky breed with a black skin not found in other breeds, the two conditions are quite distinct.

Frizzling, *F*

Frizzled fowls were described as early as 1600 by Aldrovandus, to whom a drawing of one had been sent from Parma. In England they were known to Willoughby in 1676. The mutation caused Linné to list *Gallus crispus* as a separate species in 1758, and in a later edition he referred to it as *G. pennis revolutis*. Although apparently restricted somewhat in earlier days to southeastern Asia, the East Indies, and Africa, frizzled fowls have now a world-wide distribution.

Description. Without careful breeding it is somewhat difficult to keep Frizzles free from one or more modifying genes which prevent full expression of the character and which are widespread in domestic poultry. Among unmodified frizzles there is considerable variation, but in general two types are quite distinct (Fig. 34). They are described in detail by Hutt (1930) and by Landauer and Dunn (1930). *Unmodified heterozygotes* have the shafts of contour feathers recurved, the outer surface being concave. Barbs of the rectrices and remiges curl and eventually wear off, particularly in the outer primaries. This effect is less conspicuous in the inner primaries and still less so in the secondaries. The birds cannot fly and at night squat on the floor unless given low roosts. *Un-*

modified homozygotes have the rachis extremely recurved in all feathers. The barbs are much curled. No feather has a flat vane, and all are narrow. As a result, the adult in full plumage has a somewhat woolly appearance (Fig. 34). The feathers are broken off by the crowding of the birds at night and by the treading of the males in the breeding season. Consequently, the homozygotes frequently appear quite bare in the summer.

Modified heterozygotes have less extreme frizzling in all parts of the body, and at maturity it may even be difficult to distinguish such birds

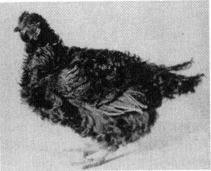

Fig. 34. A heterozygous Frizzle (*left*) and a homozygous one (*right*), both unmodified. (*From Hutt in J. Genetics, 1930.*)

from those not frizzled (Fig. 35). However, even the most modified birds still show some curling of the barbs in the outer primaries, and the feathers on the neck are slightly raised (Hutt, 1936). Secondaries of such birds are usually almost normal, and the inner ones are least affected.

Modified homozygotes lack the woolly appearance of those not modified, and the plumage seems somewhat velvety, almost as if the barbs of the feathers constituted a deep pile on an enveloping rug. Each feather is less extremely curled than in unmodified birds and is somewhat wider. Though all the barbs are curled, the curling begins farther from the rachis than in homozygotes not modified, and, as a result, there is a narrow strip on each side of the shaft where the web is flat as in normal feathers.

Genetics. Frizzling is caused by the incompletely dominant autosomal gene, F (Hutt, 1930; Landauer and Dunn, 1930), and the modified types apparently result from the interaction of F with an autosomal recessive modifier, mf. According to Landauer (1933), all birds homozygous for the modifier are affected by it, but in the material of Hutt (1936), though all Ff genotypes were modified by it, only about 40 per cent of the FF birds showed the modified plumage. The latter investigator found the modifier in 11 different breeds and varieties and in most of the non-frizzled fowls tested for its presence.

Prior to genetic analyses of frizzling, complaints of breeders that Frizzles did not breed true but always produced some birds with non-frizzled plumage led to the suspicion that homozygosity for frizzling might be lethal, leaving only heterozygotes available for breeding. After discovery that the extremely curled feathers were found only in homo-

FIG. 35. A male with modified, heterozygous frizzling that is recognizable only by the slightly raised feathers of the neck and breast.

zygotes, the reason for the fancier's complaint was made clear. With Frizzles, as in Blue Andalusians, the preference in the showroom is for the phenotype of the heterozygote, and accordingly the breeder saves only these and discards the curly-feathered, homozygous birds. His matings of the desired type, therefore, inevitably produce progeny of which only half have the kind of plumage desired in the showroom. The remainder in this 1:2:1 segregation are either not frizzled at all or homozygous for F and hence frizzled too much.

The gene F is linked with those for crest and for dominant white.

Action of the F Gene. The question arises whether frizzling results from some abnormality of metabolism, such as abnormal functioning of an endocrine gland, or from direct action of the F gene in the developing feather. In reciprocal transplants of skin between frizzled and normal fowls Landauer and Aberle (1935) found that the grafts always grew the plumage typical of the donor and never that of the host. Since skin of frizzled fowls produces only frizzled feathers on birds normally not frizzled, it is clear that the action of the gene is localized in the feather follicles and that the condition does not result from some disorder of metabolism. One graft of normal skin on an *FF* male persisted to 15 months of age, at which time the host moulted and subsequently produced simultaneously frizzled feathers over most of the body and normal feathers on the grafted skin.

Classification. Except in extremely slow-feathering birds, the presence or absence of *F* can be recognized with almost complete accuracy at 14 days of age and even earlier. Effects of the modifier are less conspicuous in young chicks than in other birds, and for most chicks of 3 weeks or so it is difficult to say with certainty whether they are modified or not.

Secondary Effects of *F*. Since homozygous frizzles are usually more or less naked, except when a new coat of plumage has just been acquired, it is to be expected that loss of the normal insulation would cause some disturbances of the physiology in such birds. These have been studied in detail by Landauer and his associates.

Metabolism. Benedict, Landauer, and Fox (1932) calculated that even at 28°C. the heat production of frizzles was greater than in normal fowls. At 17°C. the difference was much more pronounced, and in some of the homozygous frizzles the heat produced was more than twice that of normal fowls. The loss of heat from the body surface in homozygous frizzles was partially offset by an abnormally low heat loss from vaporization of water, the amount of water thus lost being 30 to 35 gm. in 24 hours per kilogram of body weight, compared with 50 to 56 gm. in normal fowls. The rectal temperatures of heterozygous frizzles did not differ from those of normal fowls, but at environmental temperatures below 15°C. the average rectal temperature for 10 homozygotes was slightly lower than in controls. One would naturally expect the homozygous frizzle fowls to eat more feed than normal ones in order to compensate for their extra heat loss, and some evidence was found that they do so.

Other Effects. In mature, homozygous frizzles, the heart is larger and beats more rapidly than in normal fowls (Boas and Landauer, 1933, 1934). The difference in females was 72 beats per minute, an increase of 27 per cent over the rate for normal fowls. It was attributed to the higher rate of metabolism in frizzles. Landauer and Upham (1936) found that in homozygous frizzles there was an increase over normal in the relative weight of the heart, blood, spleen, kidneys, adrenals, pancreas, crop, and gizzard and in the relative capacity of the duodenum, small intestine, caeca, and large intestine. However, since the normal birds were Leghorns and the frizzled ones were not, it is possible that some of these differences might be associated with the several physiological traits by which Leghorns differ from other breeds (Hutt, 1941) and not caused entirely by the deficiency of plumage in the frizzled birds. According to Landauer and Aberle (1935), the thyroid gland and adrenals of homozygous frizzles are not normal in structure. The thyroid shows "exhaustion atrophy" attributed to overwork in the effort to maintain body temperature by a higher metabolism.

Landauer (1932) maintains that the hatchability of eggs laid by heterozygous frizzles is subnormal and that it is still lower in eggs from homozygotes, but the evidence on this point is hardly conclusive.

Significance of F and mf in Evolution. The gene *F* is not a desirable one from the standpoint of a species trying to survive in competition with others. Apart from the fact that unmodified frizzles are unable to fly and tend to squat on the ground instead of roosting, it is clear that the secondary effects of the mutation are more likely to shorten life than to lengthen it. There are some indications that even under optimum conditions of domestication the mortality among frizzled fowls is higher than in normal ones. Landauer found the males to be somewhat slow in reaching sexual maturity. For all these reasons, it is highly improbable that the mutation could persist long in nature. Its preservation by fanciers is quite a different matter.

On the other hand, the modifying gene, *mf*, which to a considerable extent overcomes the action of *F* and makes the plumage almost normal, is a very desirable one. Perhaps this accounts for its presence in at least 11 different breeds and varieties (Hutt, 1936). According to Fisher's theory of the evolution of dominance, this modifying gene is exactly of the kind that would be preserved and accumulated under natural selection. It is possible that a widespread distribution of it among the ancestors of our domestic fowls, even before Jungle Fowls were distributed to the four corners of the world, may be responsible for its presence and prevalence in our modern breeds.

Flightless, *Fl*

Description. Warren (1932) described a mutation which causes the shafts of the remiges and rectrices to break off (Fig. 36). As a result, the affected birds are quite incapable of flight and cannot even reach roosts at the usual height. The mutation was very fittingly dubbed "flightless." Some of the larger body feathers are also broken. After a moult the new feathers break off as soon as they become dry. The condition is recognizable in chicks at 1 month of age, by which time some of the wing feathers are broken and others are irregular in length.

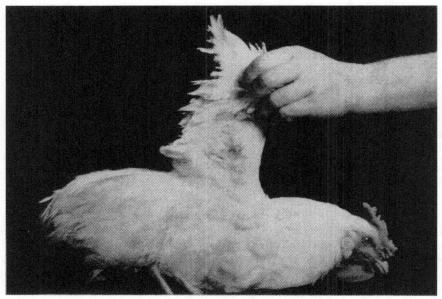

FIG. 36. Flightless, a mutation that causes breaking of the wing and tail feathers. (*From Warren in J. Heredity. 1932.*)

FIG. 37. The rough, pitted, and broken feathers of birds heterozygous for the flightless mutation (*left*) compared with normal feathers (*right*). (*From Warren in J. Heredity, 1932.*)

Genetics. Subsequent studies showed that all fowls like that shown in Fig. 36 were heterozygous for a dominant gene, *Fl*, and that most of the homozygotes apparently died before an age at which they could be recognized (Warren, 1937).

Conclusive evidence on this point was not obtained because the few birds considered homozygous that were reared to maturity were apparently sexually undeveloped and could not be used for breeding. These unusual birds were found only in the progeny of heterozygotes mated *inter se*. At hatching they were normal in appearance, but 4 weeks later it was evident that the feathers were not developing normally and that growth was retarded. Even those reared to maturity remained featherless except for undeveloped pinfeathers on the feather tracts. The beak and the toenails were defective in structure and frequently broken. Because of this, and the lack of feathers, mortality among these birds was high.

Physiological Basis. In heterozygous, flightless birds, the stubs of the broken feathers have shafts that are rough and pitted (Fig. 37). The outer layers of the rachis come off in small scales. Further evidence of abnormality was found in chemical studies of such feathers by Marlow and Caldwell (1934). The amount of phosphorus in them (0.18 per cent) is more than twice the normal figure, but the flightless feathers have a subnormal content of cystine. This suggests that the real effect of the gene *Fl* is to cause some abnormality of protein metabolism.

Fray, *fr*

The bird shown in Fig. 38 has a peculiar abnormality of the plumage which is usually confined to the large feathers of the wing and tail. In extreme cases other feathers may lack smoothness and show a "ropy" appearance. The frayed appearance of the feathers results from defects in the barbules, particularly in the distal ones and their hooklets. As a result, there is an imperfect interlocking of anterior and posterior barbules, and the barbs are not held together as in a normal feather.

This peculiarity was found by Warren (1938) to be a simple recessive character. A deficiency of "frayed" birds in backcrosses suggested either that some of those most affected died before they could be recognized or that some frayed birds were not recognized as such. Chicks show no sign of the defect at hatching and very little in the first set of chick feathers. However, in chicks that feather out early, the frayed condition is recognizable at 1 week of age in feathers that have just emerged from their sheath. The mutation is quite evident in the second set of juvenile feathers and in those of adults. It is designated by the symbol *fr*.

Fig. 38. Fray, an autosomal recessive mutation. (*From Warren in J. Heredity.*)

Naked, n

Description. Chicks affected with this mutation show varying degrees of nakedness at hatching (Fig. 39). Some have only a few scattered strands of down; others have up to 75 per cent of the normal covering. They are worst affected at about 4 weeks of age, when the down has worn off and is not quickly replaced by other feathers. Adults have more feathers than chicks, but some of them are almost completely naked. Others have almost a normal covering of body feathers, but all lack the remiges except for an occasional stub.

The *pterylosis*, or distribution of the feather tracts over the body, is normal in these naked fowls. The bare areas are covered with little stubs of feathers, usually broken right at the surface of the skin. The abnormality lies in the feathers, in the follicles, or both. In some cases the follicle seems to prevent normal eruption of the feather, as is indicated by a swelling under the skin, sometimes filled with a blood clot. Some of the feathers that do erupt are broken off near the skin, leaving the follicle full of dried blood. In the down of chicks the barbs are twisted together so that the plumage, what there is of it, is wiry rather than fluffy.

Genetics. These abnormalities are caused by a single recessive, sex-linked gene, n (Hutt and Sturkie, 1938). Strangely enough, the deficiency of feathers is more extreme in the females, which can carry only one n gene (*i.e.*, they are *hemizygous*), than in homozygous males.

The mating by which the mutation is maintained from year to year in a poultry flock, even when all naked birds are kept out of the breeding pens, is that of heterozygous (carrier) males with normal females. Even when bred to entirely unrelated hens, such males produce progeny in which all the males have normal plumage but half of the females are naked. The expectation is thus 3 normal:1 naked, with all the latter be-

Fig. 39. Naked, a sex-linked recessive mutation shown in a chick about 3 weeks old. Not all are as naked as this one.

ing females. The actual numbers from several such matings were 712 normal:246 naked, a close fit to the expectation of 719:239. Over half these naked chicks were sexed, and all proved to be females.

Lethal Action of the Gene. This ratio will not be recognized by the poultryman because about half the naked chicks die during the last 2 or 3 days of incubation and therefore are not seen unless the unhatched eggs are examined. In eight different matings of heterozygous males with normal females, Hutt and Sturkie found the mortality in naked and normal chicks during the last 3 days of incubation to be as follows:

	Highest	Lowest	Average
Proportion of naked chicks dying, %.......	83	12	47
Proportion of normal chicks dying, %......	23	1	8.5

Mortality in the naked embryos was not always related to the death rate in normal ones of the same mating. This showed that, while the naked chicks are undoubtedly affected by the conditions that cause death of normal ones, they are also killed by specific factors not affecting the normal embryos. Those which die are full grown and nearly always have the yolk sac fully enclosed in the body.

Even after hatching, the naked chicks are less viable than their siblings with normal plumage. Up to 6 weeks of age the mortality was 55 per cent in naked chicks but only 13 per cent in their brothers and sisters brooded with them. Since about 50 per cent never hatch, this means that only about a quarter of the original number of naked zygotes survive to the age of 6 weeks after hatching.

Other Naked Chicks. All naked chicks cannot be attributed to this sex-linked gene. Warren (1930) reported a case of complete lack of down that was proved by suitable breeding tests not to be hereditary at all. Occasionally one finds among Rhode Island Reds, Plymouth Rocks, and other heavy breeds chickens that have normal down at hatching time and normal plumage when fully feathered but that may be almost completely naked at 6 to 12 weeks of age (Fig. 45). A genetic basis for these extremely slow-feathering birds has not yet been worked out, but Schwarz (1931) considered the condition hereditary. He found that the thyroids of such birds were abnormal, but it is not clear whether this is the cause or the effect of the lack of plumage.

Further evidence that all cases of nakedness in the fowl cannot be ascribed to the same cause is found in the fact that birds homozygous for the "flightless" mutation resemble somewhat those made naked by the sex-linked gene. However, these flightless birds have normal down at hatching, whereas the naked chicks do not. The former have defective development of the beak and toenails, but these are normal in the sex-linked type of nakedness.

"Porcupine" Pigeons

Description. In this peculiar condition found in the pigeon by Cole and Hawkins (1930), the feathers seem to lack the normal web, or vane, and as a result the bird seems to be covered with quills. The barbs of newly grown feathers remain rolled close to the rachis, as is normal while the feather is still within the sheath. Eventually they open out slightly and are rubbed off. Microscopically, the differentiation of barbs and barbules seems to have been arrested before completion of that process. The contrast between porcupine pigeons and normal ones is striking.

Genetics. This condition is caused by an autosomal recessive gene in the homozygous state. The birds studied by Cole and Hawkins originated in Wisconsin, but the same condition, apparently caused by an independent mutation, was found in Breslau, Germany, by Krallinger and Chodziesner (1932).

Although no fowls with this type of feather defect have been described in modern times, it is to be expected that a mutation similar to that in the pigeon may some day be found in the fowl. This seems all the more likely in that Aldrovandus (1600) illustrated a fowl resembling very much these porcupine pigeons and labelled as *Gallina fere petrificata.*

Feather Tumor in Canaries

Peculiar tumors in the plumage of canaries have been described by Crew and Mirskaia (1931). These are most common on the wings but may occur all over the body. As many as six were found in a single bird. They arise from the skin as rounded, glistening bodies about the size of a pea, increase in size even to the diameter of 1 inch, and eventually can be dug right out of the skin. These lumps consist of bundles of imperfect feathers in which are layers of keratin and fat. When a moult was induced with thyroxine, the new plumage contained no tumors.

Since the condition is apparently confined to one breed of canaries, the Norwich Plainhead, it would appear to be hereditary, but experimental evidence on that point has not yet been adduced.

VARIATIONS IN THE DISTRIBUTION OF FEATHERS

Naked Neck, *Na*

Fowls lacking feathers on the neck are now widely distributed throughout the world. They are variously known as Transylvanian Naked Necks, Bare Necks, Hackleless, and even Rubber Necks. At frequent intervals they are described by newspapers more interested in headlines than in accuracy as "Turk-hens" or even "Chirkens"—products of a cross between chickens and turkeys. Formerly the condition was attributed by some writers to a dermatitis, supposed to have been induced either by fighting or by depluming mites and subsequently inherited. However, a careful study of the case by Greenwood (1927) showed that it is quite unnecessary, in order to account for the naked neck, to invoke the theory that an acquired character has been inherited.

Description. In normal fowls the main feathers are found concentrated in 10 feather tracts, or *pterylae*. The spaces between these tracts, the *apteria*, carry scattered down feathers and "semiplumes," the latter being intermediate between contour feathers and down. In Naked Necks, Greenwood found that there are no feathers at all in the apteria. The head tract is absent except just around the comb; *i.e.*, this area lacks not

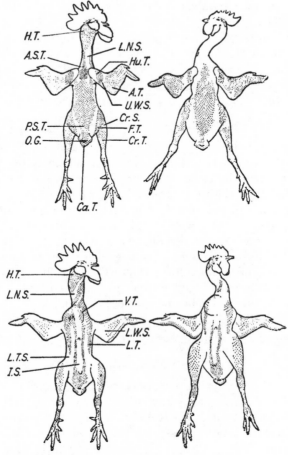

Fig. 40. Diagrams showing the reduction of the pterylae in naked-neck fowls. *Above*, dorsal views; *below*, ventral views; *left*, normal; *right*, naked neck. [*From Greenwood in Proc. Roy. Phys. Soc. (Edinburgh)*.]

A.T.—Alar tract
A.S.T.—Anterior spinal tract
Ca.T.—Caudal tract
Cr.S.—Crural space
Cr.T.—Crural tract
F.T.—Femoral or lumbar tract
H.T.—Head tract
Hu.T.—Humeral tract
I.S.—Inferior space

L.N.S.—Lateral neck space
L.T.—Lateral tract
L.T.S.—Lateral trunk space
L.W.S.—Lower wing space
O.G.—Oil gland
P.S.T.—Posterior spinal tract
U.W.S.—Upper wing space
V.T.—Ventral tract

only feathers but also feather follicles. There are no feathers on the dorsal surface of the neck, except those of the anterior spinal tract. The ventral tract is absent except for two small patches on each side above the crop. Davenport (1914) had a bird without those, and its offspring also lacked them. The lateral tracts on the breast are much reduced. The bare skin of the neck becomes reddish at sexual maturity, as does any other exposed skin. In histological structure it resembles the wattles (Freund, 1925).

These differences between normal and naked-neck fowls in the distribution of feathers are shown in Fig. 40, which also serves to illustrate the normal feather tracts of this species.

Genetics. This peculiarity was found by Davenport (1914) to be caused by a single dominant gene. Warren (1933) found a ratio of 1,388 naked neck:1,341 normal in backcrosses, a close fit to the expectation of 1,364.5 in each class. These fowls provide a good example of a breed differentiated from other fowls by a single gene. The symbol, *Na,* was assigned by Hertwig (1933).

One might suppose that the Naked Necks would interest only the fancier and have little appeal to practical poultrymen, but this is not the case. They are quite abundant in the West Indies. Davenport's birds came from Barbados. Mr. W. O'Brien Donovan, agricultural superintendent in Grenada, advised the author in 1937 that the bare-necked fowls were increasing in popularity there, being preferred to imported birds because of their superior hardiness and other good qualities. It seems likely, however, that these virtues should be attributed not so much to the gene for naked neck as to the probability that the stock carrying that mutation is thoroughly acclimatized and therefore thrives better than fowls recently introduced.

Apterylosis, *Ap*

This term is suggested for the bizarre type of nakedness studied by Sturkie (1942), partly because it describes the abnormality more specifically than does the word "nakedness," but also to differentiate it from the sex-linked mutation, naked.

Description. Affected birds show varying degrees of nakedness resulting from corresponding degrees of reduction of the pterylae, or feather tracts (Fig. 41). In that respect it resembles the naked-neck condition, but the apterylosis is more extreme. The tracts most reduced or absent are the anterior and posterior spinal, the humeral, and the femoral. The ventral tracts are absent or small in extreme cases, but only slightly reduced in others. The head tract is almost normal except for a small bare area above the eyes. Because the alar tract (on the wing) is normal and the crural tract (on the thigh) always carries some feathers, a fowl with extreme apterylosis presents a most bizarre appearance.

Genetics. This apterylosis is caused in heterozygotes by a single dominant autosomal gene. In the offspring of naked × normal parents, the ratio of chicks with apterylosis to normal ones was 623:616, while heterozygotes mated *inter se* yielded an F_2 ratio of 89 naked:27 normal. Apparently homozygotes are not affected more than heterozygotes. The mutation occurred in Rhode Island Reds. Because it is dominant and

Fig. 41. Apterylosis in a young chick. The pterylae are reduced according to a most peculiar pattern. (*Courtesy of P. D. Sturkie.*)

recognizable at hatching, it should be useful for linkage tests with other genes that are recognizable in the newly hatched chick.

As the backcross ratio shows, apterylosis has no lethal effect prior to hatching. Under conditions of brooding that were normal for most chicks, hardly a quarter of those with apterylosis survived to 5 months of age. Sturkie observed that during the first 10 days the abnormal chicks ate about one-third less feed than their normal siblings, and by feeding the mash wet, instead of dry, thus inducing greater consumption of feed, the lethal effect of the mutation was postponed. It was not averted, however, for mortality increased after feeding of wet mash was discontinued, and at later stages practically as many were dead as among those reared on dry mash. This is an interesting example of a case in which the lethal effect of a gene can be delayed by improving the environmental conditions (Table 13).

TABLE 13. LETHAL EFFECT OF APTERYLOSIS, AND ITS POSTPONEMENT BY FEEDING MASH WET INSTEAD OF DRY (STURKIE)

Cumulative mortality to age, days	Mortality, per cent, in chicks with apterylosis			Mortality, per cent, in their normal siblings, dry mash only
	Wet mash to 10 days (118) *	Wet mash to 30 days (99) *	Dry mash only (221) *	(330) *
10	22	21	54	2
15	31	28	58	3
30	53	37	64	6
60	69	52	72	9
150	..	67	78	23

* Number of chicks started.

Feathers on the Feet

Feathers on the shanks or feet are a breed characteristic in Brahmas, Langshans, Cochins, Silkies, Mille Fleurs Bantams, Faverolles, and some other breeds. The condition is variously designated as "foot feathering," "shank feathering," and "ptilopody." Since the feathers are on the toes and the metatarsal region, the term "feathered feet" or its equivalent from the Greek, "ptilopody" (suggested by Danforth, 1919), seem more appropriate than the commonly used "feathered shanks."

Description. The extent and degree of the feathering vary greatly. Of the 10 arbitrary grades of Davenport (1909), Cochins showed all but the lowest, and Brahmas all but the lowest 2. In Silkies only the 4 lower grades were found. Some birds have only a few tiny feathers between the toes or on the "hocks." These are known to poultrymen as "stubs," and, according to the standards of the American Poultry Association, they constitute a disqualification from the showring in breeds not supposed to have feathered feet. In general, the feathers are most dense down the outer side of the tarso-metatarsus and on the outer toe. Serebrovsky (1926) made distinctions between seven types of ptilopody which he considered genetically different, but since with two exceptions these all intergraded from one to another, it is questionable to what extent their arbitrary demarcation is justifiable.

Genetics. From several genetic studies of feathered feet, no interpretation has emerged that satisfactorily explains all the different types and degrees of the condition. In crosses between ptilopodous and "clean-footed" fowls, the F_1 generation usually have feathered feet, but exceptions are numerous. These exceptions might be ascribed to heterozygosity for feathered feet in one of the parents.

In a cross of Langshans with Leghorns and Hamburgs, Punnett and Bailey (1918) found dominance in the F_1, a 3:1 ratio in the F_2, and a 1:1 ratio in the backcross to clean-footed fowls. They concluded that a single dominant gene was responsible for the type of foot feathering they studied and that variability in the F_1 and backcross was caused by modifying genes. They also showed that some of the results in earlier investigations with Brahmas and Cochins, which have more feathers on the feet than Langshans, could be accounted for by duplicate genes, with the dominant allele of either pair causing feathered feet. However, this same hypothesis was invoked by Lambert and Knox (1929) to explain their results with Langshans and by Dunn and Jull (1927) to account for ptilopody in Silkies. In contrast, Hays (1943) attributed stubs to homozygosity for either of two recessive genes, the dominant alleles of which caused clean shanks and toes. From all these studies one gets the impression that a close fit of observed to expected ratios can be misleading when the latter are based upon genotypes assumed, but not proved, for the parents. This is especially so when arbitrary classifications are made in a character showing continuous variation or, as in this case, when there is some doubt about how to classify those showing only traces of the character.

Serebrovsky (1926) considered that the type of feathered feet found in Pavloffs is recessive but that about 40 per cent of the heterozygotes show a "weak" type of feathering. In Pavloffs there is uniform feathering on all the toes and feathers on the inside of the tarso-metatarsus. Serebrovsky attributed the "heel-tuft" type of feathering to a single gene. This is the condition that the fancier calls "stubs on hocks," when a few tiny feathers appear in the region just below the tibio-tarsal joint. However, this is a very difficult condition to analyze genetically because, while it may show in some chicks at hatching, other fowls may have clean hocks for 2 years but still develop stubs after that age.

Considering all the evidence, some of which is not very conclusive, the present state of our knowledge concerning feathered feet may be summed up as follows: (1) the number of genes involved is unknown; (2) there are probably genetically distinct types of feathering, but a definite genetic basis for any one type has not yet been incontrovertibly demonstrated; (3) duplicate dominant genes may possibly be responsible for some forms of feathered feet, and a single incompletely dominant gene for others, but further evidence on these points is desirable; (4) the genotype with respect to feathered feet cannot be determined from the phenotype; (5) any future investigation of this condition is not likely to extend present knowledge unless carried further than an F_2 and a backcross.

Down on Toes. Birds of clean-footed breeds frequently have varying amounts of down on the toes. This is found either on the sides of the toes or on the web between the toes, usually between the middle toe and the outer one. Sometimes only a single tuft of down is present, but it is not unusual to have the whole web covered. Since families containing birds with down or stubs on the toes or between them frequently include also specimens with stubs right up the side of the shank, it seems probable that all these forms are dependent upon some of the genes causing the lesser degrees of shank feathering.

By selection, Warren (1930a) differentiated two strains of White Leghorns, in one of which the proportion of adults with such down was less than 2 per cent, while in the other the proportion ran as high as 90 per cent. Reciprocal crosses between these two strains yielded the following proportions of adults with down on the toes:

	Per cent
In the F_1 generation	37
In the backcross of $F_1 \times$ downy	76
In the backcross of $F_1 \times$ non-downy	1

Since the 3 years' selection practised did not produce a strain breeding true for down on the toes, and since the proportion of downy birds in the F_1 generation was intermediate between that in the two strains crossed, it seems probable that more than one pair of genes is responsible for the condition. Classification was difficult and subject to some error because some of the tufts are extremely minute and (as every fancier knows) the down is so easily removed that even a cake of adhering mud might pull it out. Warren's studies brought out the interesting fact that, while chicks with down nearly always had down at maturity, many of those without down at hatching subsequently showed it as adults. In his F_1 generations and the backcross to downy birds, only 7 per cent of 434 chicks were classified as downy, whereas in 417 adults the proportion so classified was 51 per cent.

The complexity of the genetic basis for stubs and down was illustrated in a number of diallel crosses made by Cole and Hutt (1947) in each of which three full brothers, none with detectable stubs, were mated in turn with the same flock of hens. In one such case, the first brother had stubs in 13.5 per cent of his daughters (at maturity), the second had none at all, but among pullets from the third brother the incidence was 40 per cent. Similar variability with other trios of full brothers is shown in

Table 67, page 515. It is clear that with respect to this character phenotypes do not reveal genotypes; hence anyone seeking to eliminate this condition or to reduce its frequency can do so most rapidly by using the progeny test.

Variations Associated with Feathered Feet. The association of feathered feet with brachydactyly is discussed in Chap. 3. Danforth (1919a) believed that *syndactyly*, a condition in which the middle and outer toes are held together by a web of skin, is caused by the same gene, or complex of genes, as is responsible for feathered feet and brachydactyly. A similar view is held by Jaap (1939), who found 9 birds with distinct syndactyly among 55 that were brachydactylous. Further studies are necessary to show whether such an association is significant or fortuitous. Evidence reviewed later in this chapter suggests that the condition known to poultrymen as "vulture hocks" is also associated with feathered feet.

Ragged Wing

This abnormality, which to some extent resembles the flightless mutation, is apparently not uncommon, as it was found in eight flocks in different parts of the United States and in two different breeds. It is described by Hutt, Mueller, and Warren (1944).

Description. In its most extreme form, the mutation eliminates all the remiges from the adult plumage. In its least evident expression, all these feathers are present but shortened. Birds of this latter type may not be recognized as abnormal unless special search is made for them. Between the two extremes, the more common types have some of the flight feathers present, others missing (Fig. 42). The two wings are often asymmetrical in this respect.

Ragged wing differs from flightless in that the remiges are not broken off but are either absent or shortened. The rectrices of ragged-wing birds are not affected, whereas in flightless ones both tail and wing feathers are broken. The ragged-wing birds are not recognizable until the adult remiges begin to grow in at 6 to 12 weeks. Those then showing abnormal wing feathers are abnormal at maturity, but of 76 birds with clearly ragged wings at 30 weeks of age only 21 per cent had shown abnormalities at 12 weeks. Similarly, among 62 adults that had short flight feathers only 11 per cent had been recognizable at the earlier age.

Genetics. Independent studies at two experiment stations agreed in finding that the ragged-wing abnormality is an autosomal recessive mutation, apparently unifactorial, but manifested by only about half of the homozygotes. The other half are indistinguishable from other fowls, presumably because their remiges are shortened either not at all or too little to be recognized.

Fig. 42. Ragged wing; a common intermediate form of this character, with some remiges missing and others short. (*From Hutt et al. in J. Heredity.*)

Table 14 gives the combined data. These are consistent with the hypothesis given above, if one makes allowance for modifying genes affecting the expression of a gene with major effects. That such modifiers exist was shown by diallel matings in which females all homozygous for the mutation, but some with ragged wings, some with short wings only,

TABLE 14. SEGREGATION OF RAGGED WING (HUTT ET AL.)

Parents	Progeny		Expectation with 50 per cent penetrance	
	Normal	Ragged	Normal	Ragged
Normal × ragged..........	184	3	187	0
Ragged × ragged..........	303	303	303	303
Backcross to ragged........	285	88	279.75	93.25
F₂ generation..............	113	1	99.75	14.25

and some normal, were all mated with the same ragged-wing males. In the progeny, the proportion showing ragged wings (not merely short) was 39 per cent in chicks from dams of that type but only 10 per cent in those from dams apparently normal. Evidently modifiers suppressing the mutation in the dam tend to do the same in the offspring.

Congenital Baldness

Sometimes chicks show, when hatched, areas lacking down on top of the head just above the orbit (Hutt, 1932). Such bald spots lack feather follicles and therefore remain bare even in adults. The peculiarity may be bilateral, with the affected areas separated by a strip of normal down, or may be unilateral. Sometimes the bald spot is in the centre of the top of the head. In extent they vary from a diameter of about half an inch down to barely recognizable spots from which only one or two follicles are missing. In mature birds the bald spots become red like the comb but are often inconspicuous because of overlying feathers.

Affected embryos show at 11 days of incubation quite conspicuous blebs at the site of the bald spots. These are filled with clear fluid. Sturkie (1941) found that these blebs form at 8 days and attain maximum development 3 days later. The fluid is then gradually resorbed, being all gone by 16 days of incubation. The source of this fluid is not known. Sturkie concluded that it was the effect, rather than the cause, of the separation of the dermis and epidermis between which the bleb is formed.

Genetics. This condition is hereditary, and it has appeared in several unrelated flocks of fowls. It was at first considered by Hutt to be a simple recessive character. His later studies and those of Jaap (1937) have shown that, if only one pair of genes is responsible, the *penetrance* of the character is low, *i.e.*, it does not show in some of the birds homozygous for the causative gene.

Penguin Guinea Fowls

McCrady (1932) has described a peculiar condition in guinea fowls which may some day be found in chickens. The affected birds appeared at first sight to be wingless, but this illusion was caused by the absence of the remiges. Dissection showed the bones of the wing to be normal. The tail feathers were also missing, but, apart from this and the remiges, the plumage was apparently normal. In this case, the big feathers do not develop, whereas in the "flightless" fowls, which are superficially similar, the remiges and rectrices do grow out normally but then break off.

Breeding tests showed that this abnormality was caused by a single recessive gene in the homozygous condition.

VARIATIONS IN THE LENGTH OF FEATHERS

Crest, *Cr*

In Silkies, Houdans, Crèvecoeurs, all varieties of Polish, and other breeds, a crest of feathers on top of the head is a breed characteristic.

Description. This results from some of the feathers being unusually long and from their being more or less erect rather than fitted closely to the head as in uncrested birds. In extent the crest may vary from a very large knob-like structure with feathers falling over and hiding the eyes and face, down to a few elevated feathers barely distinguishable from the normal uncrested condition. Because the crest is right behind the comb, and because the size of one seems to vary inversely as the size of the other, Bonhote (1914) and others believed that a large comb prevented full development of the crest.

Association with Cerebral Hernia. It was pointed out by Tegetmeier (1856) that in the skulls of crested fowls the cranium is vaulted, sometimes forming a great tuberosity in which lie the cerebral hemispheres of the brain. The underlying cause of this abnormality was shown by Krautwald (1910) to be an excessive accumulation of fluid in the brain. It fills the third and fourth ventricles and thus causes an upthrusting of the cerebral hemispheres and of the frontal bones which overlie them. The cerebellum lies back on the medulla instead of up toward the hemispheres, and the latter are elongated.

As a result of these abnormalities, chicks severely affected show at hatching varying degrees of cerebral hernia recognizable by enlargement of the skull and often detectable by palpation. The frontal bones are raised at the posterior and interior borders. As the chick grows, ossification proceeds in the membranes of the fronto-parietal region. In mature fowls the brain is completely encased, but the roof of the cranium is perforated with holes of various sizes. These are less evident in the oldest birds.

Just how these abnormalities cause the elongation and erection of the feathers that form the crest is not clear, but since the size of the crest is directly proportional to the extent of the abnormalities in the cranium and in the brain, there can be no doubt that the latter do cause the crest. Krautwald found the skin underlying the crest to be thickened and highly vascularized, conditions which could affect the activity of the feather follicles.

Genetics. Crest is caused by an incompletely dominant autosomal gene, *Cr*. It was one of the first characters to be studied after the rediscovery of Mendel's laws. By Hurst (1905) it was shown to be hereditary and dominant, and Davenport (1906) demonstrated that only one pair of genes is involved. This has since been confirmed by many others.

Some confusion was temporarily caused by some investigators who considered crest to be induced by a dominant gene and cerebral hernia by homozygosity for an independent recessive gene. This was straightened out by Fisher (1934) and by Warren and Hutt (1936). Experiments reported by the latter show that, while *Cr Cr* birds usually have both crest and hernia, in some cases the latter is not evident, at least in living birds. From a mating of *Cr Cr* birds with heterozygotes, the 218 progeny were all crested, as expected, but hernia showed in only 18 per cent instead of half of them, as would be expected if all homozygotes were herniated. On the other hand, a backcross of *Cr cr* fowls to non-crested birds yielded 167 progeny, of which half were crested as expected, but 19 of the 84 crested fowls, presumably all heterozygous, were also herniated. This irregularity in manifestation of the hernia matters little so far as the genetic interpretation is concerned. In some adult heterozygotes, the crest is so small that one cannot be sure of its presence. The range from this extreme to the relatively enormous crests developed by fanciers in some of the breeds suggests that there are modifying genes affecting the expression of *Cr*. This is supported by the statements of earlier writers that the crest was originally confined chiefly to females but that by selection these fowls were bred so that the males also showed crests. One must remember also that the crest and hernia are merely secondary effects of the causative gene and hence subject to considerable variation.

Crest is linked with frizzling and dominant white.

Classification of homozygotes with hernia is fairly easy at hatching time. Apart from the abnormal shape of the cranium, its softness on the top can be detected by palpation. In homozygotes without hernia, the crest can be recognized by the raised down. In heterozygotes, recognition of crest is less easy, but with practice it can be made with an accuracy of 90 per cent.

Crest in Ducks. "The American Standard of Perfection" recognizes Crested White ducks as a distinct breed, the outstanding characteristic of which is a crest that is "large, well-balanced on crown of head." This affords a good example of a very undesirable gene being adopted as the distinguishing feature of a breed, as is also the case with Creepers.

In this species the crest is at the back of the head. Krautwald (1910) found that in the underlying parieto-occipital region of the skull there is a hole through which protrudes an encephalocele, or hernia of the brain. The protruding parts may include posterior parts of the cerebral hemispheres, the cerebellum, one or both optic lobes, or part of the medulla. These are still enclosed in the meninges.

Studies by Rüst (1932) showed that crested ducks are heterozygous for an incompletely dominant gene, that the homozygotes do not hatch, and that only about half the heterozygotes show a crest. In the homozygotes death occurs at the end of the incubation period, or before, the affected embryos having the upper beak reduced to a nubbin and variable deficiencies in the cranium.

Muffs and Beard, *Mb*

In Houdans, some Polish, Faverolles, Mille Fleurs, Orloffs, and some other breeds, there is an elongation of the feathers at the sides of the face and under the lower beak. This condition is known as "muffs and beard." Both are caused by one incompletely dominant autosomal gene, and neither occurs without the other. The character is quite variable in heterozygotes. It is usually recognizable in newly hatched chicks but occasionally is hard to classify with accuracy even in birds 5 months old. The symbol *Mb* is proposed because it suggests the character better than the *Ba* (for *bart*, beard) used by Hertwig (1933). The muffs are usually more evident than the beard.

The genetic basis for it was indicated by Davenport (1906) and confirmed by Serebrovsky and Petrov (1930) and others.

Vulture Hocks, *v*

In this condition, which is a breed characteristic in Sultans and in Mille Fleurs, the feathers on the posterior part of the crural feather tract (in the region of the tibia) are large and stiff, resembling flight feathers more than the soft, fluffy feathers usually found in this region. They project backward beyond the tibio-tarsal joint.

Genetics. The earlier evidence of Davenport (1906) that vulture hocks is recessive was confirmed by Jull and Quinn (1931), who found it in about a quarter of the F_2 generation from a cross of vulture-hocked male $\times$ normal females. Since none of the 202 F_1 progeny showed the peculiarity, it is apparently completely recessive. For the autosomal gene responsible, the symbol *v* is proposed.

Although the area affected by this gene is above the tibio-tarsal joint, the peculiarity is associated with feathering of the feet below that joint. The proportions showing vulture hocks among the clean-legged, medium-feathered, and heavily feathered birds in the F_2 generation of Jull and Quinn were apparently 0, 20, and 75 per cent ,respectively. A similar association was noted earlier by Dunn and Jull (1927). The basis for it is not yet known.

Long Tail

In the Japanese breeds variously called Yokohama, Phoenix, or Tosa, the tail is said to be, in average birds, 7 to 8 feet long. A 12-foot tail is a rarity, but apparently some have attained a length of 18 feet (Chamberlain, 1900). Actually, the elongation is comparatively slight in the true tail feathers, the rectrices, but is most striking in the sickle feathers and the saddle coverts. The number of these which are elongated varies from 15 up to 24.

The genetic basis for this peculiarity is not clear. In the F_1 generations from the crossing of normal $\times$ long-tailed birds, both Davenport (1906) and Bonhote (1914) found the length of the tail feathers to be intermediate between that of the parents. Bonhote raised an F_2 generation of 24 birds in which the length of these feathers was hardly the same in any two birds. He classified 19 as long-tailed but doubted that the others were as short as in normal fowls.

Length of Down Feathers

A very interesting relationship between the length of the down feathers in newly hatched chicks and their color was demonstrated by Kabystina and Petrov (1935). They arranged matings to produce the two colors to be compared in 1:1 ratios and then measured the length of the down in several chicks of each color from each mating. The residual inheritance was thus as nearly alike for the two classes compared as it was possible to get it, and any differences in length of down were properly attributable to the effects of the single genes by which the two classes differed. The samples of down came from the middle of the back. Their results with the four pairs of genes tested most extensively are given in Table 15.

TABLE 15. LENGTH OF DOWN FEATHERS IN RELATION TO COLOR
(KABYSTINA AND PETROV)

Different matings, number	Color of down	Feathers measured, number	Mean length, mm.	Color of down	Feathers measured, number	Mean length, mm.	Difference, mm.
17	Striped (wild type)	65	11.05	Not striped	7	11.54	−0.49
28	Blue	130	11.25	Black	127	9.87	+1.38
14	Dominant white	55	10.68	Black	47	9.83	+0.85
42	Restricted black	158	11.07	Extended black	184	10.09	+0.98

Length of down was unaffected by the striping found in Brown Leghorns and some other varieties. The other three comparisons all showed highly significant differences. Solid black chicks have shorter down than their full siblings with blue, dominant white, or restricted black. This last is the pattern found in Rhode Island Reds or Columbian fowls, in which black is restricted to the neck, wings, and tail. The comparison in this class was thus between feathers black and not black, the former proving the shorter, as in the other contrasting pairs.

Similar tests were made with respect to 14 other dominant mutations and their recessive alleles, but these did not reveal differences so striking or so consistent as those caused by the three genes for color just discussed. Since these 14 were mostly mutations affecting structure, such as polydactyly, creeper, naked neck, crest, etc., this is not surprising. The genes for barring and three others affecting pigmentation of the shanks and skin seemed to have little or no effect on the length of down.

VARIATIONS IN THE RATE OF GROWTH OF FEATHERS

Thus far, only three mutations have been identified that affect the rate of growth of feathers. Apart from these, there is a great deal of variation in the rate at which feathers grow in different regions of the body, in different sequences of plumage, and even in different individuals of common age and breeding maintained in the same environment. A detailed study of the normal development of feathers is beyond the scope of this book, and therefore only a very brief review of this "normal" variation in the growth of feathers can be given here. Details may be found in the investigations cited.

Normal Variation

Regional Variation. Careful observation of a dozen Plymouth Rock or Rhode Island Red chicks will show in what order the down is replaced in different regions by the first teleoptiles, usually called the "chick feathers," and also how great is the variability among different individuals. First to appear are the primary and secondary feathers on the wing. According to Hosker (1936), these are evident in sections through the wing on the thirteenth day of incubation. At hatching, a dozen or more of these remiges project beyond the down in rapidly feathering breeds like Leghorns, but they are less conspicuous and fewer in number in slowly feathering breeds like Rhode Island Reds. Thereafter the down is gradually replaced by chick feathers in all the pterylae. The last region to be thus transformed is the head tract.

The order in which different pterylae lose the down and acquire chick feathers has been studied in Silver-spangled Hamburgs by Dunn and Landauer (1930), in Barred Rocks by Gericke and Platt (1932), in White

Leghorns and Rhode Island Reds by Radi and Warren (1938), and in Brown Leghorns by Chu (1938). Although the Leghorns feather out much more rapidly than the heavier breeds because of the sex-linked gene for rapid feathering which they carry, the order in which the different pterylae displace down with chick feathers is about the same in these two classes of fowls. An exception is found in the tail feathers, some of which are evident in Leghorns at 3 days, whereas chicks of slowly feathering breeds seldom show any tail feathers till after 12 days of age. Feathers appear in the following tracts in about the order given but with considerable overlapping: humeral (shoulder), femoral (thigh), lateral (breast), anterior spinal (neck), alar (wing), posterior spinal (back), crural (leg), ventral (abdomen), and cephalic (head).

Within each of these areas there seems to be a more or less orderly sequence in the appearance of the feathers. This applies particularly to the first plumage but is also evident to some extent in the juvenile and adult plumages which succeed it. The process has been studied by Holmes (1935) in the remiges, by Warren and Gordon (1935), and by Juhn (1938). It is somewhat irregular in the secondary feathers but is so constant in the primaries that in moulting fowls poultrymen have long been accustomed to measuring the time elapsed since inception of the moult by the number of new feathers to be found among the 10 outer primaries. The innermost of these is the first to be moulted and replaced. The others follow in more or less regular order proceeding outward, and the outer primary is the last to grow in.

Sequence of Plumages. During growth, loss of one set of feathers results from their being pushed out by the succeeding set. This is evident in almost any chick up to 3 weeks of age or more, at which stage the new chick feathers often carry on their tips the down feathers that they have displaced. Although the latter soon wear off, there are sometimes enough of them present to give the chick a rather ragged, woolly apearance. In rapidly feathering birds, such as Leghorns, the chick feathers are often practically complete in all the feather tracts at 4 weeks of age. In other breeds, the growth of chick plumage is slow; in exceptional cases in Rhode Island Reds and Barred Rocks, some males are practically naked at 10 or 12 weeks of age. By that time the down is gone, but its replacement has been retarded.

From the studies of Marble (1934), it appears that between the chick feathers and the plumage of adults there is normally only one other set of body feathers. These comprise the juvenile plumage. The order of their appearance is much less regular than that of the chick feathers, and Chu (1938) even concluded that the number of successive generations of feathers prior to the adult plumage is not the same for all regions or for different follicles within a single region. Marble (1934) and Warren and Gordon (1935) agree in finding that the remiges of chicks are usually replaced directly by the definitive ones of the adults. In some chickens there are two sets of juvenile feathers before the final plumage is attained. On the other hand, it is not unusual to find persisting in the adult one or two of the outer primaries that were the first feathers to appear in the chick. Marble found that birds with such persistent primaries matured earlier than others. In the tail the chick feathers are replaced, according to Dunn and Landauer (1930), by juvenile ones, and these in turn by those of the adult.

Effect of Sex. Female chicks usually feather out more rapidly than males. This is most evident in Barred Rocks because in that breed the two sexes differ slightly in color and the comparatively quick feathering of the females is conspicuous. Feathers of capons are longer than those of comparable normal males. Horowitzowa (1931) found this to apply not only to the sickle feathers of the tail, where it is most conspicuous, but also to the remiges and to feathers of the saddle and cape. In his material the feathers of capons weighed 40 gm. more than those of uncastrated males, the relative weights (in proportion to body weight) being 5.21 per cent for males and 6.78 for capons. Another effect of sex on feather growth is seen in the moult. This is usually somewhat less precipitate, and correspondingly less conspicuous, in males than in females, but in capons, as Horowitzowa and Benoit (1929) have shown, there is a continuous growth of new feathers throughout the year. Greenwood and Burns (1940) found that this process was most active in May and June. Their three capons shed during the year more feathers per bird than were taken from controls plucked clean at one time.

Other Modifying Influences. The rate of growth of the whole body has much less effect upon the rate of growth of the feathers than one might expect. The correlation between these two variables was found by Jaap and Morris (1937) to be only .23 at 8 weeks of age. Similar studies by Radi and Warren (1938) with Rhode Island Reds yielded coefficients of correlation of .05, .19, .24, and .38 between body weight at 8 weeks and grade of feathering. These indicate very little relationship between these two variables. In Barred Rocks, Gericke and Platt (1932) found that the rate of feathering in chicks raised on different diets increased as the protein content of the diet was raised. Feather growth is somewhat more rapid at low temperatures than at high ones, but, conversely, it is more rapid at a high humidity than at a low one (Radi and Warren, 1938). The growth of feathers can be accelerated by the administration of thyroxine. Large quantities of this, whether administered in pure form or by feeding thyroid gland, induce a precipitate moult (Zavadovsky, 1925).

Rapid Feathering, *k*

In Leghorns, Minorcas, Anconas, and some other breeds, the chicks feather out much more rapidly than those of the Asiatic, English, or American breeds and some others. The discovery by Serebrovsky (1922) that this difference results from the action of a single pair of sex-linked genes is one of the most important contributions to poultry genetics since

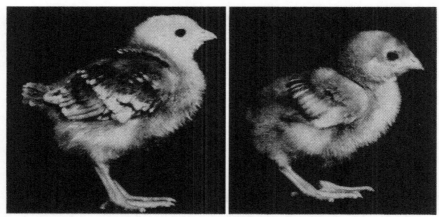

Fig. 43. Ten-day-old chicks showing the differences between rapid feathering (*left*) and slow-feathering (*right*), as given in the context.

the rediscovery of Mendel's laws. It has been verified by Warren (1925) and many others.

Description. Differentiation of the two classes with respect to feathering is most accurate at 8 to 12 days of age. Chicks with rapid feathering then have tail feathers up to an inch in length and the wing feathers extend almost to the tail or beyond it (Fig. 43). In slowly feathering birds of the same age there are no tail feathers and growth of the wings is comparatively slight. Most of the rapidly feathering chicks are recognizable earlier than at 10 days of age.

Later studies by Warren (1930*b*) showed that the two types could also be differentiated with a high degree of accuracy as soon after hatching as the chicks were thoroughly dry. At that stage the primary and secondary feathers of the rapid-feathering chicks project well beyond the down, but in slowly feathering chicks they do not. In the latter, the feathers in the wing all seem of about the same length, but in the chicks feathering rapidly the primaries are much longer than the next row of feathers, the primary coverts. These differences in the wings are not so evident 2 or 3 days after hatching as they are on the first day.

Genetics. Slow feathering is dominant to rapid feathering. The symbol K used by Hertwig and Rittershaus (1929) was the first applied to this condition that had not previously been used for some other mutation. In reciprocal crosses between birds homozygous or hemizygous (as the females must be) for these conditions, results are as follows:

	Parents		Progeny	
	♂♂	♀♀	♂♂	♀♀
(1)	KK slow	$k-$ rapid	Kk slow	$K-$ slow
(2)	kk rapid	$K-$ slow	Kk slow	$k-$ rapid

There are undoubtedly modifying genes which affect the expression of K and k, since in some matings chicks intermediate between the two types are produced. In spite of this, Warren (1930b) found that the proportion wrongly classified did not exceed 5 per cent. These were mostly females classified as males, i.e., as slow instead of rapid.

A point of considerable interest, both theoretical and practical, is that the differences in rate of feathering caused by these sex-linked genes provide one of the few cases known in animals in which a distinct modification of a physiological process depends upon a single pair of alleles. By some geneticists inherited traits are separated into "morphological characters," affecting form, structure, color, or other more or less superficial variations, and "physiological characters," or variations in function. In the fowl most of the latter, such as rate of growth, body size, fecundity, and viability, depend upon multiple factors, the exact number of genes being impossible to determine by existing techniques. This makes breeding for improvement in these physiological characters a very slow process, whereas traits dependent on a single pair of genes are easy to eliminate or acquire as may be desired.

In this case, as is shown below, rapid feathering is a very desirable mutation. It is not only a physiological character but one that is usually sharply distinct from the alternative allele. At the same time, because it is unifactorial, it can be transferred from one stock to another and utilized as may be desired by the simplest kind of genetic procedures.

Economic Significance. Chicks with this type of rapid feathering are better protected against chilling than their slowly feathering relatives. They have a further advantage in being able to fly to the roosts at an earlier age, thus getting some measure of protection against predators and against the risks of crowding on the floor in corners of a brooder house.

An advantage important to the poultryman is that in crosses of the second type given above the female chicks can be distinguished from the males by the type of feathering. Sex-linked crosses of this sort have been understood since 1910, when the fact became known that barring is sex linked. However, such crosses are sometimes difficult to make when they involve barred and non-barred breeds, or silver and gold ones, because highly improved strains with the desired colors are not always easy to find. Some of them yield females that have predominantly black plumage and are therefore less desirable in some markets. None of them in which differentiation of the sexes is based on color of the down permits the use of White Leghorns. This is unfortunate because highly improved strains are more readily available in this breed, at least in the United States, than in any other. However, crosses of Barred Rock or Rhode Island Red females with White Leghorn males will yield chicks in which the pullets can be recognized at hatching with an accuracy of 95 per cent. Females of any other slowly feathering breed will serve equally well. At maturity these birds are predominantly white, except those from Rhode Island Reds, in which varying amounts of red are found. Such crossbreds are likely also to exhibit some hybrid vigor. If crosses between breeds are not desired, slowly feathering strains of White Leghorns and rapidly feathering strains of Plymouth Rocks and Rhode Island Reds can be developed for crosses within breeds. These would have to be maintained as separate varieties, with regular inspection of chicks to make sure that chicks with slow feathering did not get into the rapidly feathering strain, or vice versa. Whether or not this method of differentiating the sexes at hatching is as desirable as the alternative one—examination of the cloaca —remains to be seen.

Even if the gene k be not used for identification of sex, it affords the best way yet known of overcoming the very undesirable type of autosomal slow feathering which is discussed later in this section.

Effect of k on Growth. In four lots of New Hampshire chicks, Warren and Payne (1945) found those with rapid feathering to be consistently heavier at 12 weeks of age than the ones with slow-feathering. This was so in both sexes. It seems probable, therefore, that the gene k, formerly considered as accelerating merely the growth of the feathers, is really a mutation that causes more rapid growth of the whole organism. Another interpretation could be that the greater covering of the body in the rapid-feathering chicks affords them a lower requirement of energy for maintenance of body temperature and thus leaves more of their nutriment available for growth.

The Tardy-Retarded Series, *t*, *t*^{s}, and *T*

While the difference between slow-feathering and rapid-feathering chicks depends on a pair of sex-linked genes, there are also autosomal genes that may prevent full expression of rapid feathering. These account for the somewhat bare chicks with ragged plumage that are not infrequently seen in White Leghorns. They are particularly conspicuous in thrifty flocks of chicks that have grown normally and appear well feathered with the exception of these ragged specimens. The latter are caused by either of two recessive autosomal mutations, tardy (*t*) and retarded (*t*^{s}), which, together with their normal allele *T*, comprise a series of multiple alleles. Retarded was first recognized by Warren (1933*a*), while tardy was identified as a separate mutation and proved to be a third allele by Jones and Hutt (1946).

Descriptions. These apply only to rapid-feathering chicks, *kk* or *k−*, as ways of recognizing the two mutations in slow-feathering chicks are not known. Males and females do not differ in the expression of these mutations.

At hatching the normal rapid-feathering chick has at least six primary feathers and as many secondaries. The retarded chick, which is less abnormal than the tardy one, has normal primaries but only the first three (outer) secondaries. The tardy chick has also normal primaries but no secondaries whatever.

At 10 days the differences are even more marked (Fig. 44). The normal chick has at least six well-developed primaries, six secondaries equal in length, and a small tail. The retarded and tardy chicks both lack tails. The former has only the first three or four primaries and secondaries of normal length, and each succeeding one is shorter than the previous one. The tardy chick shows little or no development of the secondaries, and the primaries, though normal in number, are narrower and shorter than in normal chicks. Both retarded and tardy chicks look somewhat ragged at this stage.

At 3 weeks, retarded chicks still have fewer primaries and secondaries than normal ones, and only the first three of the secondaries are equal in length to the primaries. There are small tails on the retarded chicks, but not on the tardy ones. The latter show at 3 weeks almost exactly the same stage of wing feathering as the retarded ones do at 10 days (Fig. 44).

By 6 weeks of age the retarded chick is almost normal in appearance, but tardy ones continue to show abnormally slow growth of feathers. Their tail feathers do not appear until at least 8 weeks of age. How-

Fig. 44. Ten-day-old chicks showing the three phenotypes of the tardy-retarded series of multiple alleles. A, normal, TT; B, retarded, $t^s t^s$; C, tardy, tt; D, tardy at 8 weeks.

ever, at maturity retarded and tardy birds are indistinguishable from normal ones.

Classification. If a batch of chicks contains only normal ones and one mutant type without the other, classifications can be made with almost complete accuracy at hatching. When both retarded and tardy chicks were present, Jones and Hutt found that about 12 per cent were not correctly identified at hatching. For practical purposes, such as the elimination of the defects from any stock carrying them, retarded chicks should be sorted out at 10 or 12 days, and tardy ones at any time up to 8 weeks of age.

Genetics. Some of the data of Warren (1933a) and of Jones and Hutt (1946) are given in Table 16. These show that (1) retarded and tardy are both unifactorial mutations, recessive to the normal condition T; (2) retarded (t^s) and tardy (t) are alleles, with the latter recessive to the former; and (3) all types can be obtained from the mating $Tt \times t^s t$.

TABLE 16. SEGREGATION OF NORMAL, RETARDED, AND TARDY IN VARIOUS TYPES OF MATINGS

Source of data	Parents		Offspring		
	Phenotypes	Genotypes	Normal	Retarded	Tardy
Warren.........	Normal × retarded	$TT \times t^s t^s$	325	—	—
	Normal × retarded	$T t^s \times t^s t^s$	210	234	—
	Retarded × retarded	$t^s t^s \times t^s t^s$	...	78	—
Jones and Hutt...	Normal × tardy	$TT \times tt$	102	—	—
	Normal × tardy	$Tt \times tt$	41	...	45
	Normal × normal	$Tt \times Tt$	125	...	46
	Tardy × tardy	$tt \times tt$	...	...	85
	Retarded × tardy	$t^s t^s \times tt$	...	41	—
	Retarded × tardy	$t^s t \times tt$	...	104	116
	Normal × retarded	$Tt \times t^s t$	7	4	1

Altogether, these results prove that T, t^s, and t comprise a series of multiple alleles. This was the second such series to be recognized in the fowl. The superscript s in the symbol for retarded is used as a reminder that the gene exerts its effect on the secondary flight feathers.

The full genotypes for normal, rapid-feathering chicks are thus: kk TT for males, and $k-$ TT for females. Both t^s and t were found in White Leghorns. Warren's studies showed that it is difficult to follow the segregation of retarded in slow-feathering chicks, and this is probably true also of tardy.

Autosomal Slow Feathering

Economic Significance. In the so-called "heavy" breeds, such as Plymouth Rocks, Rhode Island Reds, and Wyandottes, the gene k for rapid feathering is seldom found. Chicks of these breeds, therefore, usually show the sex-linked type of slow feathering, but among them there are great differences in the rate of feather growth caused by autosomal genes that have not yet been analyzed. Though all are slow to feather in comparison with Leghorns, some are so much worse than others that they constitute a serious problem to the producer of broilers, who wants to market at 8 or 10 weeks of age a uniformly well-feathered lot of chickens (Fig. 45). Those with bare backs, sunburned and full of pinfeathers, are a serious cause of loss. It is not uncommon to find chickens of these breeds almost naked, except for a few feathers on the wings, at 10 or 12 weeks of age. Females are less subject to this condition than males.

Where many of these occur in a flock, one might suspect some nutritional deficiency, especially since Gericke and Platt (1932) found poor

Fig. 45. Two Barred Rock cockerels 12 weeks old, and both with sex-linked slow feathering. The one on the left is well feathered out, but the other is still half naked because of the action of other genes.

feathering on diets low in protein. In most cases, however, the bare-backed broilers are found in flocks receiving a diet obviously adequate for normal growth of feathers in most of the birds. This suggests that those birds extremely slow to feather out are genetically different from the others, and this has been confirmed by experimental breeding.

Genetics. By selection in Rhode Island Reds, both Radi and Warren (1938) and Hays and Sanborn (1942) differentiated two contrasting strains, one characterized by good feathering on the back at 7 or 8 weeks of age, the other by poor feathering or lack of it. The rapidity with which selection improved the degree of feathering suggests that the number of genes concerned is not large. Hays and Sanborn concluded that a dominant autosomal gene exerts a major influence in producing good back feathering at 8 weeks. This is consistent with the fact that crosses between their two strains by Radi and Warren yielded offspring resembling the well-feathered parents. Together these results suggest that even by mass selection breeders should be able to improve the degree of back feathering. This procedure is effective in reducing the amount of plumage (Jaap and Morris, 1937), but it has not yet been proved equally effective in improving it. Breeders should use the progeny test and make selection on the basis of family averages whenever possible. When enough males are tested to reveal the good ones, this should produce the desired results rapidly. In 1940, only 59 per cent of the males in the strain selected by Hays and Sanborn had at 8 weeks the degree of back feathering sought, but in the next 2 years all of them had good feathering and were fully comparable with the females in that respect.

Use of the Gene k. Radi and Warren found that even after four generations of selection the degree of feathering attained in their well-feathered strain was not nearly so good as that prevailing in Leghorns made to feather out rapidly by the sex-linked gene k. This fact, together with the other advantages of that gene, mentioned earlier, suggests that it is highly desirable to eliminate the sex-linked gene for slow feathering from stocks used for production of broilers (and perhaps even from all breeds) and to substitute in them its recessive allele. This is a comparatively simple operation. Mutations from K to k have already been found in some of the breeds hitherto characterized by slow feathering, and there is little doubt that careful observation will reveal more chicks with rapid feathering among the heavy breeds. Any breeder of Rhode Island Reds can easily replace K with k by introducing the latter from New Hampshires, most of which have rapid feathering. However, the response to this suggestion, when it was made by the author to a group of Rhode Island Red breeders in Massachusetts, indicated that most of them would rather lose their right hands.

The matings given on page 135 show that, when the gene is introduced to a slow-feathering stock by a kk male, female chicks with the desired rapid feathering are obtained in the first generation. By mating them back to the same male or to another of the same genotype, only progeny carrying k are obtained. If the desired gene is introduced through a rapidly feathering female, the F_1 females show slow feathering, but in the F_2 generation females of the desired genotype, $k-$, will appear. By mating these to Kk males (which can be identified by a breeding test with any females), half the progeny (whether male or female) will have rapid feathering. These may be identified before 2 weeks of age and carefully tagged as the parents of the next generation, all of which should have only the k gene. Once K is eliminated, all the chicks in succeeding generations should show rapid feathering. However, since errors in classification can occur, it would be best to examine the chicks each year at 10 days of age to make sure that a slowly feathering one has not cropped out from some breeder incorrectly classified in the previous year.

HEN FEATHERING, *Hf*

Males of most breeds differ from the females in having longer, pointed, fringed feathers in the neck, saddle, back, and wing bow. Since ovariotomized females revert for a time to a type of plumage resembling that of males, it is evident that the ovarian hormone is responsible for the rounded feathers, with little or no fringe, found in females in the areas where sex dimorphism in feather structure occurs. However, in some breeds the males have hen feathering of exactly the same type as the females. This is a breed characteristic of the Golden and Silver Sebrights, an interesting breed developed by Sir John Sebright early in the nineteenth century. Hen-feathered cocks are also found in some strains of Campines and occasionally in Hamburgs, Silver-laced Wyandottes, and Games. This aberrant type of feathering has so piqued the curiosity of biologists that it has been studied in several different ways, and as a result the genetic and physiological bases for the condition are fairly well understood.

Genetics. From the studies of Morgan (1920) and Punnett and Bailey (1921), it is now clear that hen feathering is caused by a single dominant autosomal gene, which, like most others, is often incompletely dominant. The analysis has been difficult because some heretozygotes may show only a few henny feathers in their first adult plumage. This is because in such males, *mirabile dictu*, the development of henny feathers requires a male hormone, and in some cases the definitive plumage is acquired before the testes are functioning normally. However, Punnett and Bailey found that such birds become almost completely hen feathered when, after a moult, they acquire their second coat of adult plumage. They also found, as did Krizenecky (1934), that old Sebright males sometimes revert to cock feathering, a peculiarity best explained by the assumption that testicular activity was subnormal when these old birds moulted.

For this mutation the symbol *Hf* is proposed in preference to the *H* used by Punnett (1937), which had previously been preempted for the normal allele of silky plumage. Hen feathering is a good example of a mutation that is autosomal but *sex limited*, *i.e.*, that can be manifested only in one sex.

In an ingenious attempt to relate the hen feathering found in these males to that in females of ordinary breeds, Punnett (1937) has suggested that the latter carry *Hf* on the Y chromosome, so that it is never found in males of the ordinary breeds, all of which lack that chromosome. By a translocation *Hf* was presumably attached to an autosome and thus transmitted to males. According to this theory, there should be some females that lack *Hf* in their Y chromosome. Although they would be hen feathered like other females because of their ovarian hormone, skin grafts from them to normal males would produce feathers of the male type. Females of this sort would provide a critical test of the theory, but thus far none have been discovered.

Physiological Basis. It was found by Morgan (1915, 1920*a*) and others that castration of hen-feathered males causes their next plumage to be male-like or, more correctly, like the long neutral type of plumage found in capons and poulardes (ovariotomized females). This evidence that secretion of the testis is necessary for henny feathering in cocks was followed by a theory that the gonads of these birds contained special luteal cells responsible for the aberrant type of plumage. This was subsequently disproved when Pease (1922), Benoit (1922), and Nonidez (1922) found these same cells in the testes of immature males of cock-feathered breeds.

Final evidence that the gonads of hen-feathered males do not differ from those of normal cocks was provided when Roxas (1926) showed that Leghorn testes transplanted into Sebright capons induced hen feathering just the same as the Sebrights' own testes did. In the reciprocal transplantation, Sebright testes in Leghorn capons restored the masculinity of these birds but did not cause them to be hen feathered. In a similar experiment, Greenwood (1928) found that the testes of hen-feathered Campines did not induce hen feathering in Leghorn capons, although these birds did develop normal male head furnishings. It is clear that hen-feathered cocks and normal ones have gonads that are equipotential, so far as their endocrine secretions are concerned, and that hen feathering is not expressed except when the feathers develop under the influence of testicular hormones. The effect on the plumage is the same whether the hormone comes from the bird's own testis, or from a graft, or is injected in purified form as testosterone (Caridroit, 1937, and others).

Further evidence of the nature of hen feathering was provided by Danforth (1930) and Danforth and Foster (1929). Danforth found that skin grafts from females of ordinary breeds to cock-feathered males grew only feathers of the male type. However, when such a graft was made from a female of hen-feathered stock to a Leghorn male, the feathers grown on it were henny. In another experiment, skin from a Sebright female transplanted to a male of the same breed produced henny feathers, and when the host was subsequently castrated, all its feathers, graft included, were of the male type. These tests showed that the gene for hen feathering affects the feather follicles of the females just as it does the males, even though the character is never recognizable in females except in a skin graft.

It is clear that hen feathering is a genetically induced peculiarity of the feather follicle in the skin. To that extent it is like frizzling, silkiness, and other variations of the feathers; but it differs from them in being evident only in males and in requiring male hormone for its manifestation. Since ovariotomized females of hen-feathered breeds assume the neutral plumage of poulardes (Eliot, 1928; Pézard, 1928), one might also say that they require female hormone to be hen feathered, but in this respect they do not differ from females of ordinary breeds.

Hen feathering can also be induced in males by feeding thyroid gland or administering thyroxine, but the reason for this phenomenon is not yet clear.

Literature Cited

Aldrovandus, U. 1600. "Ornithologiae." Tomus Alter.

Bateson, W. 1894. "Materials for the Study of Variation." London: Macmillan & Co., Ltd.

———— and R. C. Punnett. 1908. Experimental studies in the physiology of heredity. Poultry. *Repts. Evol. Comm. Roy. Soc.*, **IV**:18–35.

Benedict, F. G., W. Landauer, and E. L. Fox. 1932. The physiology of normal and frizzle fowl, with special reference to the basal metabolism. *Storrs (Conn.) Agr. Expt. Sta. Bull.* 177.

Benoit, J. 1922. Sur les cellules interstitielles du testicle du coq domestique. *Compt. rend. soc. biol.*, **74**:1383–1384.

————. 1929. Le déterminisme des caractères sexuels secondaires du coq domestique: Etude physiologique et histophysiologique. *Arch. zool. exptl. et gén.*, **69**: 217–499.

Boas, E. P., and W. Landauer. 1933. The effect of elevated metabolism on the hearts of frizzle fowl. *Am. J. Med. Sci.*, **185**:654–665.

———— and ————. 1934. The effect of elevated metabolism on the heart of frizzle fowl. II. Increased ratio of heart to body weight. *Am. J. Med. Sci.*, **188**: 359–364.

Bonhote, J. L. 1914. Preliminary notes on the heredity of certain characters in a cross between Silky and Yokohama fowls. *Cairo Sci. J.*, **8**:83–90.

Caridroit, F. 1937. Contrôle des caractères pigmentaires raciaux par une hormone masculinisante (propionate de testostérone). *Compt. rend. soc. biol.* **126**:732–734.

Chamberlain, B. H. 1900. Note on a long-tailed breed of fowls in Tosa. *Trans. Asiatic Soc. Japan*, **27** (pt. I B): 1–5.

Chu, J. P. 1938. Studies on plumage in the male Brown Leghorn fowl. *Trans. Roy. Soc. Edinburgh*, **59** (pt. III): 533–562.

Cole, L. J., and L. E. Hawkins. 1930. Studies on inheritance in pigeons. VIII. Porcupine pigeons. *J. Heredity*, **21**:50–60.

Cole, L. J., and W. F. Hollander. 1939. The inheritance of Silky plumage in the domestic pigeon. *J. Heredity,* **30**:197–201.

Cole, R. K., and F. B. Hutt. 1947. A genetic study of feathered feet in White Leghorns. *Poultry Sci.,* **26**:536.

Crew, F. A. E., and L. Mirskaia. 1931. A peculiar feather tumor of the canary. *Vet. Record* (n.s.), **11**:541–542.

Danforth, C. H. 1919. The developmental relations of brachydactyly in the domestic fowl. *Am. J. Anat.,* **25**:97–115.

———. 1919a. An hereditary complex in the domestic fowl. *Genetics,* **4**:587–596.

———. 1930. The nature of racial and sexual dimorphism in the plumage of Campines and Leghorns. *Biol. Generalis,* **6**:99–108.

——— and F. Foster. 1929. Skin transplantation as a means of studying genetic and endocrine factors in the fowl. *J. Exptl. Zoöl.,* **52**:443–470.

Davenport, C. B. 1906. Inheritance in poultry. *Carnegie Inst. Wash. Pub.* 52.

———. 1909. Inheritance of characteristics in domestic fowl. *Carnegie Inst. Wash. Pub.* 121.

———. 1914. The bare necks. *J. Heredity,* **5**:374.

Dunn, L. C., and M. A. Jull. 1927. On the inheritance of some characters of the Silky fowl. *J. Genetics,* **19**:27–63.

——— and W. Landauer. 1930. Studies on the plumage of the silver-spangled fowl. I. The expression of the spangled pattern during growth. *Storrs (Conn.) Agr. Expt. Sta. Bull.,* **163**:31–46.

Eliot, T. S. 1928. The influence of the gonads on the plumage of Sebright Bantams. *Physiol. Zoöl.,* **1**:286–324.

Fisher, R. A. 1934. Crest and hernia in fowls due to a single gene without dominance. *Science,* **80**:288–289.

Freund, L. 1925. Besonderheiten der Vogelhaut als Artcharaktere angeblich pathologischer Herkunft. *Z. ind. abst. Vererb.,* **36**:426–429.

Gericke, A. M. M., and C. S. Platt. 1932. Feather development in Barred Plymouth Rock chicks. *New Jersey Agr. Expt. Sta. Bull.* 543.

Greenwood, A. W. 1927. The "hackleless" fowl. *Proc. Roy. Phys. Soc. (Edinburgh),* **21** (pt. 3): 123–129.

———. 1928. Studies on the relation of gonadic structure to plumage characterization in the domestic fowl. IV. Gonad cross-transplantation in Leghorn and Campine. *Proc. Roy. Soc. (London)* B, **103**:73–81.

——— and M. Burns. 1940. The problem of the moult in the castrated Brown Leghorn fowl. *Quart. J. Exptl. Physiol.,* **30**:163–171.

Hays, F. A. 1943. Inheritance of mottled earlobes and stubs in Rhode Island Reds. *Am. Naturalist,* **77**:471–475.

——— and R. Sanborn. 1942. Breeding Rhode Island Reds for rapid feathering. *Massachusetts Agr. Expt. Sta. Bull.* 396.

Hertwig, P. 1933. Geschlechtsgebundene und autosomale Koppelungen bei Hühnern. *Verhandl. deut. zoolog. Ges.:* 112–118.

——— and T. Rittershaus. 1929. Die Erbfaktoren der Haushühner. I. Beitrag: Die Ortsbestimmung von 4 Faktoren im X-Chromosom. *Z. ind. Abst. Vererb.,* **51**:354–372.

Holmes, A. 1935. The pattern and symmetry of adult plumage units in relation to the order and locus of origin of the embryonic feather papillae. *Am. J. Anat.,* **56**:513–537.

Horowitzowa, R. 1931. Morphological research on capons. *Mém. inst. nat. polon. écon. rurale Pulawy,* **12**:305–345.

Hosker, A. 1936. Studies on the epidermal structures of birds. *Phil. Trans. Roy. Soc. B,* **226**:143–188.

Hurst, C. C. 1905. Experiments with poultry. *Repts. Evol. Comm. Roy. Soc.,* **II**: 131–154.

Hutt, F. B. 1930. The genetics of the fowl. I. The inheritance of frizzled plumage. *J. Genetics,* **22**:109–127.

———. 1932. Eight new mutations in the domestic fowl. *Proc. Intern. Genetic. Congr. 6th Congr., Ithaca, N.Y.,* **2**:96–97.

———. 1936. Genetics of the fowl. V. The modified Frizzle. *J. Genetics,* **32**:277–285.

———. 1941. The association of physiological traits with breed characteristics in the fowl. *Proc. Intern. Genetic. Congr. 7th Congr., Edinburgh,* 1939:156–157.

——— and P. D. Sturkie. 1938. Genetics of the fowl. IX. Naked, a new sex-linked mutation. *J. Heredity,* **29**:370–379.

———, C. D. Mueller, and D. C. Warren. 1944. Inheritance of ragged wing in the fowl. *J. Heredity,* **35**:27–32.

Jaap, R. G. 1937. Inherited congenital baldness in the domestic fowl. *Proc. Oklahoma Acad. Sci.,* **17**:41–43.

———. 1939. Brachydactyly and syndactyly in ptilopod domestic fowl, *Gallus domesticus. Proc. Oklahoma Acad. Sci.,* **29**:27–29.

——— and L. Morris. 1937. Genetical differences in eight-week weight and feathering. *Poultry Sci.,* **16**:44–48.

Jones, D. G., and F. B. Hutt. 1946. Multiple alleles affecting feathering in the fowl. *J. Heredity,* **37**:197–205.

Jones, S. V. H. 1921. Inheritance of silkiness in fowls. *J. Heredity,* **12**:117–128.

Juhn, M. 1938. Emergence orders and growth rates in the juvenile plumages of the Brown Leghorn. *J. Exptl. Zoöl.,* **77**:467–487.

Jull, M. A., and J. P. Quinn. 1931. Inheritance in poultry. *J. Heredity,* **22**:147–154.

Kabystina, P. A., and S. G. Petrov. 1935. The genetics of down lengths in chicks (trans. title). *Genetika Selekcija seljsk.-hoz. Zivotn.,* **1**:321–336.

Krallinger, H. F., and M. Chodziesner. 1932. Die "Stachelschweintauben." *Züchter,* **4**:53–55.

Krautwald, F. 1910. "Die Haube der Hühner und Enten. Ihre Ursache, Entstehung und Vererbung." Inaugural Dissertation, zootech. u veterinär. Institut, Universität Bern.

Krizenecky, J. 1934. Zur Analyse der Hennenfedrigkeit der Sebright-Bantam-Hühner und anderer Rassen. *Z. Zücht.: Reihe B. Z. Tierzücht. Züchtgsbiol.,* **31**:201–216.

Kuhn, O. 1932. Entwicklungsphysiologische Untersuchungen an der Vogelfeder. *Arch. Entwicklungsmech. Organ.,* **127**:456–541.

Lambert, W. V., and C. W. Knox. 1929. The inheritance of shank feathering in the domestic fowl. *Poultry Sci.,* **9**:51–64.

Landauer, W. 1932. The effect of irradiating eggs with ultra-violet light upon the development of chicken embryos. *Storrs (Conn.) Agr. Expt. Sta. Bull.* 179.

———. 1933. A gene modifying frizzling in the fowl. *J. Heredity,* **24**:152–156.

——— and S. D. Aberle. 1935. Studies on the endocrine glands of frizzle fowl. *Am. J. Anat.,* **57**:99–134.

Landauer, W. and L. C. Dunn. 1930. The "frizzle" character of fowls. Its expression and inheritance. *J. Heredity,* **21**:290-305.

—— and E. Upham. 1936. Weight and size of organs in frizzle fowl. *Storrs (Conn.) Agr. Expt. Sta. Bull.* 210.

Lillie, F. R. 1940. Physiology of development of the feather. III. Growth of the mesodermal constituents and blood circulation in the pulp. *Physiol. Zoöl.,* **13**: 143-175.

—— and M. Juhn. 1932. The physiology of development of feathers. I. Growth-rate and pattern in the individual feather. *Physiol. Zoöl.,* **5**:124-184.

—— and ——. 1938. Physiology of development of the feather. II. General principles of development with special reference to the after-feather. *Physiol. Zoöl.,* **11**:434-450.

—— and Hsi Wang. 1940. Physiology of development of the feather. IV. The diurnal curve of growth in Brown Leghorn fowl. *Proc. Nat. Acad. Sci. U.S.,* **26**:67-85.

—— and ——. 1941. Physiology of development of the feather. V. Experimental morphogenesis. *Physiol. Zoöl.,* **14**:103-133.

Marble, D. R. 1934. Relation of juvenile plumage to growth and sexual maturity. *Poultry Sci.,* **13**:195-201.

Marlow, H. W., and M. J. Caldwell. 1934. A chemical and x-ray study of "flightless" feathers. *J. Heredity,* **25**:265-268.

McCrady, E., Jr. 1932. The "penguin" guinea fowl. *J. Heredity,* **23**:201-207.

Morgan, T. H. 1915. Demonstration of the appearance after castration of cock-feathering in a hen-feathered cockerel. *Proc. Soc. Exptl. Biol. Med.,* **13**:31-32.

——. 1920. The genetic factor for hen-feathering in the Sebright Bantam. *Biol. Bull.,* **39**:257-259.

——. 1920a. The effects of castration of hen-feathered Campines. *Biol. Bull.,* **39**:231-247.

Nonidez, J. F. 1922. Studies on the gonads of the fowl. III. The origin of the so-called luteal cells in the testis of hen-feathered cocks. *Am. J. Anat.,* **31**:109-124.

Pease, M. S. 1922. Note on Professor T. H. Morgan's theory of hen-feathering in cocks. *Proc. Cambridge Phil. Soc.,* **21**:22-26.

Pézard, A. 1928. Die Bestimmung der Geschlechtsfunktion bei den Hühnern. *Ergeb. Physiol.,* **27**:552-656.

Punnett, R. C. 1937. Henny feathering in the fowl: a fresh interpretation. *J. Genetics,* **35**:129-140.

—— and P. G. Bailey. 1918. Genetic studies in poultry. I. Inheritance of leg feathering. *J. Genetics,* **7**:203-213.

—— and ——. 1921. Genetic studies in poultry. III. Hen-feathered cocks. *J. Genetics,* **11**:37-57.

Radi, M. H., and D. C. Warren. 1938. Studies on the physiology and inheritance of feathering in the growing chick. *J. Agr. Research,* **56**:679-705.

Roxas, H. A. 1926. Gonad cross-transplantation in Sebright and Leghorn fowls. *J. Exptl. Zoöl.,* **46**:63-119.

Rüst, W. 1932. Lethalfaktoren und unvollkommene Dominanz bei Haubenenten. *Arch. Geflügelk.,* **6**:110-116.

Schwarz, E. 1931. Schilddrüsenerkrankung beim Haushuhn und ihre mutmassliche Erblichkeit. *Züchter,* **3**:154-158.

Serebrovsky, A. S. 1922. Crossing over involving three sex-linked genes in chickens. *Am. Naturalist,* **56**:571-572.

Serebrovsky, A. S. 1926. The genetics of the domestic fowl. II. The genetics of leg feathering (trans. title). *Mem. Anikowo Genetic. Sta.*, cited from the abstract by L. C. Dunn (*J. Heredity*, **20**:111–118) from the translation by B. F. Glessing.

———— and S. G. Petrov. 1930. On the composition of the plan of the chromosomes of the domestic hen. *J. Exptl. Biol.* (Russian), **6**:157–179 (from a translation by B. F. Glessing of the U.S. Department of Agriculture).

Sturkie, P. D. 1941. Studies on hereditary congenital baldness in the domestic fowl. I. Embryological and physiological bases of the character. *J. Morphol.*, **69**:517–535.

————. 1942. A new type of autosomal nakedness in the domestic fowl. *J. Heredity*, **33**:202–208.

Tegetmeier, W. B. 1856. On the remarkable peculiarities existing in the skulls of the feather-crested variety of the domestic fowl, now known as the Polish. *Proc. Zool. Soc. London*, **1856**:366–368.

————. 1867. "The Poultry Book." London: George Routledge & Sons, Ltd.

Warren, D. C. 1925. Inheritance of rate of feathering in poultry. *J. Heredity*, **16**:13–18.

————. 1930. Non-heritable downlessness in chickens. *J. Heredity*, **21**:408.

————. 1930a. The inheritance of two standard disqualifications in White Leghorn chickens. *Poultry Sci.*, **9**:271–282.

————. 1930b. Crossbred poultry. *Kansas Agr. Expt. Sta. Bull. 252.*

————. 1932. Flightless—a heritable variation in the domestic fowl. *J. Heredity*, **23**:449–452.

————. 1933. Nine independently inherited autosomal factors in the domestic fowl. *Genetics*, **18**:68–81.

————. 1933a. Retarded feathering in the fowl. *J. Heredity*, **24**:430–434.

————. 1937. The lethal nature of flightlessness in the fowl. *J. Heredity*, **28**:16–18.

————. 1938. A heritable variation of feather structure in the fowl. *J. Heredity*, **29**:91–93.

———— and C. D. Gordon. 1935. The sequence of apearance, molt, and replacement of the juvenile remiges of some domestic birds. *J. Agr. Research*, **51**:459–470.

———— and F. B. Hutt. 1936. Linkage relations of crest, dominant white, and frizzling in the fowl. *Am. Naturalist*, **70**:379–394.

———— and L. F. Payne. 1945. Influence of the early feathering gene upon a chick's growth rate. *Poultry Sci.*, **24**:191–192.

Zavadovsky, Boris. 1925. The effect of feeding fowls on thyroid gland. *Endocrinology*, **9**:125–136.

CHAPTER 6

VARIATIONS IN THE COLOR OF THE SKIN

Differences in the color of the skin are most noticeable in the shanks and in the beak. In these regions the fowl may be yellow, yellowish white, pinkish white, black (with either yellow or pinkish soles), blue, slate, green, or greenish black. Explanation of these apparently complex variations is simple when one knows (1) the structure of the skin, (2) the pigments involved, and (3) the genes affecting the distribution of these pigments.

STRUCTURE OF THE SKIN

The bird's skin is made up of two layers, a comparatively thin outer one called the *epidermis* and a thicker, inner layer known as the *dermis, corium,* or *cutis* (Fig. 46).

The epidermis is composed of (1) a thick outer layer, the *stratum corneum,* which is modified in the shank to form scales, and (2) a thin inner layer, the *rete Malpighii,* or *stratum germinativum.* The stratum corneum is composed of many rows of flattened cells but shows little evidence of cellular structure. It is, in effect, somewhat like a coating of

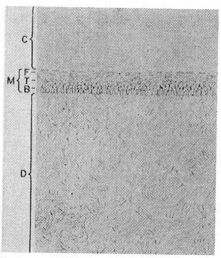

FIG. 46. Drawing of a vertical section of the skin from the shank of a white-shanked hen, showing its structure. *C,* stratum corneum, or outer layer of the epidermis; *M,* rete Malpighii, with layers of flat (*F*), transitional (*T*), and basal or columnar cells (*B*); *D,* dermis. (*From Barrows in Maine Agr. Expt. Sta. Bull. 232.*)

translucent shellac through which the pigments of the underlying dermis may be visible, though not seen clearly. Elsewhere than in the shank and beak, the stratum corneum is relatively thinner than it is shown to be in Fig. 46. Underneath this horny exterior layer of the epidermis lies the rete Malpighii, which is composed of several layers of cells. The lowest of these, a layer of columnar cells perpendicular to the surface of the skin, makes a sharp line of demarcation between the epidermis and the underlying dermis. Above it are several layers of polyhedral cells which gradually become flatter as they approach the stratum corneum. There are no blood vessels or nerves in the epidermis.

The dermis is composed of connective tissue with masses of fat scattered through it, these being particularly abundant in the lower levels. The dermis, unlike the epidermis, is highly vascular and is supplied with nerves.

PIGMENTS AFFECTING SKIN COLOR

All the skin colors thus far known in the domestic fowl arise from the presence, either singly or in combination, of two principal pigments, melanin and xanthophyll. The pinkish-white skin lacks both.

Melanin. This is the same complex protein that is responsible for black and blue in the plumage. According to Barrows (1914) it may occur in the dermis, in either layer of the epidermis, or in all three.

Xanthophyll. The yellow color in the body fat, eggs, and skin (including shanks and beak) is not produced by the cells of the fowl, as is melanin. According to Palmer (1915) this yellow color depends, to a small extent, upon the presence of carotene but mostly upon the presence of the yellow carotinoid pigment, xanthophyll, which has the general formula $C_{40}H_{56}O_2$. This is manufactured by plants, ingested by the fowl with corn, alfalfa, grass, and other feeds, and stored in various parts of the body. In a non-laying bird, xanthophyll is stored in the body fat, blood, and skin. In laying birds it goes into the egg, and as Palmer and Kempster (1919) have shown, the laying hen eliminates all the xanthophyll in her food through the egg, it being impossible for her to store it in the skin, even when the diet is very high in xanthophyll.

According to Palmer and Kempster, the xanthophyll in the skin is in the form of granules, with little or no fat associated with it. Barrows (1914) found that this pigment might be present in both layers of the epidermis or in the stratum corneum only. It is also found in the dermis, particularly along the blood capillaries. In young birds it is concentrated in the rete Malpighii, but this is not so noticeable in mature birds.

Red Color. The so-called "horn color" seen in the shanks and beak of fowls with plumage like that of Rhode Island Reds is merely an extension of the red color of the plumage and is therefore melanin in some variant form. It is confined to the epidermis. The bright red in the shanks of fowls, particularly noticeable in males, is caused by the blood in the blood vessels of the dermis. This is responsible for the pinkish cast in the feet of birds such as White Orpingtons and others that lack both yellow and black pigments in the skin.

MUTATIONS AFFECTING SKIN COLOR

With the exceptions of the genes causing white in the ear lobes and in the face and a mutation responsible for the peculiar "yellow-head" condition, all the genes affecting skin color seem to cause effects that are general throughout the skin and not localized in certain regions. One frequently reads of genes for yellow shanks, or for blue shanks, or for some other color of shank, when the writer really means genes with generalized effects on the skin. It is true that these effects are most marked in the shanks and that some of them may not be evident in the feathered areas without microscopic examination, but they are usually revealed just as clearly in the beak as in the shanks.

White Skin and Yellow Skin, *W* and *w*

Leghorns, Plymouth Rocks, Rhode Island Reds, Wyandottes, and many other breeds have a yellowish skin, but in Orpingtons, Sussex, Dorkings, and Langshans, in some Minorcas, and in other breeds the skin is white.

Description. Black varieties of white-skinned breeds may have the lack of xanthophyll in the skin obscured almost completely by black pigment in the beak and shanks, but their true nature can usually be seen upon examination of the soles of the feet, where the black is less intense. Both Jersey Black Giants and Australorps have black shanks, but the former have yellowish soles, the latter pinkish-white ones.

The yellow is pale in the beak and shanks of fowls not getting an abundance of green feed, yellow corn, or other good sources of xanthophyll in their diet. There is apparently something in certain fish-liver oils which, according to Hammond and Harshaw (1941), prevents normal yellow pigmentation in young chicks amply supplied with xanthophyll. Hens that begin laying with bright yellow shanks and beak subsequently lose some or all of that color, the amount lost depending upon the duration of the laying period. Conversely, in periods of non-laying the pigment is again stored up in the skin. In some birds the shanks appear to be almost orange. Another variation is produced when the yellow-skinned condition is associated with the mutation causing deposition of melanin in the dermis. The result of this combination is a green, or willow, color in the shanks and beak, which is a breed characteristic in the Polish Greenleg and in Sicilian Buttercups.

The gene causing white skin must be considered not as one preventing the storage of xanthophyll by the fowl but rather as one restricting it to the blood and body fat and preventing, in some way yet unknown, its extension to the skin. Palmer and Kempster (1919) point out that the blood serum, egg yolks, and body fat of the white-skinned fowl are normally as rich in xanthophyll as they are in any yellow-skinned breed. In young chicks the restriction is less complete, for White Minorca, Orpington, and Sussex chicks may show yellow in the shanks and beak up to 10 or 12 weeks of age.

Genetics. It was found by Bateson (1902) in a cross of White Dorking × Leghorn that white skin is dominant to yellow, and Hurst (1905) observed the same in another cross. The reappearance of yellow-shanked birds in Bateson's F_2 generation suggested, although the numbers of each kind were not given, that yellow skin is a simple recessive character. This was confirmed by Dunn (1925), who found it to be autosomal and assigned the symbols w and W to the two alleles, and also by Lambert and Knox (1927).

It is difficult to classify young birds as white-skinned or yellow-skinned until they are over 3 months of age. Under some environmental conditions, differentiation of the two types is not easy even at that age.

On extracting the yellow pigment with acetone and measuring it quantitatively with a photoelectric colorimeter, Heiman and Tighe (1943) found that the amounts actually present at 6 weeks of age did not correspond to the degree of pigmentation visible to the eye. This is because successive increments of pigment above the lower levels do not increase proportionately the visible intensity of yellow color. The variability among their chicks in pigmentation at 6 weeks was not related to the rate of growth.

Mosaics with respect to color of skin or shanks are found occasionally. Sometimes the birds have one white leg and one yellow one; in others one whole half of the body may differ in color from the other. These are discussed in Chap. 13 (pages 475–478).

Economic Significance. White-skinned fowls are preferred to yellow-skinned ones in the markets of Great Britain, but in the United States the preference, if any exists, is for the yellow ones. Canadians attempting to make their yellow-skinned fowls conform to the standards for "milk-fed" birds acceptable in the English market were advised to feed them on diets low in xanthophyll for several weeks before the birds were killed. Since such diets are likely to be low in vitamin A, their desirability is questionable. Moreover, yellow corn is one of the best cereals for fattening fowls. As one means of solving the problem, various ways of bleaching the unwanted yellow fat were investigated by Maw (1942), who found bone char particularly useful for this purpose. To the geneticist it would seem that the easiest solution is to employ the gene *W*, which ensures a white carcass even on diets high in yellow corn or in other substances containing xanthophyll. It could easily be incorporated into the breeds used for market purposes or, perhaps better still, could be utilized in crosses specially designed to produce the kind of poultry desired for the market in mind. Since *W* is almost completely dominant in heterozygotes, its desirable effect would be fully manifested in the crossbred generation.

The recessive allele *w* has a special value to which poultrymen are now so accustomed that they give it little thought. Of all the criteria that have been invoked as aids in the differentiation of good and poor layers, none is more valuable than the degree of bleaching of the yellow pigment. This measure is effective only in fowls that have the yellow pigment, xanthophyll, extended to the beak and the shanks. For that reason, the gene *w*, which, when homozygous, permits that extension, is a particularly valuable one to the poultryman and to the poultry industry, even though it may be of no special biological value to the yellow-skinned bird.

A mutation in sheep with effects somewhat similar to those of *w* causes the affected animals to have yellow fat. This greatly lowers the value of their meat, since mutton with fat anything other than pure white is unheard of and undesired in most markets.

Melanin in the Dermis, *id*

Description. The breeds with yellow shanks or with white ones mentioned in the foregoing section lack melanin in the dermis, because they carry genes preventing its deposition there. However in Blue Andalusians, Hamburgs, Campines, Silkies, Polish, and other breeds the shanks appear to be blue in color.

Barrows (1914) found that such blue-shanked fowls had melanin in the dermis but lacked it in the epidermis. This black pigment in the dermis appears blue because it is seen dimly through the colorless stratum corneum of the epidermis. The following shades are to be found in the shanks:

1. *Bluish,* in white-skinned birds, when not obscured by melanin in the epidermis (Fig. 47, *left*).
2. *Slate, or black,* in white-skinned birds, when partially or wholly obscured by epidermal melanin (Fig. 47, *right*).
3. *Willow, or green,* in yellow-skinned birds, from the mixture of dermal melanin and epidermal xanthophyll.

Genetics. Melanin in the dermis is caused by a sex-linked recessive gene, *id*, in either the homozygous or hemizygous condition. The dominant allele *Id* (inhibitor of dermal melanin) is apparently only incompletely dominant, for Dunn (1925) found some heterozygotes with enough flecks of dermal melanin to give their shanks a pale blue cast. Moreover, Barrows found that some birds apparently white-shanked had

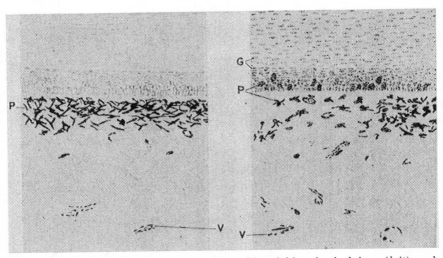

Fig. 47. Drawings of vertical section from skin of blue-shanked hen (*left*) and black-shanked hen (*right*). The former has melanin cells (*P*) thickly scattered in the upper part of the dermis, but none in the epidermis. *V* shows melanin around blood vessels. The black-shanked hen has melanin granules (*G*) in the epidermis (including the rete) and typical melanophores in the dermis. (*From Barrows in Maine Agr. Expt. Sta. Bull. 232.*)

small amounts of melanin in the dermis that were detectable only upon histological examination.

The first evidence that the inhibitor of dermal melanin is sex linked was found by Davenport (1906) in a cross of Dark Brahma ♀ (yellow shank) × Tosa ♂ (willow shank) which yielded males all with yellow shanks and females all with willow shanks. Sex-linked genes were then unknown, and the significance of this case was not appreciated. It seems probable that the sex-linked gene found by Bateson and Punnett (1911) to inhibit the peculiar black pigmentation of the Silky fowl is identical with the gene *Id*, considered here. Final proof that the inhibitor of dermal melanin is sex linked was provided by Punnett (1923) and Dunn (1925). Its action in reciprocal crosses between Polish Greenlegs and White Leghorns has been studied by Kaufman (1947).

The deposition of melanin in the dermis by *id* is quite independent of the action of genes affecting melanin in the epidermis and in the feathers that arise from it. White Hamburgs and White Langshans, with no melanin in the plumage, have blue shanks because of the melanin in the dermis. Punnett (1923) suggested that this gene and its allele are responsible for differences in color of the iris observed in reciprocal crosses between Black Langshans and Brown Leghorns. This seems quite likely because the dark-eyed Langshans are known to have dermal melanin and the red-eyed Leghorns to lack it.

Because classification of young birds as *id* or *Id* is difficult till they are 3 months old or more, these genes are unsatisfactory for the identification of sex at hatching in sex-linked crosses. Even in older birds classification is difficult in those with black plumage because the epidermal melanin may completely obscure the melanin in the dermis. Mosaics involving *Id* and *id* are considered in Chap. 13 (pages 475–478).

Melanin in the Epidermis

Although most fully black birds (*CC EE*) have black pigment in the beak and in the epidermal layer of the shank, this is not always the case. For example, Black Leghorns have bright yellow shanks. However, black is apparently not found in the epidermis of the shank or in the beak when it is absent from the plumage.

Genes that reduce the amount of black in the plumage, such as *B* (barring), *e* (Columbian restriction), *Sp* (spangling), and others, also reduce the amount of black in the shanks and beak. The effect of barring on shank color is discussed in the next chapter. Comparison of a Black Wyandotte with a Columbian one shows that the genes *ee* which convert the black to the Columbian pattern have also eliminated practically all the black from the shanks. Similarly, while Black Hamburgs have black shanks, their transformation to a spangled variety by the genes *Sp Sp* removes most of the epidermal melanin from the shanks and beak, leaving those parts with the blue appearance caused by the melanin in the dermis.

Although the melanin in the skin associated with black in the plumage is referred to here as epidermal melanin, its distribution is not strictly limited to the outer layer of the skin. Barrows (1914) found that birds with melanin in the epidermis also had it in the underlying dermis. The blackest shanks had dense deposits of melanin in the dermis as well as in the epidermis and were presumably *id id CC EE*, but even the lightest of the black ones, described as "black over white" and therefore *Id–*, *Id Id*, or *Id id* showed a few spots of melanin in the dermis of the shank when they were examined histologically.

Interaction of Genes Affecting Color of the Shank and Beak

For convenient reference, the different combinations of pigments to be found in the shanks and beak of the fowl are summarized in Table 17. Heterozygotes are not considered in the column of genotypes because it is assumed that W is fully expressed in heterozygotes and that any difference between the effects of one and two of the id and Id pair will not prevent accurate classification. Genes restricting or diluting black in the plumage are omitted to facilitate recognition of the main phenotypes and genotypes.

TABLE 17. PRINCIPAL COLORS IN THE BEAK AND SHANKS

Dermal melanin	Xantho-phyll	Epidermal melanin	Phenotype	Genotype	Examples
Absent	—	—	White, pinkish white	$Id\ Id\ WW$	Buff Orpington, Light Sussex
	—	+	Black (pink soles)	$Id\ Id\ WW$	Black Orpington
	+	—	Yellow	$Id\ Id\ ww$	White Leghorn, White Plymouth Rock
	+	+	Black (yellow soles)	$Id\ Id\ ww$	Jersey Black Giant, Black Wyandotte
Present	—	—	Blue	$id\ id\ WW$	White Hamburg, White Langshan
	—	+	{Black	$id\ id\ WW$ }	Black Hamburg, Black Langshan
			{Slaty blue	$id\ id\ WW$ }	Blue Andalusian
	+	—	{Green, willow	$id\ id\ ww$	Sicilian Buttercup
			{Greenish black	$id\ id\ ww$	Polish Greenleg
	+	+	Black	$id\ id\ ww$	Black Sumatra Game

Variations in the amount of epidermal melanin will provide shades intergrading with the main ones given in Table 17. The Polish Greenleg would probably show some epidermal melanin upon microscopic examination but not enough to obscure the green, as is the case with the Black Sumatras.

Fibromelanosis of the Silky

Description. In the Silky fowl the beak and shanks are bluish as in some of the other breeds mentioned earlier in this chapter, but, in addition, the skin all over the body is black (Fig. 48). This usually has a purplish hue, particularly in the wattles, comb, and face, from the combined effects of the black pigment in the skin and the red of the blood in the capillaries. In some parts of the world this black-skinned condition is found in fowls not having the peculiar plumage of Silkies. The association of these two peculiarities (and others) in the Silky would

FIG. 48. Chicks from which down has been plucked to show the black skin of the Silky (*right*) in contrast to the yellowish skin of the other chick. The Silky shows two other breed characteristics—polydactyly and feathered shanks.

therefore seem attributable to fanciers' whims rather than to any biological relationship.

The distribution of the melanin in Silkies was studied by Kuklenski (1915), who found it in varying amounts in the dermis of the skin, in the sheaths of muscles and nerves, in tendons, mesenteries, and walls of blood vessels, and in the dura and pia mater of the brain. The lungs contained only small flecks of black, but the trachea and air sacs were heavily pigmented. No melanin was found in bones or in cartilage, but periosteal and perichondrial membranes were heavily pigmented. Most of the glands had little pigment except for that in their fibrous capsules, but the gonads contained much melanin. There was none at all in the liver. Kuklenski found the pigment only in connective tissue, never in epithelium. A similar restriction of the melanin was noted by Stiefel (1926), who studied the heart and adjacent regions of the Silky.

This type of pigmentation was designated by Dunn and Jull (1927) as "mesodermal," to differentiate it from the dermal melanin induced by the gene *id*. However, since the dermis of the skin is of mesodermal origin, the pigmentation in it may also be considered as mesodermal. Since the melanophores of the Silky originate in the neural crest (Eastlick and Wortham, 1946) as do those of the plumage, it would seem appropriate to name this type of pigmentation according to its distribution rather than by its source in the embryo. For that reason, the term "fibromelanosis," meaning melanotic pigmentation of connective tissue, is proposed as more nearly fitting the distribution of melanin found by Kuklenski in the Silky.

Genetics. The genetic basis for this condition is not fully understood. The discovery by Bateson and Punnett (1911) that it is inhibited by a sex-linked gene carried by Brown Leghorns was confirmed by Wriedt (1927) and by Dunn and Jull (1927), who found a similar inhibitor in White Leghorns and concluded that it was either identical with the gene *Id*, inhibiting dermal melanin, or very closely linked with it. There was some indication in their birds that the gene for barring carried by the White Leghorns might also reduce somewhat the amount of melanin in birds derived from Silkies. In crosses where the results were not complicated by the action of the inhibitor, one of which was made by Bateson and Punnett and another by Wriedt, all the F_1 birds had black skin. Although this shows that fibromelanosis is dominant over its absence, the gradual gradation from the lightest to the darkest condition in segregating populations suggests that the condition depends upon multiple factors. Since black-skinned fowls may have either white or colored feathers, it is obviously quite independent of genes affecting color of the plumage.

Although unattractive to most people in the Western world, the flesh of the black-skinned birds does not taste (to the author) different from that of other chickens, and in some parts of the Orient it is considered a delicacy.

White Ear Lobes

In Leghorns, Minorcas, Blue Andalusians, Sicilian Buttercups, and some other breeds the ear lobes are white. Ear lobes of other breeds appear red because of the extremely heavy vascularization of the dermis. Since this red tends to appear in white ear lobes, fanciers consider too much of it a showroom disqualification in the breeds listed above and make a special effort to exclude birds with this defect from their breeding pens. Conversely, poultrymen breeding other varieties are equally alert in excluding from their show stock and breeding pens birds with any "enamel" white in ear lobes that should be all red to conform to breed standards. Intermediate conditions are common.

The basis for the white ear lobes is not known. Louvier (1934, 1934a) found evidence that purine bases in a form not found in other parts of the skin are associated with the white. The effect is apparently produced by some white substance which prevents excessive formation of blood capillaries or obscures them.

In the White-faced Black Spanish breed, the ear lobes are white and so greatly enlarged that they fall below the wattles in good specimens. The white is extended anteriorly to cover all of the face. In other breeds with white ear lobes, white in the face is considered undesirable.

Genetics. Since white ear lobes constitute a breed characteristic, the condition is hereditary. An analysis attempted by Warren (1928) showed that the genetic basis is very complex and that multiple factors are responsible. The F_1 generation from crosses of white $\times$ red were mostly intermediate, but in 7 of his 10 F_1 populations there were birds with white ear lobes and others with red ones in addition to those with a mixture of both colors. Classification of ear lobes with respect to color was most accurate in birds over 6 months old. There was some evidence that a sex-linked gene may affect this character, but this was found in only one of several crosses and could not be confirmed in the study by Hertwig (1930), or by Hays (1943).

Breeds with white ear lobes usually lay white-shelled eggs, but this must be merely a chance association, for Warren found no relation between the color of ear lobe and any of 10 arbitrary grades of shell color. Similarly there was no association of any particular color of ear lobe with black or white plumage or with single or rose comb.

Yellow Head, g

Deakin and Robertson (1935) found in Barred Plymouth Rocks a peculiar mutation which caused the skin of the comb, face, and wattles to remain yellow instead of becoming red as the birds matured. The condition was noticeable at a few weeks of age. Males had yellow heads until approaching sexual maturity, at which time the parts affected became orange. During the first winter, the vascularization of the head furnishings obscured the character as the comb became almost of the normal dark red color. The yellow-headed females did not turn red to the same extent as the males, but during periods of egg laying most of the yellow pigment faded out, as it ordinarily does in the beak and shanks, leaving the birds with pale pinkish heads, by which they were readily distinguished from other fowls. The physiological basis for this peculiarity was not determined, but it was suggested that the yellow appearance resulted in part from reduction of the vascularization of the head furnishings.

Genetics. The yellow-headed birds were found to be homozygous for an autosomal recessive gene, *g*. A mating of yellow heads *inter se* yielded 29 progeny, all showing the same peculiarity as the parents. In tests for linkage of *g* with other genes, Deakin and Robertson (1937) found that the yellow-head character could not be recognized with certainty in white-skinned birds of the genotype *gg Ww*.

Literature Cited

Barrows, H. R. 1914. The histological basis of the different shank colors in the domestic fowl. *Maine Agr. Expt. Sta. Bull.* 232.

Bateson, W. 1902. Experiments with poultry. *Repts. Evol. Comm. Roy. Soc.,* I: 87–124.

———— and R. C. Punnett. 1911. The inheritance of the peculiar pigmentation of the Silky fowl. *J. Genetics,* 1:185–203.

Davenport, C. B. 1906. Inheritance in poultry. *Carnegie Inst. Wash. Pub.* 52.

Deakin, A., and G. Robertson. 1935. The inheritance of yellow-pigmented heads in domestic fowl. *Am. Naturalist,* 69:378–380.

———— and ————. 1937. Linkage tests with the yellow-head and dominant-white plumage and white-skin characteristics in domestic fowl. *Sci. Agr.,* 17:451–452.

Dunn, L. C. 1925. The genetic relation of some shank colors of the domestic fowl. *Anat. Record,* 31:343–344.

———— and M. A. Jull. 1927. On the inheritance of some characters of the Silky fowl. *J. Genetics,* 19:27–63.

Eastlick, H. L., and R. A. Wortham. 1946. An experimental study on the feather-pigmenting and subcutaneous melanophores in the Silkie fowl. *J. Exptl. Zoöl.,* 103:233–258.

Hammond, J. C., and H. M. Harshaw. 1941. Some factors influencing shank and skin color in the growing chicken. *Poultry Sci.,* 20:437–444.

Hays, F. A. 1943. Inheritance of mottled earlobes and stubs in Rhode Island Reds. *Am. Naturalist,* 77:471–475.

Heiman, V., and L. W. Tighe. 1943. Observations on the shank pigmentation of chicks. *Poultry Sci.,* 22:102–107.

Hertwig, P. 1930. Die Erbfaktoren der Haushühner. 2. Beitrag: Die Ortsbestimmung von zwei weiteren Faktoren im X-Chromosom. *Biol. Zentr.,* 50:333–341.

Hurst, C. C. 1905. Experiments with poultry. *Repts. Evol. Comm. Roy. Soc.,* II: 131–154.

Kaufman, L. 1946–1947. Genetical studies on poultry. II. The inheritance of shank- and of plumage-color in Polish Greenleg—White Leghorn crosses. *Mém. inst. nat. polon. écon. rurale Pulawy.* 18, E., Mém. 2:1–16.

Kuklenski, J. 1915. Über das Vorkommen und die Verteilung des Pigmentes in den

Organen und Geweben bei japanischen Seidenhühnern. *Arch. mikroskop. Anat. Entwicklungsmech.*, **87**:1–37.

Lambert, W. V., and C. W. Knox. 1927. Genetic studies in poultry. II. The inheritance of skin color. *Poultry Sci.*, **7**:24–30.

Louvier, R. 1934. Recherches chimiques sur la pigmentation de l'oreillon du coq domestique. *Compt. rend. soc. biol.*, **116**:811–812.

———. 1934a. Recherches microchimiques sur la pigmentation de l'oreillon du coq domestique. *Compt. rend. soc. biol.*, **117**:328–329.

Maw, W. A. 1942. Personal communication.

Palmer, L. S. 1915. Xanthophyll, the principal natural yellow pigment of the egg yolk, body fat and blood serum of the hen. The physiological relation of the pigment to the xanthophyll of the plant. *J. Biol. Chem.*, **23**:261–279.

——— and H. L. Kempster. 1919. The physiological relation between fecundity and the natural yellow pigmentation of certain breeds of fowls. *J. Biol. Chem.*, **39**:313–330.

Punnett, R. C. 1923. "Heredity in Poultry. London: Macmillan & Co., Ltd.

Stiefel, K. 1926. Das Herz des melanotischen Seidenhuhns. *Anat. Anz.*, **61**:177–201.

Warren, D. C. 1928. Inheritance of earlobe color in poultry. *Genetics*, **13**:470–487.

Wriedt, C. 1927. Vererbung von schwarzem Pigment bei Silkyhühnern. *Hereditas*, **9**:223–224.

CHAPTER 7

VARIATIONS IN THE COLOR OF THE PLUMAGE

Variations in the colors of feathers have thus far been much more difficult to explain genetically than variations in their structure or arrangement. This is partly because the genetic bases for buff and red are unknown, partly because the interaction of genes to produce patterns in the feather is little understood, and also because of inadequate information concerning the relations between the color of the down and the color in the adult plumage. In the following pages, our present knowledge of feather color is summarized under the headings of (1) some general principles, (2) solid colors, (3) dilutions, (4) extension and restriction of color, and (5) patterns within single feathers.

SOME GENERAL PRINCIPLES

The Nature of Colors. The various colors in the feathers of birds may be divided into two general classes. In one of these, the color results merely from the presence of a pigment and from the size and arrangement of the pigment granules. In the other, comprising the so-called "structural colors," what one sees depends, not only upon the pigment present, but also upon the number of cell layers overlying it, their structure, and the way in which they reflect, diffract, disperse, or absorb the rays of light. Examples of structural colors in the domestic fowl are the green and purple iridescent sheens commonly seen in black feathers. White may also be considered as a structural color, because it reflects all light rays, but it is somewhat easier to think of it as resulting from the absence of the pigments found in colored feathers.

The other colors found in the fowl are black, buff, and various shades of brown. These latter vary from the light salmon breast of Brown Leghorns to the dark mahogany color of some strains of Rhode Island Reds. The pigment responsible for black color is the complex protein, melanin. It seems probable that the brown (red) and buff colors are caused by variant forms of this same substance. These are sometimes called "phaeomelanins," but this means merely brown melanin and tells nothing else of their nature.

Size and shape of the pigment granules were studied in 8 different

162

breeds by Ladebeck (1922) and again in 37 breeds or varieties by Bohren *et al.* (1943). In black feathers the granules are rod-shaped, varying little in size, which is about 0.5 by 1.3 microns. Red and buff feathers have oval granules about 0.7 by 1.0 microns and some smaller spherical ones. Ladebeck found in buff feathers some granules much smaller than those in red ones. Similar relations between the type of granule and color of feather were earlier noted in pigeons by Lloyd-Jones (1915). They suggest that black, red, and buff might result merely from differences in the size and shape of the pigment granules, but other evidence disproves this view.

Koller (1929) and Dorris (1938), who studied the development of black pigment in vitro, observed that the granules were first pale yellow but gradually changed through brown to black. If melanin is formed, as seems most likely, from the action of an enzyme (tyrosinase) upon a colorless chromogen (tyrosine), the resulting color could be yellow, light red, dark red, or black according to the stage at which oxidation of the tyrosine stopped. This view of the difference between red and black pigments is doubted for several reasons by Nickerson (1946). He was unable to oxidize newly formed red melanin in developing feathers to black, nor could he find transitional forms between red and black melanophores. The oval granules of red and buff feathers are readily soluble in 0.5 *N*. NaOH and in 6 *N*. HCl, but the black granules and the round ones of red feathers are soluble only in NaOH and not in HCl (Bohren *et al.*, 1943). Solutions of the two pigments differ when analyzed spectrophotometrically, the difference in transmission of light being greatest with light of wave length 440 to 560 millimicrons (Nickerson).

Melanophores.   The granules of pigment are produced by special cells called *melanophores*. These have long processes, which may be branched, and the cells often have more than one nucleus (Fig. 49). In the embryo incubated from 23 to 40 hours, the precursors of these melanophores are concentrated in the neural crest (Dorris, 1938), but at that stage they contain no pigment granules. The experiments of Eastlick (1939) and of Willier and Rawles (1940) show that the melanophores migrate from the neural crest to other parts of the body. The latter investigators proved by transplants of embryonic skin from colored donors to white hosts, and vice versa, that the melanophores have reached the wings and legs after 4 days of incubation. At the time of feather formation, according to Strong (1902, 1917), these melanophores are abundant among the intermediate cells of the feather follicle, from which most of the feather is formed, and by means of long processes they distribute granules of melanin to the cells of the barbs and barbules.

The distal barbules (with hooks) have more pigment than the proximal ones except in blue feathers.

Genetic Control of Pigmentation. From a number of interesting experiments in which skin has been grafted from one bird to another, it

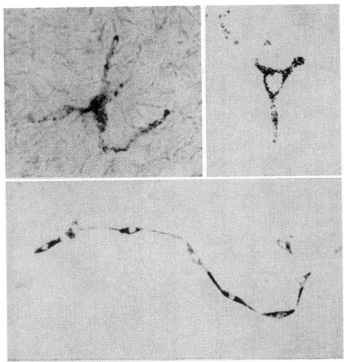

Fig. 49. Melanophores. *Upper left,* from a White Leghorn, ×360; *upper right,* from a White Plymouth Rock, ×250; *below,* multinucleate melanophore of Jersey Black Giant, showing eight nuclei, ×250. (*Left by courtesy of B. F. Willier; right and below from Hamilton in Anat. Record.*)

is now clear that the color of a feather is determined by the genetic constitution of the cells which give rise to the feather, though it is modified in some cases by the endocrine secretions to which the developing feather is exposed. This was first shown by Danforth and Foster (1929), who transplanted skin from the back of one young chick to that of another. In 125 pieces of transplanted skin that produced feathers, the color and color pattern of feathers on the graft were the same as in the donor. Skin from White Leghorns produced pure white feathers in 26 hosts representing five different breeds. Similarly, feathers of black, brown, buff, black-red, and recessive-white donors of eight other breeds yielded feathers true to the color found in the donor. The consistency of these results was all the more striking because in every case the structure and shape of the feathers on the graft (*i.e.*, whether male-like or henny) were the same as those of the host. The only exceptions to the general rule that the cells of the donor determined the color were a few

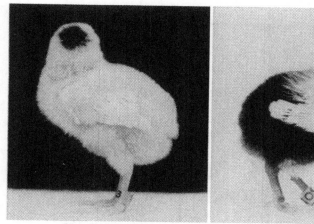

Fig. 50. *Left,* a 5-day-old White Leghorn showing on top of the head an area of black down resulting from a graft of ectoderm from a Barred Plymouth Rock at 70 hours of incubation. *Right,* a Black Minorca chick showing an extensive white area caused by a similar graft from a White Wyandotte donor. (*From Willier and Rawles in Physiol. Zoöl.*)

exceptional mosaic feathers found at the margins of some grafts in which the characteristics of both donor and host were combined.

Similar experiments, but with embryos only 3 or 4 days old instead of newly hatched chicks, have been made by Willier, Rawles, and Hadorn (1937) and Willier and Rawles (1940). These investigators successfully transferred from donor to host bits of skin ectoderm less than 0.5 sq. mm. in area. As in Danforth's experiments, the host chick developed at the site of the graft feathers of the same color as the donor. Thus, skin transplanted from a Barred Plymouth Rock embryo to the head of a White Leghorn embryo resulted in a black patch on the head of the host at hatching (Fig. 50); a graft from a White Wyandotte donor to a Black Minorca host gave the latter a white wing at hatching (Fig. 50); and skin from the head of a Barred Rock embryo transplanted to the wing bud of a White Leghorn embryo caused the latter to show at 2 weeks wing feathers with the same kind of barred feathers as are normal in

Barred Rocks (Fig. 51). Grafts from White Leghorns were exceptional in failing to cause white areas on black hosts or in inducing at best comparatively small areas of white down. This is discussed further under the heading of Dominant White.

These grafts of embryonic skin ectoderm differed from those of Danforth with hatched chicks in one important respect. They did not persist. When the chick down was replaced by chick and juvenile feathers,

Fig. 51. A 14-day-old White Leghorn male showing the effect of a graft containing melanophores from a Barred Plymouth Rock embryo when both had been incubated 71 hours. (*Courtesy of B. F. Willier and M. Rawles.*)

the latter were typical of the host's breed in shape, size, distribution in the feather tracts, and rate of growth. Thus, transplants from White Silkies produced on Black Minorca hosts areas of white feathers, but none of these had the structure typical of Silkies. Similarly, transplants from Barred Plymouth Rock embryos to the wing bud of White Leghorn hosts induced barred wing feathers, but these grew at the rapid rate characteristic of Leghorns, not at the slower rate normal in Barred Plymouth Rocks. Clearly no feather follicles of the genetic constitution of the donor persisted in the host.

This was also shown by the gradual decrease in the donor-colored area as the chick shed its down and acquired its later plumage. Eventually, all the colored feathers were lost, and the plumage became like that of the host. Later feathers in some cases showed the color of the donor at the tip (formed first) but the color of the host at the base. Apparently the melanophores introduced with the grafts eventually died.

Results similar to these of Willier and Rawles were also obtained by Dorris (1939), who, instead of waiting till the melanophores had migrated to all parts of the embryo, took pieces of neural crest from embryos

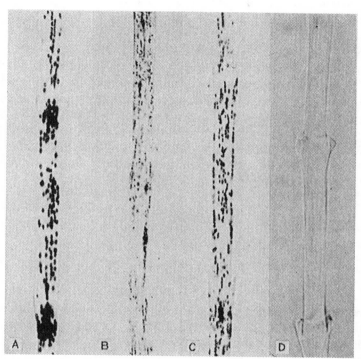

Fig. 52. Photomicrographs of unstained barbules showing differences in the types of melanin granules found in different breeds. *A*, Black Minorca; *B*, New Hampshire; *C*, Barred Plymouth Rock; *D*, White Leghorn, devoid of granules. (*From Willier and Rawles in Physiol. Zoöl.*)

incubated only about 24 to 30 hours. Similar experiments, with like results, were made by Eastlick (1939), who transplanted the primordia of limb buds and found donor-colored areas on the host whenever his grafts included cells from the neural-crest region.

Breed Specificity in Melanin Granules. Willier and Rawles (1940) found that feathers of the donor-colored areas in their grafted chicks contained melanin granules characteristic of the donor breed. Those from Black Minorca donors contained more large masses of melanin than feathers colored by grafts from Barred Plymouth Rocks (Fig. 52). Buff Minorca melanophores deposited small, round, yellowish granules.

Feathers colored by grafts from New Hampshires contained both black rod-shaped granules and red spherical ones, just as Ladebeck found in Rhode Island Reds. It is clear that the differences in color result from differences in the type of pigment granule produced by the melanophore and that this in turn depends upon the genetic constitution of those cells. It is remarkable that transplanted melanophores of one genotype are apparently able to function quite independently of the cells of the host through which they migrate and to which they supply pigment, even when those host cells are genetically quite different.

According to Hamilton (1940), even two breeds having black plumage may differ in the type of pigment granule. He found that Black Silkies and Jersey Black Giants had melanophores containing as many as six or eight nuclei, in contrast to the two or three most common in other breeds, but the Silky produced melanin in short, blunt rods, the Jersey Black Giant in long, thin rods with truncated ends. Similar differences in the melanin granules of various black breeds were not found by Lippincott (1921) or by Bohren *et al.* (1943).

SOLID COLORS

Black

A number of breeds that include representatives of different colors have a solid black variety. Examples of these are found in Leghorns, Minorcas, Wyandottes, Orpingtons, Langshans, Hamburgs, Cochins, and other breeds. In addition, there are a number of breeds in which only black birds are recognized as typical. These include the Australorps, Black Sumatras, White-faced Black Spanish, Jersey Black Giants, and some others.

However, many fowls that are not solid black have a genotype with respect to black color that is the same as a Black Minorca's but have in addition some mutation that lessens the black. The barring pattern and the mottling of Houdans and Anconas are good examples. There is considerable evidence that even buff fowls are genetically black, with the latter type of pigment restricted almost to the vanishing point.

So far, there is no evidence that the black color is not genetically the same in all of these breeds and varieties, but Hamilton's report of differences in the granules of melanin, just cited, suggests that there may be more than one kind of black, just as there is more than one kind of white. The symbol generally used to designate the presence of black pigment of any kind is C (color), but birds with solid black pigment must also carry a gene, E, which permits extension of color to all parts of the plumage. This is discussed in detail later. Most black fowls probably carry mutations that are recessive to black and therefore are not revealed. For example, many of them have been found to carry the recessive gene, *s*, for gold color, the effects of which are more likely to be masked by black than those of its allele, *S*, a gene which induces silver plumage of several different kinds.

Chicks of black breeds have black down at hatching but show various degrees of white and greyish white on the abdomen. They frequently have one or more white feathers in the chick or juvenile plumage. The fact that the down of black chicks is shorter than that of chicks colored otherwise is discussed in a previous chapter.

Dominant White, *I*

This kind of white is found in White Leghorns, Pile Games, and La Bresse. It is also frequently present in breeds that are ordinarily recessive white, such as White Minorcas, White Wyandottes, and White Rocks. It has been found in Buff Leghorns by Danforth (1933) and in Buff Minorcas by the author. In both these buff breeds the presence of dominant white was not evident and was quite unsuspected until revealed by breeding tests. The presence of the Leghorn type of white in these other breeds probably resulted from crosses made to introduce some of the desirable qualities of White Leghorns.

Genetics. Dominant white was one of the first characters in poultry that was shown to be inherited in accord with Mendel's laws. This was reported by Bateson (1902), who said that the F_1 chicks from a cross of White Leghorn $\times$ Indian Game were "white or dingy white . . . more or less speckled or 'ticked' with black" (in the down). His reciprocal crosses yielded the same results, except that the female crossbreds from White Leghorn females were "more or less dingy brownish-white." In the F_2 generation, there were 149 light:41 dark chicks, a good fit to the expected 3:1 ratio. Confirmation of this early analysis was found in later work by Bateson and Punnett (1906), Hurst (1905), and many others.

The autosomal gene responsible is designated by *I* (inhibitor of black pigment), a symbol introduced by Hadley (1913).

That the inhibitor is not completely dominant in heterozygotes is clear from the fact that ticking and spotting are usual in heterozygous chicks and that feathers partly or wholly black are common in adults. When White Leghorns are crossed with a non-barred colored breed, such as the Rhode Island Red, there is a difference in the degree of apparent dominance of *I* in reciprocal crosses. A White Leghorn sire begets progeny with about the same amount of black color in both sons and daughters, but a White Leghorn dam produces daughters somewhat darker than her sons. This is shown in part by more black flecking, but often by a dingy white shade throughout the plumage. This peculiarity was noted by Bateson (1902) and has since been observed by others. It results from the fact that White Leghorns carry the sex-linked gene for barring (Hadley, 1913, 1915), there being two of these in the male and one in the female. In the type of cross under consideration, the White Leghorn sire passes a gene for barring to all his offspring, but the White Leghorn dam can give it only to her sons. This gene, B, reduces the melanic pigment in the plumage and the shanks. Accordingly, her sons, which are $Ii\ Bb$, have less black in the feathers and in the shanks than their sisters, which are $Ii\ b-$.

By the label "dominant white" the geneticist means a white that is dominant to black. That it is not dominant to red is readily seen in the F_1 progeny of any White Leghorn $\times$ Rhode Island Red cross. In some of these birds so much red is present that it almost obscures the white. In those with little red, that color is usually found over the shoulders and back of males and on the breast of females. As was stated above, dominant white can be so completely *hypostatic* (*i.e.*, masked or obscured) to buff that its presence in some Buff Minorcas was evident only after a breeding test.

From this discussion it is evident that the White Leghorn is really a barred, colored fowl in which both the color and the pattern are suppressed by inhibiting genes which, when homozygous, completely prevent development of melanin in the plumage. They do not affect the melanin of the eye. The genotype of the White Leghorn is therefore: for $\male\ \male$, $II\ CC\ BB$; for $\female\ \female$, $II\ CC\ B-$.

Variations in Down Color. Except for brassiness in some males, the creamy cast of newly acquired plumage, and the dirt that inevitably shows in white fowls, adult White Leghorns are all of one shade of white. In the chicks it is quite different. These may vary in color from a pale creamy white, through various shades of yellow, to a burnt orange.

Classifying them as dark, medium, or light, Lamoreux and Hutt (1942) found the proportions of these shades in an unselected population to be 28, 59, and 13 per cent, respectively. They were able by progeny testing to differentiate two strains, in one of which the proportion of chicks with dark down varied from 83 to 94 per cent. In the other strain the proportion of dark chicks was reduced to about 4 per cent. Since most of the differentiation occurred in the first 2 years of selection and was later easily maintained, it is probable that the modifying genes responsible for variations in the down color of dominant white chicks are few in number. In the F_1 generation from crosses of the two strains the proportion of dark chicks was intermediate between those in the parent strains. However, among the F_1 chicks from dark dams the proportion of dark chicks was over 2.5 times as high as in chicks from light dams. In backcrosses of F_1 birds to the dark and light strains the proportions of dark chicks were 53 and 8 per cent, respectively.

The common belief among poultrymen that the paler Leghorn chicks are less desirable than the dark ones was refuted by this study. Lamoreux and Hutt found that the color of the chick has no relation to its viability, age at sexual maturity, or ability to lay eggs.

One of the factors affecting color of the down in White Leghorns is sex. In unselected populations and in others containing chicks of different colors, the proportions of males in the dark, medium, and light chicks were 71, 50, and 39 per cent, respectively. This does not mean, however, that by breeding a dark strain one gets a predominance of males. In both the dark and light strains, the sex ratios were normal.

Dark spots in the occipital region of the head are associated with the darker downs. They were found in 76 per cent of an unselected population of White Leghorn chicks, but in the dark strain 99 per cent had such spots, whereas in the light strain only 36 per cent showed them. Like the dark downs, head spots are more likely to be found in males than in females. However, the color of the down and the incidence of head spots are not sufficiently good criteria to permit recognition of sex in White Leghorn chicks with the accuracy desirable in commercial hatcheries.

Lethal Dominant White. There is a dominant white in the canary, *Serinus canarius,* which Duncker (1924) has shown to be lethal in the homozygous state. All white canaries tested proved to be heterozygous, yielding white and colored birds in the ratio of approximately 2:1. The homozygotes apparently die at an early stage of development.

Physiological Basis. Just how one pair of genes is able to prevent formation of melanin in birds that would otherwise have black feathers has not yet been conclusively demonstrated. A powerful chemical reaction is indicated. Melanin is normally formed by the action of an oxidase, apparently tyrosinase, upon a chromogen. Gortner (1911) found that certain m-dihydroxyphenols prevent the oxidation of tyrosine by tyrosinase but do not destroy the latter, nor are they oxidized in place of the tyrosine. He suggested that a similar reaction may cause dominant white. Charles and Rawles (1940) found tyrosinase in the feather germs of black fowls and New Hampshires, but this enzyme was absent from White Leghorn feather germs or, if present, was rendered inactive.

An entirely different interpretation has developed from recent studies of the melanophores in different breeds. To begin with, Koller (1929) found that explants of mesoderm from Black Leghorn embryos were able to develop normal melanophores when transferred to extracts of tissue and plasma from White Leghorn embryos. Similarly, Willier and Rawles (1940), Dorris (1939), and Eastlick (1939) found that White Leghorn hosts did not prevent in any way the development of black feathers when grafts from embryos of black breeds were introduced. On the other hand, it was difficult to find white feathers when grafts from White Leghorns were transferred to Barred Plymouth Rock hosts, and no effects whatever were obtained when the hosts were New Hampshires. Grafts to Black and Buff Minorcas were somewhat more successful, but, even in these, the areas of white down feathers were smaller than the donor-colored areas in the reciprocal grafts. A similar deficiency of dominant-white feathers after grafts to pigmented hosts was also noted by Dorris (1939).

Her discovery (1938) that, quite contrary to what one would expect, White Leghorns have melanophores and that these actually produce pigment permitted a new approach to the problem. Willier and Rawles (1940) found that, while normal branched melanophores containing granules of black pigment (Fig. 49) are present in the epidermal collar of a developing White Leghorn feather germ, these retract their long processes, round up, and die without depositing many pigment granules, if any, in the feather. Subsequently, Hamilton (1940), who studied the melanophores of different breeds in vitro, reported that in cultures from embryos 6 or 7 days old there were great differences in the viability of melanophores of different breeds. Some from Barred Plymouth Rocks were still alive 10 days after explantation, but all the White Leghorn melanophores died within 4 days. Melanophores of F_1 hybrids (from the cross B. P. R. ♀ × W. L. ♂) lived slightly longer, but all degenerated within 6 days. Some White Leghorn embryos yielded few melanophores or none. This does not mean that all the melanophores die during early development of the White Leghorn embryo. On the contrary, Hamilton found them in the base of developing feathers in chicks (of an age unstated), but there they seemed viable only in the lower third of the feather germ. At higher levels, degeneration was indicated by retraction of their branches, and, in the region where deposition of pigment is at a maximum in black breeds, only a few granules were to be found in White Leghorns. This contrast is strikingly shown in Fig. 53.

It would appear from these facts that White Leghorns may be white because their melanophores are fewer and less viable than those of colored breeds, being quite unable to persist above a certain level of

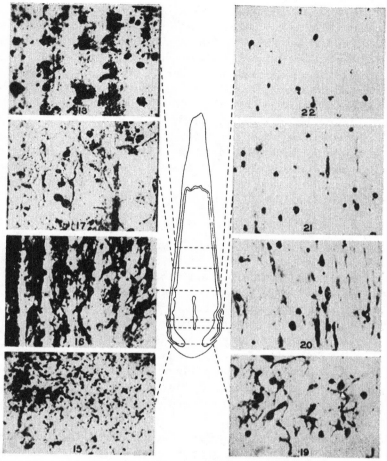

F<small>IG</small>. 53.   Changes in the melanophores at different levels of developing feather germs, showing differences between a pigmented breed and a dominant white one.

Barred Plymouth Rock, *left:* 15, region of multiplication of melanophores; 16, melanophores are packed with pigment and are depositing it in the barbs along which they are aligned; 17, region of keratinization; degeneration of melanophores under way; 18, completely degenerate melanophores at a higher level of the feather germ.

White Leghorn, *right:* 19, melanophores at the base of the germ, some rounded off, indicating their degeneration; 20–22, successive stages in the degeneration and disappearance of melanophores at higher levels of the feather germ.   (*From Hamilton in Anat. Record.*)

the feather follicle. Hamilton also found their pigment granules to be somewhat smaller than in other breeds. On this basis, the comparatively small effect of White Leghorn grafts on pigmented hosts could be attributed to the smaller number of melanophores introduced and to their comparatively rapid degeneration. Their early death in Hamilton's cultures was ascribed to an inability to tolerate the exhaustion of food and accumulation of wastes as the cultures aged. It remains to be determined what there is in the epidermis of the White Leghorn that is incompatible with survival of the melanophores. Whatever it may be, it does not weaken the other cells of the body, for the superiority of White Leghorns over other breeds in resistance to certain kinds of bacterial infection, to extreme heat, and to dietary deficiencies is fully proved. This is discussed in Chap. 12.

Recessive White, *c*

The white varieties of Dorkings, Plymouth Rocks, Wyandottes, Minorcas, Orpingtons, and several other breeds are called recessive whites because their kind of whiteness, unlike that of the Leghorn, is completely recessive to black plumage. Phenotypically, the two kinds of white seem identical in the adult, and they can be differentiated only by a breeding test. In the down of chicks there is a tendency for the White Leghorns to show more of a yellowish shade than the chicks of recessive whites, but it is not known whether or not this is because they are dominant white. Adult White Plymouth Rocks are identical in color with adult White Wyandottes, but chicks of the former breed are often a rather greyish white, in sharp contrast with the creamy-colored Wyandottes.

Genetics. It was shown by Bateson and Punnett (1906, 1908) that the white variety of the Dorking is homozygous for an autosomal recessive gene preventing color. This is designated by the symbol *c*, the recessive allele of the gene (*C*) permitting development of color in the plumage. This same type of white was found by Bateson and Punnett in Rose-comb Bantams and in White Wyandottes. It has since been found in White Cochin Bantams (Davenport, 1906), White Langshans (Goodale, 1910), White Plymouth Rocks (Hadley, 1914), and other breeds.

Cryptomeres. A bird unable to form color is obviously unable to show what genetic potentialities it possesses with respect to colors and patterns. Recessive whites may really be potentially barred, silver, spangled, or otherwise, but never reveal that fact except in a breeding test. Such hidden characters, called *cryptomeres*, are present in all recessive-white fowls. The simplest hidden color would be the fully extended black found in all-black varieties. White Wyandottes arose by mutation from the silver-laced variety of that breed, and one would therefore expect them to carry that pattern. Most of them do, but Crew (1933), Quinn (1936), and Jeffrey (1947) found some of them to be genotypically barred. The proportion of White Wyandottes that were gold instead of silver was 17 per cent in Quinn's birds and 30 per cent in Jeffrey's. A number of their White Plymouth Rocks had the genotype of Columbian varieties and Light Sussex in which pigment is restricted to the neck, wings, and tail. Only 40 to 80 per cent of Jeffrey's White Rocks carried the gene for barring, and that must mean that they carried a considerable admixture of genes from breeds other than the Barred Plymouth Rocks from which the white variety originated. Similarly, White Malines were found by Legrand (1939) to carry genes for barring, silver, and solid (extended) color and therefore to be identical with the barred Coucou de Malines except for being *cc*.

If such an assortment of genes in white birds is incompatible with any reader's idea that all individuals within a breed or variety have the same inheritance, it may be useful to recall the origin of a comparatively new white breed, the Chantecler. This was developed by Wilfrid (1927) from no less than five different breeds or varieties, one of which was dominant white and two recessive white. It is inevitable that these birds should for some years carry a variety of genes contributed by their assorted progenitors. Many of these were eliminated in the process of "fixing" the new breed, but those masked by white color must have been retained.

These examples are enough to explain why unexpected results sometimes follow crosses with recessive-white fowls. For that reason their usefulness in sex-linked crosses made to permit identification of sex at hatching is not so great as with breeds in which the genotype with respect to color can be more accurately predicted from the appearance of the birds.

Dominant × Recessive White, The 13:3 Ratio. The most common complication in the use of recessive-white breeds for sex-linked crosses is that many of these breeds carry the gene for dominant white. This probably results from attempts to improve White Wyandottes, White Plymouth Rocks, or other white breeds by the infusion of a little White Leghorn blood. Most poultrymen who have tried this have not realized, till colored birds appeared in later generations, that the Leghorn white is different and that the two kinds do not mix as well as one might expect.

What really happens in such a cross was first shown by Bateson

(1902), who found in the F_2 generation from the cross White Leghorn $\times$ White Wyandotte, not only the chicks with white or light down that were expected, but also dark ones. The proportions of each are given in Table 18. The explanation of this unexpected result was not known till Bateson and Punnett (1908) proved the fact that there are both dominant and recessive whites and showed that the F_2 generation from a cross of the two kinds should yield white and colored birds in the ratio of 13:3. However, as they themselves found, this is not always realized because both dominant and recessive whites may carry the other type. In a cross of White Leghorn $\times$ White Plymouth Rock, Hadley (1914) found in the F_2 generation a remarkably close fit of the observed and expected ratios (Table 18).

TABLE 18. THE 13:3 RATIO IN THE F_2 FROM DOMINANT $\times$ RECESSIVE WHITE

	Bateson		Hadley	
	Light down	Dark down	White	Colored
Observed.............	215	55	134	33
Expected, 13:3.......	219	51	136	31

In both Bateson's and Hadley's crosses the genotypes of the parental breeds were *II CC* (Leghorn) $\times$ *ii cc* (recessive white). The F_1 birds were therefore *Ii Cc*, and each breeder could produce four kinds of gametes: *I C, I c, i C,* and *i c.* Allowing for random mating, *i.e.*, fertilization of each kind of egg by each type of sperm, the 16 possible combinations of *I, C,* and their alleles are as shown in Fig. 54. Considering the phenotypes, there are 9 *I C,* 3 *I c,* 3 *i C,* and 1 *i c.* The first two and the last of these four classes are all white, or nearly so, leaving only 3 colored birds out of the 16.

Actually, birds heterozygous for *I* show small amounts of black in the plumage if they are *CC* or *Cc* but are pure white if *cc.* All birds homozygous for *I* are pure white. The F_2 ratio from this cross may therefore be stated either as 13 white (or nearly so):3 colored, or as 7 pure white:6 with black flecks:3 colored. In Hadley's cross the colored birds were all barred, because both parental breeds carried barring, though neither could show it.

Complementary White, The 9:7 Ratio. Pure recessive whites mated together yield only white birds, but an exception to this rule was found by Bateson and Punnett (1908). Six crosses of White Silkies with recessive whites produced 113 fully colored F_1 birds, and these in turn yielded an F_2 generation containing both colored chicks and some "light, with or without buff."

This result was attributed to the interaction of two pairs of complementary genes, such as these same investigators had found to produce

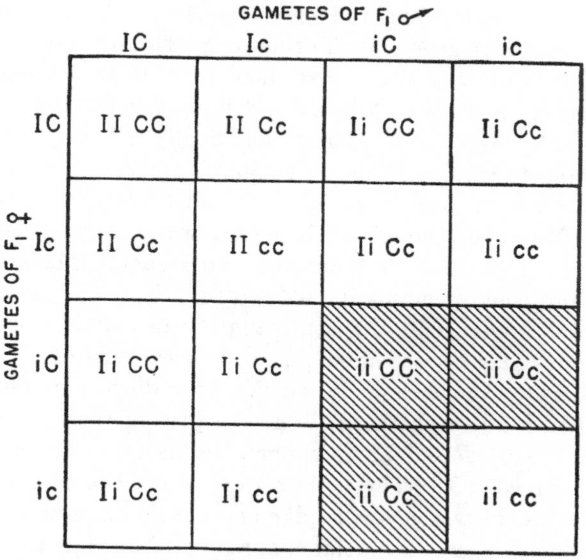

GAMETES OF F_1 ♂

	IC	Ic	iC	ic
IC	II CC	II Cc	Ii CC	Ii Cc
Ic	II Cc	II cc	Ii Cc	Ii cc
iC	Ii CC	Ii Cc	ii CC	ii Cc
ic	Ii Cc	Ii cc	ii Cc	ii cc

GAMETES OF F_1 ♀

FIG. 54. Genotypes in the F_2 generation from the cross White Leghorn (*II CC*) × White Wyandotte (*ii cc*). All phenotypes are white, or predominantly so, except those for the three crosshatched squares; hence the F_2 ratio is 13 white : 3 colored.

purple sweet peas, when two white varieties were crossed. On this basis, and assuming that the genes *O* and *C* are both necessary for color, the Silky would be *oo CC* and the recessive whites *OO cc*. The F_1 *generation* would be *Oo Cc* and colored, while in F_2 the phenotypic ratio would be 9 *O C*:3 *O c*:3 *o C*:1 *o c*. Since only the first of these four classes could be colored, the theoretical ratio would be 9 colored:7 white. The F_2 ratio observed—116 colored:87 light—fitted closely the expected 9:7 ratio of 114:89.

Because of this reasoning, it has been assumed by some writers that color in the plumage depends upon the presence of two genes, one permitting development of a chromogen, the other producing an oxidase (presumably tyrosinase). The White Silky is supposed to carry one of these, and other recessive whites the other. On this theory, colored birds have been designated as *CC OO*, with these symbols representing the chromogen and the oxidase. However, so far as the author knows, no one has ever been able to duplicate the original experiment and get colored fowls from a cross of two pure whites. Moreover, four different strains of White Silkies tested by Quinn and Godfrey (1937) all proved to carry only the ordinary recessive white found in other white breeds. It is possible that the Silkies used by Bateson and Punnett may have carried the pile pattern, in which red color is present but sometimes barely detectable, or that other genes for dilution or restriction could have made them appear practically white. The fact that their F_2 chicks were classified merely as colored or "light" and that some of the latter were buffy supports this possibility. Chicks genetically colored, but with the pigment restricted to the wing tips, as is common in those with the silver or Columbian pattern, are often almost indistinguishable from pure white ones at hatching, though their true nature is revealed as they mature. It is quite possible that Bateson and Punnett did have a complementary white, but, pending its rediscovery, it seems reasonable to say only that there is a gene, *C*, permitting the production of color and that birds homozygous for its allele, *c*, are recessive whites.

Melanophores. Considering the smoky-grey down commonly found in White Plymouth Rock chicks, it is not surprising that Dorris (1938) and Hamilton (1940) found melanophores in tissue cultures from embryos of that breed. However, Hamilton also obtained them from White Wyandottes, in which black pigment is seldom seen in chicks or adults. According to him, the melanophores of white breeds are smaller than those of colored breeds, containing smaller granules of pigment and fewer of them. Those of White Rocks degenerated in his cultures within 2 to 3 days—slightly earlier than those of White Leghorns and much ahead of the melanophores of colored breeds. He was unable to find melanophores in developing feathers of White Wyandottes, but they were present, though degenerate, in feathers from one of two White Plymouth Rock chicks examined. In cultures from the neural crest of very young embryos (up to 20 somites), Dorris found the proportion yielding no melanophores to be higher with White Rocks than in any of four colored breeds studied, and higher than in White Leghorns. This, together with Hamilton's study, suggests that recessive whites are white partly because they produce fewer melanophores than colored breeds and partly because those they do have die at early stages. What there is about the *cc* genotype that causes this peculiarity remains to be proved.

Albinism

While any white animal might be considered in general terms as an albino, geneticists restrict that term to those with more or less elimination of melanin from the eye, as well as from the skin and feathers or hair. In this sense, dominant and recessive whites are not albinos but merely white fowls in which melanin is restricted to the eye. Many of the cases of albinism reported in wild birds are of the kind discussed later, in which white feathers appear on birds originally fully covered. However, several instances of true hereditary albinism have been found in birds. In the fowl, three different types are known so far, one of which ("pink eye") is considered in this book as a dilution of pigment rather than as albinism.

A characteristic common to all albinos is that they are sensitive to light. Those with no melanin whatever in the eye are somewhat more sensitive in this respect than birds with imperfect albinism in which some of the pigment is retained in the retina. Those with all melanin gone have eyes that are practically pink (from the blood in the capillaries), but in others the eye is darker. The similarities and differences in two kinds of albinism in the fowl and one in the turkey are given in the following sections.

In the Fowl; Autosomal, a. In White Wyandottes, Warren (1933) found a type of albinism, apparently complete, that was induced in birds homozygous for a recessive autosomal gene, a. Since White Wyandottes have white plumage anyway, these albinos were recognizable only by their bright red eyes. In adult birds the eyes seemed darker, but histological studies showed the iris and retina to be completely devoid of melanic pigment. The yellow carotinoid pigment of the skin (xanthophyll) was not affected by the mutation, and the birds laid eggs with normally yellow yolks.

These albinos had such defective eyesight that the females did not use the trap nests provided. The chicks seemed to have difficulty in locating their feed. All were so sensitive to the brilliant Kansas sunlight that they preferred to remain indoors and seldom ventured outside.

In the Fowl; Sex Linked, al. The imperfect albinism studied by Mueller and Hutt (1941) was quite different in many respects. It was first found in Barred Plymouth Rocks.

Description. Affected chicks varied in color from almost pure white to a dusky chocolate color. Barring was faintly visible, first as the usual white head spot in the occipital region of the newly hatched chick, and later as faint "ghost barring" in the adult plumage. Granules of melanin were easily found in the feathers. The carotinoid pigments of the skin and beak were unaffected by the mutation. At hatching the albinotic chicks had bright pink eyes, but as the birds matured, the iris became blue-grey in color, though the pupil showed dull red. Histological studies showed that there was melanin in the eye but that it was limited to the pigment layer of the retina and to the retinal portions of the ciliary body and iris. Even in these areas there was only enough melanin to give a brownish appearance, in marked contrast to the intense black of the normal eye. Embryos with this type of albinism were recognizable as such at 5 days of incubation by the deficiency of melanin in their eyes. Peculiarly enough, the down of these albinos is shorter than that of other chicks.

Genetics and Effects. This type of imperfect albinism was caused by a single, sex-linked recessive gene, *al.* Crosses of these albinos with Warren's autosomal albinism and with his pink-eye mutation described later yielded only dark-eyed colored birds showing no trace of albinism. Carrier males, normal in appearance, can pass the mutation to half their daughters, which will be albinos, and also to half their sons, but these will show no trace of albinism.

This same mutation was later found in another flock of Barred Rocks and in White Leghorns. Both of these were in other states and were apparently mutations quite independent of the one originally studied (Hutt and Mueller, 1943).

The condition is markedly different from the type of albinism studied by Warren and from that in the turkey (discussed later) because it apparently has little or no ill effect upon the albinotic birds. Their vision seemed practically as good as in normal fowls. They suffered no heavier mortality, either before hatching or after, than normal chicks of the same matings. The original albinotic Barred Rock laid 240 eggs in her first laying year, a creditable record for any hen.

In the Turkey; Sex Linked. A type of imperfect albinism similar in some respects to that just considered was studied in Bronze turkeys by Hutt and Mueller (1942).

Description. The albinotic poults were dingy white in appearance and showed faintly the irregular stripes and pattern of dark pigment normally found in the down of bronze poults. Similarly, adults retained enough melanin in the plumage to show clearly the barring of the wing feathers and traces of the black bands near the ends of the contour feathers. The eye was pale blue. Melanin was absent from the choroid coat, the pecten, and the pigment epithelium of the functional retina in the posterior part of the eye (Fig. 55). However, melanin was found, in subnormal quantities, in the ciliary body and in the retinal (posterior) part of the iris. There was none on the anterior surface of the iris. The blue appearance of the eye in these birds resulted from the melanin at the back of the iris being seen through a layer of stroma containing many unpigmented cells. All the albinos were blind.

Genetics and Effects. This condition is caused by a single sex-linked gene, *al,* which is apparently lethal, either during incubation or

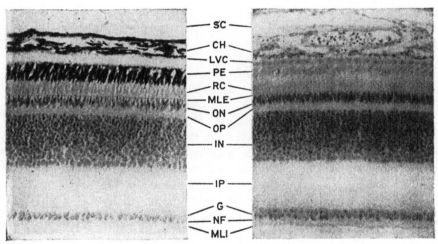

FIG. 55. Photomicrographs of sections through the posterior part of the eyes of day-old poults showing normal condition (*left*) and the elimination of melanin from the choroid coat and pigment epithelium of the albino (*right*). (*From Hutt and Mueller in J. Heredity.*)

SC—Sclera
CH—Choroid coat
LVC—Lamina vitrea choroidea
PE—Pigment epithelium
RC—Layer of rods and cones
MLE—Membrana limitans externa
ON—Outer nuclear layer

OP—Outer plexiform layer
IN—Inner nuclear layer
IP—Inner plexiform layer
G—Layer of ganglion cells
NF—Layer of nerve fibres
MLI—Membrana limitans interna

after hatching, to most of the poults that receive it. In the experiments of Hutt and Mueller, mortality among albinotic poults during the last 5 days of incubation was 75 per cent, while only 20 per cent of the colored poults in the same settings died during that period. Moreover, of those which did hatch, nearly all died in the first 6 weeks. Being blind, they had difficulty in finding feed and water. They were also recognized by the normal poults as weaklings and consequently were driven from the feeders and pecked so badly that they had to be destroyed. While blindness was probably the main cause of death in these hatched albinos, the fact that the gene killed many embryos during the later stages of incubation indicates that it may have caused some unfavorable effect on the poults after hatching, apart from blindness.

Although both are caused by sex-linked genes, this imperfect albinism in the turkey differs from the similar condition in the fowl in that it eliminates melanin in the posterior part of the retina, it causes blindness, and it is lethal to most of the affected birds.

Albinism in Other Birds. In the literature of ornithology there are many records of birds wholly or partially albinotic, but few of these cases have been studied genetically. In recent years McIlhenny (1940) found a true albinism in the mockingbird, *Mimus polyglottos,* to be inherited as a simple recessive character. The albinism reported by Cook (1939) in the American robin, *Turdus migratorius,* was evidently hereditary. The sex-linked albinism studied by Kokemüller (1935) in the budgerigar, *Melopsittacus undulatus,* is particularly interesting because it eliminated melanin and the structural blue color found in one mutant of that species but did not affect the lipochrome pigments at all. As a result, budgerigars normally green with some black were converted by the mutation to bright yellow birds with pink eyes.

In the canary, *Serinus canarius,* there is a variety with eyes pink at hatching, but darker in older birds, and with plumage described as cinnamon. It seems probable that this is a less extreme form of albinism, perhaps more comparable with the "pink-eye" mutation in the fowl considered later. The discovery by Durham and Marryat (1908) that these canaries were pink-eyed and cinnamon because of a sex-linked gene was the first experimental demonstration of sex-linked inheritance in birds after the rediscovery of Mendel's laws. It afforded the first proof that the type of sex determination found in the moth Abraxas, in which the females are heterogametic, is also found in birds.

Depigmentation

Ordinarily, the color of the fowl's definitive plumage does not change, except in so far as it may be bleached or rusty, from action of the sunlight, or made to appear brighter by the contrast of the new feathers grown after a moult with the old ones they displaced. However, white feathers are occasionally found in birds that once had only black or colored plumage. They may develop spontaneously, be caused by injury, or be induced by excessive doses of thyroxine. It is convenient to consider these cases here along with other kinds of white plumage.

Spontaneous. There are at least 9 or 10 records of colored fowls becoming more or less white after their first moult as adults. In one Black Leghorn hen that became more than half white, the anomaly was associated with a large ovarian tumor (Crew, 1922), but the same type of depigmentation occurred in a normal La Bresse hen in which the ovary was found by Krizenecky (1928) to be quite normal. Loss of pigment has also been noted in a crossbred capon by Hesse (1927) and in a Brown Leghorn capon by Juhn (1933). The latter case was particularly interesting because the bird became entirely white, thus showing that the depigmentation affects both black and the red or brown colors. Breeding tests with a Blue Andalusian that gradually became completely white over a period of about 4 years (Lippincott, 1920) showed that the bird

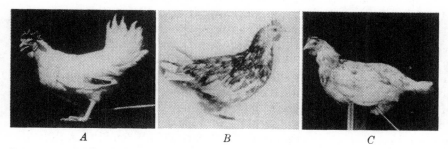

A   *B*   *C*

Fɪɢ. 56. Successive plumages assumed by a mottled Ancona hen at her first, third, and fourth annual moults are shown in *A*, *B*, and *C*, respectively.

continued to breed as a normal Blue Andalusian. Godbey and Reid (1931) found that a Barred Plymouth Rock hen which became almost entirely white at her first adult moult produced colored chicks when mated with a White Plymouth Rock. This bird was rather unusual in that when 3 years old she again assumed the normal colored plumage of her breed. Changes of this sort in the plumage of two Ancona hens were observed by the author, and Fig. 56 gives some idea of the variation in color of one of these birds over a period of 4 years.

The fact that both these whitened Anconas occurred in the same flock and in one year suggested that the condition might be hereditary. A crossbred black hen that became three-quarters white was found by Finch (1909) to produce a daughter with variable plumage that finally became pure white. Two black Australorps that became entirely white were mated by Gericke (1938) to a pure black Australorp male and produced 7 chicks, 1 of which, though black earlier, was pure white when 1 year old. In 96 birds of the F_2 and backcross generations that reached 6 months of age, 5 had begun to lose color at 4 or 5 months, and these subsequently became all white. Two years later 1 of these reverted to black plumage after her moult.

Though some types of depigmentation are evidently hereditary, neither the genetic basis nor the physiological one is yet known. The condition is not unlike the premature whitening of the hair frequently seen in man.

Traumatic. White feathers are sometimes found in colored birds at the site of injuries. Sometimes they occur where incisions have been made for caponizing or on the heads of birds that have been badly picked by others. Krizenecky (1930) found a white patch of feathers growing in at the site of exposure to X rays. The cause of the loss of pigment in these feathers is not known, but it is probably the same as that responsible for white hairs at the site of injuries in mammals.

Thyrogenous. It has been shown by Giacomini (1924), Zavadovsky (1925), and others that large quantities of thyroid substance cause a precipitate moult and varying degrees of depigmentation in the new feathers. Smaller doses of the same material make new feathers darker in the Brown Leghorn (Cole and Reid, 1924) and in some other breeds. In Black Minorca females studied by Hutt (1930), the minimum daily dose necessary to cause marked depigmentation of new feathers was 4 mg. of thyroid iodine to 5,000 gm. of body weight. White feathers were most prevalent in the birds that declined in weight. This response is not uniform in all breeds, for Emmens and Parkes (1940) found that 1.0 mg. of thyroxine daily caused darkening of the feathers in Welsummers (brown and black) but increased the amount of white in Anconas and Speckled Sussex, which normally have white-tipped feathers.

Silver and Gold, S and s

Descriptions. All fowls are either silver or gold. For that reason, these colors are here considered under the class of solid colors, even though in no case except in buff fowls are they found without some pattern or epistatic colors superimposed upon them. These gold and silver colors are obscured in solid black birds and in white ones. They are sometimes difficult to distinguish in birds showing autosomal red or with complex combinations of different patterns. The genes for these colors, S (silver) and s (gold), are located in the sex chromosomes. Some of the various phenotypes and all of the genotypes possible for silver and gold birds are given in Table 19.

Genetics. The sex-linked nature of the S and s alleles was demonstrated by Sturtevant (1912) in reciprocal crosses between Brown Leghorns and Columbian Wyandottes and by Davenport (1912) with crosses between Brown Leghorns and Dark Brahmas. It has since been learned that, while both silver and gold fowls can be identified in many cases by their appearance, the genotypes of blacks and whites with respect to the S and s alleles can be determined only by breeding tests. Taylor (1932) found his Black Minorcas to be gold; the Langshans of Punnett

TABLE 19. GENOTYPES AND PHENOTYPES OF SILVER AND GOLD BIRDS

Color	Possible genotypes	Phenotypes	
		Chicks	Adults
Silver	♂ $\begin{cases} SS \\ Ss \end{cases}$ ♀ S–	White, silver, black. Striping, marbling, or other pattern on silver ground	White, barred; silver-spangled, -laced, or -pencilled; Columbian; stippled grey as in Silver Leghorns and Dorkings; mottling and other patterns
Gold	♂ ss ♀ s–	Buff, red, chocolate, black. Striping, marbling, or other pattern on gold ground	Buff, red, black, white; gold-barred, golden-spangled, -laced, or -pencilled (partridge); stippled brown as in Brown Leghorns; the black-red combination and others

(1923) were the same, as were some Black Sumatras studied by the author. This is no assurance that other black fowls, or even other specimens of these breeds, must be gold. Barred Rocks are silver, as were the Anconas used by Asmundson and Milne (1930). Most White Wyandottes are silver, but Quinn (1936) found that 5 out of 28 tested were gold.

While buff fowls might be considered as all gold in color, there is no breed all silver, unless one considers white fowls as such, keeping in mind that white fowls can also be genetically gold. Silver is really most obvious in breeds with some feather pattern, such as lacing or pencilling, because in them the silver color shows clearly in the sexually dimorphic areas of the males' plumage. Even in females the combination of white with black gives the plumage a silvery appearance in laced, spangled, pencilled, and stippled varieties. Fowls predominantly black may show silver or gold in the neck feathers. In chicks that show striping in the down (Fig. 63), the difference between silver and gold birds is not always readily seen. It shows best in the narrower stripes on the back, which are light in silvers and brownish in gold chicks. In chicks with extremely dark downs, differences between golds and silvers are still evident, according to Punnett (1923), in the down on the sides of the head.

Gold and Silver Breeds. To save space, no lengthy list of gold and silver breeds is given here. Most of them can be identified, so far as is possible without a breeding test, from the phenotypes listed in Table 19. It is of interest to note that there are a number of paired color varieties which differ chiefly, if not entirely, in that one member is silver, the other gold. Some of these are

Silver and Golden Sebrights.
Silver and Brown Leghorns.
Partridge and Silver-pencilled Wyandotte, or Plymouth Rock.
Golden-laced and Silver-laced Wyandottes.
Golden and Silver Campines.
Golden and Silver Polish.
Golden- and Silver-spangled Hamburgs.

Punnett (1923) states that the Silver Duckwing Game differs from the Black-red Game only by having S instead of s. The Red Jungle Fowl is gold. Whether the mutation to silver occurred after its domestication or was brought in by crossing with the Grey Jungle Fowl, *Gallus sonneratii*, is not known, but it is evident that this pair of genes has been of great importance in contributing to the diversity of breeds and varieties in the domestic fowl.

Sex-linked Crosses. Any silver female mated with a gold male produces chicks in which the males are genetically silver, the females gold. The latter have buff down color, while the silvers appear white or silvery grey. If these "ground" colors are not obscured by striping or by other dark color in the down, the sexes can be separated at hatching according to the down color. Some crosses give sharp differentiation. A favorite in Great Britain is the cross Light Sussex ♀ × Rhode Island Red ♂. Both the parent breeds in this cross have the Columbian type of restriction of black pigment (see pages 192 to 196), and that ensures a clear down in which the difference between S and s is quite evident.

When breeds with striped down are involved, such as Brown Leghorns or partridge or silver-pencilled varieties, differentiation of the sexes is more difficult. A number of these crosses were tested by Punnett (1923). When a Silver-laced Wyandotte female was mated with a Buff Orpington male, the difference between the male and female chicks was just as marked as in the Light Sussex cross mentioned above. However, when a Silver-laced Wyandotte female was mated with a Brown Leghorn male, the down was very dark and striped, so that differences between the sexes were not so obvious.

In North America, few improved silver breeds are available for such crosses except the Barred Plymouth Rock, and in crosses with that breed the barring is a more useful indicator of sex than is its silver plumage. White Wyandottes and White Plymouth Rocks could be used, but many of these carry dominant white, while others may be gold instead of silver. These deviations from expectation lessen the value of these breeds for crossing. White Leghorns are silver, but useless as silver females in a silver × gold cross because of their dominant white. For these reasons, it seems probable that this type of cross will be used less than those involving the sex-linked gene for barring (either from Barred Rocks or in auto-sexing breeds) or the K and k alleles affecting the rate of feathering (see pages 136, 206 and 209).

Sex Dichromatism. It is worth noting that differentiation of the sexes in adults is more striking in breeds that show gold or silver with some pattern than in most other fowls. For example, the female of a silver-pencilled variety shows that pattern throughout the body, except for some silver lacing on the neck, but the male has black plumage all over the body, with silver lacing prominent in the hackle and saddle feathers and a silver "duckwing" showing in the wing. Corresponding differences between males and females are found in partridge varieties, which have the pencilling pattern on a gold ground. From experiments with Brown Leghorns, in which similar differences between the sexes are also found, it seems probable that the remarkable sex dichromatism in these gold and silver patterned breeds is caused by hormones of the ovary which lessen the black in the plumage of females and permit manifestation of the pattern involved.

DILUTIONS

Diluted colors are here considered as those in which pigment is distributed uniformly throughout the plumage but is reduced in amount or otherwise affected, so that the color is paler than in fowls with undiluted pigment. Five different mutations are put in this class, the latest addition being Munro's sex-linked blue.

Blue, *Bl*

This is a breed characteristic in Blue Andalusians and a varietal color in Orpingtons, Polish, Bredas, Plymouth Rocks, and other breeds.

Description. Feathers of this breed are described as slaty blue in color, but those of the male appear black or bluish black in the regions of sexual dimorphism—the neck, back, saddle, and wing bow. Similarly, the blue feathers of both males and females appear to have a narrow black lacing. This black appearance is found only in the parts of the feathers that lack barbules, but it is not solely the result of a different structure, for Lippincott (1918) found the granules of pigment in the black parts to be rod-shaped, as in other black feathers, whereas in the blue portions these granules are mostly round. It is not merely the shape of the granules that makes the feather blue or black, but also their arrangement. In black feathers and in black parts of blue feathers, the granules are scattered throughout the barb and barbule, but in blue feathers they are restricted somewhat to little clumps. These same differences between pigment granules in black and blue feathers were earlier found in pigeons by Lloyd-Jones (1915).

A peculiarity of blue feathers observed by Lippincott and confirmed by Bohren *et al.* (1943) is that the proximal barbules (carrying the scrolls or flanges) are more heavily pigmented than the distal, hooked ones. This is just the reverse of the distribution of melanin in black feathers.

The down of blue chicks is variable in color, and it is sometimes difficult to differentiate between black and dark blue in newly hatched chicks which are still wet or in those which failed to hatch. Lippincott (1921) made the distinction in some cases by determining microscopically the type of pigment granule. In others this could not be done because of a tendency in some families for the chicks to appear black and to have the rod-shaped granules characteristic of black feathers but later to show blue in the definitive plumage.

Genetics. When blue fowls are mated together, they produce black, blue, and blue-splashed white progeny in the ratio of 1:2:1. This interesting behavior—much more of a puzzle when it was solved than it would be now—was cleared up by Bateson and Punnett (1906), who showed that all blues are heterozygous. The ratios in the progeny from their different types of matings are shown in Table 20.

TABLE 20.   RATIOS OBTAINED FROM MATINGS OF THREE COLORS IN ANDALUSIANS

Parents	Progeny		
	Black	Blue	Blue-splashed white
Blue × blue..............	1	2	1
Blue-splashed × blue.....	...	1	1
Black × blue............	1	1	—
Blue-splashed *inter se*.....	...	...	All
Black × black...........	All	—	—
Black × blue-splashed....	...	All	—

These results, which have since been confirmed by Lippincott (1918), show that Blue Andalusians are heterozygous for a gene, *Bl*, which, when homozygous, makes the bird predominantly white except for a few blue feathers. A somewhat more complex interpretation was proposed by Lippincott, but its correctness cannot be proved unless a true-breeding blue fowl be found.

As the symbol *Bl* indicates, blue is considered here as an incompletely dominant character. One might almost equally well consider the blue-splashed type as recessive, with black incompletely dominant. The important points to remember are that the blue-splashed white is homozygous for a gene that converts black to blue, that the blue is heterozygous, and that the blacks from Andalusians are in no way different from any other black fowl so far as color is concerned.

Other Blue Breeds. Blue Orpingtons and blue mutants from White Leghorns were proved by Lippincott (1921) to have the same gene for blue as Blue Andalusians. Punnett (1923) refers to reports of Blue Madras Games and Blue Polish producing blue females but black males. Pending further study, it would seem probable that such reports might arise from the fact that blue males always have considerable black plumage in the areas of sexually dimorphic feathers, whereas blue hens are blue throughout.

An interesting "true-breeding" blue described briefly by Munro (1946) is apparently caused by a sex-linked gene that is either an allele of barring or closely linked to it. For this the symbol *Sd* (for sex-linked dilution) is proposed. Females with the gene are blue and barred; so are heterozygous males. These show the head spot in the down, but most of them are then black or greyish like chicks of Barred Rocks. Homozygous males are almost pure white when adult. Tests for linkage of the gene for blue with *B* yielded 159 either barred and blue or non-barred and black, plus 13 of doubtful classification.

Blue × Recessive White. The Hagedoorns (1914) found that this cross yields blue and black fowls in the ratio of 1:1. So did Lippincott (1921), who proved that blue and black progeny are obtained in equal numbers, whether blue fowls are mated to black birds or to recessive white ones. Similarly, his *Bl Bl* birds had only blue offspring whether mated to White Wyandottes, White Plymouth Rocks, Black Langshans, or Black Orpingtons. The reason why recessive whites give the same results as black fowls in these crosses is that the Andalusians are *CC* (whether black, blue, or splashed white) and so give to their F_1 progeny a gene for color that is lacking in the recessive whites. Since *C* is completely dominant, the blue is shown as well when superimposed on a *Cc* genotype as in the *CC* birds from the black breeds mentioned above.

Blue × Dominant White. *Bl* and *I* both restrict black; the former produces a blue-splashed homozygote, the latter a black-flecked heterozygote. The question arises whether two entirely different genes are involved or whether they might be multiple alleles. This was answered by a cross of blue-splashed white Andalusians × White Leghorns made by Lippincott (1923), in which *I* and *Bl* segregated quite independently in the F_2 and backcross. This case provides an unusual modification of the familiar 9:3:3:1 ratio found in the F_2 generation of a dihybrid cross. Since both parents are CC, their genotypes may be shortened to ii $Bl\,Bl$ for the homozygous Andalusians and II $bl\,bl$ for the White Leghorns. Apparently the amount of black flecking in Ii birds is reduced when Bl is present. At any rate, Lippincott's F_1 birds were all classified as white. The F_2 genotypes and the observed and expected phenotypic ratios are given in Table 21.

TABLE 21. THE F_2 GENERATION FROM THE CROSS BLUE-SPLASHED
ANDALUSIAN × WHITE LEGHORN

Genotypes	Propor-tion	Phenotypes	Lippincott's population	
			Observed	Expected
II Bl Bl	1	White		
Ii Bl Bl	2	White		
II Bl bl	2	White	106	106.5
Ii Bl bl	4	White		
II bl bl	1	White		
Ii bl bl	2	White, black flecks		
ii Bl Bl	1	Blue-splashed white	9	8.875
ii Bl bl	2	Blue	18	17.750
ii bl bl	1	Black	9	8.875

Such a close agreement of observed and expected ratios is not likely to be obtained very often. The segregation in a 12:1:2:1 ratio shows that the genes I and Bl are quite independent.

Sex Dichromatism. The Blue Andalusian male is much darker in general appearance than the female, because of the wide black fringe on its feathers in the neck, back, saddle, and wing-bow regions. While this difference is a secondary sex character, dependent, as is the sex difference in the comb and in behavior, upon secretions of the gonads, it is clear that the difference in color is only incidental and that the real difference between the sexes lies in the structure of the feathers in sexually dimorphic areas. In that respect there is no greater difference between the sexes in Blue Andalusians than in White Leghorns.

In blue males feminized after castration by implantation of an ovary (Lippincott, 1921; Régnier, 1937), the fringe on the feathers is reduced to a minimum, and the plumage is blue as in normal females. Conversely, as Régnier has shown, when the blue female is ovariotomized, new feathers in the sexually dimorphic areas become fringed as in males or capons, and predominantly black. It is not yet known why there should be rod-shaped granules of melanin and black color in the fringed areas where the barbs lack barbules, but round granules and blue color where barbules are present.

Pink Eye, *pk*

An autosomal recessive gene diluting pigment so much that the eye appears pink and the plumage of colored birds blue was studied by Warren (1940). In the White Plymouth Rocks in which this mutation was first found, the eyes were so much like those of fowls with autosomal albinism that the two conditions were considered identical until a breeding test proved them otherwise. The extent to which melanin is reduced in the eye was not determined, but it was noted that the pink eyes of colored birds seemed darker than the pink eyes of white ones.

The symbol *pk* is assigned. The mutation could be considered as a type of imperfect albinism, but it seems preferable to restrict that term to conditions making the birds whiter than the pink-eye gene does.

Cream, *ig*

A gene, *ig* (inhibitor of gold), diluting gold color to a cream that varied in shade from reddish yellow to silver, was found by Taylor (1932a) in Silver-spangled Hamburgs. It proved to be autosomal and recessive. The fact that the darkest shades of cream were found in descendants of Rhode Island Reds indicated that it dilutes autosomal red less than gold. Some of the cream-colored birds showed so little gold that they were easily confused with brassy silvers.

A similar autosomal mutation studied by Punnett (1948), when in combination with the Columbian restriction of Buff Leghorns, induces a rich cream color in females but makes the males so pale that some could be mistaken for silvers. Hens of the Brown Leghorn type of plumage, but homozygous for this mutation, appear silver-grey, with straw-tinged hackles. The corresponding males have the golden brown replaced by white in the hackles, in the outer webs of the secondaries, and elsewhere. As a result these birds appear to be silver except for the autosomal red or chestnut, which is little affected. The effects of the gene are clearly brought out by the excellent colored plates in Punnett's paper.

Although their mutations appear to be identical, Punnett's interpretation differs somewhat from that of Taylor given above. He considers that the cream mutant is not an inhibitor or diluent of gold but that the sex-linked gold is an intensifier of the autosomal cream.

Taylor suggested that this gene might account for the apparently aberrant results observed by Caridroit and Régnier (1930) in a cross of Silver Ardennes ♂ ✕ Gold Ardennes ♀, which yielded only gold progeny, where only silver were expected. If the Silver Ardennes male were really a dilute gold or cream, as seems possible from its description, the birds from this cross should have been gold, as they were found to be.

Light Down, *Li*

Hertwig and Rittershaus (1929) found in Barred Plymouth Rocks a dominant sex-linked gene, *Li* (light down), which prevents or lessens the manifestation of brown color in the down of chicks which are not black. The affected birds had down that was whitish yellow without brown. This mutation is considered here as a dilution of brown, though it might be more correct to view it as an inhibitor of that color. The effect of *Li* on adult plumage was not determined, but it was noted that some of the chicks with light down developed into adults with much brown and gold in the plumage.

EXTENSIONS AND RESTRICTIONS

Under this heading are considered various conditions in which color— black, red, or buff—is present but not evenly distributed to all parts of the plumage.

The Columbian Pattern and Extension of Black, *e* and *E*

In Light Brahmas the black pigment visible on the surface of the plumage is restricted to the neck, large wing feathers, and tail.

Genetics. This pattern, which makes the Columbian varieties of Plymouth Rocks and Wyandottes, was found by Dunn (1923) to be caused by a recessive autosomal gene, *e,* in the homozygous condition. The dominant allele is present in birds with black distributed throughout the plumage. Although the recessive gene was first recognized by Dunn and designated as e^m, the dominant allele was earlier considered by Lippincott (1918) responsible for the distribution of blue and black throughout the plumage of Blue Andalusians and their black derivatives. It was later shown (Lippincott, 1923a) that this same gene is found in many breeds. Because of his priority and the modern practice among geneticists of not using superscript symbols except for multiple alleles, it seems preferable to designate the genes for extension of black and for Columbian restriction as *E* and *e*, the symbols used by Lippincott.

These appear to be distributed as follows:

E:

1. In all solid black birds.
2. In all blacks with patterns, such as barred, silver-pencilled, and mottled varieties, and others.
3. In White Leghorns and in most recessive whites.
4. Probably also in Brown Leghorns and in partridge varieties.

C:

1. In all birds with the Columbian pattern, including Light Brahmas, Light Sussex, Black-tailed Japanese Bantams, and probably Lakenvelders.
2. In Rhode Island Reds, Redcaps, Red Sussex, Black-tailed Red Leghorns, and others with similar color.
3. In Buff Orpingtons and probably in all fowls appearing predominantly buff.
4. In some recessive whites, and even in some dominant whites.

The *ee* birds are usually recognizable by inspection except those which are buff or white. Of 11 White Plymouth Rocks tested by Quinn (1936), 6 were *ee*, 4 *Ee*, and 1 *EE*. Most buff birds of pure breeds show little or none of the Columbian pattern, but black is not uncommon in the tail. The Buff Orpingtons of Dunn (1923) were *ee*, as were the Buff Wyandottes tested by Asmundson and Milne (1930). It seems likely that other buffs are of that same genotype, although not many have been adequately tested. It is probable that most colored birds in which black pigment is not absent or obviously restricted to the neck, wings, and tail are homozygous or heterozygous for *E* and for *C*.

Anconas are birds with extended black, but, in addition, they are homozygous for a recessive gene that eliminates the black from the tips of some of the feathers. Barred Plymouth Rocks are *EE*, plus a dominant gene causing the barring pattern of their feathers. Agar (1924), who made the cross Barred Rock ♀ × Golden-laced Wyandotte ♂, with a backcross of F₁ ♂ × Golden-laced Wyandotte, considered both breeds potentially laced and these Wyandottes *ee*, but his data can be explained equally well on the assumption that the Golden-laced Wyandotte is *EE* and homozygous for a recessive gene for lacing, the dominant allele of which is carried by the Barred Plymouth Rock. This seems more likely because in Golden-laced Wyandottes the black pigment is not restricted to the neck, wings, and tail, as it is in Columbian varieties, in Rhode Island Reds, and in other breeds with the type of restriction common to birds homozygous for *e*.

Segregation of Columbian Chicks from Crosses between Breeds. In recent years, when millions of chicks have been produced from the popular cross, Barred Rock ♀ × R. I. Red or New Hampshire ♂, many hatcherymen have been perplexed to find some of these chicks white or red instead of the usual black color. These "sports" appear merely because some of their Barred Rock mothers are *Ee* instead of *EE*. Since all Barred Rocks carry the sex-linked genes *B* (barring) and *S* (silver), while the red males are *bb ss ee*, hens of the genotype *B– S– Ee* will produce in equal numbers the following kinds of chicks:

Genotype		Phenotype
Bb Ss Ee	♂	Black, with white head spot indicating barring
b– s– Ee	♀	Black, no head spot, usually some red around head
Bb Ss ee	♂	Silver or white
b– s– ee	♀	Gold

The first two of these four types are those normally expected from this cross. Extension of black in these *Ee* chicks permits easy recognition of those that are barred (as shown by their head spots) and those that are not (*i.e.*, the females). This same extension of black obscures almost completely the fact that the barred birds are also silver, while the non-barred ones are gold.

This situation is reversed in the last two of the four kinds of chicks listed above. These have the Columbian restriction of black, which removes black pigment entirely from the downy plumage. While this prevents differentiation of males and females by the presence or absence of a head spot, it reveals clearly the difference between the silver chicks, which are the males, and the gold ones. Although the Columbian pattern is not manifested in the down, it can be recognized at hatching, either in silver chicks or in gold ones, by what appears to be black skin in the wing tips. This is caused by the black pigment in the follicles from which the chick's first primary feathers develop.

Because poultrymen the world over have a special penchant for the preservation of "sports," it is not surprising that the barred, silver, Columbian males produced in this way should be used to develop another new breed, the "Delaware." It gives promise of being excellent for crossing with New Hampshire females to produce good broilers. Since the offspring of that cross are silver and Columbian in both sexes, they all have the light-colored plumage considered desirable in the broiler trade.

Endocrine Modification. In birds that are genetically extended black (whether *EE* or *Ee*) but heterozygous for some gene or genes causing a pattern in the feather, the black is not extended as fully in males as in females, and the former may even not be recognizable as fowls with extended black. The fact that some crosses yielded black females but males with red in the neck, shoulders, and saddles was long ago noted by Darwin (1890) and Davenport (1909). In the F_1 generations from crosses of Black Langshans with Brown Leghorns and with Golden-pencilled Hamburgs made by Punnett (1923), the females were full black, but the males had more or less gold in the hackles. Since all three of the parent breeds were genetically gold, and not silver, the manifestation of gold only in the F_1 males was not the result of sex-linked genes but more probably was caused by action of the male hormones. Evidence to that effect has since come from other experiments.

Taylor (1933) found that the F_1 females from the cross Black Minorca ♂ × Silver-spangled Hamburg ♀ ♀ were predominantly black but that the males were spangled. However, when the latter were treated with the urine of pregnant women, new feathers growing in were black, not spangled. The complete extension of black in these treated males was attributed to estrogenic (female) hormone in the urine. The fact that it converted the male phenotype to the same one as in the females indicated that the original difference in color between the sexes resulted from the presence of female sex hormone in females and its absence in males.

Caridroit and Régnier (1934), who made the cross Rhode Island Red ♂ × Blue Andalusian ♀, found the F_1 females to be blue (half should have been black) without any trace of red, whereas the F_1 males had varying amounts of red in the neck and across the shoulders. When these blue F_1 females were ovariotomized, the resultant poulardes showed red as did the males. Conversely, when a male with red in the neck and shoulders was castrated and feminized with an ovarian graft, the new feathers were like those of females in structure and completely blue without a trace of red. In this case the effect of the sex hormones is not directly upon the color of the plumage but primarily upon the structure and incidentally upon the color. The red showed only in the sexually dimorphic areas, and there only in the fringe of the feather where barbules were lacking. Feminization caused extension of the area with barbules within each feather to the same degree as in females. This eliminated the fringes without barbules, and with them went the red color, leaving the feminized male with black color (in this case, blue) fully extended just as in females of the same genotype. Similar results were obtained by Régnier (1934) in another cross involving Buff Leghorns, Coucou de Malines (barred), and Black Minorcas and by Nickerson (1946a) in what were said to be pure Silver Campine capons. It is difficult to explain why these last should have shown any red or gold if they were homozygous for silver, but if they were *Ss*, some red was to be expected in feathers in the sex-dimorphic areas, just as it occurred in Régnier's heterozygotes. In both cases, transformation to the female type of feather by endocrine treatments eliminated the red. The chief difference was that this had to be done in Régnier's birds by ovarian hormones, while in Nickerson's hen-feathered Campines feminization of the capons was possible with either male or female sex hormones.

Again, Quinn and Burrows (1935) found solid black females and males with black plumage but with silver hackles and saddle feathers in the F_1 generation from the cross Black Sumatra ♂ × White Wyandotte ♀. Feminization of these males by castration and the administration of theelin caused their new feathers to be female in structure and pure black in color. Conversely, castration of a black female resulted in its new plumage showing red in the wing bow and saddle. As this cross should yield silver males and gold females, the results were in accord with expectation.

These cases show that the extension of black is more complete in a milieu that includes the female hormone (or the male one in the case of hen-feathered males) than in males or in the neutral capon and poularde.

Red

Red color is characteristic of Rhode Island Reds, New Hampshires, Redcaps, Red Sussex, Black-tailed Red Leghorns, and other breeds. In all these cases, the birds of both sexes are predominantly red but have varying amounts of black in the tail and wings, occasionally also in the neck. A comparatively new breed, the Red Leghorn, is said to be red in all parts of the plumage, but it seems probable, from its description in "The American Standard of Perfection," that the breed has the same major genotype for color as the other red breeds mentioned, except that by constant selection modifying genes have been accumulated which reduce the black pigmentation almost to the vanishing point. In the showroom these birds are not disqualified if they have one solid black feather in the wings or tail, nor even if the tail is as much as one-third black.

Genetics. It is evident that these red breeds and varieties have genes for red and for black but that the latter color is restricted to the wings, tail, and neck, as in Columbian varieties, by the gene *e* in the homozygous state. This was first suggested by Dunn (1922). The restriction is even somewhat greater in the red birds because they have very little black, or none at all (in most males), in the neck. Genetic evidence that Rhode Island Reds carry *e* is provided by the typical Columbian males obtained from a cross popular in England, that of Light Sussex ♀ ♀ × Rhode Island Red ♂. These show that both breeds are *ee*.

It is well known also that these red and black birds carry the sex-linked gene, *s*, for gold, the recessive allele of silver. In addition, there is an undetermined number of autosomal genes for red, which have not yet been satisfactorily analyzed. Since the shades of color found vary from the light red, sometimes even approaching buff, found in New Hampshires, to the dark mahogany color of some strains of Rhode Island Reds, one would expect that a considerable number of genes affect the density of the red pigmentation. In an attempt to analyze these, Warren and Gordon (1933) found that variations in the shade of red seemed to be hereditary and dependent upon multiple factors. Although the color often varies in different regions—the hackle being frequently lighter than the back—no evidence was found of separate genes affecting the intensity of red in different regions. There was apparently a genetic basis for variations in the amount of black in the wings, which seemed to be distinct from variations in the shade of red. In general, males were darker red than females in all sections. Hays (1935) found in Rhode Island Reds that the progeny of exhibition strains (dark) crossed with production strains (light) were of intermediate color but that the birds from the dark mothers were distinctly darker in color than those from the light ones.

Down Color. Rhode Island Red chicks vary in color from pale buff to dark chestnut. A few are striped. Using five arbitrary classes of color, Warren (1929) differentiated in 4 years two strains distinctly different so far as down color was concerned. In the light strain, 82 per cent were of the lightest grade, and none had either of the two darkest shades. In the dark strain, none showed the lightest of the five grades, and 49 per cent qualified for the two darkest shades. Selection toward a light shade of down was evidently more effective than selection in the opposite direction. When these two strains were crossed, the F_1 generation was mostly of grade 3 (intermediate) but in the F_2 all five grades reappeared, though the majority were again of grade 3.

Warren found little or no relationship between color of the down and surface color in the adult. Some chicks with light down developed into very dark adults, though dark chicks seldom showed light plumage color when they matured. Chicks with light down were more likely than dark ones to develop into adults with characteristics considered defects in this breed—undercolor (beneath the surface of the plumage) that is pale red, white, or showing smut (black). Most of the striped chicks had these same defects. Obviously, the poultryman trying to maintain Rhode Island Reds free of these defects should select his breeders, in so far as possible, from the birds that had dark down as chicks.

Sex Dichromatism. It was noted by Warren that the majority of the striped chicks were females. Byerly and Quinn (1936) confirmed this and found also that most of the chicks with little spots of black color at the back of the head were females. Their data and some calculations from those of Hays (1940) are given in Table 22.

Although identification of the striped and spotted chicks as females is likely to be accurate in over 80 per cent of such cases, these classed together formed only 27 per cent of Hays's large population. Since sex

TABLE 22. SPOTS, STRIPES, AND SEXES IN RHODE ISLAND RED CHICKS

Pattern in the down	Byerly and Quinn, 1,102 chicks		Hays, 8,713 chicks	
	Proportion of population, per cent	Females, per cent	Proportion of population, per cent	Females, per cent
Spots on head or neck.......	36.2	82	24.7	81
Stripes on back.............	11.3	94	2.1	87
Neither...................	52.4	22	73.2	37.5

cannot be identified so accurately in those without spots or stripes, a class that includes considerably more than half the chicks, the limitations of this method of identifying sex in newly hatched Rhode Island Red chicks are evident. Hays distinguished between black spots and brown ones and found that about 85 per cent of the chicks with black spots were females, while only 74 per cent of those with brown ones were of that sex.

A much more accurate method of identifying sexes in Rhode Island Red chicks at hatching was discovered by Homer Rowell, of Essex County, Massachusetts, and demonstrated several times at the school for poultry breeders held annually at the University of Massachusetts at Amherst, Massachusetts. When the chicks are held so that both wings are outstretched, the difference is quite clear in all but those having down that is comparatively light in color. Wings of females are uniformly reddish. In males there is a white spot, the extent of which varies considerably in different chicks (Fig. 57). In its smallest expression there is merely a short streak of white or creamy down in the prepatagium, or web of the wing; but there are all gradations in size from that to the other extreme with white or cream over the whole web and part of the anterior border of the metacarpal region.

According to Jaap (1946) the sexes may be sorted by this method with an accuracy of 90 to 95 per cent in Rhode Island Reds and 80 to 90 per cent in New Hampshires. Jaap found also that the accuracy of the procedure is increased in stock selected to enhance the difference between the sexes. The important thing is to get chicks that are uniformly reddish in color on the head and back and to use males that showed large wing spots as chicks.

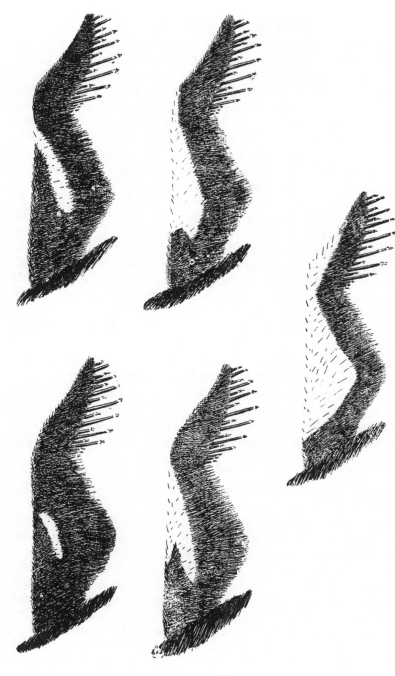

Fig. 57. Diagrams showing the location and variation of the spot of light-colored down in male chicks of the Rhode Island Red and New Hampshire breeds by which they may be distinguished from females. (*From Jaap.*)

Red-Splashed Whites, rs

A mutation that apparently restricts black even more than does the *ee* genotype and eliminates most red color as well was found by Quinn (1934, 1935) in Rhode Island Reds.

Description. Chicks of that breed homozygous for this character were white or white with a red spot at the back of the head. They developed into adults that were predominantly white but had variable amounts of red in the plumage. When these were crossed with black fowls, all the chicks were black; but in the F_2 and backcross (to red-splashed whites) there appeared not only white chicks and whites with red spots but also white ones with black head spots. These were apparently white at maturity, with a few black feathers.

Genetics. This rather complete restriction of red and black is found in birds homozygous for an autosomal recessive gene, which Quinn designated as *p*. Since this symbol has been used for pea comb since 1906 (Appendix, page 547), it seems preferable to use some other notation in the present case, and *rs* (red-splashed) is therefore proposed. The gene resembles that for dominant white in that it apparently eliminates a greater proportion of the black pigment than of the red. However, it was completely recessive in Quinn's crosses. His F_2 generation from the cross Jersey Black Giant × red-splashed white suggests that restriction of pigment by the *rs rs* genotype was equally effective in birds *EE*, *Ee*, or *ee*, although this was not specifically shown.

In a later study, Quinn (1938) reported that in Rhode Island Red chicks with this mutation the majority of the unspotted chicks were males. Sexes were evenly divided in those with one red head spot, but of the 10 per cent of the population that had black head spots 78 per cent were females.

Buff

Buff varieties are found in Orpingtons, Wyandottes, Plymouth Rocks, Brahmas, Cochins, Leghorns, and other breeds.

Genetics. The number of genes responsible for buff color is still unknown. It is true that buff birds carry the sex-linked gene, *s*, for gold, and Dunn (1923) has shown that Buff Orpingtons have the same type of restricted black as Rhode Island Reds and Columbians. Buff Wyandottes are the same, according to Asmundson and Milne (1930). Buff males are therefore *ss ee* and buff females *s– ee*. However, these same genotypes are found in Rhode Island Reds. The genes that make buffs different in color from Rhode Island Reds have yet to be discovered.

A cross of Black Hamburg × Buff Cochin made by Hurst (1905) yielded birds predominantly black. In the F_2 generation, about a quarter of the chicks had various shades of buff, the remainder being black. Similar results were recorded by Davenport (1909) except that the lighter shades in his F_2 chicks were designated as white. These results could be explained by the segregation of E and e in the F_2 generation of each cross, but that does not account for the inheritance of buff. Both these investigators found the dominant white of White Leghorns to be dominant over buff, though incompletely so. On the other hand, Danforth (1933) and the author have both extracted dominant white from buff birds that showed no trace of it.

Knox (1927) found buff dominant over recessive white and, from other data, concluded that two pairs of genes with cumulative effects differentiate buff fowls from black ones. Any three of these genes would convert a black fowl to a buff one. The conclusion of Dunn (1923) was that, apart from modifiers restricting black in buff birds more than in Columbians, fowls with the latter color and pattern differed from buffs only in having the gene for silver, S, instead of its recessive allele. The black commonly found in the neck, wings, and tail of buff birds supports the contention that most of them are genetically black fowls with the ee type of restriction.

Salmon Breast and Red Pile

In White Leghorns it is not uncommon to find females with more or less red on the breast and in the neck. The condition is known to breeders as "salmon breast." In the male counterpart of this coloration, there is red color, usually more of an orange shade, in the wing bows but none on the breast. Sometimes only one or two feathers show the red in males. One cock used by the author with other pure White Leghorns showed no trace of red till his second year, when small portions of one or two feathers in the wing bow had the characteristic orange-red color.

Studies of this salmon-breast condition by Warren (1930) indicated that it is in general recessive, although manifested in some of his F_1 birds from salmon-breasted × normal Leghorns. When affected birds were mated *inter se*, 92 per cent of the female progeny had salmon breasts but only a third of the males showed red in the wing bow. Some of Warren's matings suggested that a single pair of genes was responsible for salmon breast, but others did not.

This type of restriction of red coloration is similar to that found in Pile Games and in the Pile Leghorns described by Brown (1906) as having originated from the crossing of White and Brown Leghorns. However, good Pile males are red, not only in the wing bows, but also in the neck, saddle, back, and flight feathers; elsewhere they are white.

The females are salmon-breasted. Nothing has been added to knowledge of the red pile pattern since the review by Punnett (1923), which showed that it may be present in both dominant and recessive whites. He suggested that Leghorns with the pile pattern might be gold and pure white ones silver, but in Warren's reciprocal crosses between the two types there was no evidence that the salmon breast is caused by the sex-linked gene for gold. However, it is not certain that the salmon breast of White Leghorns is the same thing genetically as the distribution of red found in Pile Games. Cunningham (1919) developed a strain of white birds with the pile pattern from a cross of Red Jungle Fowl × White Silky. These must have been recessive whites.

This peculiar distribution of red is also found in Brown Leghorns but is not usually recognized as a separate entity in the complex coloration of that breed. The salmon breast is more evident in the lighter females than in the dark ones. The same thing was described by Goodale (1926) in black fowls, the females of which had salmon breasts and the males some red in feathers of the "mid-dorsal region."

Pending further study, it seems probable that, in the unanalyzed complex of autosomal genes causing red color, there are one or more with effects restricted to the breast and neck of females and to the shoulders and back of males but visible in varying degrees in both white and colored fowls. It is not inconceivable that by selection, by the accumulation of modifying factors, and through the interaction of genes this pattern could be developed into that of the Red Pile Game in white breeds or reduced to the vanishing point in those with dark color.

PATTERNS WITHIN THE FEATHER

The genes for color considered thus far have affected either the kind of color throughout the entire plumage or its distribution in different regions. This section deals with mutations affecting the distribution of pigments within the individual feathers, *i.e.*, with the feather pattern.

Sex-Linked Barring, *B*

This type of rather wide barring is found in Dominiques, Barred Plymouth Rocks, Scots Greys, Barred, or Cuckoo, Leghorns, and the Coucou de Malines. The pattern is a pleasing one, and the Barred Plymouth Rocks are deservedly popular. The logical belief of some poultrymen that, because of their natural camouflage, barred birds are less subject to attack from predaceous birds than are fowls all one color was disproved by Pearl (1911), who found both kinds almost equally susceptible to such marauders.

Description. The gene for barring inhibits the deposition of melanin, thus causing white bars to be superimposed on a feather that would otherwise be all black. The width and sharpness of the barring vary in the two sexes, in different strains, in different birds within strains, and in different regions within one bird. The two factors responsible for most of this variation are (1) sex and (2) rate of growth of the feathers.

Sex Differences. Because barring is caused by a dominant gene located in the sex chromosomes, females can have normally only one such gene, *i.e.*, they are hemizygous. Males can be heterozygous or homozygous and are now usually of the latter type in pure breeds. As with most other dominant mutations, the gene for barring is incompletely dominant. In other words, two such genes produce a greater effect than one. Accordingly the white bar is wider in homozygous males than in females, and as a result the latter are in general appearance darker than the males. Similarly, any barred male progeny from the cross of barred ♂ × non-barred ♀ ♀ are usually darker than their sire because these F_1 males are heterozygous, but in color they do not differ much from their sisters as do brothers and sisters in pure barred breeds.

The attempts of breeders of showroom Barred Plymouth Rocks to cope with a color pattern that is one shade in females and another in males have been very interesting. Barred Plymouth Rocks were admitted to "The American Standard of Perfection" as a properly accredited variety in 1874. As late as 1930 that guide for breeders and judges still called for the same color and width of barring in both sexes, "each feather crossed by narrow, parallel, sharply-defined dark bars that stop short of positive black . . . ; the light and dark bars to be of equal width." It is a tribute to the breeders' unremitting efforts to attain perfection that a way was found and utilized over many years to meet this genetically unsound, single standard for both sexes. Two kinds of matings were utilized as follows:

Light, or pullet, mating. Females of standard color were mated with lightly colored males having the white bars wider than was desirable in the showroom. This mating produced females of a color (*i.e.*, width of barring) that conformed to the standard set for the breed. The male progeny of this mating were useless for exhibition purposes because they were altogether too light.

Dark, or cockerel, mating. Males of standard color were mated with darkly colored females having very narrow white bars and not conforming to the standard. This mating produced cockerels with black and white bars of about equal width, giving a darker appearance than that of males not so bred. These were used for exhibition, but the female progeny of this mating were too dark for the showroom.

With pullets from one mating and cockerels from another, the fancier was thus enabled to meet the requirement that both sexes have the same color and dark and white bars of equal width. This interesting though somewhat wasteful practice was recognized by a supplement to the 1930 edition of the "Standard," which considered the birds suitable for the pullet mating as one variety and the darker ones as another. Separate standards for barring were set up for Light Barred Plymouth Rocks and Dark Barred Plymouth Rocks.

Finally, the 1938 edition conceded that the barring was caused by "a sex-linked factor for barring so that the male receives twice the amount of light barring as the female." It described color standards, effective in March, 1942, whereby males are expected to have light and dark bars of approximately equal width, but in females the light bar is to be about half the width of the dark one. This provides a workable set of standards. It is not inevitable that two genes for barring should make the dark and light bars equal in width or that one of them alone should cause a white bar half the width of the dark one, and the fancier will therefore still have ample scope for exercise of his skill in breeding Barred Rocks with straight, regular barring of the kind called for in the two sexes. The establishment of these new standards, 34 years after the genetic basis for barring was discovered, has eliminated many of the difficulties with which breeders of Barred Plymouth Rocks for exhibition purposes had to cope in the first 68 years after the breed was introduced.

Effects of Different Growth Rates. In most barred birds, the white bars are somewhat uneven in outline. In females, which have narrow bars anyway, those in some regions contain such a mixture of black and white that the bars are not easily recognizable. This is particularly so in the wing feathers, which grow more rapidly than most of the others. Here the bars are often V-shaped, and conform least to the demand of the "Standard" for regular, parallel, sharply defined bars. The black pigment extends irregularly into the white bars. On the other hand, the feathers that grow more slowly, such as those on the back, have the white bars straighter and more sharply defined. It has long been known that early maturing strains of Barred Rocks usually have less sharply defined barring than others and that the slowly maturing strains are more likely to yield birds with narrow, even bars. For some years the author maintained a flock of Barred Leghorns, which, like other Leghorns, had the sex-linked type of rapid feathering. In these, the barring was much less distinct than in pure-bred Barred Rocks raised at the same time, which, like other Plymouth Rocks, carried the gene, K, for slow feathering.

Down. Barred black chicks differ from non-barred ones in having a creamy-white patch at the back of the head. In some females (Fig. 58) this is so small as to be barely recognizable. Barred chicks also show varying amounts of greyish white on the abdomen. Differences between

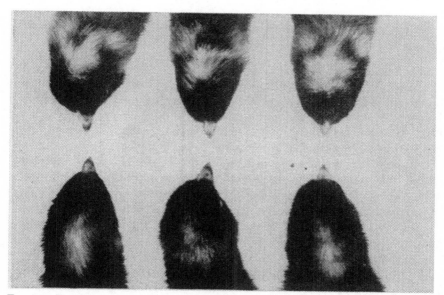

FIG. 58. Heads of Barred Plymouth Rock chicks showing sex dimorphism in the spots of creamy-white down on the heads. *Above,* males; *below,* females. The latter tend to have longer, narrower spots.

the action of the two genes for barring in males and the single gene in females are evident in the chicks as well as in adults. It has long been known that the females have darker down, smaller head spots, and darker shanks than the males. The last of these three differences is usually the most consistent and most conspicuous. In females, the black color in the foot ends abruptly at a line sharply dividing the black from the yellow found in the toes. In males, the shanks are lighter throughout, and there is no sharp distinction between black and yellow. Jerome (1939) pointed out that while the head spot is usually oval in females, with its long axis running down the median line of the back of the head, in males this spot is irregular in outline, has black and white feathers intermingled, and appears wide at the anterior end rather than narrow as in females. These differences are shown in Fig. 58. By considering them and the others mentioned, Jerome was able to determine sex in Barred Rock chicks with an accuracy as high as 98 per cent.

Genetics. The suggestion that barring is caused by a sex-linked gene was first made by Spillman (1908) and was quickly confirmed by Goodale (1909, 1910), Pearl and Surface (1910), Morgan and Goodale (1912), and others. In reciprocal crosses between barred and non-barred fowls, the following results are obtained:

Barred δ × non-barred $\female$ → all progeny barred
Non-barred δ × barred $\female$ → barred $\delta \delta$, non-barred $\female \female$

This case, so familiar in texts on genetics, has probably been used more often to illustrate sex-linked inheritance than any other. The symbol for barring is B. The fact that it may be carried by recessive whites and is apparently present in most White Leghorns was mentioned earlier in this chapter. Apart from the barring pattern and the white head spot of barred chicks, B exerts the following effects:

1. It dilutes the epidermal pigment in the shanks and beak. Barred females have enough black in the shanks to give them a greyish cast, but not always enough to obscure the yellow, and much less than such non-barred black breeds as Jersey Black Giants. However, in homozygous barred males so much of the melanin is eliminated that the shanks appear bright yellow. When White Leghorn females are mated with Rhode Island Reds or with other non-barred males, the female progeny have darker shanks than the males. Both are Ii, with predominantly white plumage, but the males are Bb and the females $b-$. Since both parental breeds have the same genotype with respect to shank color, the lighter shade of the F_1 males can be attributed to the gene for barring that they carry.

2. It apparently enhances the inhibiting action of I in birds heterozygous for dominant white. In the cross just mentioned or that of White Leghorn $\female$ × Black Sumatra δ, the male progeny ($Ii\ Bb$) have less black flecking in the adult plumage than their $Ii\ b-$ sisters.

3. It decreases the amount of black or dark down when added to chicks that are genetically black, but with that black reduced by some pattern. This effect was noted in pied chicks by Punnett and Pease (1927) and is also seen in various "auto-sexing" breeds such as the Cambar, Legbar, Ancobar, etc.

All three of these effects are alike in that the gene for barring reduces the amount of melanin in the skin or in the feathers.

Gold Barring. Buff birds with white barring are occasionally found. Punnett and Pease (1928), who studied this color and pattern in Gold

Barred Rocks, concluded that, as in barred black birds, a sex-linked gene for barring was responsible. However, because the barring gene from these gold birds did not cause a head spot in many of the chicks with buff or brown down, whereas barring introduced from black Barred Rocks did so, they considered that the gene in the gold bird was not quite the same as the familiar *B* of Barred Plymouth Rocks, but an allele of it, differing somewhat in the intensity of action.

It seems probable, however, that the failure of the barring to show distinctly in the gold birds (both chicks and adults) may have been caused by a general incompatibility between gold color and maximum development of some pattern in the feather. An example of this is found in spangling. "The American Standard of Perfection" calls for spangled tails in Silver-spangled Hamburgs, but black tails in the gold-spangled variety, and Taylor (1932) found no spangled tails in his gold birds. It is sometimes very difficult to recognize barring in gold birds when testing for linkage of *B* and *S*. Dunn (1924) attributed this to the gene, *E*, for extension of black, which inhibits development of gold. He found that his birds with buff and white barring were gold and restricted (*ee*) like other buff fowls, with the addition of *B*.

Action of the Gene. The regularity of the alternate black and white bars has led some investigators to consider whether or not this pattern might be the outward expression of some general rhythmic fluctuation in metabolism, in the action of endocrine secretions, or in some other part of the normal physiological processes. Any such possibility was eliminated by the results of reciprocal skin grafts between Barred Rocks and non-barred breeds made by Danforth and Foster (1929). Skin from barred chicks produced typical barred feathers on Brown Leghorn, Black Minorca, Rhode Island Red, and Golden Campine hosts (Fig. 59). Conversely, grafts from White Leghorns, Brown Leghorns, and Golden Campines grew feathers on Barred Rock hosts that were characteristic of the donors. A Rhode Island Red male with a tuft of barred feathers from such a graft is shown in Fig. 59. In all these cases, the skin transplanted was subjected to the same endocrine secretions and other physiological forces as the skin of the host. This was shown by the fact that grafts from one sex to the other always grew feathers that were like those of the host in structure, though like those of the donor in color. It is clear, therefore, that barring is caused by the genetic constitution of the follicles and not by any general physiological rhythm. Additional evidence to this effect was later provided by Montalenti (1934), who found that the production of dark and light bars was not necessarily synchronous in adjacent follicles. One follicle could be producing a black bar while another nearby was making a white one.

From the report of Willier (1941), it would seem that the barring is determined by the genotype of the melanophore. Transplants of these from Barred Rock embryos to non-barred hosts caused the production of barred feathers of two types, one showing the narrow white bar and dark appearance of the barred feathers of females, the other the wider white bar and light appearance of males homozygous for barring.

FIG. 59. Two Rhode Island Reds carrying skin grafts from Barred Plymouth Rock donors. The barred pattern is the same in both birds because it is determined by the genes in the graft, but the shapes of the feathers differ because they are determined by the differing sex hormones of the two birds. (*Courtesy of C. H. Danforth.*)

Similarly, Nickerson (1944) found that melanophores of Silver Campines transplanted to Leghorn feathers induced the narrow bar typical of Campines, while melanophores of Barred Rocks similarly handled caused the formation of the wider bar characteristic of that donor. He suggested that the rhythm of barring is controlled by some diffusible substance from the melanophore which inhibits formation of melanin in the subjacent area of the feather germ.

Black Feathers. The non-barred black feathers commonly found in Barred Rock females (unless pulled out before the judge or inspector sees the birds) represent a type of somatic mosaic. They are most likely to be caused by mutation from B to b, although other interpretations have been suggested. Some strains seem to have more of it than others. The fact that these black feathers are rarely seen in males homozygous for barring results merely from the fact that such a mutation in any one chromosome would not be apparent because of the normal dominant gene B in the homologous one. Only if both chromosomes experienced the same mutation could the change be evident. It is not surprising therefore that black feathers should be rare in *BB* males but just as common in heterozygotes (*Bb*) as in hemizygous (*B–*) females. In these two last named, a single mutation leaves the feather black.

Fig. 60. R. C. Punnett, who has contributed much to our knowledge of heredity in the fowl, and who developed the first auto-sexing breed.

Slinger and MacIlraith (1944) observed that Barred Rock females with black feathers have also a "green-grey" iris more frequently than do their less conspicuous flock mates that lack the black feathers. This is to be expected because (1) birds subject to somatic mutations in the plumage are presumably equally likely to have them in the iris, (2) mutations affecting only a few cells are more likely to be evident in the iris than in a barred feather, and (3) the effect of any such mutation there would be to increase the melanin and thus cause the green-grey appearance. Apparently birds with such eyes were considered less thrifty than others, but evidence to that effect has not yet been adduced.

The Auto-sexing Breeds. The differentiation of male and female chicks in pure Barred Rocks has already been discussed. Apparently the distinction between the sexes caused by females being hemizygous and males homozygous for *B* is heightened in chicks having less black in the down than have Barred Rocks. This was first recognized by Punnett and Pease (1930), who produced the Cambars, a breed in which there is a clear distinction between males and females at hatching. This breed was produced by crossing Barred Rocks with Golden Campines and mating the barred birds back to the latter breed. The barred progeny were again mated back to Golden Campines. After several generations of such backcrossing, the barred males and females were

Fig. 61. Cambar chicks, their sexes recognizable by the pale down of the males and darker down of the females. (*Courtesy of Michael Pease.*)

mated together, thus producing males BB and Bb and females $B-$ and $b-$. The homozygous males had pale, "blotchy" down. By mating these with their barred sisters, Punnett and Pease obtained the true-breeding Cambars, which are like Golden Campines in nearly all respects, except that they carry the sex-linked gene, B, just as Barred Rocks do.

In this breed, the males have pale down, the females darker down with irregular stripes on the back and dark spots on the head (Fig. 61). The sexes can be separated at hatching with complete accuracy. The Cambars and other auto-sexing breeds developed later provide interesting examples of the synthesis of new breeds to meet a specific economic need.

By procedures similar to those employed in establishing the Cambars, the gene for barring has been introduced into Barnevelders and Brown Leghorns by Hagedoorn (1936). Jaap (1940) established the Oklabars, a gold breed combining barring with rapid feathering and a conformation considered desirable in market poultry. The Legbar, produced by adding B to Brown Leghorns, has been described by Punnett (1940). Pease (1941) has developed the Buffbar, Brussbar, and Dorbar from

Buff Orpingtons, Brown Sussex, and Dorkings, respectively. Although all these new breeds mentioned are gold, auto-sexing is not restricted to breeds of that color. Punnett and Pease bred Silver Cambars and Silver Dorbars. In these, as in the other auto-sexing breeds, the males are lighter in color than the females. In the Ancobars developed by Lamoreux (1941) from Anconas and Barred Plymouth Rocks, the sexes could be identified with an accuracy of 93 per cent at hatching because the males have less black color on the head and in the sacral region than

Fig. 62. Ancobars, *i.e.*, Anconas to which barring has been added. The usual difference between the *BB* male and the *B–* female is heightened in this breed because both sexes are homozygous for mottling, which, like the barring, reduces pigment in the plumage. (*Courtesy of W. F. Lamoreux.*)

have the females. The striking difference between the effects of two genes for barring and of one gene for barring, in birds homozygous for mottling, is shown in Fig. 62, which illustrates male and female adult Ancobars.

It was pointed out by Pease (1936) that auto-sexing Rhode Island Reds are not likely to be so satisfactory as some of the other breeds to which the barring gene has been added. This is because in pure Rhode Island Reds there is already so much variation in down color that the distinction between *BB* males and *B–* females is not likely to be so readily discernible as in breeds with less variation in the color of the down. This was confirmed by Jaap (1941), who found that identification of sex by the dichromatism resulting from the gene for barring was completely accurate in striped downs but less so in chicks with red or dark brown down.

The desirability from an economic standpoint of being able to separate pullets from cockerels at hatching is obvious. It is attested by the increasing demands upon the hatcheries for chicks that have been "sexed" by examination of the cloaca. However, the use of this method (which was first introduced by trained Japanese) is not always a source of complete satisfaction to the hatchery operator. Use of the auto-sexing breeds eliminates the need for a skilled sexer. It seems inevitable that, as soon as such breeds are developed to the point at which they meet economic requirements in egg production, conformation, color of egg, and other respects, they will play an important role in the poultry industry. This will take time because some of the colors and patterns utilized in developing the auto-sexing breeds had to come from varieties in which economically desirable strains are scarce. Fortunately, there are excellent strains of Barred Plymouth Rocks from which the barring gene can be taken.

Autosomal Barring, *ab*

A kind of barring different from that discussed in the foregoing pages is found in Golden-pencilled and Silver-pencilled Hamburgs and in Golden, Silver, and Chamois Campines. It is not clear why Hamburgs with this pattern should be called pencilled. That term is also used for the pattern in which two or more concentric lines of dark pigment run parallel with the border of the feather. This is found in Silver-pencilled Wyandottes and Plymouth Rocks, in all varieties labelled as partridge, and in Dark Brahmas.

Description. In Hamburgs and Campines, the following color combinations are found:

1. Silver variety. Narrow white bars caused by wide black bars on a white (silver) ground.
2. Golden variety. Black bars on a gold ground.
3. Chamois Campine. Same as (2), but with the black pigment removed, leaving a wide white bar on a gold ground.

Genetics. It was shown by Punnett and Pease (1921) that the Silver Campine and the Golden Campine differ only in that the latter has the sex-linked gene, *s*, for gold plumage, while the former has its dominant allele for silver. The black bars are the same in both. They are caused by an autosomal recessive gene in the homozygous condition. This may be considered as a gene restricting black pigment within the feather to the black bars. Since no symbol was assigned to this gene, it is suggested that it be designated *ab* (autosomal barring).

Punnett and Pease found that the Chamois Campine differs from the other varieties by a dominant gene that inhibits formation of melanin. Its action turns the Golden Campine into a bird with white and gold bars (Chamois) rather than the usual black and gold. It was considered probable that the inhibitor might be the gene causing dominant white in White Leghorns, but this was not proved (Punnett, 1923). The correctness of their analysis of the genetic basis for the colors and patterns in Silver, Golden, and Chamois Campines was shown when Punnett and Pease made the cross Silver ♂ × Chamois ♀. Here it was expected that the dominant white of the Chamois would prevent black bars in the progeny and that the silver would be dominant over the gold, thus causing the F_1 birds to be entirely white. This expectation was realized, except that inhibition of the black bars was not so complete as the masking of the gold ones and, as a result, some of the birds showed faint ghost barring. This same dingy white is found in some birds heterozygous for dominant white, especially in those which lack the sex-linked gene for barring. Presumably homozygosity for the inhibitor of the black bars and for silver would make such birds pure white.

Spangling, *Sp*

Description. In Golden-spangled and Silver-spangled Hamburgs, the feathers have black tips that are V-shaped proximally. Except for this spangle, the feather is white in the silver variety and gold in the other. The main tail feathers, sickles, and tail coverts of the golden-spangled variety are solid black, but in the silver birds these feathers, like those in other parts of the body, are white with a black tip.

Variation in the size of the spangle was studied by Landauer and Dunn (1930) in feathers regenerated after plucking. With few exceptions, the spangle appeared in each successive "generation" of feathers, though it varied in size. Variability in size of the spangle was not related to the size or shape of the feather. Spangled birds of crossbred origin showed more variation in size of the spangle than did purebreds. In a study of the symmetry of the spangled pattern, Landauer (1930) found that most of the feathers on the left side of the body show a spangle in which the color on the right side of the rachis extends farther toward the base of the feather than the color on the left side of the rachis. The opposite kind of asymmetry is found in most spangles on the right side of the body.

Chicks of the silver variety have pale bluish-black down with irregular dark striping over the back. There is no head streak. In gold chicks the striping is somewhat more regular, the down is reddish, and there is a narrow, dark head streak. There is little sign of spangling in the first chick feathers, but it becomes increasingly apparent as the birds mature. According to Dunn and Landauer (1930), feathers developing before the chick is 25 days old are not spangled, but later ones are.

Genetics. From the studies of Punnett (1923) and Taylor (1932), it is clear that spangling is caused by an incompletely dominant autosomal gene, *Sp*. In birds heterozygous for this gene, manifestation of spangling is more complete in males than in females. This fact, pointed out by Taylor, accounts for the erroneous belief of earlier investigators that spangling was sex linked. Actually this difference in the expression of spangling in the sexes results from the action of female hormones, which increase the amount of black in the plumage (see pages 194 to 196, also Fig. 128, page 475) and thus prevent spangling from showing well in females (Taylor, 1933). In homozygotes, the pattern is fully expressed, although females are usually darker than males.

Taylor considered his Silver-spangled Hamburgs to have the Columbian type of restriction found in birds homozygous for the gene *e*, but it is difficult to see how such birds could show black spangles all through the plumage. Moreover, the available data can be explained equally well by assuming that spangled birds are *EE Sp Sp* and that the genes for spangling restrict the black to the spangle. Their action is thus similar to that of the gene for sex-linked barring, except that one restricts black to the tip of the feather, while the other restricts it to black bars across the feather. Both genes cause a pattern within each feather in birds that would otherwise be all black and silver.

Patterns in the Down. The irregular striping in the down of silver-spangled chicks, which was called "marbling" by Hertwig (1933), was attributed by her to an autosomal gene, *ma*, which she found to be linked with the gene for pea comb. The dark head streak of the golden-spangled chicks is caused, according to Rittershaus (1930), by a sex-linked gene, *ko*.

This creates a rather anomalous situation in which two separate pairs of genes are considered responsible for the differences in the down patterns of golden-spangled and silver-spangled varieties of the same breed. As adults, these two color varieties apparently differ only by the sex-linked alleles, *S* and *s*, for silver and gold. It seems possible that the marbled down of Silver-spangled Hamburg chicks may be the normal expression in the down of the gene that causes spangling in the adult plumage. However, Taylor's *Sp* is dominant in adults, while Hertwig's *ma* is recessive in chicks.

It is even more difficult to account for the gene *ko* and its separate pattern in the gold variety, unless there are genes affecting the down without much expression in the plumage of adults. Possibly the gold and silver color varieties in this breed differ by more genes than *S* and *s*, or both may carry genes with effects that differ in gold birds and silver ones. This latter possibility is suggested by the fact that spangling is manifested in the tail feathers of adult silver birds but not in those of gold ones. The chance that the head streak caused by *ko* may be one manifestation of *s* comes to mind because both are sex linked, but in tests for linkage Hertwig (1930) found these two genes to be quite remote from each other.

Mottling, *mo*

In Anconas and in Mottled Houdans, black pigment is eliminated from the tips of a number of the feathers in all parts of the body. This pattern is thus the reverse of spangling, though it is sometimes referred to as "white spangling." There is usually more white in the wings and tail than elsewhere. In other regions, about one feather in two or three is tipped with white. Chicks of these mottled breeds have black on the dorsal surface but are light yellow below and show varying amounts of light color on the sides of the head.

Genetics. Apart from some early crosses by Davenport (1906) which showed that mottling is recessive to solid black, little was known of the inheritance of this pattern till Asmundson and Milne (1930) proved that it is caused by a recessive autosomal gene in the homozygous condition. The symbol *mo* is suggested, as it conforms to current practice with respect to symbols better than the *e'* used by Asmundson and Milne. The Anconas tested by these workers were *EE mo mo SS*.

In Speckled Sussex, the feathers are brown-red with a black spangle at the distal end, on which is superimposed a white tip. This pattern has not been analyzed. The mottling of Orloffs is apparently not caused by the gene *mo*, for Serebrovsky (1926) crossed Mottled Orloffs with Mottled Houdans and got only solid-colored progeny with no mottling.

Pied Plumage, *pi*

In Exchequer Leghorns, the plumage presents a curious mixture of black and white, giving the general appearance of a very light Ancona. Some of the feathers are all black, some all white; others are black with white tips of varying extent, or white with black spots. These pied birds, though resembling light Anconas, differ from them in having a considerable number of pure white feathers. In chicks the down is black, with light yellow from below extending up the sides, as in Ancona chicks.

Genetics. This pattern was found by Punnett and Pease (1927) to be an autosomal recessive character. The symbol *pi* is proposed. This mutation is probably carried by stocks other than Exchequer Leghorns though not revealed in pure black or white breeds. Punnett and

Pease found it in the F_2 generation from a cross involving Barred Rocks and Black Sumatras and traced it back to the latter breed. They found that pied birds were made still lighter by the addition of the gene for barring.

From their appearance, one might expect that a cross of pied birds with mottled ones would yield progeny that would be more or less black and white like the parents. However, since both patterns are caused by independent pairs of recessive genes, the geneticist's expectation is that such a cross would yield solid black birds.

Lacing, *la*

The pattern called lacing is found in Silver- and Golden-laced Wyandottes, Silver and Golden Polish, and Silver and Golden Sebright Bantams. The feather is mostly white in the silver varieties and mostly buff or brown-red in the golden ones, but bordered by a band of black in both. On the neck the feathers in both sexes are black with a silver (white) or gold border, except in Sebrights, which have the feathers uniform throughout the plumage.

Genetics. It seems probable from the experiments of Punnett (1923) and Agar (1924) that lacing is caused by an autosomal recessive gene, *la*, in the homozygous state. If so, its effects are much influenced by modifying genes. In a cross of Silver Sebright $\times$ Golden-pencilled Hamburg, Punnett recovered lacing in only 44 of 299 F_2 birds. Most of these were poorly laced and only 4 showed a pattern comparable with that of the Sebright. In Agar's study, the F_1 birds from the cross Barred Rock ♀ $\times$ Golden-laced Wyandotte ♂ were backcrossed to the latter breed and produced both silver-laced and golden-laced birds indistinguishable from pure Wyandottes with those patterns. Chicks of laced Wyandottes show in the down a pattern of striping much like that of Brown Leghorns and Jungle Fowl, though not so clear in gold chicks as in silver ones. In studies with Silver-laced Wyandottes, Rittershaus (1930) found this pattern to be dominant over non-striped, and unifactorial, as was the striping of Brown Leghorns studied by Bateson and Punnett (1906).

The "Black-breasted-Red" Complex, or Wild Type

In Brown Leghorns, Black-breasted Red Games, and other varieties one finds the same type of coloration as in *Gallus gallus*, the Red Jungle Fowl, which is considered by some to be the ancestor of all domestic breeds of chickens. This combination of colors is therefore the geneticist's original "wild type." The various colors, patterns, and restrictions of pigment found in other breeds and varieties are to be considered as mutations that have been preserved by poultry breeders after domestication of this species.

In general the males have bright orange or reddish plumage in the areas of sexually dimorphic feathers but are black elsewhere, except for a little brown in the wing feathers. In females gold shows in the neck feathers, but these have a central black stripe. The breast is salmon-

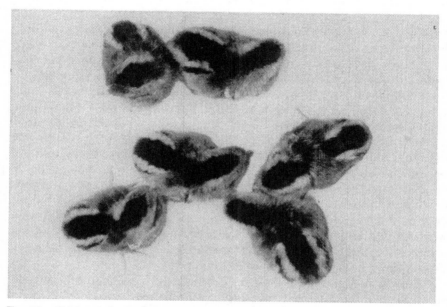

Fig. 63. Chicks of the Red Jungle Fowl showing the striped down typical of black-breasted-red breeds such as the Brown Leghorn.

colored, the wings and tail predominantly black, but the rest of the plumage is greyish brown. This type of plumage is included with the feather patterns in this book because the brown feathers and the brown parts of black ones show a mixture of dark and light brown that is sometimes described as "stippling."

Chicks of these black-red breeds and varieties have in the down the very attractive pattern of longitudinal brown, light and dark stripes shown in Fig. 63. It is of interest to note that this pattern, which is found in the down of the wild Red Jungle Fowl, is very similar to that in the down of ring-necked pheasants and of some grouse.

MacArthur and MacIlraith (1946) found that with practice the male and female chicks could be identified at hatching with complete accuracy. The females are darker than males, with broader mid-dorsal brown stripe and darker face. They show also a facial stripe extending over the eye, through the ear, to the side of the neck that is not easily detectable in males. The lower surface of the wing is of lighter color in male chicks than in females.

Genetics. It is clear that Brown Leghorns and other black-red fowls are gold birds. Silver Leghorns probably differ from brown ones only by the sex-linked gene for silver. Although there are a number of reports of crosses between Brown Leghorns and other breeds, none of these was carried far enough to reveal how black-reds differ from birds that are all black or how many genes are responsible for the stippling. From a cross of barred females with Brown Leghorn males, Régnier (1937) obtained barred sons and non-barred daughters, as expected, but some of the F_1 females were apparently just like Brown Leghorns in every respect; the others were black. Backcrossing these black females to Brown Leghorn males yielded (1) birds of both sexes like pure Brown Leghorns and (2) birds of both sexes entirely black. These results suggest that there may be a single gene for the black-red complex, but, unfortunately, the numbers of birds in the various classes were not given by Régnier, and thus no conclusion can be reached. In a similar cross made by Punnett (1923) none of the F_1 chicks showed striping of Brown Leghorns in the down as did some of Régnier's. The difference may have resulted from the fact that Punnett used a Barred Rock female, while Régnier used the Coucou de Malines.

Fanciers in America have set up different color standards for Light Brown Leghorns and Dark Brown Leghorns, which are considered as two separate varieties. The genetic difference between these has not been determined. In Polish Greenlegs two color phases similar to those in Brown Leghorns occur, and studies of Kaufman (1936) indicated that they are differentiated by a single pair of genes, the lighter phase being recessive to the dark one.

Down. Bateson and Punnett (1906) found that the striping of the down was hypostatic to full black down but dominant to the unstriped pale down occasionally found in these black-reds. The symbol St (stripe) is proposed. When a Brown Leghorn ($CC\ St\ St$) is crossed with a recessive white fowl ($cc\ st\ st$), the F_1 chicks are all colored and striped. In the F_2 generation the usual 9:3:3:1 ratio becomes 9:3:4 because the $c\ St$ phenotype is indistinguishable from the $c\ st$ one. In other words, striping cannot be manifested in a white down. The observed and expected ratios in one such cross made by Bateson and Punnett (1908) were

Ratio	Brown striped *C St*	Pale brown, unstriped *C st*	White *c St* or *c st*
Observed...........	76	29	33
Expected, 9:3:4.....	77.6	25.9	34.5

Endocrine Modification. Castration of Brown Leghorn males does not change the color of the plumage, but when females are ovariotomized, the feathers grown subsequently are like those of males and capons in color. However, when a male is feminized by removal of the testes and implantation of an ovary, the plumage becomes practically identical in color and in structure (see Fig. 124) with that of normal females (Goodale, 1916; Finlay, 1925; and others). The black breast of the male is replaced by the salmon breast of the female. Regions that have solid black feathers in normal males show in feminized males the stippling that is characteristic of females. Clearly the sexual dichromatism of Brown Leghorns depends upon secretions of the ovary. Effects upon the color of feathers similar to those just described can be induced by injecting female hormones into Brown Leghorn capons (Juhn and Gustavson, 1930; Greenwood and Blyth, 1935). In such cases, breast feathers growing during the period of injection show a transverse bar lacking black, the width of the bar varying according to the dose and the duration of treatment. Greenwood and Blyth showed that, with small doses of the hormone, feathers nearest the site of injection were most affected, while feathers remote from that site might show no effects whatever.

By feeding thyroid glands or by injection of thyroxine, the amount of dark pigment in the red feathers of male Brown Leghorns is increased (Cole and Reid, 1924; Greenwood and Blyth, 1929; and others). In Fig. 64 are shown the effects on saddle feathers of injections of thyroxine by Lillie and Juhn (1932). In the bird given 1.0 mg. every seventh day, the black areas indicating dosage were less extensive and slightly farther apart than in the bird given a 1.5-mg. dose every sixth day. In this case the change in color is associated with a change in structure, for barbules are present in the black areas just as in feathers of females. When the thyroids are removed, the amount of melanin in the plumage is reduced in both males and females and the fringed areas lacking barbules are larger than in normal fowls (Greenwood and Blyth, 1929; Parkes and Selye, 1937; Chu, 1938). A similar loss of pigment was noted by Hill and Parkes (1935) in Brown Leghorns after removal of the hypophysis, but it was attributed by them to the hypothyroid condition known to follow hypophysectomy rather than to any direct effects from absence of the usual secretions of the hypophysis. Administration of anterior-lobe extract to a male thus treated did not counteract the changes following the operation, but injection of thyroxine restored the normal black color in growing feathers.

Fig. 64. Saddle feathers of Brown Leghorn male showing increase in melanin and change to female structure induced by injections of thyroxine. *Left,* normal control; *centre,* given 1.0 mg. of thyroxine every seventh day; *right,* given 1.5 mg. of thyroxine every sixth day. (*From Lillie and Juhn in Physiol. Zoöl.*)

Patterns Not Analyzed

Patterns not yet studied or not analyzed sufficiently to provide much information include pencilling, of which there are two kinds. In Dark Cornish (Indian Games), the feather is red, laced with black and with one crescentic stripe of black. In Dark Brahmas, in the silver-pencilled varieties of Wyandottes and Plymouth Rocks, and in partridge varieties, the pencilled feather is not laced but has three narrow crescentic stripes. No one has yet accounted for the striking combination of red, black, and white in Speckled Sussex or for the white lacing of red feathers in White-laced Red Cornish. In the latter case, the white is presumably dominant white, for birds of this type are commonly produced from the cross White Leghorn $\times$ Dark Cornish, but the remainder of the complex is unknown. In Sicilian Buttercups the ground color of the feather is brown, but from the rachis there is a racemose distribution of black along the feather in two parallel rows of spangles. The genetic basis for this pattern is not known. The birchen and pile patterns of Games and Game Bantams are not yet fully accounted for in terms of specific genes.

Literature Cited

Agar, W. E. 1924. Experiments with certain plumage colour and pattern factors in poultry. *J. Genetics,* **14**:265–272.

Asmundson, V. S., and H. I. Milne. 1930. Inheritance of plumage and skin color in the Ancona. *Sci. Agr.,* **10**:293–304.

Bateson, W. 1902. Experiments with poultry. *Repts. Evol. Comm. Roy. Soc.,* **I**: 87–124.

—— and R. C. Punnett. 1906. Experimental studies in the physiology of heredity. Poultry. *Repts. Evol. Comm. Roy. Soc.,* **III**:11–30.

—— and ——. 1908. Experimental studies in the physiology of heredity. Poultry. *Repts. Evol. Comm. Roy. Soc.,* **IV**:18–35.

Bohren, B. B., R. M. Conrad, and D. C. Warren. 1943. A chemical and histological study of the feather pigments of the domestic fowl. *Am. Naturalist,* **77**:481–518.

Brown, E. 1906. Races of Domestic Poultry. London: Edward Arnold & Co.

Byerly, T. C., and J. P. Quinn. 1936. Sexual dimorphism in Single Comb Rhode Island Red down color. *J. Heredity,* **27**:319–322.

Caridroit, F., and V. Régnier. 1930. A case of sex-linked heredity disguised by the ovarian hormonic secretion in a cross between two breeds of domestic fowls. *Proc. World's Poultry Congr., 4th Congr., London:* 18–21.

—— and ——. 1934. Récessivité en presence de l'ovaire, du pigment rouge de la race Rhode Island dans le croisement de cette race avec la race Andalou bleu. *Compt. rend. soc. biol.,* **115**:371–372.

Charles, D. R., and M. E. Rawles. 1940. Tyrosinase in feather germs. *Proc. Soc. Exptl. Biol. Med.,* **43**:55–58.

Chu, J. P. 1938. Studies on plumage in the male Brown Leghorn fowl. *Trans. Roy. Soc. Edinburgh,* **59**:533–562.

Cole, L. J., and D. H. Reid. 1924. The effect of feeding thyroid on the plumage of the fowl. *J. Agr. Research,* **29**:285–287.

Cook, R. 1939. A pair of albino robins. *J. Heredity,* **30**:2.

Crew, F. A. E. 1922. A Black Leghorn which turned white. *J. Heredity,* **13**:299–303.

——. 1933. Unexpected results of matings involving sex-linked characters. *Atti del congr. mond. pollicoltura., 5th Congr.,* **2**:223–226.

Cunningham, J. T. 1919. Results of a Mendelian experiment on fowls, including the production of a pile breed. *Proc. Zool. Soc. London:* 173–202.

Danforth, C. H. 1933. The reaction of dominant white with yellow and black in the fowl. *J. Heredity,* **24**:301–307.

—— and F. Foster. 1929. Skin transplantation as a means of studying genetic and endocrine factors in the fowl. *J. Exptl. Zoöl.,* **52**:443–470.

Darwin, C. 1890. "The Variation of Animals and Plants under Domestication." New York: D. Appleton & Company, Inc.

Davenport, C. B. 1906. Inheritance in poultry. *Carnegie Inst. Wash. Pub.* 52.

———. 1909. Inheritance of characteristics in domestic fowl. *Carnegie Inst. Wash. Pub.* 121.

———. 1912. Sex-limited inheritance in poultry. *J. Exptl. Zoöl.,* 13:1–26.

Dorris, F. 1938. The production of pigment in vitro by chick neural crest. *Arch. Entwicklungsmech. Organ.,* 138:323–334.

———. 1939. The production of pigment by chick neural crest in grafts to the 3-day limb bud. *J. Exptl. Zoöl.,* 80:315–345.

Duncker, H. 1924. Einige Beobachtungen über die Vererbung der weissen Farbe bei Kanarienvögeln. *Z. ind. Abst. Vererb.,* 32:363–376.

Dunn, L. C. 1922. A gene for the extension of black pigment in domestic fowls. *Am. Naturalist,* 56:464–466.

———. 1923. Color inheritance in fowls. The genetic relationship of the black, buff and Columbia colorations in the domestic fowl. *J. Heredity,* 14:23–32.

———. 1924. Further data on the inheritance of the sex-linked barred pattern of domestic fowl. *Anat. Record,* 29:142.

——— and W. Landauer. 1930. Studies on the plumage of the silver-spangled fowl. I. The expression of the spangled pattern during growth. *Storrs (Conn.) Agr. Expt. Sta. Bull.,* 163:31–46.

Durham, F. M., and D. C. E. Marryat. 1908. Note on the inheritance of sex in canaries. *Repts. Evol. Comm. Roy. Soc.,* IV:57–60.

Eastlick, H. L. 1939. The point of origin of the melanophores in chick embryos as shown by means of limb bud transplants. *J. Exptl. Zoöl.,* 82:131–157.

Emmens, C. W., and A. S. Parkes. 1940. The endocrine system and plumage types. II. The effects of thyroxin injections to normal, caponed and thyroidectomized caponized birds. *J. Genetics,* 39:485–492.

Finch, W. C. 1909. Note on partial leucosis in a hen. *Biometrika,* 7:234–236.

Finlay, G. F. 1925. Studies on sex differentiation in fowls. *Brit. J. Exptl. Biol.,* 2:439–468.

Gericke, A. M. 1938. Black Australorps turned white. *Farming South Africa,* 13: 37–38, 45.

Giacomini, E. 1924. Colour changes in plumage of poultry after thyroid administration. *Proc. World's Poultry Congr. 2d Congr., Barcelona:* 45–47.

Godbey, C. B., and D. H. Reid. 1931. A hen with variable plumage. *J. Heredity,* 22:59–62.

Goodale, H. D. 1909. Sex and its relation to the barring factor in poultry. *Science,* 29:1004–1005.

———. 1910. Breeding experiments in poultry. *Proc. Soc. Exptl. Biol. Med.,* 7: 178–179.

———. 1916. A feminized cockerel. *J. Exptl. Zoöl.* 20:421–428.

———. 1926. Salmon blacks. *Anat. Record,* 34:171–172.

Gortner, R. A. 1911. Studies on melanin. III. The inhibitory action of certain phenolic substances upon tyrosinase. A suggestion as to the cause of dominant and recessive whites. *J. Biol. Chem.,* 10:113–122.

Greenwood. A. W., and J. S. S. Blyth. 1929. An experimental analysis of the plumage of the Brown Leghorn fowl. *Proc. Roy. Soc. Edinburgh,* 49:313–355.

——— and ———. 1935. Variation in plumage response of Brown Leghorn capons to oestrone. *Proc. Roy. Soc. (London)* B, 118:97–132.

Hadley, P. B. 1913. Studies on inheritance in poultry: I. The constitution of the White Leghorn Breed. *Rhode Island Agr. Expt. Sta. Bull.* 155.

Hadley, P. B. 1914. Studies on inheritance in poultry: II. The factor for black pigmentation in the White Leghorn breed. *Rhode Island Agr. Expt. Sta. Bull.* 161.

———. 1915. The White Leghorn. *J. Heredity,* 6:147–151.

Hagedoorn, A. L. 1936. The autosexing Barnevelder, and the autosexing Leghorn, two new breeds. *Wiss. Ber. Weltgeflügelk. 6th Congr., Berlin and Leipzig,* 2: 29–34.

——— and A. C. Hagedoorn. 1914. Studies on variation and selection. *Zeit. ind. Abst. Vererb.,* 11:145–183.

Hamilton, H. L. 1940. A study of the physiological properties of melanophores with special reference to their role in feather coloration. *Anat. Record,* 78:525–547.

Hays, F. A. 1935. Crossing production and exhibition Rhode Island Reds. *Massachusetts Agr. Expt. Sta. Bull.* 316.

———. 1940. Color markings in Rhode Island Red chicks as related to sex and adult color. *J. Agr. Research,* 61:69–74.

Hertwig, P. 1930. Die Erbfaktoren der Haushühner. II. Beitrag: Die Ortsbestimmung von zwei weiteren Faktoren im X-Chromosom. *Biol. Zentr.,* 50:333–341.

———. 1933. Geschlechtsgebundene und autosomale Koppelungen bei Hühnern. *Verhandl deut. zool. ges.:* 112–118.

——— and T. Rittershaus. 1929. Die Erbfaktoren der Haushühner. I. Beitrag: Die Ortsbestimmung von 4 Faktoren im X-Chromosom. *Z. ind. Abst. Vererb.,* 51:354–372.

Hesse, M. 1927. Veranderung der Gefiederfärbung bei einem Kapaun. *Arch. Geflügelk.,* 1:64–65.

Hill, R. T., and A. S. Parkes. 1935. Hypophysectomy of birds. IV. Plumage changes in hypophysectomized fowls. V. Effect of replacement therapy on the gonads, accessory organs, and secondary sexual characters of hypophysectomized fowls. *Proc. Roy. Soc. (London)* B, 117:202–218.

Hurst, C. C. 1905. Experiments with poultry. *Repts. Evol. Comm. Roy. Soc.,* II: 131–154.

Hutt, F. B. 1930. A note on the effects of different doses of thyroid on the fowl. *J. Exptl. Biol.,* 7:1–6.

——— and C. D. Mueller. 1942. Sex-linked albinism in the turkey. *J. Heredity,* 33:69–77.

——— and ———. 1943. Independent identical mutations to albinism in the sex chromosome of the fowl. *Am. Naturalist,* 77:181–184.

Jaap, R. G. 1940. Methods for producing autosexing varieties of chicks. *U.S. Egg Poultry Mag.,* 46:36–39.

———. 1941. Auto-sex linkage in the domestic fowl. II. Auto-sexing accuracy with the gene for barred feathers in red to black down-color genotypes. *Poultry Sci.,* 20:317–321.

———. 1946. The wing-spot method for color sexing Rhode Island Red and New Hampshire chicks. *Oklahoma Agr. Expt. Sta. Circ.* C-121.

Jeffrey, F. P. 1947. Plumage color genes in White Plymouth Rocks and White Wyandottes. *Poultry Sci.,* 26:526–528.

Jerome, F. N. 1939. Auto-sex linkage in the Barred Plymouth Rock. *Poultry Sci.,* 18:437–440.

Juhn, M. 1933. A case of spontaneous pigment loss in the Brown Leghorn capon and the plumage reaction to thyroxine. *Endocrinology,* 17:88–92.

Juhn, M. and R. G. Gustavson. 1930. The production of female genital subsidiary characters and plumage sex characters by injection of human placental hormone in fowls. *J. Exptl. Zoöl.,* **56**:31–61.

Kaufman, L. 1936. Inheritance of plumage color and certain physiological characters in two varieties of the Polish Greenleg fowl. *Mém. inst. nat. polonais écon. rurale Pulawy,* **16** (Mém. 245): 192–204.

Knox, C. W. 1927. The genetics of plumage color in poultry. *Iowa Agr. Expt. Sta. Research Bull.* 105.

Kokemüller, K. 1935. Geschlechtsgebundene Vererbung bei der totalalbinotischen Aberration des *Melopsittacus undulatus* (Shaw). *Z. ind. Abst. Vererb.,* **21**: 299–302.

Koller, P. C. 1929. Experimental studies on pigment-formation. 1. The development in vitro of the mesodermal pigment cells of the fowl. *Arch. exptl. Zellforsch.,* **8**:490–498.

Krizenecky, J. 1928. Ein Fall von spontaner Albinisierung einer La Bresse-Henne. *Arch. Geflügelk.,* **2**:266–279.

———. 1930. Über traumatischen Albinismus beim Geflügel. *Arch. Geflügelk.,* **4**:169–177.

Ladebeck, E. 1922. Die Farben einiger Hühnerassen. *Z. ind. Abst. Vererb.,* **30**:1–62.

Lamoreux, W. F. 1941. The autosexing Ancobar. *J. Heredity,* **32**:221–226.

——— and F. B. Hutt. 1942. Variations in the down color of White Leghorn chicks and their economic insignificance. *J. Agr. Research,* **64**:193–205.

Landauer, W. 1930. Studies on the plumage of the silver spangled fowl. III. The asymmetry conditions of the spangled pattern. *Storrs (Conn.) Agr. Expt. Sta. Bull.,* **163**:71–82.

——— and L. C. Dunn. 1930. Studies on the plumage of the silver spangled fowl. II. Feather growth and feather pattern during forced regeneration. *Storrs (Conn.) Agr. Expt. Sta. Bull.,* **163**:47–69.

Legrand, P. 1939. Contribution à l'étude de la couleur blanche du plumage chez les poules. *Bull. biol. France Belg.,* **73**:433–437.

Lillie, F. R., and M. Juhn. 1932. The physiology of development of feathers. I. Growth-rate and pattern in the individual feather. *Physiol. Zoöl.,* **5**:124–184.

Lippincott, W. A. 1918. The case of the Blue Andalusian. *Am. Naturalist,* **52**:95–115.

———. 1920. A hen which changed color. *J. Heredity,* **11**:342–348.

———. 1921. Further data on the inheritance of blue in poultry. *Am. Naturalist,* **55**:289–327.

———. 1923. The hereditary relation of dominant white and blue in chickens. *Poultry Sci.,* **2**:141–145.

———. 1923a. Genes for the extension of black pigment in the chicken. *Am. Naturalist,* **57**:284–287.

Lloyd-Jones, O. 1915. Studies on inheritance in pigeons. II. A microscopical and chemical study of the feather pigments. *J. Exptl. Zoöl.,* **18**:453–509.

MacArthur, J. W., and J. J. MacIlraith. 1946. Color sexing of day-old Brown Leghorns. *Poultry Sci.,* **25**:180–183.

McIlhenny, E. A. 1940. Albinism in mockingbirds. *J. Heredity,* **31**:433–438.

Montalenti, G. 1934. A physiological analysis of the barred pattern in Plymouth Rock feathers. *J. Exptl. Zoöl.,* **69**:269–345.

Morgan, T. H., and H. D. Goodale. 1912. Sex-linked inheritance in poultry. *Ann. New York Acad. Sci.,* **22**:113–133.

Mueller, C. D., and F. B. Hutt. 1941. Genetics of the fowl. 12. Sex-linked, imperfect albinism. *J. Heredity,* **32**:71–80.

Munro, S. S. 1946. A sex-linked true-breeding blue plumage color. *Poultry Sci.,* **25**:408.

Nickerson, M. 1944. An experimental analysis of barred pattern formation in feathers. *J. Exptl. Zoöl.,* **95**:361–397.

———. 1946. Relation between black and red melanin pigments in feathers. *Physiol. Zoöl.,* **19**:66–77.

———. 1946a. Conditions modifying the expression of silver in the Silver Campine fowl. *Physiol. Zoöl.,* **19**:77–83.

Parkes, A. S., and H. Selye. 1937. The endocrine system and plumage types. I. Some effects of hypothyroidism. *J. Genetics,* **34**:297–306.

Pearl, R. 1911. Data on the relative conspicuousness of barred and self-colored fowls. *Am. Naturalist,* **45**:107–117.

——— and F. M. Surface. 1910. Further data regarding the sex-limited inheritance of the barred color pattern in poultry. *Science,* **32**:870–874.

Pease, M. 1936. Auto-sex linkage in theory and practice. *Wiss. Ber. Weltgeflügelk. 6th Congr., Berlin and Leipzig,* **2**:65–69.

———. 1941. Popular new varieties of poultry. Sex-linkage within pure breeds. *Field,* **178**:614–615.

Punnett, R. C. 1923. "Heredity in Poultry." London: Macmillan & Co., Ltd.

———. 1940. Genetic studies in poultry. XI. The Legbar. *J. Genetics,* **41**:1–8.

———. 1948. Genetic studies in poultry. X. Cream plumage.[1] *J. Genetics,* **48**:327–332.

——— and M. S. Pease. 1921. Genetic studies in poultry. IV. On the barred plumage of certain breeds. *J. Genetics,* **11**:235–240.

——— and ———. 1927. Genetic studies in poultry. V. On a case of pied plumage. *J. Genetics,* **18**:207–218.

——— and ———. 1928. Genetic studies in poultry. VI. The Gold Barred Rock. *J. Genetics,* **19**:337–350.

——— and ———. 1930. Genetic studies in poultry. VIII. On a case of sex-linkage within a breed. *J. Genetics,* **22**:395–397.

Quinn, J. P. 1934. A colour mutation in the Rhode Island Red fowl. *J. Genetics,* **29**:75–83.

———. 1935. Further experiments with the *p* gene in the fowl. *J. Genetics,* **30**:477–480.

———. 1936. Genes for color and plumage pattern in white varieties of chickens unmasked by crossbreeding. *Poultry Sci.,* **15**:169–178.

———. 1938. Sexual dimorphism in red-splashed white down color of chicks. *Poultry Sci.,* **17**:170–174.

——— and W. H. Burrows. 1935. Effects of female sex hormone on plumage color. *J. Heredity,* **26**:299–303.

——— and A. B. Godfrey. 1937. Color-producing genes in White Silkie and White Rose Comb Bantam. *Poultry Sci.,* **16**:340–344.

Régnier, V. 1934. Note sur un nouveau cas de récessivité commandé par l'hormone ovarienne, dans un croisement de poules domestiques. *Compt. rend. soc. biol.,* **116**:286–288.

---

[1] According to the author's records this should be XII in Professor Punnett's series, not X. The original X, dealing with linkage data for the sex chromosome, is cited in Chap. 14.

Régnier, V. 1937. Hormone ovarienne et caractères raciaux du plumage chez le coq et la poule domestiques. Étude de génétique expérimentale. *Bull. biol. France Belg.*, Suppl. **22**:1–214 + Pl. I–V.

Rittershaus, T. 1930. Die Erbfaktoren der Dunenzeichnung der Haushühner. *Züchter.*, **2**:324–330.

Serebrovsky, A. S. 1926. Genetics of domestic fowl (Russian). *Mem. Anikowo Genet. Sta.* near Moscow, pp. 1–136. [Cited from an abstract by L. C. Dunn, in *J. Heredity*, **19**:511–519 (1928) from the translation by B. F. Glessing of the U.S. Department of Agriculture.]

Slinger, S. J., and J. J. MacIlraith. 1944. The correlation between green-gray irises and black feathers in Barred Plymouth Rock pullets. *Poultry Sci.*, **23**:533–537.

Spillman, W. J. 1908. Spurious allelomorphism: results of some recent investigations. *Am. Naturalist*, **42**:610–615.

Strong, R. M. 1902. The development of color in the definitive feather. *Bull. Mus. Comp. Zool. Harvard Coll.*, **40**:147–185.

——. 1917. Some observations on the origin of melanin pigment in feather germs from the Plymouth Rock and Brown Leghorn fowls. *Anat. Record*, **13**:97–108.

Sturtevant, A. H. 1912. An experiment dealing with sex linkage in fowls. *J. Exptl. Zoöl.*, **12**:499–518.

Taylor, L. W. 1932. Inheritance of spangling in the domestic fowl. *J. Genetics*, **26**:385–394.

——. 1932a. An inhibitor of gold color in chickens. *Proc. Intern. Genetic. Congr. 6th Congr., Ithaca, N.Y.*, **2**:197–199.

——. 1933. The use of sex hormones in determining the genotype of crossbred fowls. *Atti congr. mondiale pollicoltura. 5th Congr., Rome*, **2**:333–335.

Warren, D. C. 1929. The inheritance of Rhode Island Red chick down-color variations and their relation to color variations in adult plumage. *J. Agr. Research*, **39**:781–794.

——. 1930. The inheritance of two standard disqualifications in White Leghorn chickens. *Poultry Sci.*, **9**:271–282.

——. 1933. Inheritance of albinism in the domestic fowl. *J. Heredity*, **24**:379–383.

——. 1940. Inheritance of pinkeye in the fowl. *J. Heredity*, **31**:291–292.

—— and C. D. Gordon. 1933. Plumage and eye color inheritance in the Single Comb Rhode Island Red Fowl. *J. Agr. Research*, **47**:897–910.

Wilfrid, M. 1927. The origin of the Canadian "Chantecler" fowl. *Rept. Proc. World's Poultry Cong. 3d Congr., Ottawa:* 55–57.

Willier, B. H. 1941. An analysis of feather color pattern produced by grafting melanophores during embryonic development. *Am. Naturalist*, **75**:136–146.

—— and M. E. Rawles. 1940. The control of feather color pattern by melanophores grafted from one embryo to another of a different breed of fowl. *Physiol. Zoöl.*, **13**:177–199.

——, ——, and E. Hadorn. 1937. Skin transplants between embryos of different breeds of fowl. *Proc. Nat. Acad. Sci.*, **23**:542–546.

Zavadovsky, B. 1925. The effect of feeding fowls on thyroid gland. *Endocrinology*, **9**:125–136.

CHAPTER 8

LETHAL GENES AND MISCELLANEOUS CHARACTERS

In this chapter there are considered a number of inherited characters for some of which the physiological or anatomical bases are not sufficiently known to permit of their being classified any more definitely than as miscellaneous. Since several of these cause the death of the affected chick or embryo, a brief discussion of the nature of such mutations is warranted.

THE NATURE OF LETHAL GENES

Hereditary conditions in which the deviation from the normal is so extreme that the individual affected cannot survive practically all segregate as unifactorial characters and are usually attributed to the action of *lethal genes*. There is evidence that some lethal mutations result not from a "point" mutation in a single gene but from a sectional deficiency whereby a piece is eliminated from a chromosome. Lethal action results in other cases from loss of a whole chromosome or from transfer of part of one chromosome to another. Lethal mutations of these last three types have not yet been identified in the fowl.

It is obvious that a gene lethal to the heterozygote would be immediately eliminated from the germ plasm and hence that any lethal gene persisting long enough to be recognizable must be lethal only when homozygous, or when hemizygous, as in the case of a sex-linked lethal.

Detection of Lethals. For convenient consideration of the different ways in which the action of lethal genes may be detected, the following classification is useful. Any characters mentioned that were not discussed in earlier chapters are described later in this one.

1. *Dominant* or partially dominant genes with visible effects upon the heterozygote. These are sometimes described as "dominant genes with recessive lethal action," but it is simpler to consider the homozygote as too abnormal to survive and the heterozygote as abnormal but viable: *e.g.,* creeper; crest in the duck (which apparently affects about half the heterozygotes).
2. *Recessive* genes, autosomal, with no visible effect upon the heterozygote, but lethal to the homozygote in *late embryonic life* or *after hatching*. In these cases the lethal character is usually recognizable because of some abnormality

227

of the homozygote: *e.g.,* "stickiness," the type of chondrodystrophy studied by Lamoreux, and "congenital loco."

3. *Recessive* genes, autosomal, with effects exerted *early* in *embryonic life,* but readily recognizable because the causative gene is linked or identical with one for some color or morphological character: *e.g.,* Dunn's lethal linked with recessive white; dominant white in canaries.

4. *Sex-linked* lethals. When these operate early in development, they can be detected only by a deficiency of hatched females, by unusually high mortality at one period of incubation, and by subsequent breeding tests. When the lethal effect is exerted late in development or after hatching, the nature of the causative gene can be detected by visible abnormalities first associated only with females, or by an unusually high mortality in that sex, or by both: *e.g.,* naked; sex-linked albinism in the turkey.

5. *Recessive autosomal* genes with lethal effects first recognizable only because of abnormally high mortality in certain matings. Their existence can be proved by comparison of mortality rates with those in unrelated controls, by locating an abnormal peak of mortality at some one stage of development, and subsequently by minute examination of embryos or chicks dying at that critical period. Lethal genes of this sort are known in Drosophila, in the rat, and in other species; but although they are undoubtedly responsible for some of the early mortality in chick embryos, and probably for some of that occurring after hatching, none of this class has yet been reported for the fowl.

Time of Lethal Action. In general, the greater the abnormality caused by the lethal gene, the earlier the age at death. Most homozygous creepers die at 3 or 4 days of incubation and most "talpid" embryos at 8 to 10 days. "Sticky" embryos die during the last 4 days of incubation, and about half the naked chicks die in the 2 or 3 days before hatching time. Congenital loco is lethal within a week after hatching, whereas congenital tremor kills about 90 per cent of the affected chicks within a month, but permits a very few to live over 3 months. There is no reason why the lethal action could not be exerted in mature animals, as is the case with Huntington's chorea in man, but no lethal character with such a delayed action has yet been found in domestic birds. The hereditary dwarfism studied by Upp (1934) is apparently lethal at various ages up to a year and a half. It is true that genes heightening susceptibility to disease have a similar effect, but they are not usually classified as lethal genes.

Varying Degrees of Lethal Effect. Some mutations are lethal to all homozygotes, even in environmental conditions that are apparently optimum. Examples of this class are the sticky embryos, homozygous creepers, talpid embryos, and the embryos with defective maxillae described by Asmundson.

In other cases, some of the affected individuals die, but a varying proportion survives. Such conditions are sometimes referred to as *semi-lethal.* The proportion surviving usually depends upon the environment, but it can also depend upon modifying genes which heighten or lessen the bad effects of the lethal genes. Many chicks with hereditary blindness die, but when they are closely confined with ample feed and water, some of the blind chicks survive. This applies also to the type of imperfect albinism accompanied by blindness in the turkey. These two conditions would undoubtedly be lethal to all affected chicks in a state of nature but are not necessarily so in an extremely favorable environment when a special effort is made to keep the defectives alive. They can be considered as *facultative lethals,* in contradistinction to the *obligate* lethals like creeper, talpid, stickiness, and others that are fatal to all regardless of the environment.

With some semi-lethal mutations, survival of a few affected individuals seems to depend less upon the environment than upon individual differences, presumably caused by modifying genes, which permit a favored few to live when most of their fellows perish. For example, the sex-linked albinism in turkeys described by Hutt and Mueller is lethal to three-quarters of the affected poults during the last week of incubation, but some do hatch, and one was even raised to maturity. Similarly, 1 chick out of 35 with congenital tremor lived to a little over a year.

Effects on Hatchability. Some lethal genes in birds may not be recognized because they cause no readily visible abnormalities or are lethal at early stages of development. In such cases, the presence of a lethal gene may be suspected, and confirmed in part, by comparing the suspect matings and normal controls with respect to (1) embryonic mortality at different periods of incubation and (2) the hatchability of fertile eggs. This is nicely shown by the data of Asmundson (1945) for matings of fowls that carried the crooked-neck-dwarf lethal (Table 23). Details concerning it are given on page 236.

It is clear that the lethal gene did not raise the mortality rate in the first 2 weeks of incubation but did so in the third, thus showing the period at which homozygosity for the abnormality is lethal. In this case, that was already known because the dwarfed embryos were recognizable, but with other embryonic lethals such an easy confirmation is not to be expected. A point worth noting is that the residual mortality from causes other than the crooked-neck lethal was high, since only 64.2 per cent of the control eggs hatched. The reduction of hatchability by the lethal gene was therefore less conspicuous than it would have been if there had been less mortality from other causes. The maximum possible difference between two such matings in hatchability is 25 per cent, but this is seldom found, if ever. The difference in this example was only 11.7 per cent. A fact sometimes overlooked is that the effect of a lethal mutation on hatchability varies inversely with the amount

TABLE 23. EFFECTS OF A LETHAL GENE ON EMBRYONIC MORTALITY
AND HATCHABILITY *

Type of mating	Fertile eggs, number	Embryonic mortality			Hatched, per cent
		First week, per cent	Second week, per cent	Third week, per cent	
Parents producing dwarfs.....	202	5.9	4.0	37.6	52.5
Parents that did not.........	519	8.7	4.2	23.5	64.2
Difference................	...	−2.8	−0.2	+14.1	−11.7

* From Asmundson (1945).

of residual mortality to be expected from other causes. The hatchability expected in matings that yield the lethal character is merely three-quarters of that for control eggs produced and incubated under the same conditions. In this case, the 52.5 per cent observed is reasonably close to the 48.2 per cent expected on that basis. This relationship, which is illustrated diagrammatically in Fig. 65, applies when the

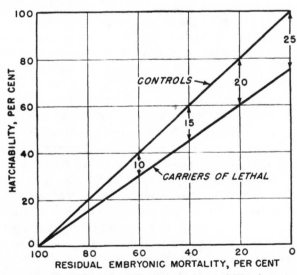

FIG. 65. Diagram showing how the difference in hatchability between (1) matings producing embryos homozygous for some specific lethal gene and (2) controls increases as residual embryonic mortality common to both stocks decreases.

mutation is lethal only to homozygotes, and not to any of the heterozygotes. When some of the latter are killed by the lethal gene, as is the case with the creeper gene, but apparently with very few others, the expectations would be slightly altered.

LETHAL CHARACTERS IN DOMESTIC BIRDS

To date, 21 lethal mutations have been described in the fowl, 3 in the turkey, 2 in the pigeon, and 1 each in the duck and canary. Of these 28 characters, 18 have been discussed in previous chapters, 9 are considered in this chapter, and 1 in the chapter on Variations in Body Size. For convenience these lethals are all listed in Table 24, where they are

TABLE 24. LETHAL CHARACTERS OF DOMESTIC BIRDS

Species	Character	Symbol	Degree of lethality	Discussed on page
Fowl...........	Creeper	Cp	Obligate	58
	Chondrodystrophy	ch	Obligate	64
	Cornish lethal	Cl	Obligate	63
	Abnormal maxillae	mx	Obligate	44
	Missing mandible	md	Obligate	46
	Wingless	wg	Obligate	66
	Diplopodia	dp	Obligate	54
	Micromelia	...	Obligate	66
	Short upper beak	su	Facultative	45
	Apterylosis	Ap	Facultative	118
	Naked	n	Facultative	114
	Dwarfism	td	Facultative	264
	Stickiness	sy	Obligate	232
	Talpid	ta	Obligate	233
	Congenital loco	lo	Obligate	232
	Lethal with recessive white	l	Obligate	234
	Crooked-neck dwarf	cn	Obligate	236
	Blindness	...	Facultative	236
	Congenital tremor	...	Obligate	235
	Bilateral microphthalmia	mi	Obligate	237
	Short mandible	sm	Facultative	46
Turkey.........	Short spine	...	Obligate	41
	Short long bones	...	Facultative	67
	Sex-linked albinism	al	Facultative	180
Duck...........	Crest	...	Obligate	128
Canary.........	Dominant white	...	Obligate	171
Pigeon.........	Lethal dwarfing	...	Obligate	67
	Creamy Gier	...	Obligate	237

classified as either obligate or facultative. While any such classification is more or less arbitrary, it does distinguish between the lethals which are fatal to all homozygotes and the cases in which some of the mutants may survive.

Stickiness, sy

Description. Byerly and Jull (1932) studied an abnormality which was lethal during the last 4 days of incubation. The amniotic and allantoic fluids were not absorbed, and because these were very viscous at hatching time, the condition was labelled as stickiness. Affected embryos were smaller than normal, though characterized by general oedema. The amount of unutilized yolk drawn into the body was therefore disproportionately large and caused unusual distention of the abdomen. About a third of the sticky embryos had the tibiae bent as in chondrodystrophy, and all the bones were extremely soft.

Genetics. This condition is caused by an autosomal recessive gene, sy, in the homozygous state. Matings of heterozygotes *inter se* yielded a ratio of 545 normal:169 sticky embryos, but when some of these same carriers were outcrossed to unrelated stock, none of the abnormal embryos were found.

Congenital Loco, lo

Description. A common abnormality in chicks and one that is nearly always lethal within a week after hatching is that designated by Knowlton (1929) as congenital loco. The Spanish word *loco*, meaning insane, has been used colloquially by cattlemen on the Western plains to describe the symptoms induced in cattle after they have eaten certain toxic plants of the genus Astragalus. Its use for the complete inability to balance that characterizes these chicks is perhaps temporarily justified till further study reveals the anatomical basis for the abnormality.

The affected chicks hatch normally but cannot stand more than a few seconds. The head is drawn back, and the beak points upward, usually on one side (Fig. 66). Finally the chick topples over backward and lies on its back or side till righted, when the whole performance is quickly repeated. The condition suggests some defect in the mechanism for balancing, but the anatomical basis is entirely unknown.

The chicks die because of their inability to feed and drink or to remain in the warm part of their brooder. Knowlton tried to raise 12 of them, but all died within 9 days.

Genetics. This condition is caused by an autosomal recessive gene, lo, in the homozygous state. From matings of carriers *inter se*, Knowlton obtained the ratio 461 normal:146 loco, which is a very good fit to the theoretical expectation of 455:152. This shows that the condition is not lethal during incubation, but only after hatching. Heterozygotes were apparently normal in every respect.

The gene responsible for this defect is widely distributed in the population of domestic fowls. Knowlton had indications of its occurrence in 30 different states or provinces in North America. The author has seen it in several different breeds, in many different flocks, and in nearly every hatching season over three decades.

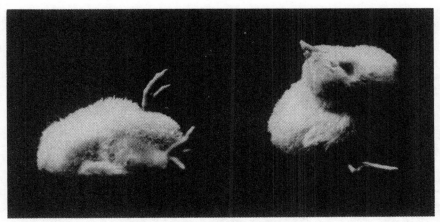

FIG. 66. Chicks with congenital loco, showing two common situations resulting from their inability to balance.

Talpid Embryo, *ta*

Description. Cole (1942) has described an extremely abnormal condition of the chick embryo which he designated as talpid because the wings have several digits and are very short and palmate, resembling the broad forefeet of the mole (Talpa). Most of the talpid embryos die at 8 to 11 days of incubation, at which stage they compare with normal embryos of the same age, as is shown in Fig. 67. The legs and wings are greatly shortened, and there may be as many as 9 or 10 digits. These are connected, as in a webbed foot, to make a polydactylous hand or foot, usually somewhat cupped. The vertebral column is shortened, and eversion of the viscera is common, being most conspicuous in older embryos. Development of the upper and lower beaks is subnormal. There is a marked oedema, which often causes large blebs in the sacral and cervical regions (Fig. 67). None showed any development of feathers, not even the one specimen that survived to the seventeenth day of incubation.

Genetics. Extensive studies by Cole showed that the talpid condition is a simple autosomal recessive character. The symbol *ta* is used for the causative gene. Since in embryos old enough to classify there was a slight deficiency of talpids in matings where 25 per cent were expected, it was concluded that sometimes the abnormality is lethal to embryos in early stages too small to permit recognition of the abnormality with the naked eye.

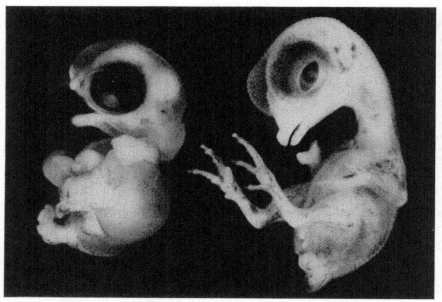

Fig. 67. Embryos of 11 days, showing differences at that age between one with the lethal talpid mutation and a normal embryo. Apart from the malformation of the face and polydactyly in both feet and in the hand, extrusion of the viscera and oedema are conspicuous. (*From Cole in J. Heredity.*)

Lethal Linked with Recessive White, *l*

Some evidence was found by Dunn (1923) that there may be a lethal gene linked with *c*, the gene for recessive white. When an F_1 cockerel (*Cc*) from the cross White Wyandotte ♀ ♀ × Pit Game ♂ was mated with his dam and six other white relatives on her side (all *cc*), three of these matings yielded ratios in the hatched chicks of approximately 2 colored:1 white, instead of the 1:1 ratio expected. The inference was that in these three matings both male and female were heterozygous for a lethal gene linked with *c*, so that one-quarter of the progeny were homozygous for *c* and for the lethal. If, for convenience, the latter be designated as *l*, the carrier male was (*C L*) (*c l*) and the carrier dams (*c L*) (*c l*).[1] The four genotypes expected in progeny from these matings were thus

(*C L*) (*c L*), colored, viable.
(*C L*) (*c l*), colored, viable.
(*c l*) (*c L*), white, viable.
(*c l*) (*c l*), white, non-viable.

The mating of the cockerel with his dam yielded 19 colored:8 white, a 2:1 ratio in accord with expectation if the dam had transmitted the lethal to her son. Similar ratios were obtained in progeny from other relatives that could have carried *l*.

Although the evidence in this instance was not conclusive, it affords the only case in the fowl of a type of lethal known in several species in which the lethal action can be detected by a deficiency of animals with some color or pattern below the numbers expected in certain matings. In the mouse homozygosity for yellow hair or for dominant white spotting is lethal. Dominant white is lethal to homozygotes in the canary, as is the creamy-headed condition in Gier pigeons, which is discussed later.

Congenital Tremor

Description. In a hereditary semi-lethal abnormality described by Hutt and Child (1934) the affected chicks showed at hatching varying degrees of tremor. In some it was barely perceptible, but in others the tremor was so violent that the chicks could not stand. It was usually not noticeable in squatting chicks, nor in the few that survived beyond 3 weeks of age. Measurements with a kymograph showed that the number of vibrations per second varied from 10 to 17 in different chicks during the first 2 days but declined thereafter.

Of the chicks with tremor, 68 per cent died within 1 week, and 88 per cent within a month of hatching. Only 2 out of 35 lived beyond 6 months. Death resulted in some cases from an inability to feed and drink. Growth was greatly retarded in the few that survived longer than a month.

Genetics. It was shown that this defect is hereditary, but the genetic basis for it is apparently complex. From matings over 4 years in which both parents produced chicks with tremor, the proportion of affected chicks was about 10 per cent. The fact that in large families (16 or more) the ratio of normal to affected chicks was about 15:1 suggested that tremor might depend upon two pairs of duplicate genes, but it seemed more likely that the character might be a recessive one with an

---

[1] Parentheses are used here to show that the two genes within them are linked.

unusually low penetrance, or manifestation. Since approximately equal numbers of males and females were affected, the condition is apparently autosomal.

Crooked-neck Dwarf, *cn*

Description. Embryos showing this lethal mutation were found by Asmundson (1945) in New Hampshires. They are apparently normal up to about 11 days of incubation but show some oedema from 11 to 13 days. Thereafter growth is retarded, being so slight from 16 to 20 days of incubation that at the latter age the dwarfs weigh only half as much as their normal siblings. Most of them apparently die on the twentieth or twenty-first day. At that time they are characterized by crooked necks and absence or marked reduction of the pectoral muscles and those of the limbs. In some cases the sternum is not fully developed. The dwarfing of the body results in an abnormally swollen appearance after the yolk is drawn into the body cavity. The tibiotarsal joints are rigid, and probably others as well, for the embryo does not make vigorous movements of the limbs, as normal chicks do at that age.

In histological studies of these dwarfs, Rosenberg (1947) found marked degeneration of the muscle fibres, some of which were hardly recognizable as such. The more common signs of degeneration included loss of fibrils, reduction of cytoplasm, loss of cellular outlines, formation of cysts, and pycnosis of the nuclei. In some cases the degenerating nuclei formed large masses of chromatin described as "skeins."

Genetics. Crooked-neck dwarfs are homozygous for a recessive autosomal gene, for which the symbol *cn* is proposed. From heterozygotes mated *inter se* Asmundson obtained a ratio of 297 normal:103 dwarfs.

None of the affected embryos hatch, and apparently all die during the last week of incubation (Table 23). A point of interest is that apparently similar abnormalities of the muscles, with resultant similar crooked neck and rigidity of the affected limbs, are inherited as simple autosomal recessive characters in sheep, cattle, and swine (for references and discussion see Hutt, 1934). In all these species the condition is lethal, as in the fowl, at the termination of foetal development.

Blindness

Another semi-lethal condition is the hereditary blindness briefly reported by Hutt (1935). The affected chicks were blind at hatching and remained so throughout life. When they were exposed to intense light, the iris did not contract as in normal fowls. As in other blind chicks, the head was slowly moved from side to side. In adults there was pronounced bulging of one or both eyes, usually asymmetrical. Although mortality in these blind chicks was higher than in their normal siblings, when they were confined in close quarters some of them learned to eat and drink. Mature females laid almost as many eggs as did their normal sisters.

This blindness was found to be a simple autosomal recessive character. It occurred in White Leghorns.

Bilateral Microphthalmia, *mi*

Description. Unilateral microphthalmia and anophthalmia are defects commonly found in chick embryos and hatched chicks which are attributed to accidents of development rather than to heredity. A type of bilateral microphthalmia found by Jeffrey (1941) in Barred Plymouth Rocks is quite different and clearly hereditary. The affected chicks have at hatching eyeballs approximately half the size of normal ones. These are not visible on the exterior, and the chicks are totally blind. The causative gene also induces a thickening of the posterior end of the comb, which is sometimes double. The condition was recognizable in embryos that died late in incubation.

Genetics. This abnormality was proved to be caused by an autosomal recessive gene in the homozygous state. Matings of carriers *inter se* yielded in 2 years a ratio of 274 normal:80 microphthalmic. The symbol *mi* is proposed.

Jeffrey considered it fully lethal because the affected chicks could not see to feed or drink and none was raised to maturity. However, blindness *per se* is not lethal, and even a chick with bilateral anophthalmia can be raised by special care. It is possible that death may be caused by other ill effects of the gene. Evidence of these was found in the fact that, although microphthalmic embryos apparently survived to the later stages of incubation (as was indicated by the normal 3:1 ratio in late embryos and hatched chicks), they then experienced a higher rate of mortality than did their normal siblings. In one year, 43 per cent of them hatched; in another year, only 25 per cent.

Creamy Gier Pigeons

According to Lienhart (1937) there is a variant form of the Meunier Carrier pigeon known as the Rosy Gier in which the plumage is of a creamy-white color, with a brownish tint on the throat and in the wing bars. Creamy heads are found only in males, never in females, which have ash-colored heads. Matings of these two types together yielded 2 ♂ ♂ :1 ♀. Half the males have creamy heads, and half ashen, but all the females have ashen heads, much to the disappointment of the breeders.   Lienhart found that the missing cream-headed females all died just before hatching time.

These results are caused by a sex-linked lethal gene, closely linked with the gene for creamy head, or identical with it.   Apparently this gene can survive only in the heterozygous males and is lethal to the hemizygous females.   This is an interesting case in which attempts to incorporate a gene as a breed characteristic are doomed to failure, because the gene is lethal to the heterogametic sex—in this case, the females.   Lethal genes that are autosomal, such as the creeper mutant in fowls and crest in ducks, can be preserved and can even be adopted, as have these two, as the distinguishing characteristics of special "breeds."

ELIMINATION OF LETHAL GENES

Since lethal genes are obviously undesirable, it is necessary to know how to eliminate them quickly, as easily as possible, and with a minimum loss of good stock.   The methods used will depend on the type of lethal involved.

A dominant gene with effects recognizable in the heterozygote, as in Creeper fowls and white canaries, can be eliminated immediately.   If it be desirable to breed Creepers, they can be mated with normal birds and the normal progeny marketed.   This is perhaps better than mating Creepers together and having one-quarter of their potential offspring die during incubation.   Similarly, lethals associated with some color or pattern, such as that linked with recessive white, can be eliminated by avoiding matings involving the "marker" character.   If the latter is a particularly desirable breed characteristic, it might be possible by breeding tests to find a crossover in which the desirable marker would be separated from the undesirable lethal.

A sex-linked lethal gene in domestic birds can be carried only by males, except for semi-lethals like albinism in the turkey, in which case a few of the females may attain maturity.   Once the carrier males are detected, their elimination and the marketing of all their male progeny will end the problem.   Normal, viable females from these carriers will not have the gene and can safely be kept.   Half the sons of carriers will not have the lethal; these could be identified by breeding tests if the stock were valuable enough to justify the effort, but the simplest plan is to dispose of the heterozygous sire and all his male progeny.

However, most of the lethal genes bothering the poultryman are likely to be simple autosomal recessives, which can be detected in heterozygotes only by suitable breeding tests.   The poultryman is comparatively fortunate in that he can afford to keep a few known heterozygotes for just such tests, whereas the breeders of cattle or of horses could hardly afford to do so. Any hen or cock that has produced a chick with congenital loco is a carrier. From the mating that yields a loco chick, two-thirds of the unaffected surviving chicks must also be carriers. The safest and easiest plan is to use for breeding none of these normal birds from the mating that showed the lethal character. However, if it seems desirable to use them, they can be tested by mating them back to their sire or dam or to any other known carrier and then hatching a dozen or so pedigreed chicks from each suspect. If no chicks with loco appear in that number, the suspect is probably not a carrier; but if there be only one loco chick and a dozen normal ones, the bird under test carries the lethal and should not be used for further breeding.

This is the progeny test in almost its simplest form. The same procedure is used to detect a gene lethal to the embryo, except that in such cases the unhatched eggs must be examined for the abnormal chicks. Even if the lethal effect is exerted at an early stage before any abnormality is recognizable, or if it should kill later embryos without causing any visible abnormality, its action may be detected by the unusually high mortality in matings of carriers *inter se,* and the fact that the excess of deaths usually occurs at some one stage of incubation.

MISCELLANEOUS CHARACTERS

Compared with the extensive information about hereditary variations in the skeleton, skin, and plumage, very little is known about variation in the internal organ systems. This brief section covers our knowledge of hereditary variations in the urogenital system, the alimentary tract, and the blood.

Unilateral Kidney

In one strain of White Leghorns, Jeffrey, Beaudette, and Hudson (1937) found in four generations 14 females with absence or atrophy of the left kidney. This was accompanied by compensatory hypertrophy of the right kidney, and it apparently had no ill effects on the duration of life, fecundity, and reproduction of the abnormal birds.

Some evidence that this condition is hereditary was found in the fact that most of the affected birds were descended from two males. There was no sign of genetic ratios, but one pair of breeders yielded two affected daughters and nine normal ones. The apparent restriction of the abnormality to females suggests that it is sex linked, but many males were marketed without examination for this character, and hence that point is still in doubt.

Pendulous Crop in Turkeys

Description. The peculiar abnormality shown in Fig. 68 in which the crop becomes distended with stagnant fluid contents was found by Hinshaw and Asmundson (1936) to affect 1 to 15 per cent of certain flocks of turkeys in the drier parts of California. It usually appeared

Fig. 68. Pendulous crop in a Bronze turkey. (*From Hinshaw and Asmundson in J. Am. Vet. Med. Assoc.*)

in poults from 8 to 16 weeks of age after excessive drinking of water during a heat wave. About 60 per cent of these eventually died or had to be killed, but some with pendulous crops lived over a year. Most of the affected birds became unthrifty and emaciated, and many died from self-inflicted lacerations of the pendulous crop, from bullying by their stronger mates, or from pneumonia. The same abnormality is found in the drier inland areas of New South Wales, where it causes considerable economic loss (Hungerford, 1939).

Genetics. It was concluded by Asmundson and Hinshaw (1938) that the pendulous crop might be caused by one pair of recessive genes but that the basis might be more complex. The condition was found only in Bronze turkeys, never in Bourbon Reds. When these breeds were crossed, very few of the F_1 birds developed pendulous crop but about a quarter of the F_2 generation showed it.

Within the Bronze breed, various matings were made in which one parent, both, or neither had had pendulous crop. Some of these breeders were still affected when used; others had recovered. The results in 29 such matings spread over 3 years are condensed in Table 25.

TABLE 25.   MATINGS SHOWING THAT PENDULOUS CROP IS HEREDITARY*

Matings, number	Type of mating	Progeny of susceptible age, number	Proportion with pendulous crop, per cent
3	Both parents normal. (a) Low incidence in progeny	4i2	8.5
3	Both parents normal. (b) High incidence in progeny	729	19.0
4	Both parents normal. Crosses of a × b	251	6.8
1	Both parents normal but from affected birds	81	35.8
12	One parent with pendulous crop or recovered	325	40.0
6	Both parents with pendulous crop or recovered	265	69.0

* Condensed from Asmundson and Hinshaw.

These data show clearly that pendulous crop is hereditary. If it were a simple recessive character, one might expect all the progeny to be affected in matings where both parents had pendulous crop. This expectation was actually realized in one of the six matings in this class; in another, 94 per cent of the poults developed the abnormality. However, because the manifestation of the character depends so much upon the environment, clear-cut genetic ratios were hardly to be expected. The sexes did not differ in susceptibility.

Influence of Environment. This condition provides a good example of a hereditary character the expression of which depends to a great extent upon the environment. Apart from the evidence in the field that the condition appeared during excessively hot weather or after it, a critical experiment by Asmundson and Hinshaw illustrated this point nicely. Poults hatched from parents with pendulous crops and therefore genetically highly susceptible to the abnormality were divided in two groups. One of these was raised in the comparatively hot, dry summer climate of Davis (California), while the other was maintained under similar conditions of management at Tomales, 2 miles from the ocean. The differences in the two lots (Table 26) show that, while pendulous crop is a hereditary abnormality, it can be completely suppressed even in highly susceptible stock, provided that the environment is cool.

TABLE 26. ROLE OF ENVIRONMENT IN MANIFESTATION OF PENDULOUS CROP

Place	Average maximum daily temperature	Humidity	Poults exposed, number	Proportion developing pendulous crop, per cent
Davis...........	92.5°F.	Low	67	67
Tomales........	74°F.	Higher	83	None

Crooked Neck

Jull and Quinn (1931) found a peculiar abnormality in Brown Leghorns in which the neck became twisted to one side, usually to the right. This was not evident until the chickens were half grown but became steadily worse thereafter, till eventually the affected birds could not eat, nor could they walk in a normal manner. The underlying cause of the defect was not determined.

Some indication that the crooked neck might be inherited as an autosomal recessive character was found in the ratio of 129 normal:27 affected among the progeny of carrier parents. However, since the deviation from the expected 117:39 was too great to occur by chance in more than 3 per cent of similar trials, it seems probable either that the character is not a simple recessive or, more likely, that it is one but that some of the genetically susceptible birds do not show the abnormality. Both males and females developed crooked necks, but since the males could not mate and the females laid very few eggs, it was unfortunately not then possible to make the critical test of mating the affected birds together.

Types of Blood

Normal agglutinins such as those occurring in the blood of man are apparently found only occasionally in the blood of the fowl. Karshner (1928) found only four agglutinations in 128 tests. Similarly, Schütt (1929) differentiated three types of blood, of which one contained an agglutinogen, another an agglutinin, and a third neither. This last was by far the most common. An agglutinin was found in only 20 birds out of 230 tested.

However, when the blood of fowls is tested against sera containing immune agglutinins induced by inoculation of one animal with corpuscles of another, the situation is found to be much more complex. Landsteiner and Miller (1924) found 8 different types of blood in 10 birds tested with a univalent serum obtained by inoculating a rabbit. In the extensive studies of Todd (1930, 1930a) with a multivalent serum, nearly every one of 48 chicks tested in three different families seemed to have red blood corpuscles that reacted differently from those of all the rest. In discussing Todd's data, Wiener (1933, 1934) maintained that in each family the reactions of certain chicks were sufficiently alike to permit of their being grouped, and by this method he reduced the number of different types to 9 in one family, 6 in another, and 4 in the third. These he accounted for by postulating that in the three families there were respectively 5, 4, and 3 different agglutinogens responsible for the different types of blood. It is true that many different types of blood could result from the combination in pairs of a comparatively small number of agglutinogens, since, with n of the latter, the number of possible blood types is at least 2^n. The fact remains that at the present time the numbers of blood groups, the numbers of agglutinogens, and the numbers of genes responsible for them are unknown so far as the fowl is concerned.

Evidence of Inheritance. However, there is ample evidence that the differences known to exist are hereditary. In Todd's Plymouth Rocks, no chick had corpuscles with antigenic properties that were not also present in the sire or the dam. This was nicely shown by the following procedure: A highly multivalent serum was produced by pooling the sera from 12 hens, each of which had been given six weekly injections of mixed blood from 22 other fowls. It presumably contained agglutinins effective against the many different kinds of antigens occurring in the blood cells of those 22 birds. A small quantity of this multivalent serum could then be "exhausted," or "absorbed," so far as any one fowl, A, was concerned, by adding to it washed red corpuscles of that fowl and repeating that procedure until the serum no longer caused agglutination of such corpuscles. This showed that all agglutinins originally in the multivalent serum that were capable of agglutinating A's blood cells had been absorbed and eliminated. Some idea of the diversity of types in the fowl's blood is conveyed by the fact that, when the serum had been thus exhausted so far as any one fowl was concerned, it still continued to agglutinate the corpuscles of most other birds with which it was tested. Even when the serum was exhausted with the blood of two different birds, it still agglutinated the corpuscles of 69 out of 78 other fowls with which it was tested.

Within any one family, however, it was quite different. When the serum was twice exhausted, so that all agglutinins effective against corpuscles of both the sire and the dam were eliminated, and then tested against the progeny of those two birds, none of the chicks showed any agglutination of its blood corpuscles. This was true for all of 61 offspring thus tested in three different families, except for one lone chick which was shown by the blood tests to belong to another family. This experiment showed that none of these 60 chicks had in its blood cells any antigens not present in its sire or dam. In other words, the agglutinogens behave as dominant characters.

Similar results were obtained by Thomsen (1934) in extensive experiments like Todd's, except that among 95 chicks in 33 families he found 3 whose corpuscles were still agglutinated by the test serum after it had been absorbed by blood cells of the sire and dam. Two of these 3 were siblings. Later, Thomsen (1936) adduced further evidence that such recessive antigens occur in the fowl and devised a special technique for identifying them.

Further evidence of the genetic nature of the blood types was found by Todd (1935) in blood tests of a family that was highly inbred after three generations of brother × sister matings. The pair used for starting this line was selected from 18 siblings after tests showed that the blood cells of these two were closely alike. In the third inbred generation, the 12 birds tested had serological reactions that were practically identical. When a multivalent test serum was exhausted for the cells of any member of the family, it would no longer agglutinate the cells of other members of the family. In other words, these birds were homozygous with respect to the genes determining the antigenic properties of their blood cells. The fact that this was accomplished in three generations shows that the number of genes concerned was rather small.

Tests by Kozelka (1933) with three different breeds indicated that no one blood type was associated with one breed more than with another. Birds of inbred stocks were somewhat more homogeneous than unrelated birds. Kozelka concluded that the number of different agglutinogens in the fowl was not great and that the diversity of blood types resulted from the many different ways in which a few agglutinogens could be combined.

In genetic studies of a single agglutinogen by Terentyeva (1933), the ratios obtained indicated that it segregated as a unifactorial dominant character, not sex linked, but the appearance of two birds carrying the agglutinogen in one of six matings of parents lacking it was difficult to explain. Boyd and Alley (1940) tested 19 different families of chickens with five solutions that were each believed to contain only a single agglutinin. In general, corpuscles of the offspring were agglutinated only by the solutions that agglutinated the corpuscles of their sire, or dam, or both, but there were five exceptions to this rule in 45 offspring tested.

An agglutinogen studied by Olson (1943) was inherited as a unifactorial, autosomal character with incomplete dominance, so that three different types of blood cells were found in the homozygous dominant, heterozygous, and homozygous recessive birds. The first two of these differed only quantitatively in their capacity for absorption of agglutinins against all three types of cells, but, in birds considered homozygous for the recessive allele, the blood cells were qualitatively different. They could absorb only agglutinins for their own type. From tested sires and dams mated together in the six possible combinations of homozygotes and heterozygotes in pairs, 472 offspring were tested, and in all six matings the segregations observed fitted closely to those expected for a single pair of alleles with dominance incomplete.

Literature Cited

Asmundson, V. S. 1945. Crooked neck dwarf in the domestic fowl. *J. Heredity.* **36**:173–176.

―― and W. R. Hinshaw. 1938. On the inheritance of pendulous crop in turkeys (*Meleagris gallopavo*). *Poultry Sci.,* **17**:276–285.

Boyd, W. C., and O. E. Alley. 1940. Individual blood differences in chickens. *J. Heredity,* **31**:135–136.

Byerly, T. C., and M. A. Jull. 1932. "Stickiness" a lethal factor in the domestic fowl. *J. Exptl. Zoöl.,* **62**:489–498.

Cole, R. K. 1942. The "talpid lethal" in the domestic fowl. *J. Heredity,* **33**:82–86.

Dunn, L. C. 1923. A lethal gene in fowls. *Am. Naturalist,* **57**:345–349.

Hinshaw, W. R., and V. S. Asmundson. 1936. Observations on pendulous crop in turkeys. *J. Am. Vet. Med. Assoc.,* **88** (n.s. **41**):154–165.

Hungerford, T. G. 1939. Pendulous crop of turkeys. *Agr. Gaz. N. S. Wales,* **50**: 231–232, 282–284.

Hutt, F. B. 1934. A hereditary lethal muscle contracture in cattle. *J. Heredity,* **25**:41–46.

―――. 1935. Hereditary blindness in the fowl. *Poultry Sci.,* **14**:297.

―― and G. P. Child. 1934. Congenital tremor in young chicks. *J. Heredity,* **25**:341–350.

Jeffrey, F. P. 1941. Hereditary microphthalmia in the domestic fowl. *J. Heredity,* **32**:310–312.

―――, F. R. Beaudette, and C. B. Hudson. 1937. An inherited kidney abnormality in the domestic fowl. *J. Heredity,* **28**:335–338.

Jull, M. A., and J. P. Quinn. 1931. Inheritance in poultry. *J. Heredity,* **22**:147–154.

Karshner, W. M. 1928. Hemoagglutination. III. Hemoagglutination in the blood of chickens. *J. Lab. Clin. Med.,* **14**:346–350.

Knowlton, F. L. 1929. Congenital loco in chicks. *Oregon Agr. Expt. Sta. Bull.* 253.

Kozelka, A. W. 1933. Individuality of the red blood cells of inbred strains of fowls. *J. Immunol.*, **24**:519–530.

Landsteiner, K., and P. Miller. 1924. On individual differences of the blood of chickens and ducks. *Proc. Soc. Exptl. Biol. Med.*, **22**:100–102.

Lienhart, R. 1937. Quelques cas nouveaux de léthalité. *Compt. rend. soc. biol.*, **126**:336–342.

Olson, C., Jr. 1943. The inheritance of an agglutinogen of the chicken erythrocyte. *J. Immunol.*, **47**:149–154.

Rosenberg, L. E. 1947. Histological studies of muscle from crooked neck dwarf fowl. *Anat. Record*, **97**:277–282.

Schütt, G. 1929. Über das Vorkommen von Blutgruppen bei Hühnern. Inaugural Dissertation, Tierärztl. Hochsch. Hannover.

Terentyeva, E. L. 1933. Inheritance of isohaemagglutinogen in the fowl (Russian). *Biol. Zhur.*, **2**:64–69.

Thomsen, O. 1934. Untersuchungen über erbliche Blutgruppenantigene bei Hühnern. *Hereditas*, **19**:243–258.

———. 1936. Untersuchungen über erbliche Blutgruppenantigene bei Hühnern, II. *Hereditas*, **22**:129–144.

Todd, C. 1930. Cellular individuality in the higher animals, with special reference to the individuality of the red blood corpuscle. II. *Proc. Roy. Soc. (London)* B, **106**:20–44.

———. 1930a. Cellular individuality in the higher animals, with special reference to the individuality of the red blood corpuscle. II. *Proc. Roy. Soc. (London)* B, **107**:197–205.

———. 1935. Cellular individuality in the higher animals, with special reference to the individuality of the red blood corpuscle. III. *Proc. Roy. Soc. (London)* B, **117**:358–366.

Upp, C. W. 1934. Further data on the inheritance of dwarfism in fowls. *Poultry Sci.*, **13**:157–165.

Wiener, A. S. 1933. Individuality of the blood in higher animals. *Z. ind. Abst. Vererb.*, **66**:31–48.

———. 1934. Individuality of the blood in higher animals. II. Agglutinogens in red blood cells of fowls. *J. Genetics*, **29**:1–8.

CHAPTER 9

VARIATIONS IN BODY SIZE

Most of the inherited conditions described in previous chapters are caused by mutation of a single gene. The majority segregate clearly in Mendelian ratios. Unfortunately for the poultryman, some of the inherited characters of greatest value are caused by so many genes that their number cannot be determined by existing techniques. Because of this it is much more difficult to predict the outcome when such "multiple-factor" characters are involved in a mating than with uni-factorial things like rose comb or congenital loco.

The problem is complicated still further by the fact that most of the economically desirable traits, such as the capacity for egg production, the ability to resist disease, and the ability to produce large eggs, are affected not only by a complex of many genes but also by various modifying influences in the environment. A good example of such a character is body size.

This chapter considers (1) how variable body size can be, (2) some of the conditions that cause its variation at different ages, (3) how differences in size are inherited, (4) increasing body size by breeding, (5) some specific genes with major effects on size, (6) genes with effects localized in certain regions of the body, and finally (7) what little is known about how genes operate to cause differences in size.

These points are considered in some detail, not merely because body size is economically important, but also to illustrate the variability, complexity, and genetic behavior of a familiar physiological character.

EXTENT OF VARIATION IN BODY SIZE

It would be difficult for anyone to say with accuracy just how big chickens can grow or how small they may remain in the bantam breeds. However, some idea of the range in size from the smaller to the larger breeds is conveyed by the following extremes found by the author in weighing 66 pairs of mature birds, representing 36 breeds and varieties, at a poultry show:

247

	Smallest, grams	Largest, grams
Among 66 females:		
Rose-comb Bantam........................	400	
Light Brahma.............................	...	3,920
Among 66 males:		
Modern Black-breasted Red Game Bantam.....	535	
White Langshan............................	...	4,970

Undoubtedly fowls larger or smaller than these extremes can be found. The "standard" weights in Jersey Black Giants (see Table 27) call for cocks weighing 5,902 gm. and cockerels of 4,994 gm. These are both heavier than the largest male mentioned above, but none of three Jersey Black Giant males weighed at the poultry show in question exceeded 4,300 gm. The extremes given merely show that it is not difficult to find large birds nearly ten times the size of the smaller varieties.

More important than the extremes in size are the weights of the breeds of economic importance. Some of these are given in Table 27, the figures quoted being the "standard" weights called for by "The American Standard of Perfection."

TABLE 27. STANDARD WEIGHTS OF A FEW IMPORTANT BREEDS
(In pounds)

	Cock	Hen	Cockerel	Pullet
Plymouth Rocks...............	9.5	7.5	8	6
Rhode Island Reds.............	8.5	6.5	7.5	5.5
Jersey Black Giants............	13	10	11	8
Leghorns.....................	6	4.5	5	4
Orpingtons...................	10	8	8.5	7
Sussex.......................	9	7	7.5	6
Various Ornamental Bantams...	1.6	1.4	1.4	1.2

In contrast with the figures for large breeds given in Table 27, the average weight of 18 mature females of the Red Jungle Fowl was found by the author to be only 749 gm., which is 1⅔ pounds. If that species is the progenitor of all domestic breeds, it is evident that the size of the fowl has been increased since its domestication to weights varying in different breeds from about three to six times that of the wild birds. Presumably this has been accomplished by selection on the part of the breeders and by the utilization of many of the mutations affecting size that have undoubtedly occurred since the first Jungle Fowls were kept in captivity.

VARIATION IN SIZE AT DIFFERENT AGES

At Hatching. The weight of the chick at hatching time depends more upon the weight of the egg than upon anything else. Under normal conditions of incubation, chicks weigh from 61 to 68 per cent of the weight of the eggs from which they hatch (Halbersleben and Mussehl, 1922; Jull and Quinn, 1925; Hays and Sanborn, 1929; and others).

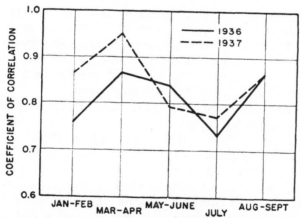

FIG. 69. Seasonal changes in the dependence of chick weight at hatching upon weight of the egg from which it hatched, as measured by the coefficient of correlation between the two. (*From Galpin in Proc. Roy. Soc. Edinburgh.*)

A better idea of the extent to which size of the chick depends upon the size of the egg is conveyed by the high positive coefficient of correlation between these two variables. This was found by Upp (1928) to vary from .68 to .84, and by Galpin (1938) to range from .76 to .95. In eggs that were weighed and put into the incubator on the day when laid, Graham (1932) found that the correlation between egg weight and chick weight was .95. Galpin noted that in hatches distributed through 9 months the dependence of chick weight upon egg weight increased from January to March and April, decreased thereafter till July, and then increased again in August and September (Fig. 69). This fluctuation she attributed to changes in the ability of the embryo to utilize the nutrients in the egg, these changes resulting from variations in the dam's metabolism associated with differences in the activity of the thyroid gland.

While it is obvious from these very high correlations that weight of the chick is determined more by the weight of the egg than by anything else, it is also generally recognized that the chicks are somewhat larger when hatched from eggs incubated in an atmosphere of high relative humidity than when the eggs are incubated at a low humidity.

When just hatched, male chicks are slightly heavier than female chicks from the same dam and also weigh more in relation to egg weight than do the females (Munro and Kosin, 1940). These differences are too small to be recognized in any small number of chicks and can be detected only by statistical study. Since the eggs that give rise to males do not differ in weight from those producing females (Jull and Quinn, 1925), the differences between the sexes at hatching must result from sex differences in metabolism, in growth, or in both, during embryonic development. According to later studies by Kosin and Munro (1941) the difference is not apparent at the eighteenth day of incubation and arises in part from a greater utilization of calcium in the shell by male embryos during the final stages of incubation.

During Growth. Contrary to a common belief among poultrymen, the size of the chick at hatching has little or nothing to do with its subsequent growth (Upp, 1928). Hays and Sanborn (1929) did find a relationship between weight when hatched and weight at 4 weeks, but at 21 weeks no such relationship was evident.

Inspection of any flock of growing chickens shows that some birds grow more rapidly than others. According to experiments by Dove (1935) those growing most rapidly are able to select a diet conducive to such growth when given an opportunity to do so. There are also differences in growth rate to 8 weeks among the families of different dams (Asmundson and Lerner, 1933) and in progenies from different sires (Jaap and Morris, 1937) within one breed. Presumably these indicate hereditary differences. Evidence to that effect is found in the demonstration by Schnetzler (1936) that in two generations of mass selection he could differentiate two strains of Barred Plymouth Rocks, one of which grew rapidly to 8 and 12 weeks of age, while the other grew much more slowly.

However, it is not clear that hereditary differences in growth within a breed, as measured by weight at 8 weeks or some later age, represent an inheritance separate from that responsible for ultimate body weight. Schnetzler found the correlations between weight at 8 and 12 weeks and weight at maturity to be +.29 and +.39, respectively. On the other hand, Jaap and Morris considered the rate of growth up to 8 weeks to be independent of the weight at maturity.

From the practical standpoint it is of considerable importance, particularly to producers of broilers, that, by breeding, strains can easily be differentiated which, like Schnetzler's, grow more rapidly than the average bird of an unselected population. It is debatable whether or not rapid growth is desirable in birds to be kept for egg production and breeding, but there can be no doubt that it is valuable in birds raised for market.

Breed Differences. In general the heavy breeds grow more rapidly than Leghorns, but in the first 4 weeks Leghorns usually grow faster than the heavy breeds. Although much of the difference in absolute weights between samples of these two classes results from growth slackening off after 8 weeks of age in the Leghorns, the heavier breeds usually grow more rapidly than the light ones after 4 weeks of age and sometimes right from hatching. These facts have been shown in comparisons of growth in heavy breeds with that in White Leghorns by Card and Kirkpatrick (1918), Warren (1930), Waters (1931), Asmundson and Lerner (1934), and others. Similarly Lerner and Asmundson (1932) found Light Sussex to grow more rapidly than Anconas. There is less definite information about breed differences in this respect within the heavy breeds, but the general impression that New Hampshires are characterized by very rapid growth was substantiated by Kempster (1941), who found that his representatives of that breed grew more rapidly than did White Plymouth Rocks, Rhode Island Reds, and White Wyandottes. This applied to the actual weights at different ages up to 40 weeks and also to the increments in weight in each 4-week period up to 20 weeks. After that age the gains in weight were greater in the other three breeds than in the New Hampshires. This indicates that birds of the latter breed attain a higher proportion of their adult weight in the first 20 weeks than do other breeds.

Sex Differences. Male chickens grow more rapidly than do females (Jull, 1923; Ackerson and Mussehl, 1930; and others). The actual body weights at any one period after 8 weeks are somewhat misleading measures of the difference between the sexes in growth rate, because they represent the differences accumulated during all the previous growth period. Actually the difference between the sexes in the rate of gain is comparatively slight up to about 8 weeks but is heightened thereafter as the rate of growth slackens in females (Fig. 70). Kempster (1941) found that the difference between the sexes at 8 weeks was greater in White Leghorns than in Rhode Island Reds. This is to be expected because growth slackens and terminates sooner in the former breed than in the latter. Adverse environmental conditions retard the growth of males more than that of females (Bird and Gutteridge, 1934).

Apart from differences in body weight, another indication that females mature sooner than males is found in the fact that, in the humerus, radius, ulna, femur, and tibio-tarsus, ossification is completed 10 to 47 days earlier in females than in males (Latimer, 1927). This is also shown, as Holmes, Piggott, and Moore (1932) found, by a higher

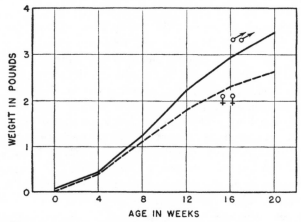

Fig. 70. Sex differences in the rate of growth of White Leghorns. (*From data of Kempster.*)

ash content of the tibia in females than in males at 6 and 9 weeks of age.

Other Factors. Growth of chicks is retarded by such environmental handicaps as overcrowding, disease, parasites, faulty diet, and similar adverse conditions. Hays and Sanborn (1929), Asmundson and Lerner (1933), and Kempster (1941) all found that early-hatched chickens grew faster than late-hatched ones. The reason for this is not clear, but Kempster's data indicate that the hot summer weather to which his later hatches were exposed during their period of rapid growth was a major factor. However, the retardation of growth caused by the hot weather was largely overcome by unusually great gains in weight (compensatory growth) later on after the peak of the summer heat had passed. Growth of chicks is also stimulated by the hybrid vigor found in some crosses of different breeds, but discussion of this is reserved for Chap. 15.

Variation in Adults. The weight of a mature, healthy fowl depends upon (1) the size of its skeleton, (2) the amount of organs, muscles, skin, and feathers supported by that skeleton, and (3) the amount of stored fat. The second and third of these variables, particularly the latter, may change considerably with differing environmental conditions, but the skeleton is little affected after maturity. Schneider and Dunn (1924) and Kopeć (1926) found the variability of body weight in White Leghorns, as measured by the coefficient of variation, to range from 12 to 18 per cent, whereas the coefficients of variation for bone measurements were only 3 to 4.5 per cent. Weight of the plumage is even more variable than that of the body (Kopeć). Genetic studies of size could be made more accurately by measuring skeletal dimensions, as Maw (1935) did, than by considering body weights, but the latter are more easily obtained.

Sex Dimorphism. Studies of the genetic basis for adult size are complicated by the fact that in all breeds the males are considerably larger than the females. This means that either (1) the weights must be considered separately for each sex, thereby reducing the numbers and necessitating consideration of two sets of data instead of one, or (2) the weights for one sex must be corrected to make them equivalent to those of the other.

The second of these alternatives was used by Waters (1931), in whose Leghorns, Brahmas, and their descendants the males were 24 to 32 per cent heavier than the females in seven different populations. He converted the weights of females to equivalent male weights by multiplying them by 1.28. Punnett (1923) used 1.25 as his conversion factor.

Sex differences in the skeleton are somewhat less. In the combined length of the humerus, ulna, femur, and tibio-tarsus (two proximal bones in the fore- and hind limbs) males exceeded females by 16 per cent in the White Leghorns of Schneider and Dunn (1924), 15.6 per cent in those of Latimer (1927), and 13.4 per cent in the miscellaneous Leghorns studied by Hutt (1929). The difference is not constant for all bones. In Hutt's material, sex dimorphism in the appendicular skeleton was greatest in the tarso-metatarsus (16.5 per cent) and least in the phalanges of the toes (7 to 10 per cent).

The difference in rates of growth of the two sexes and in their ultimate sizes is not caused by the male and female hormones. Mature capons do not differ in skeletal dimensions from normal males (Landauer, 1937) and are usually heavier because they carry more fat. Similarly poulardes remain small in size, as do normal females. Obviously the male hormones do not normally stimulate or protract growth, nor do female hormones inhibit it. The differences in the size of male and female fowls are apparently determined by sex-linked genes, of which the males, with two sex chromosomes, must have more than the females, which have only one sex chromosome. Evidence that sex-linked genes do exert marked effects upon body size is considered later in this chapter.

Measures of Size. The advantages of skeletal measurements over body weight as measures of size were mentioned earlier. Fortunately it is possible to make measurements in the living bird of a bone that gives a good indication of body size. This is the tarso-metatarsus in the skeleton, or the shank in the live bird. A special device for measuring length of the shank devised by Burmester and Lerner (1937) proved so accurate that with its use the correlation between shank length in the living bird and length of the tarso-metatarsus, as measured in the dissected and cleaned bones, was +.968. Using this device, Lerner (1937) found the correlation between shank length and body weight to be +.659. Strains of White Leghorns characterized by differences in body size showed corresponding differences in length of the shank. By selection in that breed, Lerner (1946) increased shank length by 8.1 mm., with corresponding increase of 210 gm. in body weight in December. Contrary to appearances, length of the shank is not disproportionally reduced in bantam breeds (Lerner, 1941; Jaap *et al.*, 1943).

It is not known whether any other one bone gives as accurate an indication of body size as does the tarso-metatarsus; but, apart from the fact that it is probably more accurately measured in the living bird than is any other large bone, because it is comparatively bare of both feathers and muscles, there are some indications that it is a more sensitive indicator of body size than other bones are likely to be. In the Leghorns of Latimer (1927), ossification of the tarso-metatarsus was completed relatively early in females (139 days) but relatively late in males (195 days). Of the 6 longest bones of the appendicular skeleton, the tibia and tarso-metatarsus were the latest to complete growth in length. Hutt (1929) found both variability and sex dimorphism to be greater in the tarso-metatarsus than in any other of 13 bones measured in the wing and leg. Moreover, in his three dwarf fowls the relative length of the tarso-metatarsus was reduced much more than that of the 2 other bones with which it was compared.

The tarso-metatarsus is apparently among the last bones to complete growth, but it is also more readily affected than others in the limbs by processes that cause growth to slacken early, as it does in females and (still earlier) in dwarf fowls. It is probably for these reasons that it is such a good indication of body weight.

THE INHERITANCE OF DIFFERENCES IN SIZE

Differences in body size in the fowl, as in other species, depend upon a great many different genes, the exact number of which has not yet been determined. In accord with the expectation for any character dependent upon multiple factors, a cross between two breeds differing in size yields an F_1 generation that is usually intermediate in size between the two parents, except that in some crosses hybrid vigor may

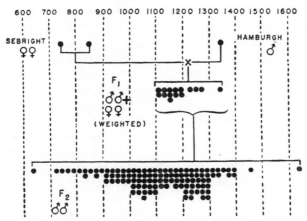

Fig. 71. Diagrammatic illustration of inheritance of body weight in a cross of Sebright Bantam ♀ × Hamburg ♂. Weights of the birds in grams are given by the figures at the top. Each dot represents one bird. Only the males are shown for the F_2 generation. Details are given in the text. (*From Punnett, courtesy of Macmillan & Co., Ltd.*)

raise the mean toward the weight of the larger parent. In the F_2 generation, variability is greater than in the F_1, and the parental sizes are likely to be recovered in large populations. F_2 birds smaller than the small parent or larger than the large ones (*i.e., transgressive inheritance*) may be found in rather large F_2 populations, but theoretically the chance of getting them will vary inversely as the number of genes differentiating the two parents with respect to size.

A Typical Example. The first detailed study of differences in size in the fowl was a cross made by Punnett and Bailey (1914) between Golden-pencilled Hamburgs and Silver Sebrights. The results afford a good example of what happens when two breeds are crossed that differ somewhat in size (Fig. 71).

Hens and cocks of the smaller breed weighed about 600 and 750 gm., respectively, while in the Hamburgs the weights were about 1,100 gm.

for hens and 1,350 gm. for cocks. In Fig. 71, the weights of the parental females (Sebrights) and of the F_1 females are converted to equivalent male weights by multiplying them by 1.25. It is clear that the F_1 generation tends to approach the Hamburg size and that there is a great variation in the F_2 generation. The fact that the smallest male in the F_2 population was smaller than the Sebright, while the largest exceeded the Hamburg, suggests that comparatively few genes for size were involved. On theoretical grounds, the chance of getting either extreme of the F_2 range is $1/4^n$, where $n =$ the number of gene pairs segregating from the F_1. Thus, if only four pairs of genes were responsible for the differences in size between Sebrights and Hamburgs, one would need a population of 4^4, or 256, to get the largest and smallest birds possible in the F_2 generation. The recovery here of extremes beyond the parental weights in an F_2 population of only 112 males led Punnett and Bailey to postulate that the differences observed could be accounted for by four pairs of genes with cumulative effects. However, as Punnett (1923) has later pointed out, the environmental conditions affecting size, particularly in an experiment conducted over several seasons, may vary enough to cause some differences in the weights, and it is therefore perhaps best not to be too positive about the actual number of genes affecting size in this cross. This is particularly so because the range of normal variation in the parental breeds was not determined, and it is therefore possible that the Sebrights and Hamburgs used may not have been average representatives.

Further evidence that the variation in the F_2 generation resulted primarily from the segregation of genes for size was found when Punnett and Bailey raised two F_3 populations. One of these came from the largest F_2 birds, which yielded progeny with average weights in females and males of 1,150 and 1,360 gm., respectively. At the other end of the range, two matings of the smaller F_2 birds yielded in one case F_3 progeny below 600 gm. in weight and in the other case, where the parents were a little heavier, progeny with weights around 700 gm., or less, for females, and 800 gm. for males. This breeding test showed that the largest F_2 birds carried several or many genes for size which were lacking in the smaller birds of the same population.

Other Studies of Body Size. Results of a cross between Silver-spangled Hamburgs and White Cornish were interpreted by May (1925) as indicating that the F_1 and F_2 generations equalled the Cornish in weight (which he attributed to hybrid vigor) and were no more variable than the parent breeds. His data show, however, that the age of 10 months, on which his conclusions were based, was adequate for measuring adult size in the Hamburgs and in the Cornish females, but not for the

Cornish males, which continued to grow beyond that age. When this is considered, his data show the F_1 birds to be intermediate between the parents, though closer in size to the Cornish. As for variability, it seems doubtful that his F_2 population contained enough birds for an adequate measure of the variation possible in the second generation from such a cross.

Waters (1931) made reciprocal crosses between White Leghorns and Light Brahmas. Weights in the latter breed at 10 months (3,940 gm. in males) were approximately twice those of the White Leghorns. The F_1 and F_2 generations were intermediate in mean weight between the two parental breeds, and there was more variation in the F_2 population than in any other. This is in accord with the expectation for the operation of an undetermined number of multiple factors with cumulative effects. Presumably some of these might have more influence on size than others. Waters considered that the difference of about 2,000 gm. between Leghorns and Brahmas (males) could be accounted for by two pairs of genes with major effects, each gene good for an increase of 500 gm. in heterozygotes, or 1,000 gm. in homozygotes, above the 2,000-gm. weight of the Leghorns. Convincing proof of this interpretation has not yet been advanced. The attempts to account for hereditary characters showing continuous variation, such as body size, egg production, and hatchability of eggs, by making arbitrary classes that are assumed to be indicative of certain simple genotypes have not been very successful. Little is lost by admitting that existing genetical techniques do not permit accurate determination of the number of multiple factors involved in such cases.

Results similar to those of Punnett and Bailey and of Waters were obtained in crosses of Silky × White Leghorn and Faverolle × Buff Leghorn made by Lauth (1935). In each case backcrosses of F_1 birds to the smaller parental one yielded offspring considerably smaller in size than did backcrosses to the larger parental race. When Phillips (1914) crossed Rouen and Mallard ducks, mean weights of males in these two parent breeds were 2,417 and 1,068 gm., respectively. The F_1 males at 1,661 gm. were somewhat smaller than the mid-point between the weights of the parental races, but the F_2 birds were heavier, with a mean weight of 1,740 gm. Weights for the females corresponded to these, though smaller in all classes. Variability was greater in the F_2 population than in any other. This is typical multiple-factor inheritance except that the F_1 birds were rather small.

An exception to this general behavior of differences in size when large and small breeds are crossed was noted by Jull and Quinn (1931) and by Maw (1935), who found the mean weights of their F_1 birds to be somewhat closer to those of the smaller parent than to the large one. In both these experiments the discrepancy in size between the two breeds crossed was greater than in any of those previously mentioned— so great, indeed, that the crosses were made possible only by utilizing artificial insemination. With allowances for sex dimorphism, the Barred Rocks used by Jull and Quinn were about four times the size of their Rose-comb Bantams, but Maw's Brahmas weighed five times as much as the Sebright Bantams that he used as the smaller breed. In both studies variability was greater in the F_2 generation than in any other, and in neither were there found any F_2 birds so large or so small as to exceed the normal ranges of variation in the parental breeds. In Maw's crosses the unusually small size of the F_1 birds was shown by a careful study to have arisen, in part at least, from the action of a sex-linked gene or genes that depressed body size. Similar genes may have been responsible for the small F_1 birds in the cross made by Jull and Quinn.

Origins of Breeds of Different Sizes. In view of the evidence from these various crosses it seems reasonably certain that large breeds are large because of the cumulative action of an undetermined number of genes inducing large size. Undoubtedly these have been accumulated by constant selection on the part of poultrymen who preferred large birds to small ones. Breeds of medium size, such as Hamburgs and Leghorns, evidently lack some genes for size that are present in larger breeds. Bantam breeds undoubtedly have still fewer of such genes; but, as is shown in the next section, the small size in some of them, at least, results not merely from a shortage of genes promoting larger size but also from the presence of dominant genes that reduce body size. It is not clear to what extent the bantams have been bred by continuous elimination of genes for size, but the production of many varieties of bantams that in color and other characteristics are miniature replicas of larger breeds suggests that this has been the usual method. The process would be greatly expedited by the incorporation of dominant genes for dwarfing, but it is not yet known how many bantam breeds carry such genes.

Comparative Influence of Environment and Heredity. The old question whether the influence of the environment is greater than that of heredity might well be asked with respect to body size. It is clear that the genetic potentialities for size are greatly limited in the newly hatched chick by the size of the egg from which that chick hatches. Other limitations may operate during the period of growth, but when the effects of these are not persistent or not too severe, the size attained at maturity is likely to be determined by heredity. The chickens of Kempster (1941), which were retarded by hot weather, recovered and by compensatory rapid growth eventually attained a weight normal for the strain. Similarly Heuser and Norris (1934) found that, in four lots of chicks on diets containing different levels of protein, growth during the period of most rapid development from hatching to 10 weeks was directly proportional to the amount of protein. Lowering of the protein content slowed down the rate of growth. At 29 weeks of age, however,

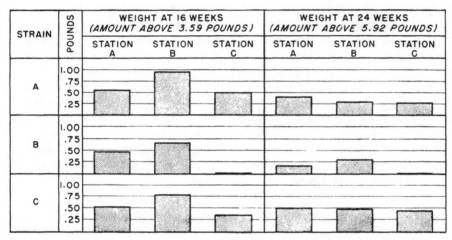

FIG. 72. Mean weights at two ages of Barred Rock cockerels of three different strains from each of which samples were reared at three different experimental stations. At 16 weeks the influence of environment predominated; the chickens were uniformly heaviest at station B and lightest at C, regardless of strain. At 24 weeks the influence of heredity was predominant; the cockerels were consistently heaviest in strain C and lightest in B, regardless of the environment. The base weights, 3.59 and 5.92 pounds, are those for strain B at station C, which happened to be lowest at both ages. (*Designed from data of Gutteridge and O'Neil.*)

the lots that grew slowly in their earlier stages had made up the deficiency, for all lots finally weighed approximately the same.

The comparative effects of heredity and environment upon growth, size, and conformation were studied in another way by Gutteridge and O'Neil (1942), who arranged an interesting experiment in which three somewhat different strains of Barred Rocks were all compared at each of the three different experimental farms on which the strains had previously been bred. The body weights of the cockerels at 16 and 24 weeks are shown in Fig. 72, where they are given as the mean increment in each lot above the mean weight of the smallest lot among the nine compared at each age.

At 16 weeks the influence of environment was very marked, for the cockerels were consistently heaviest at station B and lightest at station C in each strain. Measurements of the muscling on the breast and overlying the tibia showed also that the birds at station B were in much better flesh than those at A and C. However, even at 24 weeks of age, when these cockerels would hardly be mature, the influence of heredity was predominant over that of the environment, for the birds of strain C were consistently heaviest and those of strain B consistently lightest, irrespective of the environment in which they had been reared (Fig. 72). At that age the maximum differences due to environment were 0.14, 0.29, and 0.02 pound in strains A, B, and C, respectively, whereas at the three different stations the maximum differences between strains were 0.34, 0.20, and 0.52 pound at stations A, B, and C, respectively.

Altogether, the evidence indicates that where large size is desired at an early age, as in the production of broilers, much can be accomplished by providing the optimum environment, including a diet promoting rapid growth. Conversely, when size at maturity is the major consideration, as is usually the case in turkey production, the objective is more likely to be attained by careful breeding, and the rate of growth during the first 2 or 3 months is not nearly so important.

INCREASING BODY SIZE BY BREEDING

Up to a certain point, large hens lay more eggs and bigger ones than do small ones. Because of these facts and the prejudice against small fowls in the market, breeders of White Leghorns in the United States have by selection considerably increased the size of that breed in the last 30 years. The standard weights for Leghorns were increased in the 1930 edition of "The American Standard of Perfection" by ½ pound in all classes to stand at 6, 5, 4½, and 4 pounds for cocks, cockerels, hens, and pullets, respectively.

Body size can quickly be increased by proper breeding methods. While breeding primarily to increase egg size, Goodale (1935–1936) found that in 5 years the mean weight at first egg in his White Leghorns was increased from 3.44 to 4.23 pounds, an increase of 23 per cent. Part of this difference probably resulted from the age at first egg being 14 days later in the selected stock than in the original birds. However, in weights taken when the fiftieth egg was laid, the selected strain was still 22 per cent heavier than the birds with which selection began. Similarly, by progeny testing, Hutt, Cole, and Bruckner (1941) increased the mean mature weight of their White Leghorns from 1,690 to 1,813 gm., an increase of 7 per cent in four generations of selection. This was done even though selection was directed simultaneously toward capacity for laying, larger egg size, and resistance to disease, with more emphasis upon the last named of these objectives than on any other.

Some indication of the rapidity with which a physiological character can be modified by continuous progeny testing with a single objective in view is conveyed by the demonstration by Goodale (1941) that body size in mice could be increased about 70 per cent in 28 generations of selection. It seems probable that this remarkable change in the population resulted from the accumulation, not only of many genes for large size scattered through the original unselected stock, but also of similar mutations occurring during the course of the experiment. If other physiological characters permit of similar rapid improvement, it is obvious that progeny testing for greater production of milk, eggs, and meat would be highly profitable. In most cases, however, the breeder must keep several different objectives in view, and selection directed toward improvement in four characters proceeds much more slowly than with a single goal.

SPECIFIC GENES AFFECTING SIZE

Thus far only three hereditary variations in size have been sufficiently studied to indicate that they are caused by genes that can be considered as specific entities. One of these is the sex-linked reduction of size already mentioned, in which the birds are normal, another is an autosomal recessive dwarfism accompanied by various pathological conditions, and the third a sex-linked recessive dwarfing.

Dominant Sex-linked Genes Reducing Size

Reciprocal crosses by Maw (1935) of Light Brahmas and Golden Sebright Bantams yielded in the F_1 and F_2 generations definite evidence that the bantams carried a dominant sex-linked gene or genes that counteracted the genes for size contributed by the Brahmas and thereby depressed body size. The theoretical expectations for such a case in the cross Golden Sebright ♂ ♂ × Light Brahma ♀ ♀ are shown in Table 28. On following them through, it is clear that in the F_1 generation the size should be reduced in both sexes. In the F_2 generation all the males should be similarly affected, but only half the females. These latter are the ones that get the Sebright sex chromosome and hence are gold in color and subnormal in size.

The actual results observed by Maw conformed closely to expectations. The F_1 weights were reduced considerably below the mid-points between Brahma and Sebright weights (which were 2,407 for males and 1,851 for females), but both sexes were affected alike, and the males were

TABLE 28.　EXPECTATIONS AND RESULTS IN THE CROSS GOLDEN SEBRIGHT ♂♂ ×
LIGHT BRAHMA ♀♀ *

Population	Genotypes	Expected phenotypes		Observed	
		Color	Size	Birds, number	Mean weight, grams
P₁ Sebright ♂♂......	(sZ) (sZ)	Gold	Reduced	6	816
P₁ Brahma ♀♀......	(Sz) —	Silver	Normal	22	3,102
F₁ ♂♂..............	(sZ) (Sz)	Silver	Reduced	9	1,813
F₁ ♀♀..............	(sZ) —	Gold	Reduced	7	1,410
F₂ ♂♂..............	(sZ) (sZ)	Gold	Reduced ⎫	82	1,277
	(Sz) (sZ)	Silver	Reduced ⎭		
F₂ ♀♀..............	(sZ) —	Gold	Reduced ⎫	69	1,225
	(Sz) —	Silver	Normal ⎭		

* The Sebright sex chromosome, Z, carries dominant genes reducing size; the Brahma sex chromosome,
z, does not (S = silver; s = gold).

about 28 per cent heavier than the females, as is normal. In the F₂
generation, body weights were not given separately for the gold and
silver birds. However, since a reduction in size was to be expected only
in the gold females, not in the silver ones, but in all the males regardless of color, the net effect was to reduce the mean weight for *all* F₂
females much less than that for all F₂ males. It is not surprising,
therefore, that the usual sex difference in weight was reduced to an excess
of only 4 per cent in the males.

Final and critical evidence that the complex reducing size in this
cross was sex linked was provided by comparisons of the silver birds
with the gold ones in both sexes of the F₂ population. Measurements
were taken of five bones in the leg and wing and of two cranial dimensions. With respect to these, there was no difference between S and s
males. None was expected, as all of these carried Z, the sex chromosome from the Sebright. However, it was expected that the silver
ʼemales would be larger than the gold because the latter carried Z while
the former had z, the sex chromosome from the Brahma. In all seven
items measured the mean size for 39 S females exceeded that for 43 s
females by statistically significant differences.

In the reciprocal cross Light Brahma ♂♂ × Golden Sebright ♀♀,
size of the F₁ males should be reduced by the Z chromosome received
from their dams, but size of the F₁ females should be normal, as their
z chromosome comes from the Brahma sire. As a result, the sex di-

morphism in size should be much less in this F_1 generation than in that from the reverse cross. Maw found this to be true, although it was more evident in the skeletal measurements than in the body weights. Altogether, the evidence clearly shows that Maw's Sebrights carried a dominant sex-linked gene or genes with a significant capacity to reduce body size. Some points of similarity in these crosses and those with Rose-comb Bantams made by Jull and Quinn (1931) suggest that the same sex-linked complex may be found in other breeds of bantams.

Recessive Sex-linked Dwarfism, *dw*

The author has studied in recent years a remarkable type of dwarfism that is caused by a single sex-linked recessive gene, *dw*. Females with this gene weigh about 30 per cent less at maturity than their normal *Dw–* sisters, but the effect is even greater in males. From one mating that produced both homozygous and heterozygous males, the mean weight of the latter at about 7 months of age was 2,965 gm. For their homozygous brothers of the same age it was only 1,712 gm., a reduction of 42 per cent. Two of these males are shown in Fig. 73.

Fig. 73. Dwarfing caused by the sex-linked recessive gene, *dw*. For these two full brothers hatched on the same day, the weights at 209 days of age, when this photograph was taken, were 3,030 gm. for the *Dw dw* male on the left, but only 1,540 gm. for his *dw dw* brother on the right.

Although this mutation is still being studied, some facts concerning it are already evident. There is no sign of dwarfing when the chicks are hatched. Some of them are recognizable as dwarfs at 8 to 10 weeks of age, but classification is most accurate when the birds are 5 months of age or more. At that time the difference between dwarfs and normal siblings is obvious in all males and in about 98 per cent of the females, or more. It is apparently completely recessive.

Contrary to the situation with the type of dwarfism considered in the next section, these dwarfs mature sexually, and both sexes reproduce normally. Experiments are under way to determine possible effects of the gene upon age at first egg, egg production, and viability.

Recessive Dwarfism, td

It seems probable that the kind of dwarfism for which Landauer (1929) gave a detailed description but no genetic data is the same as that for which Upp (1934) provided extensive genetic data but less description. The connecting link was provided by Warren's dwarfs, which Landauer found to resemble closely his own specimen and which (according to Warren's data as reported by Upp) segregated from carrier parents in the same ratio as did Upp's. Moreover, an earlier brief description of the latter's birds by Mayhew and Upp (1932) conforms to that given by Landauer.

Description. These dwarfs show a general retardation of growth which is recognizable at 2 to 4 weeks of age. The outer toe is curled backward, and this is sometimes evident at hatching. The skull is broad and high in relation to its length, and the upper beak is bent downward. The tissues around the eye appear swollen. The tongue is shortened and swollen. The legs are shortened, more so in the tarso-metatarsus than in the femur and tibio-tarsus. The sacrum is disproportionately small and high, so that the tail seems abnormally high on the body. There is almost no endochondral bone in the shaft of the long bones. Landauer found the thyroids of his specimen to be enlarged and consisting mostly of aplastic tissue with very small cells entirely lacking in colloid. None of the dwarfs became sexually mature.

Upp's data indicate that, of 73 dwarfs hatched in one season, half died before reaching 4 weeks of age and the remainder between 4 and 20 weeks of age. However, Mayhew and Upp earlier reported one bird that lived to be more than a year and a half old. The condition can therefore be considered as an obligate lethal character, with delayed lethal action, or perhaps as a semi-lethal one.

Landauer considered this syndrome as resulting from hypofunction of the thyroid gland and akin to the condition in man designated as *myxoedema infantilis.* Upp (1932) was unable to modify it by treatment with pituitary preparations. Similarly a brief treatment of one bird with thyroid gland was apparently ineffective in a dwarf 190 days old.

Genetics. Dwarfs of this type are evidently homozygous for a recessive autosomal gene, for which the symbol *td* (thyrogenous dwarfism) is proposed. In one year Upp (1934) obtained from carrier parents 236 normal chicks and 70 dwarfs, which is a close fit to the expectation of 230:76. Since this observed ratio applied to chicks that hatched and did not include any that died during incubation, it is evident that the lethal action of the mutation is exerted in very few cases during incubation, if at all.

It is noteworthy that the dwarfs of this type studied by Landauer, Warren, and Upp all occurred in Rhode Island Reds, but in three different flocks that were not likely to be closely related.

CONFORMATION; GENES WITH LOCALIZED EFFECTS

Although there are on record a number of instances in which breeds differing in conformation have been crossed, there is very little definite information about the inheritance of variations localized in certain regions of the body, which are the underlying conditions responsible for differences in shape. This is chiefly because shape is so difficult to measure and to describe in accurate terms but also because variations in shape generally depend not upon single mutations but upon many factors. These are probably identical in many cases, if not most, with genes determining body size, since variations in shape must arise from variations in the rate and duration of growth in different parts of the skeleton or in the muscles that overlie it. In living birds the measurement of shape is complicated by variations in the length and density of the plumage. Kopeć (1926) found that his Orpingtons and Leghorns did not differ in skeletal dimensions and indices of shape as much as he had been led to expect from their external appearances and attributed the disparity in shape of the living birds in part to differences in the plumage, which he showed to be proportionately heavier in the Orpingtons.

Differences in conformation are most accurately measured by the dimensions of the bones and by indices showing the relation of one or more bones to others. It would seem axiomatic that differences in shape must depend upon growth processes affecting some bones differently from others, but one could still argue that the genes for growth of the skeleton have general effects and that different bones react differently to them.

Examples of genes affecting certain parts of the fowl's skeleton disproportionately are afforded by the creeper mutation, which shortens the legs more than it shortens the wings, and by rumplessness. The latter has a marked effect on conformation, but its effects seem localized in the synsacrum and the pygostyle. The lethal gene that shortens the legs of certain Cornish fowls is also in this class. Evidence that genes with effects less conspicuous than these operate to affect shape was found by Dunn (1928), whose several inbred families of White Leghorns differed in shape of the head, in femoro-tibial index, and in ulno-humeral index. Differentiation in any of these three indices was apparently independent of differences in the other two and in total size. From statistical analyses of Dunn's data, Wright (1932) concluded that the preponderant influence upon size was exerted by factors with general effects but that, in addition, other genes affected the dimensions of the head and still others affected the legs.

Breed Differences in Conformation. One has only to compare a good specimen of the Cornish (Indian Game) breed with a Leghorn or with a Rhode Island Red to realize that breeds do differ in conformation. This applies even to living birds of these three breeds as well as to dressed carcasses. Other differences in the shapes of breeds undoubtedly exist, although few are so obvious as the example given. However, some breeds that appear to differ are really more alike than they seem. Lerner (1937a) compared Plymouth Rocks and Minorcas with respect to the growth of the pectoralis major muscle and of the leg bones in relation to body weight but found no great difference between the breeds. It seems possible, however, that the measures used were not adequate to reveal differences in conformation in these two breeds, since they did not consider length, breadth, or depth of the body, dimensions in which differential growth of parts could greatly affect body shape. In the Leghorns of Dunn (1928), the families differed more in dimensions of the cranium than in proportions of bones in the limbs.

Using as a measure of conformation the ratio, (shank length)/(cube root of body weight), which Jaap had previously found to be the most satisfactory single criterion of body shape, Jaap and Thompson (1940) found significant differences in this measure among females representing five different breeds. These were fairly consistent in populations studied in 2 successive years. Plymouth Rocks (White and Barred) and Rhode Island Reds were much alike. Orpingtons and Wyandottes were alike but different from the first group, and Leghorns differed from all the rest in having longer shanks in proportion to body weight than any of the other four breeds.

Inheritance of Conformation. There is little definite information about the inheritance of body form in the fowl. This is not surprising in view of the difficulty of measuring conformation and the fact that it has been considered in only a few crosses. Ghigi and Taibell (1927) found that the F_1 generation from the cross Leghorn $\times$ Indian Game (Cornish) resembled the latter parent in shape and length of tarsus but were intermediate in size. In an F_2 generation of 55 birds, 41 were intermediate, 3 somewhat like the Indian Game and 11 more like Leghorns. No actual measurements or indices of shape were reported.

The pioneer study in this field was that of Kopeć (1926, 1927), who made reciprocal crosses between White Leghorns and Buff Orpingtons and measured in the F_1 and F_2 generations various dimensions of the body. Unfortunately, he had comparatively few birds, but enough to indicate that certain dimensions of the body are inherited independently of others. Data given for the F_1 females from both crosses and for F_1 males from the Leghorn dams showed that length of the sternum was in all three populations short like that of the Leghorn parents, or even shorter. In contrast, the tibial region was comparatively long as in the Orpingtons. One index of shape, (depth of thorax)/(length of sternum), which was greater in Orpingtons than in Leghorns, was still greater in all the F_1 populations. The relations of other dimensions and indices in the F_1 birds to those in the parental breeds were less consistent.

According to Jaap (1941) many of the differences in the conformation of different breeds and of crossbreds become evident by 12 weeks of age. His Cornish sires increased the weight of the body in their crossbred offspring in relation to depth of body and length of shank. Maw and Maw (1938) took five different measurements of shape on upward of 50 progeny from each of three different Barred Rock sires, one of which exceeded the smallest in body weight by 200 gm., the other by 700 gm. Progeny of the smallest sire were smallest in all five dimensions, and progeny of the largest sire were largest in length and breadth of back, in depth of body at the front, and in length of shank, but not in length of the keel. The sire that was intermediate in weight produced progeny smaller than those of the biggest male in most dimensions but exceeding them in length of keel. Since this applied both to his sons and to his daughters, it revealed a hereditary capacity in that male for producing progeny with keels relatively long in proportion to other dimensions of the body. This substantiates the evidence from the Leghorn $\times$ Orpington cross of Kopeć that there are special genes determining the relative length of the sternum. It would seem, therefore, that producers of market poultry should be able to increase by breeding the proportion of birds with the long keels desired in such stock.

PHYSIOLOGICAL BASES FOR GENETIC DIFFERENCES IN SIZE

The question, How do genes operate to cause differences in size? is an intriguing one. Are Rhode Island Reds bigger than White Leghorns because they have more cells, or larger cells, or both? Do chicks of these breeds differ in chemical substances affecting the rate of growth? Answers to such questions cannot be given with certainty, but some information on these points is available. Students of these problems have nearly all sought answers by comparing embryos of large breeds with those of small breeds.

Number and Size of Cells. After the first 9 or 10 days of incubation, the embryos of large breeds are slightly larger than those of small breeds (Byerly, 1930; Keller, 1933; Blunn and Gregory, 1935; Kaufman, 1936; and others). However, in such comparisons, as Byerly, Helsel, and Quinn (1938) point out, the factor limiting growth of the embryos of the smaller breed may be the smaller eggs usually laid by hens of such breeds. This complication can be overcome to some extent by comparing embryos that develop in eggs of one size but differ in genetic potentialities with respect to size. Thus, Blunn and Gregory compared the embryos from Rhode Island Red hens (average weight 3,007 gm.) with those from White Leghorn hens that weighed only 1,561 gm. (average) but apparently laid eggs as big as those of the Reds. At 72 hours, 14 days, and 19 days, the Rhode Island Red embryos were heavier than the Leghorn ones, but the differences were not significant. Similarly Byerly *et al.* (1938) found that hybrid embryos from the cross Silky × Rhode Island Red were only slightly bigger than pure Silky embryos when developing in the small eggs of Silkies. When they developed in the large eggs of Rhode Island Reds, the hybrids were closer to the size of Silkies at 14 days but actually larger than the embryos of pure Reds at 18 days. Weight of the hybrid chicks at hatching was clearly dependent to a large extent upon the size of the egg.

If the genetically large embryos are actually larger than genetically small ones, as seems probable, especially during the middle week of incubation, the available evidence, though controversial, indicates that they are larger because of more rapid cell division, not because of differences in size of cells. Blunn and Gregory found the number of cells per unit of volume to be significantly greater in embryos of Rhode Island Reds than in embryos of White Leghorns. The difference was greatest at 14 days but was present also at 72 hours and at 19 days of incubation. This would mean that there are more cells, but smaller ones, in embryos of the larger breeds. However, Byerly *et al.* did not find similar differences in number of cells per unit of volume in their embryos of differing sizes.

Keller (1933) found no difference between embryos of large breeds and those of small ones with respect to the size of erythrocytes, cells in the liver, and cells in dorsal root ganglia. She concluded that, since embryos of the larger breeds were somewhat larger, they must differ in the number of cells. Kaufman (1930) found various cells in pigeon embryos to be larger than corresponding cells in chick embryos of the same age, but this does not explain differences in size within either of these species.

Few such studies have been made with chicks after hatching. Mehner (1938) found that females of bantam, medium, and large breeds did not differ significantly in the size of erythrocytes or of certain epithelial cells but did differ in the area of cross sections of muscle fibres in the gracilis and sartorius muscles. These were smallest in bantams and largest in the large breeds.

Glutathione. A tripeptide of glutamic acid, glycine and cysteine, known as "glutathione," is found in rapidly growing tissues in comparatively high concentration. It has been shown to control cell division in root tips and in the protozoon Paramoecium. Gregory, Asmundson, and Goss (1936) found that when comparable pairs of eggs, one from a Barred Plymouth Rock and one from a White Leghorn, were incubated simultaneously, the concentration of glutathione was significantly higher in embryos of the larger breed than in those of the smaller one. Similar differences have been observed in newborn rabbits of breeds that differ in size. In chicks of the Leghorn and Barred Plymouth Rock breeds compared at 2-day intervals from hatching to 14 days of age, Gregory, Goss, and Asmundson (1937) found a similar difference. After 4 days of age the Rock chicks were consistently heavier and from 2 to 14 days of age they had a higher concentration of glutathione than did the Leghorns. Conversely, the latter breed showed a consistently higher concentration of ascorbic acid.

These observations are of great interest even though they cannot yet be interpreted as showing that big chickens are bigger than small ones because their genes for size produce more glutathione than do the genes of smaller breeds.

Retardation of Growth. All these studies of the embryological and physiological bases for differences in size have dealt with embryos and chicks at the periods when they are growing most rapidly. It is difficult to escape the conclusion, however, that ultimate body size depends much less upon the rates at which embryos grow during incubation than upon the age at which retardation of growth begins. The studies of Latimer (1927) and others show that cocks are larger than hens because growth of the skeleton continues in males after it has slowed down or ceased in females. Byerly *et al.* (1938) found that retardation of growth began during the third week in Silkies, but not till the fifth and sixth weeks in Silky × Red hybrids. It seems certain that genetic differences in size depend, not merely upon the rapidity of growth in early stages, but also upon the time at which the initial spurt terminates and the rate at which growth is decelerated. How the genes for size affect these processes remains to be determined.

Literature Cited

Ackerson, C. W., and F. E. Mussehl. 1930. Sex differences in the normal growth rate of chicks. *J. Agr. Research,* **40**:863–866.

Asmundson, V. S., and I. M. Lerner. 1933. Inheritance of rate of growth in domestic fowl. II. Genetic variation in growth of Leghorns. *Poultry Sci.,* **12**:250–255.

——— and ———. 1934. Inheritance of rate of growth in domestic fowl. III. Comparative rates of growth of Leghorns and Rocks. *Poultry Sci.,* **13**:348–352.

Bird, S., and H. S. Gutteridge. 1934. Variation of sex difference in chick growth. *Sci. Agr.,* **14**:433–437.

Blunn, C. T., and P. W. Gregory. 1935. The embryological basis of size inheritance in the chicken. *J. Exptl. Zoöl.,* **70**:397–414.

Burmester, B. R., and I. M. Lerner. 1937. A measuring device for shank length of living birds. *Poultry Sci.,* **16**:211–212.

Byerly, T. C. 1930. The effects of breed on the growth of the chick embryo. *J. Morphol. Physiol.,* **50**:341–359.

———, W. G. Helsel, and J. P. Quinn. 1938. Growth in weight and cell number. Genetic effects in the chick embryo and chick. *J. Exptl. Zoöl.,* **78**:185–203.

Card, L. E., and W. F. Kirkpatrick. 1918. Rearing chickens. *Storrs (Conn.) Agr. Expt. Sta. Bull.,* **96**:353–394.

Dove, W. F. 1935. A study of individuality in the nutritive instincts and of the causes and effects of variations in the selection of food. *Am. Naturalist,* **69**:469–544.

Dunn, L. C. 1928. The effect of inbreeding on the bones of the fowl. *Storrs (Conn.) Agr. Expt. Sta. Bull.,* **152**:53–112.

Galpin, N. 1938. Factors affecting the hatching weight of Brown Leghorn chickens. *Proc. Roy. Soc. Edinburgh,* **58**:98–113.

Ghigi, A., and A. Taibell. 1927. Results of some crosses between table and egg breeds. *Proc. World's Poultry Congr. 3d Congr., Ottawa:* 126–129.

[Goodale, H. D.] 1935–1936. "Early Egg Size." Mount Hope Farm, Williamstown, Mass.

———. 1941. Progress report on possibilities in progeny-test breeding. *Science,* **94**:442–443.

Graham, W. R., Jr. 1932. Some factors affecting the weight of egg in domestic fowl. *Sci. Agr.,* **12**:427–446.

Gregory, P. W., V. S. Asmundson, and H. Goss. 1936. Glutathione concentration and hereditary size. V. Comparative studies with Barred Plymouth Rock and White Leghorn embryos. *J. Expt. Zoöl.,* **73**:263–284.

———, H. Goss, and V. S. Asmundson. 1937. Glutathione concentration and hereditary size. VI. Comparative post-hatching studies with Barred Plymouth Rocks and White Leghorns. *Growth,* **1**:89–102.

Gutteridge, H. S., and J. B. O'Neil. 1942. The relative effect of environment and heredity upon body measurements and production characteristics in poultry. I. Period of growth. *Sci. Agr.*, **22**:378–389.

Halbersleben, D. L., and F. E. Mussehl. 1922. Relation of egg weight to chick weight at hatching. *Poultry Sci.*, **1**:143–144.

Hays, F. A., and R. Sanborn. 1929. Rate of growth in Rhode Island Reds. *Massachusetts Agr. Expt. Sta. Bull.* 259.

Heuser, G. F., and L. C. Norris. 1934. The influence of the protein level on the growth of chickens and its relation to subsequent behavior. *Atti congr. mondiale pollicultura. 5th Congr., Roma, 1933*, **2**:551–558.

Holmes, A. D., M. G. Piggott, and W. B. Moore. 1932. The influence of sex on the size and composition of tibiae of growing chicks. *Poultry Sci.*, **11**:243–249.

Hutt, F. B. 1929. Sex dimorphism and variability in the appendicular skeleton of the Leghorn fowl. *Poultry Sci.*, **8**:202–218.

———, R. K. Cole, and J. H. Bruckner. 1941. Four generations of fowls bred for resistance to neoplasms. *Poultry Sci.*, **20**:514–526.

Jaap, R. G. 1941. Body form in growing chickens. *J. Agr. Research*, **62**:431–443.

——— and L. Morris. 1937. Genetical differences in eight-week weight and feathering. *Poultry Sci.*, **16**:44–48.

——— and R. B. Thompson. 1940. Heritable differences in conformation of adult female fowl. *Poultry Sci.*, **19**:73–78.

———, R. Penquite, and R. B. Thompson. 1943. Body form in growing chickens. II. Growth of Cornish Bantams. *Poultry Sci.*, **22**:11–19.

Jull, M. A. 1923. Differential sex growth curves in Barred Plymouth Rock chicks. *Sci. Agr.*, **4**:58–65.

——— and J. P. Quinn. 1925. The relationship between the weight of eggs and the weight of chicks according to sex. *J. Agr. Research*, **31**:223–226.

——— and ———. 1931. The inheritance of body weight in the domestic fowl. *J. Heredity*, **22**:283–294.

Kaufman, L. 1930. Les différences du taux d'accroissement des oiseaux, sont-elles manifestes pendant la vie embryonnaire? *Arch. anat. microscopique*, **25**:325–335.

———. 1936. Die Entstehung der Unterschiede der Körpergrösse bei Hühnern. *Wiss. Ber. Weltgeflügelk. 6th Congr., Berlin and Leipzig*, **2**:41–43.

Keller, C. 1933. Vergleichende Zellen- und Kernmessungen bei grossen und kleinen Hühnerrassen zur Prüfung der genetisch bedingten Wuchsunterschiede. *Z. Zellforsch. u. mikroskop. Anat.*, **19**:510–536.

Kempster, H. L. 1941. The normal growth of chickens. *Missouri Agr. Expt. Sta. Bull.*, **423**:1–20.

Kopeć, S. 1926. Recherches sur l'hérédité de la forme du corps chez les poules. *Mém. inst. nat. polon. écon. rurale Pulawy*, **7**:261–293.

———. 1927. Some data on the inheritance of body shape in crosses between Leghorns and Orpingtons. *Proc. World's Poultry Congr. 3d Congr., Ottawa:* 123–126.

Kosin, I. L., and S. S. Munro. 1941. Evidence of a sex differential in the utilization of shell calcium by the chicken embryo. *Sci. Agr.*, **21**:315–319.

Landauer, W. 1929. Thyrogenous dwarfism (myxoedema infantilis) in the domestic fowl. *Am. J. Anat.*, **43**:1–43.

———. 1937. Studies on the creeper fowl. XI. Castration and length of bones of the appendicular skeleton in normal and creeper fowl. *Anat. Record*, **69**:247–253.

Latimer, H. B.   1927.   Postnatal growth of the chicken skeleton.   *Am. J. Anat.*, **40**: 1–57.

Lauth, H.   1935.   Vererbung von Körper- und Eigewicht bei Haushuhnrassen.   Ein Beitrag zur Genetik quantitativer Eigenschaften.   *Z. Zücht. Reihe B. Z. Tier-zücht. Züchtungsbiol.*, **31**:271–310.

Lerner, I. M.   1937.   Shank length as a criterion of inherent size.   *Poultry Sci.* **16**: 213–215.

———.   1837a.   Relative growth and hereditary size limitation in the domestic fowl.   *Hilgardia*, **10**:511–560.

———.   1941.   Relative growth in Bantams and Leghorns.   *Growth*, **5**:1–10.

———.   1946.   The effect of selection for shank length on sexual maturity and early egg weight in Single Comb White Leghorn pullets.   *Poultry Sci.* **25**:204–209.

——— and V. S. Asmundson.   1932.   Inheritance of rate of growth in domestic fowl. I. Methods and preliminary report on results obtained with two breeds.   *Sci. Agr.*, **12**:652–664.

Maw, A. J. G.   1935.   The inheritance of skeletal dimensions in the domestic fowl. *Sci. Agr.*, **16**:85–112.

Maw, W. A., and A. J. G. Maw.   1938.   The influence of type of sire on the body size of the progeny.   *U.S. Egg Poultry Mag.*, **44**:78–84.

May, H. G.   1925.   The inheritance of body weight in poultry.   I. In the Cornish-Hamburgh cross.   *Rhode Island Agr. Expt. Sta. Bull.* 200.

Mayhew, R. L., and C. W. Upp.   1932.   Inherited (?) dwarfism in the fowl.   *J. Hered-ity*, **23**:269–276.

Mehner, A.   1938.   Beziehungen zwischen Zellgrösse und Körpergrösse.   *Z. Zücht: Reihe B. Z. Tierzücht Züchtungsbiol.*, **40**:1–48.

Munro, S. S., and I. L. Kosin.   1940.   The existence of a sex difference in the weight of day-old chicks, with further data on the egg weight–chick weight relationship. *Sci. Agr.*, **20**:586–591.

Phillips, J. C.   1914.   A further study of size inheritance in ducks with observations on the sex ratio of hybrid birds.   *J. Exptl. Zoöl.*, **16**:131–148.

Punnett, R. C.   1923.   "Heredity in Poultry."   London: Macmillan & Co., Ltd.

———.   1930.   Some experiments concerning fecundity.   *Proc. World's Poultry Congr. 4th Congr., London:* 34–37.

——— and P. G. Bailey.   1914.   On inheritance of weight in poultry.   *J. Genetics,* **4**:23–39.

Schneider, M., and L. C. Dunn.   1924.   On the length and variability of the bones of the White Leghorn fowl.   *Anat. Record,* **27**:229–239.

Schnetzler, E. E.   1936.   Inheritance of rate of growth in Barred Plymouth Rocks. *Poultry Sci.,* **15**:369–376.

Upp, C. W.   1928.   Egg weight, day old chick weight and rate of growth in Single Comb Rhode Island Red chicks.   *Poultry Sci.,* **7**:151–155.

———.   1932.   Notes on a form of dwarfism encountered in Rhode Island Red fowls. *Poultry Sci.,* **11**:370–371.

———.   1934.   Further data on the inheritance of dwarfism in fowls.   *Poultry Sci.,* **13**:157–165.

Warren, D. C.   1930.   Crossbred poultry.   *Kansas Agr. Expt. Sta. Bull.* 252.

Waters, N. F.   1931.   Inheritance of body weight in domestic fowl.   *Rhode Island Agr. Expt. Sta. Bull.* 228.

Wright, S.   1932.   General, group and special size factors.   *Genetics,* **17**:603–619.

CHAPTER 10

EGG PRODUCTION

Students of poultry genetics sometimes expect a college course in that field to deal mostly with (1) the genetic basis for differences between hens or strains in ability to lay and (2) intricate and recondite techniques for breeding quickly a superior strain of fowls that will excel in egg production most of those now existing. This is natural, for fowls are kept under domestication primarily to produce eggs.

The literature on variations in laying capacity is voluminous. Since about 1908 this fertile field has been plowed, cultivated, and cross-harrowed with each new genetical and statistical technique that has come along. Correlations—simple, multiple, and partial—coefficients of regression and of inbreeding, the analysis of variance, sire indices and diallel crosses have all been invoked. Unfortunately, the net correlation between the number of pages written on the subject and the actual increment in knowledge is disappointingly small. This is no reflection on those who have tackled the problem. It results merely from the fact that genetic procedures known thus far are inadequate for analyzing characters affected by multiple genes.

For the benefit of the reader in a hurry, it seems desirable to state here that, in the opinion of the author, (1) the number of genes affecting egg production is unknown but apparently large and (2) the way to get more good layers is to employ the progeny test, details of which will be found in Chap. 15.

For those still reading, the present chapter reviews briefly some of the studies of egg production which have led to those conclusions and shows that there is a considerable fund of information about that character. It is covered under the headings of (1) anatomical and physiological basis, (2) environmental influences, (3) measures of egg production, (4) genetic basis, (5) contributory variables, and (6) the effect of senescence.

ANATOMICAL AND PHYSIOLOGICAL BASIS

Ovary and Oöcytes. Most birds, including the fowl, have only one ovary, which is on the left side. From the standpoint of evolution, the loss of the right ovary and oviduct is attributed to the need of reducing weight as an adaptation for flight and to lack of space for two oviducts or two eggs in the abdomen. Proponents of this theory also point out that one ovary can supply all the eggs needed for reproduction. However, in the hawks and falcons, about two-thirds of the females have right ovaries of varying sizes, as well as the normal one on the left (Gunn, 1912). According to Stanley and Witschi (1940), this tendency reaches its highest development in the subfamily Accipitrinae. In these birds there is no corresponding development of the right oviduct, which is either absent or vestigial. Conversely, in ducks, according to Wodzicki (1934), there is a tendency for the right oviduct to persist, but not the right ovary. A duck with paired ovaries and oviducts, both systems apparently functional, was reported by Chappelier (1913).

In the fowl, persistent rudiments of the right oviduct are commonly found attached to the cloaca and extending anteriorly up to 5 cm. or so in length. They are frequently distended with watery fluid, and in birds with long right oviducts this may cause trouble. Occasionally the right oviduct is as long as the left one (Crew, 1931), and it may even receive yolks from the left ovary (McKenney, 1931). An ovary is sometimes found on the right side, but it is quite rare for one of these to be functioning, as in the Wyandotte reported by Kirkpatrick and Card (1916). This had at autopsy not only a fully formed egg in the left oviduct but also a newly detached ovum from the right ovary in the right oviduct, which was functioning just as the left one.

The suggestion, engendered by such reports of double sets of reproductive organs, that a race of hens thus equipped would excel their supposedly less fortunate sisters in the numbers of eggs produced is ill founded. According to Pearl and Schoppe (1921), who counted the visible oöcytes in a number of fowls, the limiting factor is not the amount of ovarian tissue or the number of potential eggs but the proportion of these which the hen can convert into the finished product. In 24 fowls the average number of oöcytes visible to the naked eye was 1,906, which far exceeds the number of eggs that most hens lay in a lifetime. In addition to these, many more smaller oöcytes are present, but their number is not related to the actual number of eggs that a hen may lay. Thus, in one fowl which had laid only 69 eggs in 14 months, the number of oöcytes found with low magnification was 13,476. Fauré-Fremiet and Kaufman (1928) calculated that the 2-day-old chick has several million oöcytes, of which up to 1,600 seemed "privileged" at 15 days to undergo further development. The number of potential eggs must be far greater than this, for Pearl and Schoppe found that removal of more than half the ovary was followed by regeneration to such an extent that the number of visible oöcytes (together with those removed) greatly exceeded the number in control birds. It has even been suggested that, by removal of part of the ovary or by injuring it, that gland can be stimulated to a productivity greater than normal, but the fallacy of that contention was proved experimentally by Hutt and Grussendorf (1933).

Growth of the Ovum. For about 2 months prior to laying, the oöcytes increase in size very slowly, some of them attaining diameters up to 6 mm., but all contain only white yolk (Riddle, 1911). About 6 to 10 days before an ovum is released, its growth is suddenly accelerated to about 25 times the former rate (Riddle, 1916) and a layer of yolk about 2 mm. thick is added daily, thus causing an increase in diameter of about 4 mm. Stieve (1918) considers that this phase of rapid growth does not begin till the ovum is 9 to 11 mm. in diameter but agrees with Riddle that it coincides with the formation of yellow yolk. Details of the cytological changes associated with yolk formation are given by Van Durme (1914) and Brambell (1926). The whole question is reviewed by Marza and Marza (1935) with special reference to the histological structure of the follicle and to the chemistry of yolk formation.

The concentric layers of white and yellow yolk that have long been shown in diagrams of the egg in cross section are not always readily seen. They were attributed by Riddle to diurnal differences in metabolism such that white yolk was deposited from 1 to 5 A.M., when metabolism is low, and yellow yolk during the rest of the day. The yellow coloring of the yolk is mostly xanthophyll (Palmer, 1915), a carotinoid pigment obtained from the feed. From the experiments of Conrad and Warren (1939) it now seems more likely that the yellow layers represent yolk formation during a period when feed containing such pigments is being assimilated and that the narrower pale layers are formed when carotinoid pigments are no longer available. Similar bands can be induced by spaced and regular injections of the fat stain, Sudan III (Fig. 74), or by providing at different periods of the day feeds differing in their content of xanthophyll. Conrad and Warren concluded that the narrow bands of white yolk are attributable to the synthesis (after deposition in the egg of the dietary fat containing carotinoid pigments) of fat from the carbohydrates and proteins, which would presumably lack yellow pigment.

The concentric layers of yolk are added beneath the nucleus of the ovum, which is thus maintained at the periphery and gradually separated from the original mass of white yolk present before any yellow yolk was formed, which remains at the centre of the ovum. This is called the "latebra." In sections through this and also through the nucleus, or germinal disc, one can sometimes trace the path by which the latter has moved outward by the break which it has caused in the concentric layers of yolk (Fig. 74).

The ultimate size of the ovum before its ovulation depends, not upon the rate at which yolk is deposited in it, according to Warren and Conrad (1939), but rather upon the length of the period during which yellow yolk is accumulated. A normal, active ovary will show ova in all successive stages of growth, from the almost invisible oöcyte up to the one

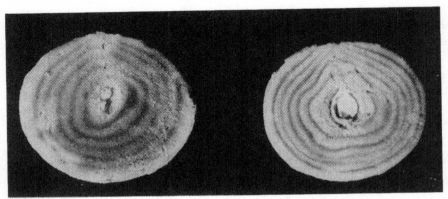

Fɪɢ. 74. Transverse sections of boiled yolks showing the bands of dye resulting from injections of the fat stain Sudan III given the hens at regular intervals. The central latebra is evident, also the irregularly vertical path of the nucleus from the centre of the yolk to the top. (*Courtesy of D. C. Warren.*)

next to be released from its follicle (Fig. 75). Ordinarily, the largest 8 or 10 of these will show yellow yolk.

Ovulation. The size attained by the ovum before it is released from the follicle varies in different birds. Young pullets just beginning to lay have smaller yolks in their eggs than after they have been laying for some months. Release of the ovum results from rupture of the stigma, a streak in the follicle which lacks blood vessels, but the forces causing it to break are still not fully understood. The old idea that pressure exerted on the follicle by the infundibulum of the oviduct is responsible was disproved by Pearl and Curtis (1914), who found that ova were liberated normally when the infundibulum was sewed up and even when the entire oviduct was removed. From observation of the process in anaesthetized fowls, Phillips and Warren (1937) concluded that the rupture results from contraction of the muscle fibres of the follicle after prolonged tension. They found that the period of time elapsing between the laying of an egg and the ovulation of the next ovum ranged from 7 to 74 minutes, the average being 32. While this is about the same as the period observed by others, it does not mean that release of an ovum from the ovary is dependent upon the laying of the previous egg, for Warren and Scott (1935) showed that premature laying (induced experimentally) did not hasten the ovulation of the next ovum.

Fɪɢ. 75. A functioning ovary showing gradations in size of immature ova and two empty follicles from which yolks have recently been released. (*From Warren and Conrad in J. Agr. Research.*)

Acquisition of Albumen, Membranes, and Shell. After its release from the ovary, the ovum is engulfed by the infundibulum of the oviduct and carried rather rapidly by peristalsis (and perhaps to some extent by ciliary action) through the albumen-secreting region to the isthmus. It was found by Pearl and Curtis (1912) that the egg spends about 3 hours in the albumen tube, less than an hour in the isthmus, and the remainder of the time in the uterus. This agrees well with similar determinations made by Warren and Scott (1935) on anaesthetized hens (Table 29). In this table the mean lengths of the different regions in 19 active oviducts of White Leghorns are also given.

These figures must not be considered applicable to every oviduct or to each egg. Hens vary, not only in the number of eggs laid per month and in the size of those eggs, but also in anatomical proportions and in physiological functions. The data in Table 29 do show, however, that the egg traverses rather rapidly the albumen-secreting portion of the

TABLE 29. AVERAGE LENGTHS OF DIFFERENT REGIONS OF THE OVIDUCT AND APPROXIMATE TIME SPENT BY THE EGG IN EACH*

Region	Average length, centimetres	Approximate time for egg to pass, hours
Body cavity (engulfing of yolk after ovulation)............	....	¼
Infundibulum...............	3.2	⅓
Albumen-secreting portion......	38.9	3
Isthmus....................	10.5	1¼
Uterus.....................	10.3	20–24
Vagina.....................	4.9	—
Entire oviduct...............	67.8	—

* From Warren and Scott (1935).

oviduct where the firm albumen is acquired. This comprises 50 to 60 per cent of the total albumen. The first of this to envelop the egg adheres to the vitelline membrane as the so-called "chalaziferous layer." It is continuous with strands of albumen before and behind the ovum which coagulate and become twisted as the egg rotates, thus forming the chalazae. In the isthmus, where the shell membranes are laid down and some thin albumen is acquired, passage of the egg is slowed down. About 80 per cent of the entire interval between ovulation and laying is spent in the uterus. Early in that period the egg acquires most of its outer layer of thin albumen and becomes plump.

A few hens lay consecutive eggs at intervals of 24 hours, others at intervals varying from 25 to 30 hours. Warren and Scott (1935a), by palpating the egg from the large intestine, determined that the longer intervals are accounted for mostly by extra time spent in the uterus.

A detailed account of the secretion and chemistry of albumen, shell, and shell membranes is beyond the scope of this book, but in Chap. 11 there is some consideration of variations in eggs and their component parts, together with what is known of the causes for them.

Laying. A long controversy over the question of which end of the egg is laid first has resulted from the fact that sometimes the blunt end is laid first, sometimes the pointed one. It is agreed that the pointed end is always, or almost always, directed caudad in the passage down the oviduct, but in hens killed shortly before laying the larger end is often found pointed toward the vagina.

Numerous investigators have sought to find the answer to this riddle by dissection, by X rays, by the direction of the streaks of blood on pullets' eggs, and by other means. Nathusius (1885) cites the ingenious Frau Ernst, who made her hens lay eggs in coal dust and concluded from the markings that all had been laid with blunt end first, thus supporting Aristotle and the other "big-endians."

According to Bartelmez (1918), the question was finally cleared up by Wickmann, who showed in 1895 that at the time of laying the egg is rotated about its shortest axis to place one end or the other oposite the opening into the vagina. He found that in most cases this rotation brings the blunt end to that opening. He considered this likely to happen with eggs that lie in the uterus with the small end buried in its posterior blind sac, considerably past the vaginal orifice. In a large number of eggs collected at the moment of laying, Olsen and Byerly (1932) found the proportion laid small end first to be about 70 per cent for Leghorns, 66 per cent for Barred Rocks, and 82 per cent for Rhode Island Reds. Individual hens differed considerably in this respect. In ducks, Motohashi (1935), using the Ernst technique mentioned above, found that 71 per cent of the eggs were expelled small end first.

According to Wickmann, the egg is not merely expelled by pressure through the vagina and cloaca but is extruded by a complete prolapse of the uterus in such a way that the egg never touches the walls of the vagina or cloaca.

Experiments of Rothchild and Fraps (1944) indicate that the time at which an egg is laid is determined in some way by the ruptured follicle from which its yolk came. When such follicles were removed, hens retained their eggs 1 to 7 days beyond the expected time of laying. Removal of other parts of the ovary had no such effect. The reason for this peculiar relationship has yet to be determined.

The Roles of Endocrine Secretions. The processes of egg formation just described are set in motion and controlled by various glands of internal secretion.

Pituitary Hormones. Following the discovery in 1926 that the anterior lobe of the pituitary secretes a hormone that stimulates the mammalian gonad, it was demonstrated that the same process is operative in doves (Riddle and Flemion, 1928), in pigeons (Riddle and Polhemus, 1931), and in chickens (Domm, 1931). Under ordinary conditions this hormone is apparently increased in amount at the time of sexual maturity, when it induces functional activity in the gonads. These, in turn, produce not only eggs or spermatozoa, but also the hormones of the ovary or of the testis. When this gonadotropic hormone is given in comparatively large doses, it can induce precocious sexual maturity in young chicks (Domm, 1937) or excessive activity of the ovary in hens already in laying condition (Bates *et al.*, 1935; Phillips, 1943). This does not mean that hens thus treated will lay more eggs. On the contrary, follicles thus brought simultaneously and suddenly to almost full size (Fig. 76) do not contain normal yolk and soon undergo regression. However, as we shall see in the section on the influence of light, by a slight stimulation an inactive ovary may be brought into full function without any immediate injurious effects.

Injection of gonadotropic hormones will also cause premature rupture of ovarian follicles (Fraps *et al.*, 1942), but it has not yet been shown

Fig. 76. Phenomenal activity of a hen's ovary (*right*) after six daily injections of 0.5 cc. of a gonadotropic extract; *left*, normal ovary of an untreated control hen. Both birds had been laying at the same rate prior to the experiment. (*From Phillips in Poultry Sci.*)

that normal ovulation in normal fowls is thus induced. Another hormone, prolactin, which causes regression of follicles and cessation of ovarian activity is discussed in the section on Broodiness (page 328). There is also a hormone of the posterior lobe of the pituitary which has an oxytocic effect and which may be concerned in the process of laying. When administered intravenously in large doses, it causes premature expulsion of an egg from the uterus (Burrows and Byerly, 1942); but it has yet to be shown that in physiological doses it is responsible for initiation of the processes which result in the laying of the egg.

Ovarian Hormones. In poulardes, females from which the ovary has been removed, the oviduct remains in an undeveloped condition. It is now known that this is because a hormone secreted by the ovary is necessary to bring the oviduct into the stage of functioning normally found in the laying hen. This has been demonstrated by Juhn and Gustavson (1930) and by many others since, who have shown that even in young chicks the oviduct becomes greatly hypertrophied after injections of female hormones. At least one preparation with the physiological properties of ovarian hormones can now be made synthetically. This is diethylstilbestrol. Its capacity for inducing development of the oviduct in chicks, as demonstrated by Herrick (1944), is shown in Fig. 77.

Up to 20 weeks of age or thereabouts, the lumen of the oviduct is occluded at the cloacal extremity by a membrane, the perforation of which is brought about by an ovarian hormone or hormones as the pullet approaches sexual maturity (Greenwood, 1935). This natural process can be simulated experimentally in young chickens only 6 to 9 weeks

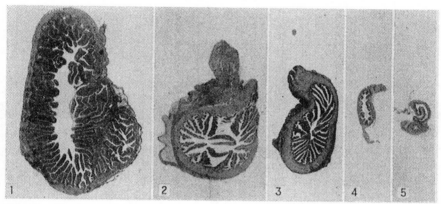

FIG. 77. Effects of hormones on the uteri of young chicks. Photomicrographs of cross sections after treatment from 18 to 40 days of age, all shown with the same magnification. 1, large dose of diethylstilbestrol; 2, lighter dose of the same; 3, estrone; 4, testosterone (male); 5, untreated control. (*From Herrick in Poultry Sci.*)

of age by injecting the female hormone, oestrin (Asmundson, Gunn, and Klose, 1937).

Another function of the ovarian hormones that is indispensable for egg production is the raising of the level of fatty materials in the blood. This is a prerequisite for the deposition of yolk in the follicles. In laying fowls and in pullets just prior to laying, the lipides in the blood are raised to a level six or seven times that in immature females (Table 30). This is caused by ovarian hormones, and, as Lorenz, Chaikoff, and Entenman (1938) have shown, it can be induced in immature females, and even in males, by treatment with oestrin.

Other Hormones. In addition to the endocrine secretions mentioned, others are undoubtedly instrumental in initiating and maintaining the state of egg production, but their roles are not yet fully understood. In laying birds, the blood calcium is higher than in immature or non-laying females by 50 to 100 per cent (Riddle and Reinhart, 1926, and many others). This is essential for the formation of eggshells. One would ex-

TABLE 30. RISE IN BLOOD LIPIDES AS THE OVIDUCT ENLARGES PRIOR TO LAYING *

Birds, number	Mean weight of oviduct, grams	Fatty acids in 100 cc. of whole blood, milligrams
8	2.9	310
6	6.7	314
3	16.2	654
8	23.9	2,116
4	33.0	2,351

* From Lorenz (1939).

pect it to be induced by the hormone of the parathyroid gland, but while some investigators have found parathormone effective in this way (Macowan, 1932; Knowles, Hart, and Halpin, 1935), others have not (Avery, Scott, and Conrad, 1940). It is possible that the parathyroid hormone acts synergistically with some other to cause the rise in blood calcium. The fact that a case of tetany caused by depletion of calcium reserves with laying could not be relieved by supplying calcium intravenously but was soon overcome by injecting parathormone (Hutt and Boyd, 1935) shows that the parathyroid must be involved in the calcium metabolism of the laying hen.

There is some ovarian hormone in egg yolk. Altmann and Hutt (1938) obtained evidence that it could cause a rise in blood calcium, but Marlow and Richert (1940) were quite unable to confirm this hypothesis, even with larger doses of estrogenic hormones. There are reports in the literature that the thymus gland is concerned in the formation of eggshells, but Ackert and Morris (1929), Morgan and Grierson (1930), and Greenwood and Blyth (1931) found that extirpation of that gland had no effect on egg production, eggshells, or blood calcium.

The thyroid gland is essential for optimum functioning of the reproductive system. Even when it is removed hens will lay some eggs, but Winchester (1939) and Taylor and Burmester (1940) found the egg production of completely thyroidectomized birds to be only a quarter or less of that for normal controls. Greenwood and Chu (1939) observed that some birds from which thyroids had been removed began to lay at the same time as controls, but others did not do so until fed thyroid substance. The relation of the thyroid to size of egg is considered in Chap. 11.

Use of Hormones to Increase Production. Because the ovary and reproductive tract are influenced by hormones, numerous attempts have been made to increase the production of eggs by administering preparations of various endocrine glands. In reports of 31 different experiments using preparations of the pituitary (11), ovary (8), thyroid (4), thyroactive casein (7), and corpus luteum (1), the author can find no consistent evidence that any of the preparations tried thus far will cause normal hens to lay more eggs than they would without it.

ENVIRONMENTAL INFLUENCES

The Role of Light. For many years it has been common knowledge that egg production could be induced in pullets slow to mature and increased in flocks not laying well by exposing the birds to more or less artificial light. Ordinarily, this stimulatory procedure is invoked in seasons when the days are short or decreasing in length. It is unnecessary in the spring, when the hours of daylight are increasing, because production seems to increase with them. Experiments showed that it matters little or not at all whether the normal hours of daylight be supplemented by artificial light in the morning or at night. Poultrymen jumped to the logical conclusion that short days did not permit consumption of enough feed to provide the heat and energy needed for long nights. Lengthening the day by the use of artificial light was believed to raise the production of eggs simply by (1) giving the hen an opportunity to consume more feed and (2) shortening the period on the roosts without feed at night. In support of this reasoning, experiments showed that a "night lunch" provided by lighting the pen for 20 minutes or so at 10 P.M. was practically as effective as an extra hour or two of feeding time at either end of the day.

It was not until this plausible philosophy had been taught by poultry professors for about three decades that it was proved to be completely erroneous. This little bit of history should be kept in mind to encourage any reader inclined to doubt what the author of this book has ventured to set before him as facts. While an effort has been made to include only those supportable by experimental proof, it is well to remember that in biology, as in other fields of science, interpretations made in any one decade may have to be changed because of new facts brought to light in the next.

The true relation of increased light to increased egg production of fowls, whether occurring naturally in the spring or induced with supplementary artificial light in the fall and winter, was eventually revealed by several remarkable series of studies with other birds. It has long been known that the urge in wild birds to migrate northward in springtime is accompanied by development of the gonads. Seeking the cause for this in juncos (*Junco hyemalis*) exposed to supplementary light, Rowan (1926) concluded that increased exercise as the days lengthened was responsible. Subsequently, in studies with the starling, *Sturnus vulgaris*, Bissonnette (1930, 1931) proved that the stimulation of the gonads is attributable, not to exercise, but to the light itself. Later (1931*a*) he showed that with increasing intensity of light up to that from a 40-watt bulb the response is accelerated, but with lights of still greater intensity no faster or greater results were noticeable. Bissonnette (1932) also found that, while red and white light were highly stimulatory, green light inhibited development of the testis. Later Benoit and Ott (1938) discovered that the maximum stimulation is caused by the red-orange portion of the spectrum, such light being 35 times as potent as the infra-red rays. Blue light has little or no effect.

All this work was done with males. It was soon shown by various investigators, not only that other species could be brought into the reproductive state by increased exposure to light, but also that females respond as males do, though somewhat more slowly. Thus, Benoit (1936) found that, while the testes of drakes exposed to extra light could be brought from the resting condition to full activity in 12 to 15 days, it took about twice as long to bring the ovaries of ducks to the laying condition. With fowls bred for increased fecundity the response to artificial lighting, as evidenced by increased egg production, is usually more rapid than Benoit found it to be in his Rouen ducks.

The mechanism whereby light brings about activation of the gonad was revealed, step by step, in a remarkable series of experiments on drakes by Benoit (1937). After proving that there is no stimulation in birds from which the pituitary has been removed, he showed (by the effects of implantations in immature female mice) that, after a bird has been exposed for some time to artificial light, the anterior lobe of its pituitary has the gonad-stimulating potency, even though transferred to another animal. Expressed otherwise, it is producing a gonadotropic hormone. It was then proved, with hooded drakes, that light on all body surfaces other than the head is ineffective. However, in drakes completely hooded except for their eyes, the normal stimulatory effect of light was obtained. Finally, it was shown that even the eyeball is unnecessary, so long as the light can strike the optic nerve in the orbit or be conveyed directly to the anterior lobe of the pituitary by means of a glass tube.

As a result of this ingenious series of experiments, it is now clear that the eye, as a photoreceptive organ, transmits the influence of the light along the optic nerve to the anterior lobe of the pituitary. That gland is induced thereby to elaborate the gonadotropic hormone (or hormones) which bring the testis or ovary into full normal function. Their activation, in turn, causes the production of testicular and ovarian hormones. Undoubtedly, still others are produced by the activated pituitary or induced by its effects on other endocrine glands. Thus the full reproductive state is brought about, or, as the poultryman sees it, the hen begins to lay.

Light and Latitude. It is now generally recognized that the increase in egg production in the spring results from the stimulus provided by daily increments in the hours of daylight, rather than from the rise in temperature associated therewith. As Whetham (1933) showed from curves of egg production and of hours of daylight at different latitudes, seasonal fluctuations are least near the equator (where the hours of daylight are most constant throughout the year) and progressively greater with increasing latitude north or south of the equator, as the differences between short days and long ones become more pronounced. At lat. 55°N., the peak of production is reached in March and April, whereas at lat. 40°S. those are the months of lowest production and the peak is reached in September or October. These differences in seasonal productivity between the Northern and Southern Hemispheres are all the more striking because, as Whetham showed, there is no difference in this respect between fowls at the same latitude in the Eastern and Western Hemispheres.

The fact that at all latitudes the peak of egg production precedes by 2 or 3 months the period of longest days suggests that after the days have reached the minimum number of hours of daylight necessary for activation of the gonad there is proportionately less effect of further lighting and that, at some point, additional light is without any corresponding effect. A common practice among poultrymen using artificial light is to start with a half-hour supplement to the available daylight and to increase the amount to the point where the birds have about 13 or 14 hours of light and 10 or 11 of darkness. Others start right off with about the same schedule. While this is fully effective, there is some indication that, when the total amount of light provided is close to the minimum essential for stimulation, a greater effect is obtained by increasing the amount each day up to that minimum than by providing all at once a slight excess above it (Burger, 1939).

Light and Hour of Laying. Hens do not often lay in darkness, except for the soft-shelled eggs sometimes laid prematurely. However, when Warren and Scott (1936) provided artificial light continuously through the 24-hour period, they found that after about a week the hens laid at any hour of the 24. When light was provided only from 6 P.M. to 6 A.M., with complete darkness during the other half of the day, the birds adjusted their habits correspondingly and laid only during the lighted (night) period. Finally, after a 24-hour period of darkness, the normal daytime light and nighttime darkness were reestablished, with the result that in about 4 days practically all the eggs were laid during the day. Apparently there is some psychological influence of the light that induces laying, apart entirely from its role in activating the complex endocrine system. Further evidence of this was provided by 48 laying hens from which Rothchild and Fraps (1944a) removed the ruptured follicles. As was expected, laying was delayed for 9 to 36 hours beyond the expected time for most of the hens. However, three-quarters of these finally laid during the hours of light, whether it was provided at the normal period of daylight or by turning night into day.

Limitations of Light. The average hen, somewhat like birds in the wild, is unable to maintain for more than 3 or 4 months the maximum reproductive activity to which she is stimulated by the lengthening days of early spring. Similarly, the laying induced by artificial light in the fall or early winter is followed after a few months by more or less of a reaction, indicated by lower production or the cessation of laying. A corresponding regression of the gonads after prolonged lighting has been observed in other species. As a result, hens induced to lay "out of season" by artificial lights are not likely to lay any more eggs in a period of 12 months than those left to do their best under the more natural urge of the approaching spring. The advantage to the poultryman is merely that he gets his peak of production when eggs are at a high price, rather than in the spring, when every old crow is laying and the markets are glutted with eggs.

A point often overlooked is that some pullets will lay well right through the shortest days. It is only the poor and mediocre ones that require the stimulus of the added light. Consequently, the breeder seeking to evaluate the genetic capacities of his pullets for egg production can do so more accurately in an unlighted flock than in one given lights. This is merely because the latter situation permits no differentiation (at least in the first 6 months of laying) between the genetically good layers and the others artificially stimulated beyond their normal capacities.

Another limitation is that light is effective only for birds that are almost full-grown and near sexual maturity. Young growing birds are insensitive (Benoit, 1936, and others), and any attempt to hasten sexual maturity by excessive illumination of immature birds is more likely to make them refractory to light than to bring about the effect desired (Callenbach *et al.*, 1944). Since the gonads of young chicks respond when gonadotropic hormone is injected, while those of birds older but still immature cannot be activated by the light treatment, it would seem that the normal attainment of sexual maturity is dependent upon development of the anterior lobe of the pituitary to the stage at which it can produce the gonadotropic hormone. The genetic constitution is apparently a factor in determining whether much or little light is necessary for activation of that process.

Domestication. There can be little doubt that some of the current prolificacy of laying hens has resulted merely from the improvement of the environment since man first decided that it would pay him to keep fowls in captivity. Contributory influences may include not only an increased or more readily available food supply but also, perhaps, better diets, particularly in the level of animal protein, which can be quite a limiting factor in the production of eggs. Shelter from the elements is also necessary in northern latitudes if the hens are to lay eggs in any season other than spring and summer.

However, the statements by enthusiastic environmentalists that improvements in our knowledge of feeding poultry are largely responsible for the high egg production attained today are not correct. If they were, then wild fowls recently domesticated might be expected to produce chicks which, when given the best diet and shelter possible, would lay as well as Leghorns which have been bred for egg production. This they do not, as is clearly shown by the following record for unselected Jungle Fowls hatched at Cornell University in 1942 and given a diet supposed to be the best known.

	Hens, alive at 500 days of age	
	Number	Egg production, mean number
Jungle Fowls, unselected....	22	62.5
White Leghorns, *C* strain...	670	181.0

While the egg production of these Jungle Fowls was barely a third of that for the Leghorns that had been bred for increased productivity, it was probably considerably higher than that of Jungle Fowls in nature. Similarly, Asmundson and Lloyd (1935) found the mean number of eggs laid by 277 turkeys in their first year to be 76.6, a figure undoubtedly higher than the number laid by wild turkeys. Individual records of well over 200 eggs are known for this species. Domestic ducks are capable of phenomenal egg production, some of which results merely from domestication, and some from selection. A good example of the increase in egg laying that results from domestication is afforded by the quail, *Colinus virginianus,* for which Coleman (1930) found the mean production of 107 birds to be 72 eggs, with individual records up to 125.

Some of the increase in egg production following domestication results merely from removing the eggs daily and thereby causing the birds to continue laying longer than they would in nature. Pearl (1912) cites instances of egg laying being thus protracted in the house (English) sparrow to 51 eggs, in the Mallard duck to 80 eggs or more, and in the wryneck to 48 eggs. Ornithologists say that not all wild species can be induced to continue laying by regular removal of the eggs, but it is evidently an important factor in raising the production of some birds under domestication.

Disease. The fact that disease decreases the number of eggs laid is well known to all poultrymen and to others who might still belong to that class if they had been able to keep disease and parasites under control. Sudden outbreaks of disease may cause production of a flock to drop in a few days almost to nothing. The influence of chronic and slowly progressive disease is less evident, but its effects may in the long run be more serious than those of a sudden outbreak from which there is quick recovery.

Accurate quantitative measures of the influence of disease on egg production are difficult to obtain. From the records in a laying test, Harris (1926, 1927) found that in all three breeds investigated the mean monthly egg production of birds that died during the year was consistently lower than that of birds which survived. The difference was least early in the year but increased steadily from November to September. That is because hens dying in July may show a normal rate of laying in the previous November but are less likely to do so in June. An important point nicely shown by Harris is that the egg production of birds that die is subnormal for several months prior to death (Fig. 78). Those which died in September and October laid 3 eggs per month less than survivors as far back as March, and the difference increased steadily with each month thereafter. As was to be expected, the maximum difference was usually found in the month prior to that in which death occurred.

Pullorum disease provides a good example of a chronic disease that may greatly reduce egg production. In the data of Asmundson and Biely (1930) comparing first-year production of birds which reacted positively to the agglutination test for *Salmonella pullorum* and those which did not (Table 31), it should be noted, not only that the reactors laid 61 eggs per bird less than the others, but also that the variability in the former group was twice as great as in the non-reactors.

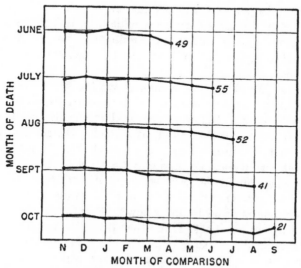

FIG. 78. Graphs showing that the egg production of hens that die is subnormal for several months prior to death; deviations of their mean monthly egg production from the corresponding means for hens that survived (straight lines). Numbers of birds that died are shown. The largest deviations equal about nine eggs. (*From Harris in Poultry Sci., 1926.*)

TABLE 31. EFFECT OF PULLORUM DISEASE ON EGG PRODUCTION
(FROM ASMUNDSON AND BIELY)

Class	Birds, number	Mean egg production, number	Coefficient of variation, per cent
Reactors..........	102	160.1	39.2
Non-reactors	587	221.7	20.5

This extreme variability of the reactors might have resulted if some of the birds had carried the infection throughout the laying year and others had caught it only toward the end of the laying year, being thus less affected. However, the variability was shown to be equally great throughout the year in birds that reacted to the test at the beginning. It seems most likely, therefore, that it resulted from the fact that some birds continued to lay well even though infected, while others could not. About 15 per cent of the reactors laid over 225 eggs in the year, while 55 per cent of the non-reactors did so.

Biely (1930) also showed that production of reactors is lower than that of non-reactors in the second year of laying, the difference resulting not only from a lower rate of production but also because the reactors tend to stop laying earlier than the non-reactors toward the end of the laying year.

Temperature. As every poultryman above lat. 40°N. knows, a sudden drop in environmental temperature or a prolonged spell of unusually cold weather will cause a decline in egg production. Leghorns are more susceptible to such changes than the heavy breeds. In general, the effect of cold winter temperatures on egg laying is slight, possibly because a lessening of that activity at one time may be offset by a more rapid rate of production when laying is resumed. At Ottawa, Canada, in 1933–1934, when the mean temperature outdoors for 4 winter months was only 8.2°F., with low points of 34 to 38° below 0°F. in each of the 3 coldest months, Gutteridge *et al.* (1944) found that Barred Plymouth Rocks laid just as well in uninsulated pens for which the mean temperatures from Nov. 15 to Apr. 14 were 39 and 42°F. as in those which were maintained 5 to 10°F. higher by insulation or by heating. Similar results were obtained in other years. Still farther north at Kapuskasing, in northern Ontario, birds in unheated houses turned in a mean production of 69.8 eggs for 5 winter months against 72.3 for birds in heated houses, an insignificant difference, in spite of the fact that, in 30 consecutive days, the temperature outdoors rose above zero only twice, and got as low as 43° below zero. Similar failures to raise egg production by heating have been reported from comparatively mild regions farther south.

Presumably, these experiments relate to hens not afflicted with disease. The simultaneous arrival of extremely cold weather and respiratory disease of one kind or another frequently precipitates a partial moult and cessation of egg laying for periods up to 6 weeks or more.

At the other end of the scale, hot summer weather may cause a decline in production, especially if its onset is sudden, but some flocks and some birds seem better able to withstand it than others.

Other Environmental Influences. It is generally recognized by poultrymen that transferring hens from one pen to another may cause a drop in egg production, and Warren (1930) found this to be so in a controlled experiment. Among pullets caught, crated, handled, and placed in another pen, 35 per cent stopped laying within 12 days, whereas of those similarly disturbed but released in their own pen only 11 per cent stopped. Single birds introduced as strangers to a flock already organized are at a disadvantage until their position in the social order has been established, and their rate of egg laying is temporarily subnormal (Guhl and Allee, 1944). The extent to which egg production is reduced by social pressure against the underprivileged in poultry society has yet to be determined, but it would seem that those continually driven from the feeders by other birds are not likely to lay so well as those not thus harassed.

It has been demonstrated that egg production can be temporarily reduced or stopped by administering kamala (see page 366) and by sulphanilamide. Doubtless there are many other drugs and toxins that would have the same effect.

It is generally considered that the date of hatching has some relation to the productivity of the birds, and this has led to varying recommendations at different latitudes concerning the best time to hatch chicks. It is not always recognized that the important fact is not the calendar date of hatching but the environment into which by that date the pullets are arbitrarily projected some 5 months later, when they are nearing sexual maturity. A major factor in that environment is the length of day, although temperatures, particularly cold weather in late fall, may also play an important role. Poultrymen have learned by experience and by experiment that late-hatched chicks take longer to come into production and that early ones may mature at undesirably young ages and are more likely to have a "winter slump." As a result, optimum periods of hatching are generally set to avoid these extremes. When the environment is artificially controlled, as when birds are raised indoors or when natural daylight is supplemented with artificial light, the season of hatching is less important, and in practice it is often adjusted to suit the poultryman's available space, his time, and his markets.

There are doubtless many other environmental influences that may affect the productivity of fowls. Enough have been mentioned to show that, in contrast to the case with many of the simple hereditary characters considered in earlier chapters, the number of eggs that a hen lays depends, not only upon her inherited capacity, but also to a great extent upon her environment. Any hen unable to produce more than 130 eggs in her first year may blame the record on a lack of the necessary genes, on poor environment (including food), on misadventure, or on all three. Many hens now lay over 300 eggs in their first year, and these should, in all honesty, attribute their prowess, not only to good ancestry and good management, but also to good luck.

MEASURES OF EGG PRODUCTION

The literature recording man's attempts to measure the laying capacities of fowls reveals a remarkable mixture of ingenuity, scientific study, and hopeful optimism.

The Trap Nest. Since the method now most practicable and the one against which most other procedures have to stand comparison is the trap nest, a few words on its history are in order. According to Cook (1937), who searched the records of the U.S. Patent Office, various kinds of nest boxes were patented in the decade after the Civil War, but these permitted the hen to escape after laying and were designed more to provide her with some privacy during that process than to record the frequency with which she was entitled to it. Not until 1899 was a patent issued for a trap nest devised specifically to measure egg-laying ability. This was taken out by George L. Lytle. However, it is clear that there must have been other inventors with the same idea, for Goodale (1937) has recorded that, at the Maine Experiment Station, Professor Gowell installed 52 trap nests in 1898 and that Professor Rice, of Cornell University, invented one sometime in the last decade of the nineteenth century.

While this gives the record for the United States, it would be no surprise to find that poultrymen in other parts of the world were using trap nests at much earlier dates. Even though the fowl has been valued through most of its few thousand years of domestication for its fighting ability rather than for its productivity, it seems probable that many people must have sought means to identify the better layers. Further information about their efforts is desirable.

While the trap nest provides the most practical means of measuring productivity, it is by no means infallible. Some hens consistently lay on the floor until they are caught and trained to use the nests. Even when all hens in a pen are using the nests more or less regularly, some eggs are laid on the floor and cannot be assigned to any one hen. Other errors result from traps getting out of order, so that birds go in and out without closing them; sometimes two hens enter one nest even though it is in perfect order. Some eggs are broken, eaten, and never recorded. Altogether these difficulties may result in errors varying at different times and in different flocks from 1 to 5 per cent.

A system used earlier with hens, and still used for ducks, is to pen the birds individually in small coops or cages early in the day or at night and to release them when they have laid.

Palpation. Hens that are going to lay during the day can be detected by palpating the egg in the uterus. This necessitates handling and examining the birds individually shortly after daylight before any of them have laid. The efficacy of this procedure was thoroughly tested by Alder and Egbert (1918), who used it for several years. During one whole year when the total daily estimates of eggs to be laid amounted to 42,886, the numbers actually gathered each day fell short of the daily estimates by only 110 and exceeded them by 128. The total error resulting was therefore only 0.5 per cent, or much less than that entailed by the use of trap nests. It was found most practicable to have one man guide the hens to another stationed near the exit, who made all the examinations and called off the records to his mate. The hens were not lifted from the floor, and became used to the routine after about 10 days of training. In one trial, two men examined over 500 hens in 46 pens in 37 minutes. Advantages of the method include a saving in labor and in the expense of trap nests, as well as greater accuracy. The chief disadvantages, which probably prevent the general use of this procedure, are (1) that people prefer not to roll out at daybreak to feel hens if they can avoid it and (2) the eggs of individual hens cannot be identified. Trap nests would thus have to be used in the hatching season if pedigree breeding is to be carried out.

Physiological Changes Indicating Laying Ability. *Depigmentation.* It is now general knowledge that with continued laying hens lose the yellow pigment in the skin, beak, and shanks; consequently the good layers can be distinguished from the poor ones with a high degree of accuracy by estimating the degree of pigmentation. The physiological basis for this is merely that the pigment, xanthophyll, is put in the yolks of the eggs as fast as it is obtained from the feed (Palmer and Kempster, 1919); consequently the reserves of xanthophyll accumulated prior to laying or in periods of non-laying are not maintained. According to Palmer and Kempster, the loss of yellow pigment is attributable not to its being transferred to the eggs but rather to bleaching and to the wearing off of the outer layers without any replacement of the xanthophyll. This does not fully explain the orderly sequence in which the yellow color is lost. Ordinarily, the skin around the vent, the eyelid, and the ear lobes (in breeds with white ones) lose their yellow cast with a week's laying. It takes a month of continuous laying, or more, to bleach the beak, and about 4 to 6 months to remove all yellow from the shanks. In the beak, the color is first lost from the base and last from the tip. A laying hen that has been out of production for 2 weeks may show, after resumption of laying, a bleached area at the tip and the base of the beak, but a yellow band in the middle, where the color was deposited during the period of non-laying.

As every experienced culler knows, these changes are most easily estimated in breeds with no black or reddish pigment in the beak and shanks, such as White Leghorns. They cannot be detected in breeds with black beaks and shanks or in Orpingtons, Sussex, and other breeds that carry the dominant gene, *W,* preventing extension of the xanthophyll to the beak and shanks.

While this relationship of depigmentation to egg production must have been noted earlier, the first reference to it in scientific literature appears to have been made by Blakeslee and Warner (1915), and critical proof was reported shortly thereafter by Blakeslee *et al.* (1917). This came from comparisons between the amount of yellow pigment in hens completing a year of production in a laying test and their actual records made in that test. Typical data are shown in Table 32.

TABLE 32. RELATION BETWEEN THE AMOUNT OF YELLOW PIGMENT IN THE EAR LOBES OF WHITE LEGHORN HENS IN OCTOBER AND THEIR EGG PRODUCTION IN THE PREVIOUS 12 MONTHS*

Per cent yellow	1913–1914		1914–1915	
	Birds, number	Mean eggs, number	Birds, number	Mean eggs, number
10–20	83	187.0	81	185.1
25–35	67	148.2	72	172.2
40–50	111	136.7	119	148.4
55–65	46	132.1	90	126.9
70–80	2	76.5	13	111.5

* From Blakeslee *et al.* (1917).

In this particular example the relationship so evident in the figures is not a direct one, for the amount of yellow in the ear lobes in October does not of itself measure the productivity of many previous months. It does reveal which birds are still laying, which have been out of production for some time, and some grades in between. The more direct relationship is that hens still laying in October are likely to have the highest records, as Harris and his associates showed later. The production over previous months is measured more directly by the color of the shanks.

Time of Moult. That hens moulting late in the laying year are better layers than those which moult early was apparently first recognized by Rice *et al.* (1908). The usefulness of this criterion in culling operations is increased by the fact that the time at which moulting began can be estimated with a high degree of accuracy by the number of new primary feathers in the wing. As a result, flocks can be easily sorted in September or October into early moulters, late moulters, and various stages in between. On making such a classification in birds finishing a year at a laying test, Blakeslee *et al.* (1917) found the following close relationship between stage of moult and egg production:

	Number	Mean annual production
Birds not yet moulted.............	96	185.6
Birds in process of moulting.......	173	156.5
Birds with moulting completed....	106	122.9

Measuring the laying capacity by the moult is complicated by a number of variables. Some hens moult rapidly, others slowly; some continue laying through part of the moulting period, but others do not. The relation of such variations to egg production has been studied in White Leghorns by Marble (1930) and in Rhode Island Reds by Hays and Sanborn (1945). Marble's report includes a good account of successive changes in the feathers of the wing as the moult progresses and their relation to loss of feathers in other parts of the body.

Limitations. Normally the first full moult does not begin until the hen is 16 to 20 months old, which is too late for poultrymen who like to have poor producers culled out earlier or who wish to identify good pullets to use as breeders. For these purposes the degree of depigmentation may be useful, although it has its limitations in birds that have not been laying long. As Palmer and Kempster (1919) pointed out, the fading of yellow measures only the length of time in which the birds have laid continuously, and not the rate of production during that period. According to Lerner (1942), who studied the pigmentation in the shanks of White Leghorn pullets at 8 months of age, it gives no clue to the rate of laying, to pauses in production, or even to the length of the laying period, although it does serve as a measure of total production. However, his pullets had been laying for an average period of only about 70 days, and it seems possible that depigmentation of the shank might be a better guide to antecedent production in flocks that have been laying for 4 or 5 months. For shorter periods the loss of pigment in the beak may also be useful, as it will indicate continuous production for the previous month or so and, on diets containing adequate xanthophyll, any pause during that period.

Other Indications of Production. The discovery in the second decade of the twentieth century that good layers could be distinguished from poor ones by lack of yellow pigment and by late moulting precipitated a period of cheery optimism in which many poultrymen sought to find other outward and visible signs of inner and less evident physiological perfection. Among such indicators of productivity, those most in favor were anatomical measurements, particularly of various dimensions in the head. One enthusiast even claimed a system by which he could predict the future egg production of pullets by study of the head. For the extensive literature dealing (pro and con) with possible relationships of body conformation, dimensions of the head, and head "type" to egg production the reader is referred to papers by Marble (1932), Miller and Carver (1934), Jull *et al.* (1933), and Bryant and Stephenson (1945), all of which report failure to find any such measure that would indicate the hen's innate capacity for laying. Several investigators have reported positive correlations of this sort, but most of them are too low to have any practical usefulness.

On the other hand, it must be recognized that there may be relationships between production and conformation that would not be revealed by the simple linear correlations that have been used by most investigators. Clevenger and Hall (1935) could find no linear correlations between various measurements of the head and production, but when their birds were classified in four groups according to "head type," those with "overly refined" and "coarse" heads were found to be poorer layers than the two intermediate classes. However, since these two extremes in head type were also the extremes in body weight, it seems probable that much of the value of the head as an indicator of production depends upon the extent to which it represents the size of the bird and the degree of fatness. Here again, numerous investigators have reported linear correlations between body weight and egg production (some positive, some negative) to be so small as to indicate little relationship. However, as Platt (1927) and others have shown, there is such a relation but it is nonlinear. The smaller birds within a breed do not lay so well as the larger ones, and the extremely heavy hens also tend to show poor records, but, between these extremes, laying ability shows little relation to body weight. This is also evident in the extensive data of Taylor (1930) for birds in the Canadian laying contests (Fig. 79), except that his heaviest Leghorns, which were apparently not much over 5 pounds in weight, laid as well as the others. Most poultrymen know that their small pullets should be discarded before housing and that hens that become excessively fat are not likely to lay well in the future. Apart from this, body weight gives little clue to productivity.

Attempts to relate laying ability to the rate of increase in egg size (Hadley, 1919) and to body temperature (Fronda, 1923) have not been successful. The size of the genital papilla in the cloaca of the chick at hatching is no indication of future egg production (Hammond and Burrows, 1937). The changes in the body that accompany the laying state,

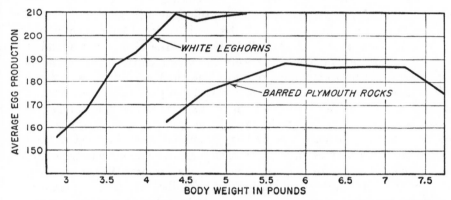

Fig. 79. Distribution of 8,195 White Leghorns and 5,766 Barred Rocks in Canadian laying tests according to body weight and egg production, showing lower production of smaller birds in both breeds. (*From data of A. G. Taylor.*)

such as enlargement of the abdomen, spreading of the pubic bones, changes in the vent, and reddening of the comb are helpful in distinguishing laying hens from non-layers but not in differentiating between high producers and low ones.

Periods Used to Measure Laying Ability. The foregoing discussion shows that the best way to measure laying ability is to use trap nests, but there are still the questions (1) how long a period is necessary to permit differentiation of good layers from poor ones and (2) at what part of the year it should come. These are considered below.

First-year Production. Presumably the common practice of measuring productivity by the number of eggs laid in the first year of laying originated from the fact that good hens lay about a year before going into the first full moult. Some poultrymen, particularly those in official tests, such as government programs for obtaining records of performance, determine the number of eggs laid in 365 days beginning with that of the first egg. This has the disadvantage that the books cannot be closed until the last late-maturing hen has had her full innings. Even though this obstacle be overcome by setting an arbitrary late finish line, it still means that the family averages, which are much more important than the record of any one hen, cannot be calculated until some of the birds are almost 22 months old. Another possible objection is that the hen beginning to lay at 190 days gets no more credit for 240 eggs than the one that lays the same number but none at all till she is 220 days old. The laying tests, faced with the practical problem of testing a new generation in the same pens each year, set arbitrary starting dates and finishing dates, usually thus reducing the testing period to 50 weeks or even to 48. While this serves their purpose, it will hardly do for a poultry breeder who has some chicks hatched 10 weeks later than others.

The 500-day Test. At Cornell University, the author has found it convenient and satisfactory to measure the laying capacity by the number of eggs laid up to 500 days of age. The chief advantage is that the chicks hatched early in March of one year finish their test about the end of July in the next one and can then be disposed of, leaving the laying house clear for new pullets to be brought in from the rearing range. At weekly intervals thereafter other hens (that had been hatched at successive weekly intervals in the previous year) complete their tests and are moved out, some to market, some to pens for prospective breeders. As they go, their quarters are taken over by pullets as the latter mature. By about Sept. 20, all the hens hatched in the previous year have completed their tests; three-quarters of them have been marketed, the rest transferred, and all the pullets of the current year are housed, with their tests well under way.

For hens that begin to lay at 190 days of age, production is measured by this test during a period of 310 days, which is 55 days less than the full year's test considered as standard by many poultrymen. It can be criticized, therefore, as not being adequate to reveal "persistency," *i.e.,* the ability to keep on laying after other hens have stopped. However, while persistency is undoubtedly an important factor in determining how many eggs a hen will lay in 365 days, there may be some question whether or not it permits any better evaluation of genetic capacity to lay than does the total production to 500 days of age. At any rate, the latter measure has proved adequate for recognition of superior families and for increasing egg production in a large flock (Hutt and Cole, 1947).

Other Test Periods. In the pioneer studies of egg production made by Raymond Pearl and his associates at the Maine Experiment Station in the decade beginning in 1908 [1] the number of eggs laid by a hen in November, December, January, and February was taken as the measure

---

[1] For a review of these and bibliography, see Hutt (1942).

of her capacity to lay. This led to the belief that the "winter cycle" of egg laying constituted some sort of a specific biological unit, and even to the suggestion that there were specific genes for high productivity in these 4 months. It is true that the hens with the highest records up to Mar. 1 are likely to have the best records for the year. This was especially so in 1908, because at that time any pullet that could shell out 50 eggs between Nov. 1 and Mar. 1 was a credit to her ancestors and a source of pride to her owner. At one time some importance was attached to the fact that the correlation between winter and annual production is of the order of +.6. However, this figure means little because it represents the correlation of a large part with a whole. In other words, the number of eggs laid in 4 months is a considerable part of the total laid in 12 months and must influence the latter figure. It was soon shown by Ball and Alder (1917), Goodale (1918*a*), and Harris and Lewis (1922) that there is no basis for considering the winter production as any special biological entity.

This does not mean that the number of eggs laid during 4 winter months has little significance. On the contrary, it is probably a more useful guide to genetic capacity for laying than any other consecutive 4 months, particularly if the birds have not been stimulated by artificial light. In other words, while any hen may show a fair record in the spring months, only the best ones will lay well before and after that natural period of high production. In a thorough statistical examination of this question, Harris *et al.* (1918), Harris and Lewis (1921), and Harris and Goodale (1922) found that the predictive value of the records for single months was higher for the 4 winter months and for August, September, and October at the end of the laying year than for the 5 months of spring and early summer. As would be expected, the accuracy of prediction is increased when the production of 2 or 3 consecutive months is considered (Harris *et al.*, 1921). In practice, this means merely that the poultryman not interested in exact records for 365 days can identify his best layers easily by trapping in the winter and in late summer and fall, without bothering to trap during the spring months. Thus Thompson and Jeffrey (1936), in predicting the annual record from the number of eggs laid from Oct. 1 to Jan. 31 and from June 1 to Sept. 22, found their estimates to deviate from the actual record by an average of about 16 eggs. It would not be surprising if accuracy adequate for selection of breeders could be attained merely by trapping in the winter and identifying by physical examination the hens still laying in late August, September, and October.

Since the invention of the trap nest, that instrument has been used chiefly to measure egg production during the first laying year. It is to be hoped that in the future the success attained in raising first-year production may be matched by similar progress in developing birds capable of several years of economically profitable laying. This question is considered elsewhere, but it is appropriate to mention here that many years ago Ball, Alder, and Egbert (1916) suggested that the period for measuring laying ability should be not just 1 year, but 3. This was based on their observation that flocks with high production in their first year sometimes did not do as well in subsequent years as those with lower first-year records.

Sampling Records by Intermittent Trapping. The current trend of events—whereby hens are bred to lay more and more and men to work less and less—increases the importance of methods for sampling the egg record so that good layers can be identified with less labor than is needed for complete daily trap-nest records kept throughout the year. This can be done by trapping as little as 1 day a week (Voitellier, 1930; Dudley, 1931; Olsen, 1939). With this method, Dudley found the correlation between the sample and the complete record to be +.90 to +.92 in three different lots of birds. Similar accuracy was attained by trapping for 4 consecutive days in each lunar month. This was to be expected, since in both cases the sample was one-seventh of the full record. These correlations mean that about 80 per cent of the variations in the full record would be revealed by corresponding variations in the sample. A better idea of the degree of error to be expected is conveyed by the deviations of the actual complete records from those estimated by the use of regression equations based on the correlations observed (Table 33).

TABLE 33. DIFFERENCES BETWEEN PRODUCTION ESTIMATED FROM TRAPNESTING FOR ONE DAY PER WEEK AND ACTUAL RECORDS *

Dudley (48 weeks)		Olsen (52 weeks)	
Difference	Proportion of records, per cent	Difference	Proportion of records, per cent
0–12 eggs..........	57	Within 10 eggs......	44
13–24 eggs..........	29	Within 15 eggs......	58
25–36 eggs..........	10	Within 20 eggs......	73
Over 36 eggs........	4	Within 25 eggs......	85
		Within 30 eggs......	89

* Data from Dudley (1931) and Olsen (1939).

According to Dudley, the simpler estimate of seven times the record for the sample is not quite so accurate as the equations he used, because the relationship is not exactly linear. This results in the estimate being too low in the case of poor layers and somewhat too high for the best ones. For practical purposes it may suffice if the poultryman using the simple estimate remembers that the extremes in his flock are neither as good nor as bad as they seem.

Still greater accuracy can be attained by trapping for 1 week each month (Voitellier, 1930; Hays, 1946) as this provides a sample of 84 days, or 32 more than the one previously considered. It is questionable whether the greater accuracy thus attained is worth the extra effort for the man trying to get records for many birds with a minimum of help. This is especially so because a difference of 15 eggs or so in a hen's record does not mean a corresponding difference in the productivity of her daughters.

Estimates of productivity that are adequate for most purposes may be made by trapping only on 3 days a month. According to Card (see Lippincott and Card, 1939, page 155), this yields a correlation between the sample and the full record ranging from $+.86$ to $+.94$. With samples of only 2 days a month the correlation is still as high as $+.77$ (Hays, 1946). On the other hand, the trap nests cost the same whether they are used often or not. Many poultrymen are now trapping only 4 days a week. The studies cited above show that 4 days a month should be adequate. Considering the time involved to put on and take off the trap-nest fronts, it would seem that 4 consecutive days may prove more satisfactory for this purpose than 1 day a week. As Dudley has shown, it is just as accurate.

Measuring Productivity of Flocks. Because all the foregoing discussion in this section has dealt with ways of measuring the productivity of individual hens, it is desirable to emphasize the fact that such records are much less important (except for advertising) than the average production of the flock, strain, or family. This has been measured in various ways, some of which are a happy mixture of eggs and euphemism. One might question how accurately the productivity of a strain was measured in laying tests when the breeder sent 13 of his best prospects and the "average production" as published was that of the 10 highest of these 13. Fortunately this system, in general use in laying tests of this country for some years prior to 1938, has been abandoned. The average production of hens still alive at the end of the laying year means little unless one knows upon what proportion of the original number that average is based. The "hen-day average," determined from the cumulative average monthly or weekly records during the year, will be high if poor layers have been culled regularly throughout the test period but lower if they have not. Similarly, one may measure productivity by the proportion of the flock that lay 200 eggs or more in a year, but this is not a true figure if the families showing poor prospects in the first 3 months are then excluded from the original number started.

Unfortunately, these various forms of lily gilding have resulted in spuriously high records being bandied around in the press until the average poultryman is led to expect much higher productivity from the average hen than she is able to deliver. As a measure of economic value, the "production index," or "hen-housed average," which is the total number of eggs laid by the flock or family during the test period, divided by the original number of birds therein, is a most useful figure. An average of 177 eggs per bird for unculled survivors to 500 days of age may seem good, but the production index of only 90 eggs for that same flock does not (Hutt and Cole, 1947). However, since the production index is influenced as much by mortality as by laying ability, or more, its use over a period of years as a measure of the improvement in laying capacity effected by selection is therefore of dubious validity unless the mortality has been constant during the period. This is a point sometimes overlooked by some investigators.

To afford comparisons of strains it would seem desirable to determine the average production of unculled samples of adequate size taken at random. This is accomplished to some extent by such excellent reports as those of the Council of American Official Egg Laying Tests giving the average production (and mortality) for all birds entered by any breeder during 3 years in all standard egg-laying tests in the country. The poultry breeder is more concerned with comparisons of families so that he may get accurate progeny tests of sires and dams. This also necessitates the testing of adequate samples, which is an expensive process because some of the birds in those samples are sure to be economically unprofitable. There is now some evidence that considerable culling of such birds can be done during the year without adversely affecting the progeny tests, provided that it is done uniformly in all families. This is discussed in Chap. 15.

GENETIC BASIS FOR DIFFERENCES IN EGG PRODUCTION

The number of genes affecting egg production is unknown. Existing techniques for analyzing characters dependent upon multiple factors are hardly adequate to warrant even an estimate. Some investigators have attempted to simplify the problem by breaking the whole into its more easily described parts and then studying each part separately. These are considered with some detail in the next section of this chapter, and the evidence concerning any genetic basis or lack of it for each of the parts, or variables, that contribute to the year's egg record is there reviewed.

Because of their historical interest, it seems justifiable to discuss briefly some of the earlier attempts to account for egg production in terms of genes. The critic must remember that these pioneering studies were made in the decade between 1910 and 1920, when geneticists were busily fitting many variations in many species into simple Mendelian ratios. It was not unreasonable to suppose that differences in egg production might conform to the rule. Raymond Pearl (1912), who made the first study of this sort, concluded that differences in egg production resulted from the action of two pairs of genes, one of which was autosomal, the other sex linked. Goodale and Macmullen (1919) invoked two pairs of genes, both autosomal, and showed that Pearl's data, as well as their own, could be explained on that basis. Hurst (1921) postulated separate dominant genes for high production at different seasons, with a recessive one for ability to lay well in autumn. By this time, Goodale and Sanborn (1922) were treating the year's egg record as the sum of genetic variation in age at first egg, rate of laying, degree of broodiness, persistency, and winter pause. Genes to account for observed segregations of these items were proposed by Hays (1924).

In all these attempts to explain variations in egg production by Mendelian ratios, the procedure followed was essentially that initiated by Pearl. The first step in this procedure was one of its greatest weaknesses, namely, the making of arbitrary classes with respect to some character showing continuous variation (*e.g.*, egg production, age at first egg, etc.). The hens were then sorted into these classes and assigned phenotypes, as good, poor, or medium in egg production, late maturing or early maturing, etc. The next step was to assume genotypes of the parents that would account for the segregation of their daughters in these arbitrary classes. This was never difficult, as most hens had small families of 4 to 12 daughters, or so, and almost any observed ratio of good:poor or high:low could be made to fit either a 3:1 or 1:1 ratio quite well. When the numbers for several dams and one sire were added, the resulting close fit of observed to expected numbers was quite impressive. The critical test of any theory thus derived would be to see if the daughters (and sons) would breed according to their phenotypic classifications and to the genotypes that they should have if those invoked for their parents were correct. Unfortunately, this critical test was never made on a scale sufficient to reveal the fallacies underlying this method of analysis.

Punnett's Test. Belief in Pearl's sex-linked L_2 gene for high fecundity dominated the poultry-breeding scene for some years, but the theory was finally disproved in an ingenious test by Punnett (1930). This study was important, not merely because it corrected an erroneous belief, but still more because it demonstrated a method of analyzing quantitative characters that had not previously been used by animal breeders. Punnett reasoned that, if high egg production depends upon a sex-linked gene, that gene should show linkage with other genes in the sex chromosome. Tests were arranged with males so bred as to contain

1. One sex chromosome from a good layer and carrying one or two dominant sex-linked genes; in this case, B (barring), S (silver), or both.
2. One sex chromosome from poor laying stock and carrying the recessive alleles b and s of the sex-linked genes in the other one.

These males were then backcrossed to females of a breed characterized by low fecundity and carrying the recessive alleles of the sex-linked genes. Silkies served for this purpose. The offspring were classified and tested under uniform conditions to determine their laying ability. Obviously, if high fecundity were sex linked, the silver and barred pullets should have proved better layers than the gold and non-barred ones. The results of three such tests (Table 34) showed clearly that there was no such difference.

TABLE 34. RESULTS IN PUNNETT'S TEST FOR A SEX-LINKED GENE AFFECTING FECUNDITY

Parentage of sires tested	Mean egg production of daughters			
	S silver	s gold	B barred	b non-barred
Light Sussex ♀ (240 eggs) × Indian Game ♂	110.9	112.4	—	—
White Wyandotte ♀ (200 eggs) × Indian Game ♂	113.0	142.0	123.7	118.1
Barred Rock ♀ × Black Sumatra ♂	.....	.....	80.0	84.0

Since the genes B and S, which were tested for linkage with any possible sex-linked gene for high fecundity, are about 45 crossover units apart in the sex chromosome, any such gene in that chromosome should have shown linkage with either one or the other, or with both. Because no such relationship was found, it seems improbable that any gene with major effects on laying ability exists in that chromosome, although there is still the possibility, as Punnett pointed out, that there might be one so remote from B and S that it could show no linkage with either of them.

This method of hunting for genes with major effects upon quantitative characters by testing for possible linkage of such genes with others that serve as markers for known linkage groups is one that has been used effectively by plant breeders. It might possibly prove more useful for analyzing multifactorial characters in the fowl than the arbitrary classifications and assumed genotypes upon which the pioneer investigators relied too much and too long. So far as the author is aware, the only similar analysis in the fowl since Punnett's study was that in which Maw demonstrated the existence of a dominant sex-linked gene reducing body size. Details of that study are given in Chap. 9.

CONTRIBUTORY VARIABLES

General Considerations

In most of the voluminous literature concerning variations in laying ability, the measure of that ability has been the number of eggs laid within a more or less arbitrary year, usually of 365 days. It is evident, therefore, that the total number of eggs laid by a hen in that year will depend entirely upon the number of days on which, for one reason or another, she abstains from laying. The various types of abstention are well known to every poultryman familiar with the capacities and caprices of hens in the matter of egg laying. They are sometimes referred to as "late sexual maturity," low "intensity," or "rate of production," "pause," "broodiness," and "lack of persistency." Although these designations suggest entirely different biological phenomena, they all refer to the same thing, so far as the year's egg record is concerned, namely, days on which the hen does not lay.

The importance of these variables was first pointed out by Goodale (1918) and Goodale and Sanborn (1922). This led to their being studied at considerable length during the ensuing 30 years. A leader in this field has been Dr. F. A. Hays, Goodale's successor at what is now the University of Massachusetts. His studies and those of others in the same field, have been directed, in general, upon four main lines as follows:

1. Ways of measuring variations in these five variables.
2. The extent to which they influence the year's egg record.
3. The extent to which they are interdependent.
4. Their genetic basis.

As was to be expected, some of these fields of study have proved more fruitful than others. Thus, there can be little argument over the fact that failure to lay on one day or on several consecutive days automatically reduces the hen's chance of achieving a perfect record and that the reduction is proportional to the number of days with no eggs. It does not necessarily follow that the abstentions commonly measured in terms of late maturity, low intensity, winter pause, broodiness, or poor persistency must represent separate and distinct genetic characters, each determined by a specific set of genes. There is evidence that this applies to some of them.

Even if all five are influenced by genes, there is no reason why such genes should be the only ones, or even the most important ones, determining the number of eggs laid by a hen in 365 days. As was shown earlier, the genes determining body size also influence the number of eggs produced. Big hens generally begin laying at a later age than small ones. Is this because they have genes for late sexual maturity or because they have genes for prolongation of the period of growth of the skeleton, *i.e.*, for large body size? The readily demonstrable inheritance of body size suggests that genes affecting size are involved. Similarly, hens laying 64-gm. eggs are less likely to do so on several consecutive days than hens laying 50-gm. eggs. Have the latter genes for "high intensity" or for small eggs? Are there separate genes for the cycle (number of consecutive daily eggs) and for small eggs, or could they be the same?

Apart from such questions, it seems probable that the number of eggs laid might depend in part upon the bird's capacity for ingesting and digesting her feed and for assimilating the end products of digestion. The proportion of these utilized for maintenance may also vary. This last would be influenced by the rate of metabolism, which is thus an important factor in determining the proportion of the feed available for production of eggs or accumulation of fat. It is inconceivable, in the light of present knowledge of genes affecting metabolism in simpler organisms, that all these processes in the fowl are not influenced by genes. Similarly, the activities of the endocrine glands—the response of the anterior pituitary to the external stimulus of light and, in turn, that of the ovary to the internal stimulus of the gonadotropic hormones— are more likely to be controlled by genes than not. Any genes influencing these important physiological processes must be considered among those affecting egg production, even though their effects are less easily measured than the number of eggs laid consecutively or the duration of a period of non-laying. In fact, one can hardly exclude from the complex of genes influencing egg production those which make some hens resistant to lymphomatosis (or to any other disease) and hence able to continue laying under conditions that cause susceptible hens to cease production and eventually to die.

With this introduction, and before proceeding to a discussion of these five variables one by one, it is appropriate to consider the extent to which they may jointly and separately affect the egg record.

In statistical studies of this problem, Knox, Jull, and Quinn (1935) considered age at sexual maturity, rate of production to Mar. 1 (intensity), and persistency to be the major hereditary traits affecting the first-year egg record. They found the coefficient of multiple correlation between these three variables together and egg production for the year to be +.866 in one breed and +.886 in another. When converted to coefficients of determination, these figures mean that differences in age at first egg, rate of production to Mar. 1, and persistency together accounted for 75 and 79 per cent of the variation in the year's record. In similar studies with these three variables, Lerner and Taylor (1937) obtained similar coefficients of determination, but with a range from 55 to 91 per cent in different years and with different measures of rate of production. (The reader unaccustomed to these various coefficients need not feel overwhelmed by them. He can reach the same conclusions merely by recalling that the hen that starts early and keeps going the longest, with the least amount of "absenteeism" from the nest, is likely to end up with the best total score for the year.)

Using certain arbitrary measures of desirable performance, Hays (1944) found that among 748 Rhode Island Reds the influence of these five variables on the year's egg production was as shown in Table 35.

TABLE 35. INFLUENCE OF DEFICIENCY IN ANY OF FIVE VARIABLES UPON NUMBER OF EGGS LAID IN THE FIRST YEAR OF LAYING *

Hens, number	Variable in which hens were deficient	Measure of deficiency	Egg production, average	Difference from best
309	None	. . . .	251.6	
19	Late maturity	Over 215 days of age	244.7	6.9
182	Low intensity	Cycle of 1 or 2 eggs	220.2	31.4
195	Winter pause	Over 7 days	227.4	24.2
20	Broodiness	In pullet year	234.8	16.8
23	Low persistency	Laying year less than 280 days	196.4	55.2

* Data from Hays.

Hens deficient with respect to several of these variables had poorer records than those deficient in only one. This was mathematically inevitable, but not necessarily of biological significance. From the differences shown in the last column of Table 35, Hays concluded that the five variables ranked, with respect to their influence on the year's record, in the following order: (1) persistency; (2) intensity; (3) winter pause; (4) broodiness; (5) age at sexual maturity. This conclusion was fully justified from his data. Lerner and Taylor (1937) also ranked persistency first.

It may be pointed out, however, that, if other similarly arbitrary measures of egg laying and of abstention from it were used, the relative importance of these five variables could be entirely different. To illustrate this fact, let us consider a flock of hens for which the average age at first egg was 190 days. If production be measured (1) for 365 days from first egg, any hen ceasing to lay at 280 days thereafter or less automatically reduces her chance of making a perfect record for the year by at least 85 eggs. However, if production be measured (2) by the number of eggs laid to 500 days of age, any hen that begins at 190 days of age and stops 280 days thereafter is handicapping her record only by some number that cannot exceed 30. Obviously persistency is of great importance in the first case, but much less so in the second. Conversely, if late starters are given just as many days for their record as early ones, the age at first egg is of little importance, except in so far as the late starter's style may be cramped toward the end of the race by the shortening hours of daylight in the late fall months. However, when the measure of performance is the number of eggs laid to 500 days of age, the hen beginning to lay at 170 days has an advantage over the average member of the flock that may be worth up to 20 eggs, while her sister beginning at 230 days is automatically handicapped by having 40 days less than the average member of the flock in which to make her record. It is evident, therefore, that with this measure of laying capacity the age at first egg might easily be the most important variable of the five considered in Table 35.

In practice, the breeder must use these different arbitrary measures of abstention from egg laying according to their importance in his own operations. The breeder of Rhode Island Reds must consider broodiness more seriously than the average owner of a White Leghorn flock. If he is breeding hens to win laying tests or to make the 365-day record (from first egg), persistency may well be his most important consideration. On the other hand, if he is more concerned about progeny tests that require the annual housing of large numbers of pullets and the measuring of viability, productivity, or other qualities that can be evaluated by the time the birds are 500 days old, persistency is of less importance and the desirable combination of optimum age at first egg with optimum body size will be a more important factor in the selection of breeding stock.

Age at Sexual Maturity

Measures. This is usually measured in females by the age at which the first egg is laid. When used for comparisons of pullets hatched at successively later dates through the hatching season, the age at first egg should be corrected for the fact that late-hatched birds mature at older ages than early ones. An alternative measure, the date of first egg, has been used, but it is less desirable for two reasons. It is more closely dependent than the other upon the date of hatching, and it renders difficult any comparisons of birds or data from different latitudes in which the seasons differ.

The good breeder is less concerned with the performance of individual females than with the mean (average) for whole families. In practice, determination of the mean age at first egg is often complicated (especially in sires' families) by the fact that one or two recalcitrant hens do not begin to lay until several months after their most precocious sisters. These "holdouts" are thus able to delay computation of the average, even if an arbitrary age be set after which they are excluded from the record. A practical suggestion by Lerner and Taylor (1940) provides a means of overcoming these difficulties. If the breeder will determine the family's rating by the *median*, rather than by the mean, the former figure is known as soon as half the family have begun to lay. The median is the mid-point in the distribution; it separates the half that begin to lay early from the other half that begin later. If the distribution be exactly uniform, it will coincide with the mean, but this is not likely to happen. When large numbers are involved, the median and the mean are so close together that either may be used. Lerner and Taylor found the correlation between the two in large populations to be +.903 and +.933 in two different years and concluded from other evidence that the quickly determined median is just as useful as the mean for evaluating families according to their age at sexual maturity.

Variation in Relation to Light. A few pullets begin laying at about 4 months of age, while others do not start until they are more than 10 months old. When differences in age at first egg occur among birds hatched on the same date and reared together, they are properly attributable to genetic variability, but this does not apply equally well to birds hatched at different dates. That is because the age at first egg is influenced to a great extent by the length of day (or amount of light, natural or artificial) at the time when they are sufficiently grown to lay if the light be adequate. Since the time (or date) at which that stage is attained depends largely upon the time of hatching, there is a close relationship between date of hatch and age at first egg. This is well known to poultrymen, most of whom have learned by experience either to hatch chicks at the dates considered optimum in their latitude or to compensate for late hatching by providing artificial light for birds reaching somatic maturity when the days are short.

This point is illustrated by the records of Upp and Thompson (1927) for Leghorns hatched from the same parent stock at fortnightly intervals throughout the year (Table 36). These data, which were taken at lat. 36°N., show clearly that pullets hatched from July to January—and thus ready to lay at various periods from the following January to August—began laying at younger ages than those maturing in the fall and early winter.

These records show no significant differences among birds hatched from Feb. 25 to May 5. This is not the usual experience, for, in a normal 10-week hatching season beginning early in March, the mean age at first egg is usually slightly greater with each successive hatch. Thus, Byerly and Knox (1946) found that, for every 2 days by which hatches fell after Mar. 21, there was a corresponding prolongation of age at first egg by about 1 day. An almost identical relation has been noted in California by Taylor and Lerner (1938). This effect applies only to birds hatched in the spring and maturing at a time when the days are becoming shorter. The opposite relationship, with later hatched pullets laying at successively earlier ages, is found among birds hatched in latitudes north of the equator from August to December (Table 36).

It follows, therefore, that, in evaluating families according to sexual maturity, some correction for hatching date is necessary. This may be done by determining for each successive hatch the mean age at first egg and deducting from the figure for each pullet the number of days by which the mean for her hatching date exceeds that for those hatched earliest. When sires are being compared, this may not be necessary if all sires have daughters distributed approximately equally through early and late hatches. It must be done if two or three series of males used in one season are to be compared, as is shown in Chap. 15.

Equally important for evaluation of families is the fact that the genetic variability in age at first egg is reduced, if not eliminated entirely, in later hatched birds that are rushed into egg production by exposure to artificial light. This applies also to pullets not given artificial light but hatched in late summer and thus hastened into laying by the lengthening days of late winter, as Greenwood and Blyth (1946)

TABLE 36. DATA SHOWING THAT PULLETS BEGINNING TO LAY IN MONTHS WHEN DAYS ARE SHORT TAKE LONGER TO DO SO THAN THOSE BEGINNING WHEN THE DAYS ARE LONGER OR LENGTHENING *

Dates of hatches	Pullets, number	Mean age at first egg, days	Mean date of laying first egg
Nov. 17–Dec. 15	?	156	May 23
Jan. 14–Feb. 11	45	185	July 27
Feb. 25–Mar. 24	45	236	Nov. 2
Apr. 7–May 5	41	234	Dec. 11
May 19–June 16	40	229	Jan. 15
June 30–Aug. 11	32	214	Feb. 18
Aug. 25–Sept. 22	34	195	Mar. 24
Oct. 6–Nov. 3	32	179	Apr. 18

* From Upp and Thompson (1927).

have shown. It follows that the pullets genetically unable to mature at the time and age desired will be recognized best if their genetic inadequacies are not masked by the provision of extra light in either of these ways.

Variation in Relation to Body Weight. It is recognized that small breeds, strains, and birds tend to begin laying at earlier ages than do big ones, but studies of this relationship have left some confusion in the literature. This is partly because of differing measures of body size and different methods of analysis. Since body weight increases with age until definitive body weight is attained, and since most pullets begin laying before that stage, it is axiomatic that, in general, the later the bird starts laying the greater will her weight be at that time.

Expressed otherwise, the correlation between age at first egg and body weight at first egg has been found in three breeds to be about +.5 (Upp and Thompson, 1927; Hays, 1933; Callenbach, 1934). In contrast, Hazel and Lamoreux (1947) found a negative correlation of .33 between age at first egg and body weight at 156 days. A similar negative correlation (.23) was also found by Lerner (1946), who determined body weight at about 5 months. This negative correlation pertained to pullets that had a mean age at first egg of 166 days, which was within about 2 weeks of the weighing. With larger birds, for which the mean age at laying was 177, there was no relation whatever between weight at 5 months and age at first egg. It seems probable that the body weights determined at such arbitrary ages could lead to confusing interpretations unless the pullets then laying or about to do so were separated from those maturing later. The former would show body weights spuriously raised by the rapid enlargement of the reproductive system, while the later maturing birds would not. For that reason, body weight at some stage prior to maturity of all birds would seem of dubious value as an aid in selection.

It does not follow that because early layers are smaller than late ones when they begin laying they must remain so. In seven groups of rather small Leghorns varying in age at first egg from 120 to 300 days, Waters (1937) found the mean weights at first egg to range correspondingly from 1,273 to 1,718 gm., but at 10 months of age the mean weights for the seven groups were all about the same. Similarly, Lerner (1946) found·the correlation between age at first egg and body weight in December to be only +.07 in one line of small Leghorns (1,666 gm.). These findings suggest that age at sexual maturity may have little or no relation to adult size within flocks comprised of comparatively small birds.

Apart from correlations, which can be misinterpreted, the fact that age at first egg is prolonged as body size increases has been frequently demonstrated. Two experiments in selection, during both of which age at sexual maturity was considered little or not at all, will serve to illustrate the point. At the Mount Hope Farm, selection by Goodale (1935–1936) to increase the size of egg automatically raised body weight and with it the age at first egg. Similarly, Lerner (1946), by selecting for longer shanks in Leghorns, raised body weight and, at the same time, the age at first egg. Their results are shown in Table 37.

TABLE 37. DATA SHOWING THAT AGE AT FIRST EGG IS RAISED AS BODY SIZE IS INCREASED BY SELECTION

Means	Mount Hope Farm		Lerner	
	Unselected line	Selected	Unselected line	Selected
Weight at first egg, pounds...	3.44	4.23	Not given	Not given
Weight at 50th egg, pounds...	3.55	4.32	—	—
Weight in December, grams..	....	....	1,666	1,903
Age at first egg, days........	186	200	166	177

The two later records of body weight shown in this table were taken at about 9 months of age and should represent approximately adult weights. Both experiments show that when adult body weight is increased by selection the age at first egg is automatically raised at the same time, even though that factor is not considered in the selection process.

Other Variation. Any environmental influence retarding growth and development may delay the commencement of laying. Sometimes this happens when birds are vaccinated at 4 or 5 months for chicken pox. Critical evidence has not yet been adduced to substantiate the common belief that the onset of laying can be delayed, when desired, by changing the quantity or quality of protein in the diet of birds nearly mature. On the other hand, Taylor and Lerner (1939) found that addition of wheat bran to an apparently complete diet did induce earlier laying, and hence the possible influence of dietary factors is not excluded.

External signs by which pullets likely to mature early may be identified when hatched are unknown. There is no relation between age at first egg and the size of the genital eminence in the cloaca at hatching (Hammond and Burrows, 1937; Phillips and Williams, 1944).

Relation to Egg Production. There has been a spate of reports on this subject, most of them ending with the conclusion that pullets beginning to lay at early ages are better layers than those starting later. These conclusions are based on negative correlations of the order of about $-.3$ to $-.5$ between age at first egg and "annual production." These are of very dubious value simply because the later maturing birds have fewer days in which to make a record. This is most obvious when the laying year terminates at some fixed date, as in laying tests. Even when allowed 365 days from first egg in which to make the year's record, the late starters, when coming down the home stretch in October and November, are so handicapped by shortening days, the corresponding reduction of light, and the temptation to moult that few of them can keep on laying to the 365-day limit unless artificial light be provided. In contrast, the early starters can finish their 365-day year in August or early September without these handicaps. As they have the advantage of longer days at both ends of their year, it is inevitable that they should turn in better records.

When laying ability is measured by the *rate of production* after laying has begun, rather than by the number of eggs in an arbitrarily determined year, the coefficients of correlation dwindle to insignificance and it is clear that age at first egg is not related to productivity (Table 38).

Entirely apart from that question, early-maturing pullets are likely to be more profitable than late ones merely because more of their production comes in the fall months, when prices are best. On the other hand, the unusually precocious birds are likely to be small, to lay small

TABLE 38. COEFFICIENTS OF CORRELATION SHOWING THAT AGE AT FIRST EGG, THOUGH HIGHLY CORRELATED WITH "ANNUAL PRODUCTION," HAS NO RELATION TO LAYING ABILITY THAT IS MEASURED BY THE RATE OF PRODUCTION

Investigators	Correlation between age at first egg and		
	Year's record	Rate	Period of measurement
Kempster (1925)................	--.23 to --.45	−.01 to −.25	Best 2 months
Knox, Jull, and Quinn (1935):			
White Leghorns.............	−.40	+.02	To Mar. 1
Rhode Island Reds..........	−.48	−.02	To Mar. 1
Lerner and Taylor (1937):			
Flock of 1933...............	−.35	+.09	Winter
Flock of 1933...............	.....	+.02	Spring
Flock of 1933...............	.....	+.14	Summer
Flock of 1934...............	−.39	+.14	Winter
Flock of 1934...............	.....	+.13	Spring
Flock of 1934...............	.....	+.03	Summer

eggs, and to be unable to maintain production. Some Leghorns will lay at less than 150 days, especially if hatched early. The breeder more concerned about having Leghorns that weigh 4 to 5 pounds as adults and pullets capable of soon laying 2-ounce eggs will find those beginning at 170 to 190 days more likely to meet his requirements.

Genetic Basis. Age at sexual maturity, as measured by age at first egg, is generally considered to be inherited. It is not always clear, in evidence cited in support of this conclusion, whether the age at first egg is inherited independently of body size or whether the real variable is size and age at first egg is merely incidental. This doubt would apply, for example, to studies like those of Godfrey and Jull (1935) showing resemblance of sisters in age at first egg and positive correlations between dams and daughters of 0.160 in White Leghorns and 0.448 in Rhode Island Reds. The selection experiments of Goodale (1935–1936) and Lerner (1946) mentioned earlier show that selection resulting in greater size of body automatically raises the age at first egg, and these results need not be interpreted in terms of specific genes for later maturity.

However, the maintenance of mean age at first egg for Rhode Island Reds at about 196 days or less, while body weight at first egg was increased during 6 or 7 years by over half a pound (Hays and Sanborn, 1939) is evidence that there are genes influencing sexual maturity directly, apart from those affecting both that variable and body weight. Other evidence was found by Waters (1934) in the F_1 and F_2 generations from the cross White Leghorn $\times$ Light Brahma. Some of these birds with adult weights over 2,700 gm. began to lay nearly as early as the Leghorns that had an average weight of only 1,600 gm. In breeding Leghorns for low fecundity, Lamoreux, Hutt, and Hall (1943) found that the lowering of the mean production (to 500 days of age) was accomplished chiefly by raising the age at first egg to 352 days. This was done without any increase in body weight, although that was not stated in the report cited.

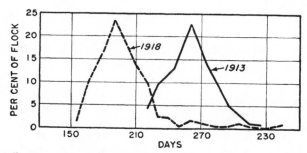

Fɪɢ. 80. Distributions of ages at first egg in the unselected flock of 1913 and that of 1918. In 5 years of selection the mean age was reduced from 256 to 194 days. (*From Goodale and Sanborn.*)

The feasibility of changing the mean age at first egg by a few years of selection was first demonstrated by Goodale and Sanborn (1922), who reduced it in Rhode Island Reds from 256 days in 1913 to 194 days in 1918 (Fig. 80).

While differences in age at sexual maturity are subject to genetic variation, the number of genes concerned is unknown. Hays (1924) suggested that sex-linked genes are involved, in addition to others. Supporting evidence was found by Warren (1934), who differentiated by selection two strains of Rhode Island Reds in one of which mean age at first egg was 6 to 7 weeks later than in the other. In reciprocal crosses between these two strains and in backcrosses of the F_1 females to the early strain, the tendency was for the daughters to resemble the paternal strain, as would be expected if they received in their sex chromosome (from the sire) a gene or genes influencing age at first egg (Table 39).

Similar evidence of sex-linked genes affecting age at first egg was seen in the F_1 generations of Waters (1934) from reciprocal crosses of early-maturing Leghorns with late-maturing Brahmas, but in the two

F_2 generations the ages at first egg showed no sign of being influenced by sex-linked genes.

Intensity, or Rate of Laying

Although poultrymen tend to evaluate laying capacity in terms of the number of eggs laid in 365 days or in 48 weeks, the record for a shorter period has some desirable features of special value. As Dryden (1921) pointed out, the real laying ability may possibly be better shown

TABLE 39. RECIPROCAL CROSSES AND OTHERS BETWEEN EARLY-MATURING AND LATE-MATURING RHODE ISLAND REDS SHOWING THE APPARENT INFLUENCE OF SEX-LINKED GENES TRANSMITTED BY THE SIRES UPON AGE AT FIRST EGG IN THEIR DAUGHTERS *

Type of mating	Daughters, number	Mean age at first egg, days
(a) Early ♂♂ × early ♀♀, 1930.....	20	216.7
Early ♂♂ × early ♀♀, 1931.....	45	222.2
(b) Late ♂♂ × late ♀♀, 1930.......	29	249.3
Late ♂♂ × late ♀♀, 1931.......	71	269.0
(c) 2 Early ♂♂ × late ♀♀, 1930....	31	222.7
3 Early ♂♂ × late ♀♀, 1931....	36	217.9
(d) 3 Late ♂♂ × early ♀♀, 1930....	42	232.9
4 Late ♂♂ × early ♀♀, 1931....	80	244.8
(e) Backcross, early ♀♀ from (c) × early ♂♂.....................	132	214.4
(f) Backcross, late ♀♀ from (d) × early ♂♂.....................	249	217.5

* Data from Warren.

in short periods than in long ones because in the short periods environmental conditions are under better control than in long ones. A pullet may demonstrate excellent productivity in the fall months, only to have her record for the year ruined by an outbreak of respiratory disease in January. Furthermore, most breeders must evaluate pullets, their families, their sires, and their dams by December or January in order to make wise selection of breeding stock for the spring hatches. To do so, they must use, willy-nilly, the evidence of laying ability up to that time, whether measured as total eggs laid in 3 or 4 months or otherwise. A further obvious advantage of short-time records is that labor is saved if trapnesting can be reduced from a 12-month job to one of a few months or weeks.

Measures. Dryden took as a short-time measure of productivity (1) the number of eggs laid in the best 2 consecutive months. Hays and

Sanborn (1927) tried (2) the number of eggs in the first 60 days of laying, (3) production from first egg to Mar. 1, expressed as a percentage of the number of days in that period after deducting all "pauses" of 4 days or more, and (4) the mean length of the cycle of production in that period, *i.e.*, the number of consecutive days of laying.

Fig. 81. D. C. Warren. Formerly of Kansas State College, now with the U.S. Department of Agriculture at Purdue University.

(The use of the term "clutch" by poultrymen in this sense seems hardly justifiable since that word has long been understood, in general usage and by ornithologists in particular, to mean the number of eggs laid by a bird before she stops laying to incubate them.) Others have measured rate of laying as in (3) above, but (5) without any allowance for the time out of production (Jull, 1934, and others), or (6) deducting from the number of days on which the percentage is based only pauses of 7 days or more (Lerner and Taylor, 1936).

In practice, the breeder will not have much occasion to use egg records to Mar. 1 unless he stops trapping on that date. He is more likely to need measures of production by which his birds can be evaluated in December. Some of those listed above can be modified for that purpose, but in most cases it will suffice to note the numbers of eggs laid per month for 2 or 3 consecutive months. With the period of test thus reduced, there would seem to be little justification for crediting any pullet with time out from laying, whether 7 days, 4 days, or 1, except for non-laying that results from adverse environmental conditions affecting only some of the birds.

Variation. Since hens rarely lay 2 eggs in one day, it is obvious that the best layers are those that miss the fewest days. Some can lay only on 2 successive days and skip the third. Others have cycles of 3 to 6 eggs or more without a break, and some have been known to lay for over 2 months without missing a day. As every experienced trapnester knows, most hens tend to lay at a later hour on each successive day until finally they skip a day and start over again on the following morning. As Atwood (1929) showed, the greater the number of eggs in the cycle, the shorter the interval between them. This was confirmed by Hays (1936) and by Heywang (1938), some of whose data are shown in Table 40. He observed a few cycles of 40 or more consecutive eggs,

TABLE 40. DATA SHOWING DIFFERENCES IN LENGTHS OF THE INTERVALS BETWEEN TWO SUCCESSIVE EGGS AT THE BEGINNING, THE MIDDLE, AND THE END OF CYCLES OF DIFFERENT SIZES*

Number of eggs in cycle	Number of such cycles	Interval between eggs, hours		
		Between first two	Between two in the middle	Between last two
2	4,768	28.21	—	—
3	2,781	26.57	. . . . .	27.37
4	1,288	25.95	25.73	26.81
5	608	25.72	25.14	26.55
6	342	25.57	24.80	26.45
7	190	25.59	24.43	26.34
8	130	25.40	24.31	26.27
9	58	24.85	24.29	26.26
10	36	24.50	24.22	26.39

* From Heywang (1938).

and, as would be expected, in these cases the average interval between successive eggs was only a few minutes longer than 24 hours.

An interesting point noted by both Atwood and Heywang is that the interval between the last two eggs of a cycle is always significantly longer than that between any other two of the preceding eggs in the same cycle. It would seem almost as if the hen realizes that she will not be laying on the following day anyway and can therefore relax and meditate at leisure while making her last contribution to the cycle that is terminating. Similarly, the interval between the first two eggs, though not so great as that between the last two, is longer than that between any other pair of consecutive eggs in the cycle. The shortest intervals come in the middle of the cycle (Table 40).

Scott and Warren (1936), utilizing an ingenious procedure for following the ovum down the oviduct by palpation, concluded that hens

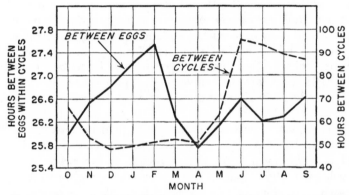

Fig. 82. Changes in the intervals (1) between eggs within cycles and (2) between cycles, at different seasons, with evidence of an inverse relation between length of day and length of the interval between eggs. Both graphs apply to the same birds. (*From Hays in J. Agr. Research, 1936 and 1938.*)

seldom ovulate in the afternoon and that when a hen lays late in the afternoon release of the next ovum does not follow until about 15.5 hours later. As a result, the cycle of successive daily eggs is terminated. This failure to ovulate is related to the onset of darkness, according to Warren and Scott (1936). They found that hens kept in the dark during the daytime and given artificial light at night adjusted their laying habits accordingly in about 60 hours and then laid only during the lighted period at night. When given light continuously (day and night), their hens laid at any hour of the 24. Further evidence of the relation of light to length of the cycle is seen (Fig. 82) in the data of Hays (1936), showing that in the fall and early winter the interval between eggs increases steadily (*i.e.,* shorter cycles) until February, but thereafter drops precipitately to the shortest interval (longest cycle) in April. The influence of light is less evident from April to September, probably because most of the days in that period provide the maximum stimulation possible, but also because some hens become refractory to the influence of light after prolonged stimulation.

Confirming these facts, Byerly and Moore (1941) showed that the cycle could be lengthened far beyond the normal by extending the lighted period to 14 hours but alternating that with a 12-hour period of darkness. Hens thus provided with a 26-hour working day (to match the average normal interval between eggs laid on consecutive days) had cycles with mean duration over 5 days. Other hens given 14 hours of light but only 10 hours of darkness between such periods laid in cycles with mean length of only 2 days or less. These last were unable to maintain egg production as well on their 24-hour day as were the hens with the 26-hour day, even though the number of hours of light was the same for both. While it is clear that most hens would prefer a 26-hour day, it seems probable that the poultryman will be more successful in breeding them to accelerate their physiological processes to suit a 24-hour day than he would be in slowing down the earth to one revolution in 26 hours.

When once a hen's cycle of laying has been demonstrated, whether two, three, four, or more eggs, it is likely to be maintained while that hen is laying. This means, not that a record with a preponderance of two-egg cycles will show none of 4 eggs, or vice versa, but merely that hens are fairly consistent in this respect. It would therefore be easy to measure the rate of laying by the length of the cycle, if it were not for one more variable, namely, that the interval between cycles is not always just 1 day. As Hays (1938) has shown (Fig. 82), this interval tends to be shorter for pullets laying in the fall and winter, thus compensating for the shorter cycles (and greater interval between eggs within cycles) to which most birds are limited by the amount of daylight then available. Obviously, while the number of eggs per cycle is some guide to rate of production, it would be more accurate if combined with a measure of the days of non-laying between cycles. Such a combination would seem to be provided (and without any special calculation) simply by the number of eggs per month, with the obvious corollary that several months show the hen's all-round capacity better than 1 only.

Relation to the Year's Record. Much has been written about the relation of intensity, or rate of laying, to egg production—the latter term being used to mean the year's record. It is hardly necessary to cite here all the columns of matching egg records and all the coefficients showing that intensity (measured in divers ways and for various periods) is significantly correlated with the total number of eggs laid in 365 days. All these coefficients are positive. Here is one point on which all investigators are agreed. Perhaps that is because the number of eggs laid in 4, 5, or 6 months is a big part of the number laid in 12 months. Another reason is that the hen's genotype is the same after Mar. 1 as before, and the laying ability demonstrated prior to that date is likely to be continued after it, except in so far as it may be modified by changes in environmental conditions. Actually, intensity of production is the same thing as production, when size of egg is not considered. There is no reason why genetic capacity for laying should not be measured in the first 3 or 4 months or in the best 2 months, except that it pays to keep some hens for a full year and poultrymen have become accustomed to a test period of 12 months. This, in turn, measures not merely genetic capacity for laying a lot of eggs in a short time but also the ability to keep on doing so for a long time and the extent to which the process may be interrupted by genes for broodiness, for susceptibility to disease, or for vacations or by the influence of faulty diets or other adverse environmental conditions. All this was clearly stated some years ago by Dryden (1921). As he pointed out, such environmental influences may account for the frequent cases in which hens with comparatively low records for the year produce daughters that appear to be much better layers than their dams.

Poultry breeders would like to know what period of the laying year is most likely to reveal the kind of egg record that a hen will make in 12 months. On this point the statisticians are not in agreement. Harris and Goodale (1922) concluded that the egg production from March to June was of less value than that of fall, winter, and late summer months in predicting the year's record. On the other hand, Hays and Sanborn (1932), who measured intensity by the average number of days per cycle, considered that the spring, summer, and winter seasons ranked in the order just given with respect to their desirability as short-time test periods. In later years, however, they (1939) adopted as the most satisfactory measure the mean length of the cycle in the period from first egg to Mar. 1 and set three eggs as the minimum figure allowable for hens good enough to use as breeders. With other procedures, Lerner and Taylor (1937) concluded that rate of production was more indicative of the year's record when measured in the spring or winter months than in the summer and fall.

While consideration of intensity is indispensable for the evaluation of pullets in their first few months of production, and although it is really the expression of genetic laying capacity, the *economic value* of the hen depends upon several other equally important factors. The highest rate of winter production is of little use if the pullet lays only 50-gm. eggs, if she dies on Mar. 2, if she spends a good part of the spring months in broodiness, or if she ceases to lay in May. Obviously, the full record for 10 or 12 months (or an estimate of it determined by sampling) has a special value of which intensity is only a part.

Genetic Basis. That there are genetic differences in laying ability, whether measured in 12 months or 3 months or by length of the cycle, is clearly evident to anyone observing the differences between families and the resemblance of sisters in this respect. The number of genes concerned is unknown. A single example will suffice to show the complexity of the problem. Because of the tendency for hens laying large eggs to produce fewer of them (page 356), one may question whether large eggs result from genes for low intensity or whether high intensity results from genes for small eggs. Should the genetic capacity for converting surplus feed into yolk (and hence into eggs) be measured only by the number of parcels in which it is wrapped, and not by the size of the parcel? Is the hen that lays 9 eggs of 50 gm. each in 10 days as good a layer as the one that produces 8 eggs weighing 60 gm. in the same period? The question is worth considering by anyone seeking to account for differences in laying ability in terms of a few pairs of genes.

Pauses in Production

Most pullets take a vacation from laying on one pretext or another during the first laying year. Sometimes it is merely a week end, sometimes 2 months or more. Often it is forced upon them by disease or by some other environmental influence so obvious that the poultryman recognizes sadly that his hens have been "knocked out of production." At other times, pullets "go into a slump" for no apparent reason except that they have laid well for a few months, and are therefore entitled to some vacation. This is especially likely to happen with early-hatched birds that begin laying in August or early September. Among their later hatched full sisters beginning to lay in December, so few may stop laying during the winter and spring that their defection is not revealed by the production of the flock as a whole.

While any abstention from laying, whether designated as a "winter pause," a "spring pause," or merely a "work stoppage," must automatically reduce the number of eggs laid by a hen in any arbitrary period such as the first year of laying, it does not necessarily follow that such a pause is a distinct biological phenomenon and, as such, entitled to genes of its own on a par with genes for early maturity or for intensity. It is clear that much of such pausing is induced by environmental influences, but it is not yet clear that any of it is attributable to specific genes. In fact, the failure of Lerner and Taylor (1947) to increase significantly the proportion of pausing birds in a strain of Leghorns selected for that objective during nine generations suggests that there can be little genetic basis for such pauses. At the same time, the proportion of pausing birds decreased in their line bred for high production, thus apparently differentiating these two lines with respect to the proportion of pausers. However, as they clearly showed, both in their own Leghorns and in the Rhode Island Reds of Hays (1944), the hens with low rate of production are more likely to go a-pausing than the good layers. Similarly, Hays (1936a) had previously found that the good layers that do pause take shorter vacations than the poor ones. It is not clear, therefore, that the differences between the two lines of Lerner and Taylor with respect to proportion of pausers resulted any more from elimination of genes for pausing than from accumulation of genes for egg production in the better line. In both these lines and in other unselected controls, the proportion of birds that paused seemed to be influenced more by changes in environmental influences from year to year than by selection. This same situation is commonly seen in most flocks. The poultryman must not attribute winter pauses to genetic variation merely because he cannot recognize any specific environmental influence that can be held responsible.

Study of these temporary work stoppages is complicated by the problem, When is a pause a real pause and when is it merely a hesitation? Different investigators have defined a pause as 4 days of non-laying (Hays, 1936a), 7 days (Lerner and Taylor, 1936, 1947), and 8 days (Hays, 1938). Since any such definition is entirely arbitrary, the point merits no debate.

An interesting question is whether or not a pause is precipitated by exhaustion from prolonged or prolific laying. If so, does the hen recuperate while on vacation and return to her labors with renewed vigor? Does she compensate for the lost time by greater productivity when laying is resumed? Apparently not. According to Lerner and Taylor (1936) the rate of production in the 15 days before a pause is slightly lower than that for the whole period of 4 months in which the pause falls, but the rate is no higher after the vacation than before it. It is true, as Hays (1936a) found, that hens with short winter pauses tend to turn in better records thereafter than hens with long pauses, but this is mathematically inevitable because the former have more days for laying before reaching the 365-day limit. This has no biological significance. For his 693 birds with pauses of 4 days or more, the average duration of the pause was 37 days, and the maximum 123 days. It is generally recognized that when the pullet stops laying and undergoes a partial moult, as early-hatched pullets frequently do, she is likely to be out of production for 6 or 8 weeks.

Persistency

The first year of laying is usually terminated by onset of the first complete moult, but good layers frequently continue laying during early stages of the moult, and occasionally a hen even lays right through that process. Since hens vary greatly in the time at which they begin moulting, there are corresponding differences in the dates at which they stop laying. Obviously, this variation must affect the egg record for the year if it be measured in some arbitrary period of the calendar, as in laying tests, or for 365 days from first egg. Because of this, persistency, or the ability to continue laying in late summer and early fall, has been so thoroughly studied that the simple underlying facts have been almost lost in the clouds of statistical mysticism thus engendered.

Measures. Hays and Sanborn (1933) measured persistency by the number of days from first egg to last egg before stopping for the moult. This figure, with some modification for the hens that did not stop laying within 365 days of first egg, was considered by them as the "biological laying year." However, there is good evidence that cessation of laying results from reduction in the length of day in late summer and fall, and since this factor would act equally on all birds whether they began laying in the previous August or in December, it would seem that the latter must, in general, have a shorter laying year than the former. That this actually happens is shown by the significant negative correlations of .615 and .566 between age at first egg and length of the biological year found by Hays and Sanborn (1926, 1933). These show that about 32 per cent of the differences in persistency, as thus measured, results from variations in age at first egg. This, in turn, as we have seen earlier, is considerably affected by genetic variation and by the date of hatching.

Persistency could be measured by the date or age at last egg, but the latter would have to be corrected for date of hatching. This is merely because the shortening days of September catch the hens hatched in April at a younger age than those hatched in March. In practice, dates and ages are difficult to incorporate in some single index of desirability. For that reason, not many poultrymen are likely to evaluate the laying qualities of their hens by the date or age at last egg. A more practical measure, even if a less exact one, is the number of eggs laid in August and September at the end of the laying year (Knox *et al.*, 1935). In fact, it would seem that anyone keeping hens until the end of September would probably be interested less in the persistency by itself than in the total number of eggs laid to that date. Lack of persistency measures only one kind of abstention from laying. The total production considers them all. Together with its component monthly records, it yields a better direct measure of the hen's net economic value as a layer than any other measure of laying or of not laying.

Variation. Some hens stop laying in June, others not till December. It seems probable that differences in this respect depend to a large extent upon genetic variations in response to shortening days. Similar differences in wild birds may account for the differences between species with respect to early and late southward migrations. The relation of decreasing light to cessation of laying is shown by the fact that a flock that is declining in production in September can be restored to a high rate of laying merely by supplementing the available daylight with artificial light. However, just as some pullets lay well in shortening days at the start of their laying year, so do some hens continue laying at the end of their year in November without artificial light, long after most of the flock have stopped. These are likely to be the same birds, but on that point further evidence is desirable. While these exceptionally persistent layers are interesting, both as biological phenomena and as economic assets, it is sometimes necessary to force them to stop laying, in order that they may complete their moult and be ready for reproduction in January.

While the range in persistency from early moulters to late ones is very great, there is evidence that the differences are attributable to genetic variations in the birds and not solely to environmental conditions. In 911 Rhode Island Reds, Hays and Sanborn (1933) found the length of the biological laying year to vary from 80 to 484 days, the mean for all birds being 364 days. Nevertheless, there is a strong tendency for the hen to cease laying at the same time in each successive year. When this was measured by the correlation between that time in the first and second laying years, Harris and Lewis (1923) found the coefficient of that correlation to be significant and high, $r = +.503$. The tendency is shown still more clearly by the figures of Greenwood *et al.* (1940) for 129 birds for which dates were known of last eggs at the end of 3 successive laying years. In these the following relationships were observed:

	Number	Per cent
Birds with all 3 dates within 6 days.....	13	10.1
Birds with all 3 dates within 20 days....	60	46.5
Birds with 2 out of 3 dates within 6 days	69	53.5
Birds with 2 out of 3 dates within 13 days	108	83.7

Their most remarkable case was a Brown Leghorn hen that in successive years from 1931 to 1938 terminated the year's laying on Oct. 17, 17, 3, 22, 18, 12, 10, and 20, respectively. While individual birds show an innate tendency to stop laying at about the same time each year, Greenwood *et al.* concluded that the genetic potentiality in that respect is not reliably revealed by the date when laying stops at the end of the pullet year. This point seems worth emphasizing, because in most other studies of persistency to date nothing else has been considered than the persistency at the end of the pullet year.

Consideration of the time at which the moult begins invites a few words about its duration. As most observant poultrymen know, the hens that keep on laying till October or November then do their moulting in a hurry and get back to laying about as soon as the loafers that began moulting in July and August. This has been verified statistically by the finding that the duration of the period of non-laying associated with the moult shows a significant negative correlation with persistency, whether measured by the length of the laying year (Hays and Sanborn, 1930), by the date of last egg, or by the age of the hen when she lays it (Lerner and Taylor, 1941).

Relation to Laying Ability. The novice starting out to breed better layers might conclude from various studies and statements in the literature that the success or failure of his efforts would depend largely upon selection for persistency. There are the consistent and highly significant coefficients of partial correlation between persistency and the year's total egg production of $+.75$ (Hays and Sanborn, 1927) and $+.73$ and $+.77$ (Knox *et al.*, 1935). These show, in both studies, a much greater effect of persistency on total number of eggs than that of any other contributory variable. There is the conclusion of Lerner and Taylor (1937) that "age at last egg is the most important single factor affecting egg production." Finally there is the evidence of Hays (1944) that hens ceasing to lay prior to 280 days from first egg lay 55 eggs per bird less than those which continue after that dividing line, and his conclusion therefrom that persistency appears to be the most important of "the five inherited physiological characters" affecting the first-year production.

Concerning all this the author is somewhat skeptical. This is partly because he and his colleague have been able over a period of years to raise considerably the average egg production of two strains of Leghorns and to do so with little or no consideration of persistency (Hutt and Cole, 1947). It was disregarded merely because good management of successive generations of these birds made it impracticable to keep them for 365 days from first egg and necessitated measuring their laying ability by their performance to 500 days of age (page 298). For the average hen, this was about 55 days short of a 365-day laying year. The statistics and conclusions cited in the previous paragraph are undoubtedly correct if one thinks of egg production only in terms of the number laid in 365 days. They merely represent other ways of saying that the hen ceasing to lay in July will not have so many eggs to her credit by Oct. 1 as will the bird that keeps on laying right up to that date.

There is some evidence, however, that the persistent hens are better layers than the early stoppers even before the latter have stopped. Co-efficients of correlation between persistency and winter or spring rate of production are all positive and are given as .137 to .271 by Lerner and Taylor (1937), .150 by Knox *et al.* (1935), and .184 by Hays and Sanborn (1926). These last found that the total number of eggs laid up to the end of February is a still better indication of the probability that a hen will keep on laying beyond 315 days from first egg. Among 1,136 hens that did so, the proportion with winter egg production above the average was 63 per cent, whereas among 1,015 hens that stopped laying within 315 days the corresponding proportion was only 34 per cent. In this case, however, the figures are somewhat misleading because the pullets that begin early have a better chance, not only to roll up a good score before Mar. 1, but also to achieve persistency (*i.e.*, to lay beyond their 315-day deadline) before the shades of approaching autumn shorten too much the days of August and September.

Because of these and other indications that the good layers prior to 500 days of age are most likely to be persistent layers thereafter, because the eggs of early-maturing hens count on the record just the same as those of their late-persisting sister, and because problems of management, of record keeping, and of selection make it impracticable to evaluate families by the 365-day production of their members, it would seem more satisfactory for the breeder to close the test period at some fixed age, such as the 500 days already discussed. Persistency can still be measured, if desired, in those hens of the better families that are kept for breeding. Those not good enough for that purpose can be exploited to better advantage after 500 days by keeping them in large pens, not trap-nested, but given artificial light in order to get the maximum possible number of eggs. Since hens of that age are usually laying eggs of large size (except for the influence of hot weather), such a program should prove more profitable than maintaining them under test conditions merely to see when they will stop laying.

Genetic Basis. The evidence available to date seems hardly adequate to prove that persistency is inherited as a distinct biological entity apart from laying ability and uncomplicated by differences in age at first egg. As has been emphasized earlier, when persistency is measured by the number of days from first egg to last egg, the pullets beginning early have a better chance to finish late. This led to the suggestion that genes for persistency are linked with those for early maturity, but the spurious nature of this apparent linkage was made clear by Knox *et al.* (1935), Lerner and Taylor (1937*a*), and Hays (1939). This does not mean that there is no relation between the two, but merely that it is not accurately indicated when persistency is measured by the length of the laying year. Since both the beginning of laying and its termination are influenced by the amount of available light, one would expect that genes determining the response to light must affect both processes. It does not follow that for any one hen the initiation of laying and its cessation will both be decided by the same fixed rate of change in available light. One would hardly expect exactly the same response from the weary veteran that has shelled out a couple of hundred eggs as from the young and impetuous pullet that has yet to experience the thrill of her first one.

Broodiness

In wild birds, incubation of the eggs is a normal and indispensable part of the process of reproduction. A few atypical parasitic groups, including many of the cuckoos, some cowbirds, and a few others, have succeeded in foisting the entire responsibility (apart from egg laying) upon other, more gullible, members of the avian society. The Megapodes, or brush turkeys, escape the dreary hours of sitting by having their eggs incubated in a warm compost pile, with additional heat provided by the dependable Australian sun. Apart from these special cases, broodiness is necessary for preservation of the species. With domestication, it proved more desirable to have the eggs hatched in incubators and to keep the hens laying. As a result, while some hens still show strongly a maternal instinct, broodiness has been reduced by selection in some breeds and strains almost to the vanishing point. Most poultrymen now regard it, not as a normal consequence of egg laying, but rather as an abnormality interfering with that process.

Variation. Selection against broodiness is complicated by the rather high variability in its manifestation. Some pullets become broody after laying only a dozen eggs or so, and others not till 1, 2, or even 3 years old. Among 47 Rhode Island Reds that went broody, Hays (1940) found that 27 did so in the first laying year, 16 not until the second laying year, and 4 did not go broody until their third year. Even among those which do not show the trait in their first year there is great variation. Some hens go broody only once, but others have been known to do so 13 times in the first laying year. Among 1,122 Rhode Island Reds broody in their first laying year, Hays and Sanborn (1926*a*) found the frequency of "re-peaters" within that year to be as follows:

Times broody, number	Proportion of population, per cent	Times broody, number	Proportion of population, per cent
1	27.8	5	6.4
2	23.1	6	4.2
3	19.6	7	2.5
4	13.3	8–13	3.1

As is well known, some environmental conditions are more conducive to broodiness than others. The advent of hot weather warns the owner of heavy breeds that his troubles with broodiness are likely to increase. Another important factor is the removal of the eggs as they are laid, or at least daily. This practice will prevent the onset of broodiness and cause continued laying in some wild species (page 288). It is also an important factor in preventing domestic fowls from becoming broody. As many poultrymen have found, leaving eggs to accumulate in some secluded nest is equivalent to an invitation to go broody that some hens find irresist-ible. Professor R. C. Punnett (1923) cites his experience with two ban-tam females that showed no sign of broodiness during their first 2 laying years. During that period the eggs had been removed from the nest as they were laid. In their third year, the two were given to Dr. Gadow, the well-known ornithologist, who allowed their eggs to accumulate in the nest. Confronted with this stimulus, hitherto unexperienced, both the hens went broody and hatched chicks. Darkness is apparently conducive to the onset of broodiness. By keeping laying hens in darkened quarters, at high temperatures, and confronting them with orphaned chicks peep-ing their plaintive pleas for adoption, Burrows and Byerly (1938) suc-ceeded in arousing maternal instincts and evoking complete broodiness even in White Leghorns.

The problem of reducing broodiness by selection is obviously compli-cated by this extreme variability and the resultant difficulty of identi-fying potentially broody females. Another difficulty is that still less is known about the males, and their genotypes can be estimated only from the amount of broodiness in their sisters and daughters.

Physiological Basis. Broodiness apparently results from the secre-tion by the anterior lobe of the pituitary of a hormone known as "pro-lactin." It induces lactation in mammals and desquamation of the epithelial cells of the crop to form "crop milk" in pigeons. When injected into laying fowls, it causes a cessation of laying, resorption of yolk, and marked regression of the ovary (Bates *et al.,* 1935). In all but 1 of 19 laying hens of heavy breeds thus treated by Riddle *et al.* (1935), laying stopped within 6 days and varying degrees of broodiness followed. Leghorns similarly treated were somewhat more resistant, although some of them clucked and a few sat on the nest. From later experiments, Bates, Riddle, and Lahr (1937) and Nalbandov (1945) concluded that the prolactin thus injected exerts its remarkable effects by inhibiting the production of the follicle-stimulating gonadotropic hormone of the anterior pituitary.

If these experiments have their counterpart in the endocrine secretions of normal laying hens at the onset of broodiness, as seems likely, there is still to be determined the nature of the stimuli that cause the pituitary to increase its production of prolactin at the expense of the follicle-stimulating hormone. Attempts to interrupt broodiness by administration of various hormones have not been successful. One might conclude, therefore, either that the process, when once initiated, must run its full course or that some forces apart from hormones exert a predominant influence on the balance of endocrine secretion in broody hens. The former alternative seems less likely because broodiness can be quickly terminated by proper management, especially if the hens are put in broody coops while still in the early stages of the "attack."

Whatever the stimuli may be that initiate the process, the changes that take place in the pituitary of broody hens are remarkable. They have been studied in detail by Payne (1943). A large part of the gland, in some cases almost all of it, is modified by transformation of the acidophile and basophile cells and most of the chromophobes into cells of a special type. These "broody cells" are characterized by small size but have large and vesicular nuclei and appear to be functioning actively. They are not found in the pituitaries of laying hens but are present in the early stages of brooding, before the hen actually sits on the eggs. They persist in some cases, but not in all, while the hen is caring for her chicks. It would be interesting to learn if variation in the retention of the broody cells is related to the well-known variation among hens with respect to their acceptance of maternal responsibilities after their chicks have hatched. From differences in the stimulation of the crop in pigeons following transplants of pituitaries from hens, Burrows and Byerly (1936) concluded that the glands from broody hens contained more prolactin than those from laying hens. In later studies a similar difference could not be detected. This by no means controverts the role of the pituitary, since its effect on broodiness might depend, not upon the amount of prolactin it contains, but on the amount secreted. The cytological changes in the pituitaries of broody hens are in accord with the other evidence that prolactin inhibits the production of the follicle-stimulating hormone. Other processes must induce the same effect, since many hens stop laying and undergo ovarian regression without going broody.

The fact that capons will brood chicks shows that broodiness is not limited to the female. Their behavior when mothering chicks has been described by Goodale (1916). Some capons seem refractory, even when given injections of prolactin. Similarly, attempts to induce broodiness in normal males by that treatment are only partially successful. So far as males are concerned, it is apparently quite all right to cluck around and look after the chicks, but sitting on eggs is quite a different matter. The range of genetic variation in broodiness is indicated by the fact that in phalaropes the incubation is done mostly by the male.

Contrary to common opinion, the temperature of the broody hen differs little from that of laying hens, except in showing less diurnal fluctuation (Simpson, 1911; Eigemann, 1937). It is true that broody hens feel hotter than others on the breast, but this results from the increased vascularization that causes the reddish areas of the skin on the breast known as "brood spots." Details of their formation are given by Lange (1928), but other changes in the anatomy and physiology of broody hens have apparently not been studied.

Relation to Egg Production. The general opinion that broodiness lowers the egg record for the year is confirmed by such data as the records cited in Table 41.

TABLE 41. COMPARISONS OF THE EGG PRODUCTION OF BROODY AND NON-BROODY HENS

Breed and authority	Mean first-year egg record		
	Non-broody hens	Broody hens	Difference
Rhode Island Reds (Hays and Sanborn, 1926a)..	181.3	164.9	−16.4
Rhode Island Reds, broody line (Hays, 1933a)..	184.9	177.5	− 7.4
Rhode Island Reds, non-broody line (Hays, 1933a)................................	212.2	203.4	−8.8
Rhode Island Reds (Jull, 1940)...............	205.0	180.0	−25.0
White Leghorns (Jull, 1940)..................	194.0	153.0	−41.0
Rhode Island Reds (Lanson, 1948)............	271.4	269.1	−2.3

The lack of uniformity in the effects of broodiness on the year's record, as given by these investigators for different flocks and strains, suggests that the subject could stand further investigation. A point overlooked by some poultrymen in their general dislike of broody hens is that some of these birds must compensate for temporary lapses into maternal yearning by laying at a faster rate after they recover from them, or before. Some evidence was found by Hays and Sanborn (1926a) that the hens laying best in the winter are more likely to go broody when the season for that activity arrives. Similar evidence that broody hens show a higher rate of laying than others has been adduced by Lanson (1948) in data restricted by culling to birds of unusually high laying ability. Among these the average for non-broody hens was 271 eggs, but for 17 hens each of which went broody three times the average was also 271. Since the average hen loses about 16 days of egg laying with each spell of broodiness, it is clear that these 17 must have laid at a faster rate than the others to make up for their days out of production.

Genetic Basis. The fact that breeds differ in the degree of broodiness exhibited by them shows that the trait is hereditary. The genetic basis is unknown. The hypothesis of Goodale *et al.* (1920) that complementary genes are involved and that non-broody hens lack one of these or carry an inhibitor of both is supported by the fact that the proportion of broody hens is usually high in the offspring from the crossing of two different breeds.

Evidence that sex-linked genes may be involved was found by Roberts and Card (1933) in reciprocal crosses between Leghorns and Dark Cornish. In the latter breed 88 per cent of the birds went broody. In the F_1 generations the proportion of broody birds was 88 per cent in the pullets from the Cornish sire, but only 37 per cent in those from the Leghorn sire. Similar patroclinous inheritance of broodiness was noted by Warren (1942) and Kaufman (1946–1947) in various crosses between breeds. On the other hand, Hays (1940) could find no evidence of sex-linked genes for broodiness in Rhode Island Reds. In his birds, the degree of broodiness shown by the dam was clearly related to the proportion of her daughters that went broody. Thus dams for which the number of broody periods in the first laying year was 0, 1, 2, 3, or more had proportions of broody birds among their daughters of 11, 28, 72, and 90 per cent, respectively.

The feasibility of reducing broodiness in a strain by selection was demonstrated by Goodale *et al.* (1920), who in 5 years lowered the proportion of broody birds in their flock of Rhode Island Reds from 91 per cent in 1913 to 19 per cent in a special non-broody line. The number of broody periods per broody hen was reduced from 5.4 to 1.9. In later years, selection by Hays and Sanborn (1939) decreased the proportion of broody hens in this flock to 2.2 per cent. It seems doubtful that anything less than such a frequency is to be expected because of the impossibility of recognizing in their first year the hens that will not go broody until their second or third.

SENESCENCE IN RELATION TO EGG PRODUCTION

It is unfortunate for the producer of market eggs—but not for the hatcheryman—that only a small proportion of the pullets raised each year is kept for more than 1 year of laying. The annual expense of renewing the flock is a heavy one. This is not merely because of the 5 or 6 months of growth necessary before laying begins but also because it takes a considerable period of laying to get the eggs up to the 2-ounce weight currently considered standard in many markets. If mature birds would only lay enough eggs in successive years to justify keeping them for even 2 years, the industry could be spared some of its highest costs. The poultry breeder makes it a regular practice to keep his best birds for several years. In every commercial flock there are undoubtedly hens that could profitably be kept for 2 or even 3 years, but the general practice is to dispose of such flocks annually and to replace them with younger birds.

Rate of Decline in Egg Production. The data in Table 42 are representative of numerous reports in the last 36 years showing the relation of the number of eggs laid in the second and third years to the number produced in the first year. Other similar records are given by Jull (1928).

In the last (right) column of this table it is seen that the number of eggs laid in the second year has been found to vary from 68 to 105 per cent. This last figure requires some explanation, as it would not apply to modern flocks at all. Nixon's 3-year records for 88 hens are included because hers was apparently the first study of the effect of age on egg production. Her birds had rather low egg production in the first year, possibly because they were enrolled in various other experiments, and it is not surprising that their second-year records, though still low in comparison with those of the later investigators, should be slightly higher than their own first-year records. A similar superiority in the second year for low-producing hens was noted about the same time by Ball *et al.* (1914).

With the exception of Nixon's data, the second-year production is seen to vary from 66 to 86 per cent of the first-year record. That this measure considered by itself can be deceptive is evident from comparison of the Leghorns of Hall and Marble with those of Zander *et al.* In the former, the second-year record was 86 per cent of the first. In the latter,

TABLE 42. DATA FROM SEVERAL SOURCES SHOWING THE EFFECT OF SENESCENCE ON THE NUMBERS OF EGGS LAID IN THE SECOND AND THIRD YEARS, AS COMPARED WITH THE FIRST-YEAR RECORDS OF THE SAME BIRDS

Investigator	Breed	Birds with records for 2 years or more, number	Mean egg production per bird			Second year as proportion of first, per cent
			First year	Second year	Third year	
Nixon (1912)......	White Leghorns	88	92	97	86	105
Harris and Lewis (1922a) *........	White Leghorns	443	174	140	...	76
Hall and Marble (1931)..........	White Leghorns	1,867	169	146	124	86
Hall and Marble (1931)..........	Rocks, Reds, etc.	372	192	138	110	72
Hoffa (1932), I *...	Leghorns	66	167	126	...	76
Hoffa (1932), II *..	Leghorns	120	183	121	...	66
Hoffa (1932), III *.	Leghorns	115	200	134	...	67
Clark (1940)*......	White Leghorns	178	169	136	106	80
Zander et al. (1942)	White Leghorns	117	263	179	151	68

* In these cases, the data are from unculled, unselected populations.

it was only 68 per cent, but the mean production for these hens was 179 eggs, or 33 more than for the Leghorns of Hall and Marble. One must remember also that in most cases the records given for hens in their later years are restricted to hens that were retained when others were culled out. In other words, a hen with low first-year production would not be kept for a second year, and, similarly, some hen whose production was good in the second year might be discarded because her eggs did not hatch well. In spite of this, figures derived from these selected populations are useful as a guide to what the poultryman might expect in populations culled as he would, of necessity, wish to cull them. Thus the high second-year average of 179 eggs for the Leghorns of Zander et al. is attributable in large part to the fact that these birds were evidently a highly selected group, as one may recognize by their first-year average of 263 eggs.

Data for the second-year performance of unculled populations are available from some laying tests in which birds are kept for 2 years. The figures given (in Table 42) by Harris and Lewis for such a test at Vineland, New Jersey, agree fairly well with the data of Hoffa for three successive 2-year trials in Bavaria. In these unculled populations the mean second-year production varied from 121 to 140 per bird.

Some idea of the decline in egg production after the second year is given by the records of Hall and Marble (1931) and of Clark (1940) for Leghorns kept up to 11 years of age (Fig. 83). Clark's figures are particularly interesting because they pertain to a flock that originally

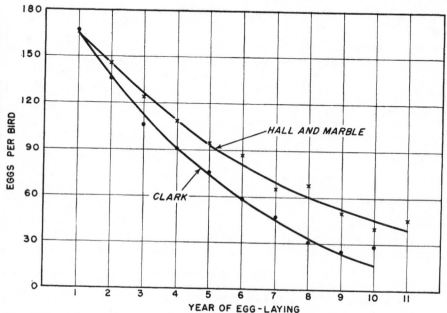

Fig. 83. The decline in egg production in successive years of laying. (*Drawn from the data of Clark and of Hall and Marble.*)

numbered 200 pullets in which no culling whatever was done during over 10 years. In the tenth year of laying, the 26 survivors had an average production of only 27.2 eggs. In the Leghorns for which Hall and Marble gave records up to 11 years, the production appears to have declined less rapidly, but this illusion results merely from the fact that their data apply to hens that were retained in the flock when others were culled and hence that must have been somewhat superior to the average. Egg production in these birds declined each year about 13 per cent below that of the previous year, while the corresponding figure for Clark's unculled flock was 19 per cent.

Relation of Laying Ability to Rate of Decline. In general, hens with the best records in the first year are likely to be the best layers in the second year. The correlation between the two records was found to be +.548 by both Nixon (1912), who studied rather poor layers, and Harris and Lewis (1922a), who had somewhat better ones. The same relationship has been shown in other ways in other studies. This does not mean that for every hen the second-year production is directly proportional to the first. On the contrary, the same principle applies to individuals as to flocks, namely, that the reduction in the second year is proportionately less for low producers than for high ones (Jull, 1928; Hoffa, 1932). From the practical point of view, the important fact is that the greatest numbers of eggs in the second year are likely to be obtained from the best layers of the first year. Since these will be the ones that continue laying till late September and October, any poultryman who has consistently eliminated from the flock the hens that stopped laying in July, August, and early September will then have left the hens worth keeping a second year (Table 43).

TABLE 43. RELATION OF PERSISTENCY IN THE FIRST YEAR TO THE NUMBER OF EGGS LAID IN THE SECOND *

Status of hens in last 3 months of first year		Hens, number	Mean production in second year
Laying	Not laying		
August....................	August, September, October	24	91.4
August and September.........	September and October	107	127.5
August, September, October....	October	144	138.8
	....	144	157.5

* Data from Harris and Lewis (1922a).

The relation between the number of eggs laid in the first and third years is not so close as that between the first and second. In Brown Leghorns with first-year records ranging from 150 to 259 eggs that were kept without any culling until they died, Greenwood (1937) found little relation between first-year production and that of the third. Further data on this point are desirable.

It is generally recognized that the lower production in the second laying year results mostly from charging against the second laying year much of the inevitable period of non-laying that is associated with the annual moult. This applies particularly to the good layers that do not moult until October, or even later. However, there is evidence that, for the average hen, senescence is already an important factor reducing the output even in the second laying year. This is demonstrated by the data of Zander *et al.* for 117 selected White Leghorns which, presumably because of their high first-year records, were kept for 3 laying years (Table 44).

TABLE 44. EFFECTS OF SENESCENCE ON CERTAIN VARIABLES INFLUENCING EGG RECORDS IN 3 YEARS OF LAYING *

Variable	First year	Second year	Third year
Egg production, mean number.......	263 ± 33	179 ± 34	151 ± 41
Length of laying year, days.........	385 ± 35	274 ± 40	249 ± 51
Rate of laying (number of eggs in March)........................	24.3 ± 2.3	22.5 ± 2.5	21.7 ± 2.4
Date of last egg (mean date ± days)	Oct. 26 ± 33	Oct. 9 ± 33	Sept. 20 ± 45

* Data from Zander *et al.* (1942).

While reduction of the second laying year to a period 111 days shorter than the first one resulted mostly from time out for moulting, it should be noted that the average hen stopped laying 17 days earlier in the second year and 36 days earlier in the third year than in the first one. The rate of laying declined in the second year and still more in the third. Although that is shown in Table 44 only for 1 month, similar declines or greater ones were found in all 12 months. Obviously, these hens were slowing down even in their second year.

Possibilities in Avian Gerontology. All the data concerning senescence considered thus far relate to whole groups of birds, *i.e.*, they are averages. As such, they may be misleading. One must remember that, while the breeder measures his results in terms of averages for successive generations, his inspiration and aims are provided by the exceptional individuals whose performance far excels the mediocrity of the population to which they belong. The average duration of life in man may decide annuity rates, but it had little influence on Thomas Parr, who lived to 152 years, or on Liberty Hyde Bailey, who spent his ninetieth birthday searching for palms on the Island of Grenada and found on that day three new species that had never been described. Similarly, some unusually meritorious hens maintain production of eggs for several years at a rate that shows complete disregard for averages such as those shown in Tables 42 and 44, and in Fig. 83.

To illustrate this point a few records of exceptional hens are given in Table 45. The 1,515 eggs laid by Cornell R 1149, as reported by Hall (1938), provide the highest record for a lifetime known to the author, but it must not be taken as the limit for the species. This is merely because so few hens get a chance to show how many eggs they might lay in a lifetime that one can hardly conclude that the upper limit has been determined.

TABLE 45. SOME UNUSUAL RECORDS OF EGG PRODUCTION THAT WAS SUSTAINED AT HIGH LEVELS FOR SEVERAL YEARS

Year of laying	Oregon 1911—B 14 Dryden (1921)	White Leghorn 1914—E 21 Dryden (1921)	Oregon 1915—F 284 Dryden (1921)	White Leghorn 1927—R 1149 Hall 1938)
First..............	215	259	235	241
Second............	206	249	210	221
Third.............	208	172	227	214
Fourth............	198	215	192	210
Fifth.............	189	193	213	188
Sixth.............	148	127+	...	152
Seventh...........	81	...	...	175
Eighth............	31	...	...	114
Ninth.............	2+			
Total............	1,278	1,215	1,077	1,515
Average for first 5 years.......	203.2	217.6	215.4	214.8

In Table 45, records of three hens bred by Dryden (1921) are given because of their remarkably high average egg production for the first 5 years. The poultryman now facing the annual expense of renewing his flock, together with high losses from mortality in the first year of laying, may well dream of what life might be if all hens could live for 5 years and yield in that time an average production exceeding 200 eggs per year! It is worth noting that as early as 1921 Dryden had found 20 hens that laid over 1,000 eggs in a lifetime, and Hall (1938) stated that between 1910 and 1938 about 80 such hens were found in the Cornell flock of White Leghorns. From the few records available for study, it would seem doubtful that many hens could lay enough eggs after 5 years to pay for their feed, but many of them might be worth keeping for breeding.

Most of the emphasis in breeding for increased egg production has been placed thus far on high records for the first year. This is attributable largely to the importance given to first-year records by laying tests and the inevitable publicity attached to the high records made in them. Some laying trials have encouraged breeding for sustained production by testing the birds for 2 years of laying. This is desirable, but it would seem that what is most needed is research that might lead to means of identifying in their first year, or in the first 2, those birds that are capable of maintaining economically profitable production for several years.

In recent times, considerable interest has been aroused in the science of gerontology, the study of changes associated with old age, as a special field of human biology. Scientists interested in biology of the fowl might well follow suit. In fact, the hen is more likely to profit from such studies than man is. While the aged of both species can be plied with vitamins, calcium, and sociology, the fact remains that longevity in man is determined by genes. This probably applies also to the fowl, although it has not been demonstrated quite so clearly in that species. So far as *Homo sapiens* is concerned, man seems to find it least perturbing to ignore his own genes, to shut both eyes, and to acclaim with pride the preservation and multiplication of the unfit. Geneticists can do somewhat better with *Gallus gallus*.

Breeding for productive longevity in the fowl will not prove easy. This is partly because of the difficulty in recognizing the type desired while it is still young. While the best layers of the first year are likely to be best in the next year, they are not necessarily the hens that will keep on laying for 4 or 5 years. The Oregon hen B 14, whose record is given in Table 45, laid only 215 eggs in her first year. While that was good for hens hatched in 1911, such a bird would now be culled out by most breeders after 1 year of laying, and yet her average for 5 years proved to be 203 eggs. Another problem is that senescence seems to be accompanied by a decline in fertility and hatchability of eggs (Hyre and Hall, 1932). This cannot apply to all hens, for Martin and Insko (1934) found some groups with higher hatchability in the fourth and fifth years than at earlier ages. If the birds capable of sustained egg production should prove also able to maintain efficient reproduction, this problem would not be serious. Another effect of senescence is a steady decline in size of egg (see page 359).

Literature Cited

Ackert, J. E., and M. H. Morris. 1929. Studies on the effect of thymectomy on growing chickens. *Anat. Record*, **44**:209.

Alder, B., and A. D. Egbert. 1918. A quick method of obtaining accurate individual egg records without the trap nest. *Utah Agr. Expt. Sta. Bull.* 162.

Altmann, M., and F. B. Hutt. 1938. The influences of estrogens in egg yolk upon avian blood calcium. *Endocrinology*, **23**:793–799.

Asmundson, V. S., and J. Biely. 1930. Effect of pullorum disease on distribution of first year egg production. *Sci. Agr.*, **10**:497–507.

Asmundson, V. S., C. A. Gunn, and A. A. Klose. 1937. Some responses of the immature female fowl to injections of mare gonadotropic hormone and oestrin. *Poultry Sci.,* **16**:194–206.

———— and W. E. Lloyd. 1935. Effect of age on reproduction of the turkey hen. *Poultry Sci.,* **14**:259–266.

Atwood, H. 1929. Observations concerning the time factor in egg production. *Poultry Sci.,* **8**:137–140.

Avery, T. B., H. M. Scott, and R. M. Conrad. 1940. Effect of parathyroid preparation on the blood calcium of the fowl. *Poultry Sci.,* **19**:321–323.

Ball, E. D., B. Alder, and A. D. Egbert. 1916. Breeding for egg production. I. A study of annual and total production. *Utah Agr. Expt. Sta. Bull.* 148.

———— and B. Alder. 1917. Breeding for egg production. II. Seasonal distribution of egg production with especial reference to "winter" egg production. *Utah Agr. Expt. Sta. Bull.* 149.

————, G. Turpin, and B. Alder. 1914. A study in annual egg production. Based on the records of a flock of seven-year-old hens and their progeny. *Utah Agr. Expt. Sta. Bull.* 135.

Bartelmez, G. W. 1918. The relation of the embryo to the principal axis of symmetry in the bird's egg. *Biol. Bull.,* **35**:319–361.

Bates, R. W., E. L. Lahr, and O. Riddle. 1935. The gross action of prolactin and follicle-stimulating hormone on the mature ovary and sex accessories of fowl. *Am. J. Physiol.,* **111**:361–368.

————, O. Riddle, and E. L. Lahr. 1937. The mechanism of the anti-gonad action of prolactin in adult pigeons. *Am. J. Physiol.,* **119**:610–614.

Benoit, J. 1936. Facteurs externes et internes de l'activité sexuelle. I. Stimulation par la lumière de l'activité sexuelle chez le Canard et la Cane domestiques. *Bull. biol. France Belg.,* **70**:488–533.

————. 1937. Facteurs externes et internes de l'activité sexuelle. II. Etude du mécanisme de la stimulation par la lumière de l'activité testiculaire chez le Canard domestique. Rôle de l'hypophyse. *Bull. biol. France Belg.,* **71**:394–437.

———— and L. Ott. 1938. Action de lumières de différentes longueurs d'onde sur la gonado-stimulation chez le Canard male impubère. *Compt. rend. soc. biol.,* **127**:906–909.

Biely, J. 1930. Effect of pullorum disease on second year egg production. *Sci. Agr.,* **10**:221–227.

Bissonnette, T. H. 1930. Studies on the sexual cycle in birds. I. Sexual maturity, its modification and possible control in the European starling (*Sturnus vulgaris*). *Am. J. Anat.,* **45**:289–305.

————. 1931. Studies on the sexual cycle in birds. V. Effects of light of different intensities upon the testis activity of the European starling (*Sturnus vulgaris*). *Physiol. Zoöl.,* **4**:542–574.

————. 1931*a*. Studies on the sexual cycle in birds. IV. Experimental modification of the sexual cycle in males of the European starling (*Sturnus vulgaris*) by changes in the daily period of illumination and of muscular work. *J. Exptl. Zoöl.,* **58**:281–319.

————. 1932. Studies on the sexual cycle in birds. VI. Effects of white, green, and red lights of equal luminous intensity on the testis activity of the European starling (*Sturnus vulgaris*). *Physiol. Zoöl.,* **5**:92–123.

Blakeslee, A. F., J. A. Harris, D. E. Warner, and W. F. Kirkpatrick. 1917. Pigmentation and other criteria for the selection of laying hens. *Storrs (Conn.) Agr. Expt. Sta. Bull.* 92.

Blakeslee, A. F., and D. E. Warner. 1915. Correlation between egg-laying activity and yellow pigment in the domestic fowl. *Science*, **41**:432–434.

Brambell, F. W. R. 1926. The oogenesis of the fowl (*Gallus bankiva*). *Phil. Trans. Roy. Soc. B.*, **214**:113–151.

Bryant, R. L., and A. B. Stephenson. 1945. The relationship between egg production and body type and weight in Single Comb White Leghorn hens. *Virginia Agr. Expt. Sta. Tech. Bull.* 96.

Burger, J. W. 1939. On the relative roles of increased and constant periods of illumination in the sexual photoperiodic activation of the male starling. *J. Exptl. Zoöl.*, **80**:249–257.

Burrows, W. H., and T. C. Byerly. 1936. Studies of prolactin in the fowl pituitary. I. Broody hens compared with laying hens and males. *Proc. Soc. Exptl. Biol. Med.*, **34**:841–844.

—— and ——. 1938. The effect of certain groups of environmental factors upon the expression of broodiness. *Poultry Sci.*, **17**:324–330.

—— and ——. 1942. Premature expulsion of eggs by hens following injection of whole posterior pituitary preparations. *Poultry Sci.*, **21**:416–421.

Byerly, T. C., and C. W. Knox. 1946. Date of hatch and day length affect age at first egg. *Poultry Sci.*, **25**:587–592.

—— and O. K. Moore. 1941. Clutch length in relation to period of illumination in the domestic fowl. *Poultry Sci.*, **20**:387–390.

Callenbach, E. W. 1934. Interrelationship of body weight, egg weight, and age at sexual maturity. *Poultry Sci.*, **13**:267–273.

——, J. E. Nicholas, and R. R. Murphy. 1944. Influence of light on age at sexual maturity and ovulation rate of pullets. *Pennsylvania Agr. Expt. Sta. Bull.*, **461**:1–12.

Chappelier, A. 1913. Persistance et développement des organes génitaux droits chez les femelles adultes des oiseaux. *Bull. sci. France Belg.*, **47**:361–376.

Clark, T. B. 1940. The relation of production and egg weight to age in White Leghorn fowls. *Poultry Sci.*, **19**:61–66.

Clevenger, L. C., and G. O. Hall. 1935. Head type in relation to annual egg production and egg weight. *Poultry Sci.*, **14**:54–60.

Coleman, W. B. 1930. Method of breeding quail at White Oak Quail Farm, Richmond, Virginia. Mimeographed circular sent out April, 1930.

Conrad, R. M., and D. C. Warren. 1939. The alternate white and yellow layers of yolk in hens' ova. *Poultry Sci.*, **18**:220–224.

[Cook, R. C.] 1937. A trap-nest postscript. *J. Heredity*, **28**:424–425.

Crew, F. A. E. 1931. Paired oviducts in the fowl. *J. Anat.*, **46**:100–103.

Domm, L. V. 1931. Precocious development of sexual characters in the fowl by homeoplastic hypophyseal implants. I. The male. II. The female. *Proc. Soc. Exptl. Biol. Med.*, **29**:308–312.

——. 1937. Observations concerning anterior pituitary-gonadal interrelations in the fowl. *Cold Spring Harbor Symposia Quant. Biol.*, **5**:241–257.

Dryden, J. 1921. Egg-laying characteristics of the hen. *Oregon Agr. Expt. Sta. Bull.* 180.

Dudley, F. J. 1931. Short period trapnesting as a means of estimating annual egg production and average annual egg weight. *Harper Adams Util. Poultry J.* **16**:557–562.

Eigemann, M. 1937. Experimentelle Untersuchungen über die Brütigkeit der Hühner. *Arch. Geflügelk.*, **11**:273–292.

Fauré-Fremiet, E., and L. Kaufman. 1928. La loi de décroissance progressive du taux de la ponte chez la poule. *Annal. physiol. physicochim. biol.*, **4**:64–122.

Fraps, R. M., M. W. Olsen, and B. H. Neher. 1942. Forced ovulation of normal ovarian follicles in the domestic fowl. *Proc. Soc. Exptl. Biol.*, **50**:308–312.

Fronda, F. M. 1923. Can the body temperature of a hen be used as a clue to her egg-laying capacity? *Poultry Sci.*, **3**:34–38.

Godfrey, A. B., and M. A. Jull. 1935. Statistical studies on the inheritance of sexual maturity in White Leghorns and Rhode Island Reds. *Poultry Sci.*, **14**:346–350.

Goodale, H. D. 1916. Note on the behaviour of capons when brooding chicks. *J. Animal Behav.*, **6**:319–324.

———. 1918. Internal factors influencing egg production in the Rhode Island Red breed of domestic fowl. *Am. Naturalist*, **52**:65–94, 209–232, 301–321.

———. 1918*a*. Winter cycle of egg production in the Rhode Island Red breed of domestic fowl. *J. Agr. Research*, **12**:547–574.

[———]. 1935–1936. "Early Egg Size." Williamstown, Mass.: Mount Hope Farm.

———. 1937. The trap-nest and scientific breeding. *J. Heredity*, **28**:344–345.

——— and G. Macmullen. 1919. The bearing of ratios on theories of the inheritance of winter egg production. *J. Exptl. Zoöl.*, **28**:83–124.

———, R. Sanborn and D. White. 1920. Broodiness in domestic fowl. *Massachusetts Agr. Expt. Sta. Bull.* 199.

——— and ———. 1922. Changes in egg production in the station flock. *Massachusetts Agr. Expt. Sta. Bull.* 211.

Greenwood, A. W. 1935. Perforation of the oviduct in the domestic fowl. *Trans. Dynamics Development*, **10**:81–92.

———. 1937. Constitutional vigour in poultry. *Empire J. Exptl. Agric.*, **5**:32–38.

——— and J. S. S. Blyth. 1931. Thymus extirpation in the laying hen. *Proc. Soc. Exptl. Biol. Med.*, **29**:38–40.

——— and ———. 1946. Sexual maturity in Brown Leghorns. *Poultry Sci.*, **25**:597–605.

———, ———, and N. Galpin. 1940. A study of fecundity in the domestic fowl: The behaviour of persistency in individual hens. *J. Agr. Sci.*, **30**:202–209.

——— and J. P. Chu. 1939. On the relation between thyroid and sex gland functioning in the Brown Leghorn fowl. *Quart. J. Exptl. Physiol.*, **29**:111–119.

Guhl, A. M., and W. C. Allee. 1944. Some measurable effects of social organization in flocks of hens. *Physiol. Zoöl.*, **17**:320–347.

Gunn, T. E. 1912. On the presence of two ovaries in certain British birds, more especially the Falconidae. *Proc. Zool. Soc. London*, 63–79.

Gutteridge, H. S., S. Bird, H. I. MacGregor, and J. M. Pratt. 1944. The effect of heat, insulation and artificial light on egg production and feed consumption of pullets. *Sci. Agr.*, **25**:31–42.

Hadley, P. 1919. Egg-weight as a criterion of numerical production in the domestic fowl. *Science*, **49**:427–429.

Hall, G. O. 1938. An unprecedented record of sustained high egg production. *J. Heredity*, **29**:50–53.

——— and D. R. Marble. 1931. The relationship between the first year egg production and the egg production of later years. *Poultry Sci.*, **10**:194–203.

Hammond, J. C., and W. H. Burrows. 1937. The female genital eminence is not a measure of future egg production. *Poultry Sci.*, **16**:285–286.

Harris, J. A. 1926. The monthly egg record of birds which die during the first laying year. *Poultry Sci.*, **6**:1–8.

Harris, J. A. 1927. Further studies of the monthly egg record of birds which die during the first laying year. *Poultry Sci.,* **6**:215–224.

———, A. F. Blakeslee, and W. F. Kirkpatrick. 1918. The correlation between egg production during various periods of the year in the domestic fowl. *Genetics,* **3**:27–72.

——— and H. D. Goodale. 1922. The correlation between the egg production of the various periods of the year in the Rhode Island Red breed of domestic fowl. *Genetics,* **7**:446–465.

———, W. F. Kirkpatrick, A. F. Blakeslee, D. E. Warner, and L. E. Card. 1921. The egg records of limited periods as criteria for predicting the egg-production of the White Leghorn fowl. *Genetics,* **6**:265–309.

——— and H. R. Lewis. 1921. The interrelationship of the egg records of various periods during the first and second year of the White Leghorn fowl. *Poultry Sci.,* **1**:97–107.

——— and ———. 1922. The "winter cycle" in the fowl. *Science,* **56**:230.

——— and ———. 1922a. The correlation between first- and second-year egg production in the domestic fowl. *Genetics,* **7**:274–318.

——— and ———. 1923. The correlation between the time of beginning and the time of cessation of laying in the first and second laying year in the domestic fowl. *Genetics,* **8**:37–74.

Hays, F. A. 1924. Inbreeding in the Rhode Island Red fowl with special reference to winter egg production. *Am. Naturalist,* **58**:43–59.

———. 1933. Relation between body weight and age at sexual maturity. *Poultry Sci.,* **12**:23–25.

———. 1933a. Characteristics of non-broody and intense broody lines of Rhode Island Reds. *Massachusetts Agr. Expt. Sta. Bull.* 301.

———. 1936. Time interval between eggs of Rhode Island Red pullets. *J. Agr. Research,* **52**:633–638.

———. 1936a. Winter pause in Rhode Island Reds. *Massachusetts Agr. Expt. Sta. Bull.* 329.

———. 1938. Time interval between clutches in Rhode Island Red pullets. *J. Agr. Research,* **57**:575–581.

———. 1939. Absence of linkage between genes for early sexual maturity and genes for high persistency in egg production in the domestic fowl. *Proc. World's Poultry Congr. 7th Congr., Cleveland:* 70–72.

———. 1940. Inheritance of broodiness in Rhode Island Reds. *Massachusetts Agr. Expt. Sta. Bull.* 377.

———. 1944. The significance of inherited characters affecting egg production. *Poultry Sci.,* **23**:310–313.

———. 1946. The value of limited trapnesting in poultry breeding. *Massachusetts Agr. Expt. Sta. Bull.* 438.

——— and R. Sanborn. 1926. Annual persistency in relation to winter and annual egg production. *Massachusetts Agr. Expt. Sta. Tech. Bull.* 9.

——— and ———. 1926a. Broodiness in relation to fecundity in the domestic fowl. *Massachusetts Agr. Expt. Sta. Tech. Bull.* 7.

——— and ———. 1927. Net correlations of characters concerned in fecundity. *Massachusetts Agr. Expt. Sta. Tech. Bull.* 12.

——— and ———. 1930. Duration of annual molt in relation to egg production. *Massachusetts Agr. Expt. Sta. Bull.* 264.

Hays, F. A., and R. Sanborn. 1932. Types of intensity in Rhode Island Rèds. *Massachusetts Agr. Expt. Sta. Bull.* 286.

―― and ――. 1933. The significance of length of biological laying year in production breeding. *Massachusetts Agr. Expt. Sta. Bull.* 298.

―― and ――. 1939. Breeding for egg production. *Massachusetts Agr. Expt. Sta. Bull.* 307.

―― and ――. 1945. Annual molt in Rhode Island Reds. *Massachusetts Agr. Expt. Sta. Bull.* 429.

Hazel, L. N., and W. F. Lamoreux. 1947. Heritability, maternal effects and nicking in relation to sexual maturity and body weight in White Leghorns. *Poultry Sci.,* **26**:508–514.

Herrick, E. H. 1944. Some influences of stilbestrol, estrone, and testosterone propionate on the genital tract of young female fowls. *Poultry Sci.,* **23**:65–66.

Heywang, B. W. 1938. The time factor in egg production. *Poultry Sci.,* **17**:240–247.

Hoffa, H. 1932. Vergleichende Untersuchungen über die Leistungen von Hennen leichter Rassen im ersten und zweiten Legejahr. *Arch. Geflügelk.,* **6**:225–272.

Hurst, C. C. 1921. The genetics of egg production in White Leghorns and White Wyandottes, and its application to poultry breeding. *Trans. World's Poultry Congr. 1st Congr., The Hague:* 3–20.

Hutt, F. B. 1942. Contributions of Raymond Pearl to poultry science. *Poultry Sci.,* **21**:98–107.

―― and W. L. Boyd. 1935. Idiopathic hypoparathyroidism and tetany in the fowl. *Endocrinology,* **19**:398–402.

―― and R. K. Cole. 1947. Genetic control of lymphomatosis in the fowl. *Science,* **106**:379–384.

―― and D. T. Grussendorf. 1933. On the fecundity of partially ovariotomized fowls. *J. Exptl. Zoöl.,* **65**:199–214.

Hyre, H. M., and G. O. Hall. 1932. The constancy of hatching power in hens. *Poultry Sci.,* **11**:166–171.

Juhn, M., and R. G. Gustavson. 1930. The production of female genital subsidiary characters and plumage sex characters by injection of human placental hormone in fowls. *J. Exptl. Zoöl.,* **56**:31–61.

Jull, M. A. 1928. Second year production in relation to first year egg production in the domestic fowl. *Poultry Sci.,* **7**:276–286.

――. 1934. The inheritance of sexual maturity, rate and persistence of laying in the domestic fowl. *Poultry Sci.,* **13**:286–289.

――. 1940. "Poultry Breeding," 2d ed. New York: John Wiley & Sons, Inc.

――, J. P. Quinn, and A. B. Godfrey. 1933. Is there an egg-laying type of the domestic fowl? *Poultry Sci.,* **12**:153–162.

Kaufman, L. 1946–1947. Etudes génétiques sur les poules. I. Hérédité de l'instinct de couver. *Mém. inst. nat. polon. écon. rurale Pulawy.* 18, E., Mém. **1**:1–12.

Kempster, H. L. 1925. The correlation between sexual maturity and egg production. *Missouri Agr. Expt. Sta. Bull.* 78.

Kirkpatrick, W. F., and L. E. Card. 1916. Fourth annual international egg-laying contest. *Storrs (Conn.) Agr. Expt. Sta. Bull.,* **87**:200–244.

Knowles, H. R., E. B. Hart, and J. G. Halpin. 1935. The variation in the calcium level of the blood of the domestic fowl. *Poultry Sci.,* **14**:83–89.

Knox, C. W., M. A. Jull, and J. P. Quinn. 1935. Correlation studies of egg production and possible genetic interpretations. *J. Agr. Research,* **50**:573–589.

Lamoreux, W. F., F. B. Hutt, and G. O. Hall. 1943. Breeding for low fecundity in the fowl with the aid of the progeny test. *Poultry Sci.*, **22**:161–169.

Lange, B. 1928. Die Brutflecke der Vögel und die für sie wichtigen Hauteigentümlichkeiten. *Gegenbaur's Morph. Jahrb.*, **59**:601–712.

Lanson, R. K. 1948. A study of the association between broodiness and intensity. *Poultry Sci.*, **27**:207–212.

Lerner, I. M. 1942. The relation of shank color to winter egg production characteristics of Single Comb White Leghorn pullets. *J. Agr. Research*, **64**:333–338.

———. 1946. The effect of selection for shank length on sexual maturity and early egg weight in Single Comb White Leghorn pullets. *Poultry Sci.*, **25**:204–209.

——— and L. W. Taylor. 1936. The relation of pauses to rate of egg production. *J. Agr. Research*, **52**:39–47.

——— and ———. 1937. Interrelationships of egg production factors as determined for White Leghorn pullets. *J. Agr. Research*, **55**:703–712.

——— and ———. 1937a. The spurious nature of the linkage between length of laying year and sexual maturity in the fowl. *Am. Naturalist*, **71**:617–622.

——— and ———. 1940. The use of the median as a measure of sexual maturity in White Leghorn pullets. *Poultry Sci.*, **19**:216–218.

——— and ———. 1941. Factors affecting the duration of the first annual rest. *Poultry Sci.*, **20**:490–495.

——— and ———. 1947. Further observations on winter pause in Single Comb White Leghorn pullets. *Poultry Sci.*, **26**:198–205.

Lippincott, W. A., and L. E. Card. 1939. "Poultry Production," 6th ed., Philadelphia: Lea & Febiger.

Lorenz, F. W. 1939. Relation of blood-lipid level to reproduction in the domestic fowl. *Proc. World's Poultry Congr. 7th Congr., Cleveland:* 113–115.

———, I. L. Chaikoff, and C. Entenman. 1938. The endocrine control of lipid metabolism in the birds. II. The effects of estrin on the blood lipids of the immature domestic bird. *J. Biol. Chem.*, **126**:763–769.

McKenney, F. D. 1931. A persistent right oviduct in the domestic fowl. *Anat. Record*, **49**:51–57.

Macowan, M. M. 1932. Observations on the ductless glands, the serum calcium and egg-laying in the fowl. *Quart. J. Exptl. Physiol.*, **21**:383–392.

Marble, D. R. 1930. The molting factor in judging fowls for egg production. *Cornell Univ. Agr. Expt. Sta. Bull.* 503.

———. 1932. The relationship of skull measurements to cycle and egg production. *Poultry Sci.*, **11**:272–278.

Marlow, H. W., and D. Richert. 1940. Avian estrogens and blood calcium. *Endocrinology*, **27**:274–278.

Martin, J. H., and W. M. Insko, Jr. 1934. Relationship between age, fecundity and hatchability. *Poultry Sci.*, **13**:188–190.

Marza, V. D., and E. V. Marza. 1935. The formation of the hen's egg. I–IV. *Quart. J. Microscop. Sci.*, **78** (pt. II): 133–189.

Miller, M. W., and J. S. Carver. 1934. The relationship of anatomical measurements to egg production. *Poultry Sci.*, **13**:242–249.

Morgan, A. H., and M. C. Grierson. 1930. The effects of thymectomy on young fowls. *Anat. Record*, **47**:101–117.

Motohashi, H. 1935. Orientation of the duck's egg at the moment of laying. *Trans. Tottori Soc. Agr. Science*, **5**:203–230.

Nalbandov, A. V. 1945. A study of the effect of prolactin on broodiness and on cock testes. *Endocrinology*, **36**:251–258.

Nathusius, W. 1885. Besteht eine ausnamslose Regel über die Lage der Pole des Vogeleies im Uterus im Verhältnis zur Kloakenmundung. *Zool. Anz.*, **8**:415–417.

Nixon, C. 1912. A study of the first, second and third-year production of White Leghorn hens. *Ann. Rept. Am. Breeders' Assoc.*, **7**:279–288.

Olsen, M. W. 1939. The value of periodical trap-nesting. *Poultry Sci.*, **18**:232–235.

—— and T. C. Byerly. 1932. Orientation of the hen's egg in the uterus and during laying. *Poultry Sci.*, **11**:266–271.

Palmer, L. S. 1915. Xanthophyll, the principal natural yellow pigment of the egg yolk, body fat and blood serum of the hen. The physiological relation of the pigment to the xanthophyll of the plant. *J. Biol. Chem.*, **23**:261–279.

—— and H. L. Kempster. 1919. The physiological relation between fecundity and the natural yellow pigmentation of certain breeds of fowls. *J. Biol. Chem.*, **39**:313–330.

Payne, F. 1943. The cytology of the anterior pituitary of broody fowls. *Anat. Record*, **86**:1–13.

Pearl, R. 1912. The mode of inheritance of fecundity in the domestic fowl. *J. Exptl. Zoöl.*, **13**:153–268.

—— and M. R. Curtis. 1912. Studies on the physiology of reproduction in the domestic fowl. V. Data regarding the physiology of the oviduct. *J. Exptl. Zoöl.*, **12**:99–132.

—— and ——. 1914. Studies on the physiology of reproduction in the domestic fowl. VIII. On some physiological effects of ligation, section, or removal of the oviduct. *J. Exptl. Zoöl.*, **17**:395–424.

—— and W. F. Schoppe. 1921. Studies on the physiology of reproduction in the domestic fowl. XVIII. Further observations on the anatomical basis of fecundity. *J. Exptl. Zoöl.*, **34**:101–118.

Phillips, R. E. 1943. Ovarian response of hens and pullets to injections of ambinon. *Poultry Sci.*, **22**:368–373.

—— and D. C. Warren. 1937. Observations concerning the mechanics of ovulation in the fowl. *J. Exptl. Zoöl.*, **76**:117–136.

—— and C. S. Williams. 1944. Relationship between the genital eminence of day-old female chicks and age of sexual maturity. *Poultry Sci.*, **23**:348–349.

Platt, C. S. 1927. Relationship between body weight and egg production in the domestic fowl. *Poultry Sci.*, **6**:285–289.

Punnett, R. C. 1923. "Heredity in Poultry." London: Macmillan & Co., Ltd.

——. 1930. Some experiments concerning fecundity. *Proc. World's Poultry Congr. 4th Congr., London*: 34–37.

Rice, J. E., C. Nixon, and C. A. Rogers. 1908. The molting of fowls. *Cornell Univ. Agr. Expt. Sta. Bull. 258.*

Riddle, O. 1911. On the formation, significance, and chemistry of the white and yellow yolk of ova. *J. Morphol.*, **22**:455–491.

——. 1916. Studies on the physiology of reproduction in birds. I. The occurrence and measurement of a sudden change in the rate of growth of avian ova. *Am. J. Physiol.*, **41**:387–396.

——, R. W. Bates, and E. L. Lahr. 1935. Prolactin induces broodiness in fowl. *Am. J. Physiol.*, **111**:352–360.

—— and F. Flemion. 1928. Studies on the physiology of reproduction in birds.

XXVI. The role of the anterior pituitary in hastening sexual maturity in ring doves. *Am. J. Physiol.*, **87**:110–123.

Riddle, O., and I. Polhemus. 1931. Studies on the physiology of reproduction in birds. XXXI. Effects of anterior pituitary hormones on gonads and other organ weights in the pigeon. *Am. J. Physiol.*, **98**:121–130.

———— and W. H. Reinhart. 1926. Studies on the physiology of reproduction in birds. XXI. Blood calcium changes in the reproductive cycle. *Am. J. Physiol.*, **76**:660–676.

Roberts, E., and L. E. Card. 1933. Inheritance of broodiness in the domestic fowl. *Atti congr. mondiale pollicultura. 5th Congr., Rome*, **2**:353–358.

Rothchild, I., and R. M. Fraps. 1944. On the function of the ruptured ovarian follicle of the domestic fowl. *Proc. Soc. Exptl. Biol. Med.*, **56**:79–82.

———— and ————. 1944a. Relation between light-dark rhythms and hour of lay of eggs experimentally retained in the hen. *Endocrinology*, **35**:355–362.

Rowan, W. 1926. On photoperiodism, reproductive periodicity, and annual migrations of birds and certain fishes. *Proc. Boston Soc. Nat. Hist.*, **38**:147–189.

Scott, H. M., and D. C. Warren. 1936. Influence of ovulation rate on the tendency of the fowl to produce eggs in clutches. *Poultry Sci.*, **15**:381–389.

Simpson, S. 1911. Observations on the body temperature of the domestic fowl (*Gallus gallus*) during incubation. *Trans. Roy. Soc. Edinburgh*, **47** (pt. **3**): 605–617.

Stanley, A. J., and E. Witschi. 1940. Germ cell migration in relation to asymmetry in the sex glands of hawks. *Anat. Record*, **76**:329–342.

Stieve, H. 1918. Über experimentell, durch verändert äussere Bedingungen hervorgerufene Rückbildungsvorgänge am Eierstock des Haushuhnes (*Gallus domesticus*). *Arch. Entwicklungsmech. Organ.*, **44**:530–588.

Taylor, A. G. 1930. Report of the ninth and tenth annual Canadian National Egg Laying Contests. *Domin. Canada Dept. Agr. Bull.* 139 (n.s.).

Taylor, L. W., and B. R. Burmester. 1940. Effect of thyroidectomy on production, quality and composition of chicken eggs. *Poultry Sci.*, **19**:326–331.

———— and I. M. Lerner. 1938. Breeding for egg production. *California Agr. Expt. Sta. Bull.* 626.

———— and ————. 1939. Effect of varying levels of wheat bran on age at sexual maturity. *Poultry Sci.*, **18**:323–326.

Thompson, W. C., and F. P. Jeffrey. 1936. The usefulness of winter and summerfall egg yield records as criteria of poultry breeder selection. *New Jersey Agr. Expt. Sta. Bull.* 612.

Upp, C. W., and R. B. Thompson. 1927. Influence of time of hatch on hatchability of the eggs, rate of growth of the chicks, and characteristics of the adult female. *Oklahoma Agr. Expt. Sta. Bull.* 167.

Van Durme, M. 1914. Nouvelles recherches sur la vitellogenèse des oeufs d'oiseaux aux stades d'accroissement, de maturation, de fécondation et du début de la segmentation. *Arch. biol.*, **29**:71–200.

Voitellier, C. 1930. Possibilities with regard to introducing various kinds of periodical testing of egg production in place of permanent testing. *Proc. World's Poultry Congr. 4th Congr., London:* 11–18.

Warren, D. C. 1930. The effect of disturbances upon the rhythm of egg production. *Poultry Sci.*, **9**:184–193.

————. 1934. Inheritance of age at sexual maturity in the domestic fowl. *Genetics*, **19**:600–617.

Warren, D. C. 1942. The crossbreeding of poultry. *Kansas Agr. Expt. Sta. Bull.* 52.

—— and R. Conrad. 1939. Growth of the hen's ovum. *J. Agr. Research,* **58**: 875–893.

—— and H. M. Scott. 1935. The time factor in egg formation. *Poultry Sci.,* **14**:195–207.

—— and ——. 1935a. Physiological factors influencing the rate of egg formation in the domestic hen. *J. Agr. Research,* **51**:565–572.

—— and ——. 1936. Influence of light on ovulation in the fowl. *J. Exptl. Zoöl.,* **74**:137–156.

Waters, N. F. 1934. Growth and sexual maturity in Brahma and Leghorn fowl. *Iowa State Coll. J. Sci.,* **8**:367–384.

——. 1937. Body weight, egg weight, sexual maturity, and growth rate in the domestic fowl. *Poultry Sci.,* **16**:305–313.

Whetham, E. O. 1933. Factors modifying egg production with special reference to seasonal changes. *J. Agr. Sci.,* **23**:383–418.

Winchester, C. F. 1939. Influence of thyroid on egg production. *Endocrinology* **24**:697–701.

Wodzicki, K. 1934. Beobachtungen über das Vorkommen des rechten Eileiters bei der Hausente. *Bull. acad. polon. sci. lettres B,* **II**:385–395.

Zander, D. V., I. M. Lerner, and L. W. Taylor. 1942. The decline in annual egg production with age. *Poultry Sci.,* **21**:455–461.

CHAPTER 11

VARIATIONS IN EGGS

It is unnecessary to dilate on the value and importance of eggs as food for man. There are many different variations in eggs, some of which are induced genetically, while others are caused by environmental differences. Some of them are important because they affect the size and keeping qualities of the egg. Some are important because they make the eggs undesirable or unattractive as food. Others, such as the color of the shell, are important in markets where the consumers are finicky, but less so where food is scarce. There are also variations, some genetic and some environmental, which modify directly the nutritional value of eggs.

As a matter of convenience these variations will here be grouped as those affecting (1) size, (2) shape, (3) shell, (4) albumen and yolk, and (5) chemical composition, followed by a brief consideration of (6) abnormal eggs.

Knowledge of the genetic factors responsible for variations in eggs is by no means as exact as that about genetic variations in structure and color of the plumage or in the skeleton. This is because, with only a single exception, all the genetic variations thus far known in eggs are influenced by an undetermined number of multiple factors. The lone exception is the mutation causing blue color in the shell.

Because this book is concerned primarily with genetic variation, it is impossible to review here the voluminous literature on the formation of eggs, their chemical composition, nutritive value, and other pertinent matters. Valuable information on some of these points may be found in the compilations by Needham (1931, Vol. I) and Grossfeld (1938), but all of them are reviewed in the recent comprehensive monograph by Romanoff and Romanoff (1949).

VARIATIONS IN SIZE

Variation and Correlation of Dimensions and Parts. As a matter of convenience, egg size is usually measured by weight, although in any but new-laid eggs the weight is more subject to change than the volume or the dimensions of the shell. With respect to variability there is agree-

ment by Pearl and Surface (1914), Curtis (1914), Kopeć (1924), and
Asmundson (1931), each of whom measured several hundred eggs, that
weight of the hen's egg is more variable than length or breadth, this last
being the least variable of the three measures. This applies also to
turkey eggs (Funk, 1937).

Weight of the egg is closely related to its length, but even more so
to its breadth. The relationships determined by Asmundson (Table 46)

Fig. 84. V. S. Asmundson, of the University of California.

are fairly typical of those found by the other investigators mentioned
above. Contrary to what one might think, there is little or no relation
between the shape of an egg and its weight, the coefficients of correlation determined by different investigators being sometimes positive, sometimes negative, but always low.

The albumen, yolk, and shell contribute to the egg about 58 to 61,
28 to 31, and 10 to 11 per cent, respectively, of its total weight. One
would expect, therefore, that the correlations of these parts with weight
of the whole egg would rank in the order given. This they were found
to do by Curtis and by Jull (1924), but, in Asmundson's material, weight
of the shell was more highly correlated with that of the whole egg than
was weight of yolk. Some of his extensive data, based on 707 eggs laid
by 67 hens, are given in Table 46. It will be noted that the variability

of the three parts of the egg is inversely proportional to their weights, a point noted also by Curtis, by Jull, and by Olsson (1936).

TABLE 46. DIMENSIONS AND PARTS OF EGGS, THEIR VARIABILITY AND RELATION TO THE WHOLE *

Item	Mean	Coefficient of variation	Correlation with weight of egg
Length, millimetres..........	56.9	5.3	+.628
Breadth, millimetres.........	41.0	3.7	+.810
Index, breadth/length × 100..	71.8	5.6	−.085
Weight of egg, grams........	53.6	10.1	—
Weight of yolk, grams........	16.1	13.1	+.538
Weight of albumen, grams....	31.5	12.6	+.899
Weight of shell, grams.......	5.6	14.4	+.636

* From Asmundson (1931).

Relation between Egg Size and Body Size. Most poultrymen know that small hens tend to lay small eggs. This relationship was first expressed numerically by Asmundson (1921), who found a correlation of +.384 between egg weight and adult body weight in White Leghorns. Similar correlations and higher ones have since been reported by Atwood (1923), Jull (1924a), and many others. The relationship apparently persists after both egg weight and body weight have become maximum, for Atwood and Clark (1930) found the correlation between these two variables to be +.458, +.434, and +.426 in the first, second, and third years of laying.

However, this relationship is expressed more accurately by the correlation ratio than by simple coefficients of correlation, for it is not a linear one. In other words, the biggest birds do not lay proportionately bigger eggs. It seems probable that this non-linearity, first pointed out by Marble (1931a), is merely the manifestation among representatives of a single species of a general principle that applies to birds as a class. The extensive studies by Heinroth (1922) of the relationship between egg weight and body weight in 436 species of birds showed that, while the relative egg size differs from group to group, the general tendency within each family or order (and in birds as a whole) is for it to decrease as body size increases. Notable exceptions include one of the kiwis, *Apteryx australis,* which weighs about 2½ kg. and lays an egg of 455 gm., which is almost a fifth of its body weight. At the same rate any good Rhode

Island Red would lay a 1-pound egg. Another exception is the cuckoo, which lays a disproportionately small egg, presumably as an adaptation for its parasitic mode of reproduction.

On further analysis of Heinroth's data, Huxley (1927) found that the relation between egg weight, y, and body weight, x, within any group could be expressed by the equation $y = bx^k$, in which b is a constant. In the smaller birds of a family or order, k is approximately 1.0, but it gradually decreases with increasing body weight to about $\frac{2}{3}$ in the largest birds. In

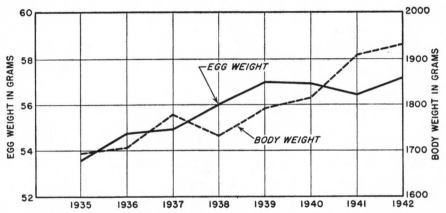

Fig. 85. Increase in egg weight associated with increase in body weight of White Leghorns of the C. Resistant strain at Cornell University.

other words, egg size in the smaller birds is directly proportional to body size, but in the larger birds this relationship cannot be maintained, and egg size seems to be proportional to some surface area, possibly that of the body. The similarity of Huxley's curves for whole families to those found by Marble in the fowl suggests that the same principles determine the relation of egg size to body size both within a species and within such taxonomic groups as families or orders.

Obviously anyone attempting to increase egg weight by breeding should at the same time pay attention to body size. The general tendency for these two variables to rise together is illustrated in Fig. 85, which shows their increase during several years of selection in White Leghorns of the C. Resistant strain at Cornell University. The changes from year to year were not always parallel, perhaps because selection for body size and egg size was incidental to the main objective, which was genetic resistance to lymphomatosis, and also because body weight is much influenced by environmental conditions prior to weighing. Egg size was increased from 53.6 to 57 gm. in four generations and thereafter remained relatively constant because no effort was made to increase it above the so-called "standard" weight of 56.7 gm. Concurrently, body weight was raised from 1,690 gm. in the unselected population of 1935 to 1,786 gm. in the fourth generation of the C. Resistant strain.

Similarly, while Goodale (1935–1936) was raising the weight of the fiftieth eggs laid by his White Leghorn pullets from 48.7 to 58.2 gm. in five generations of selection, body weight at first egg automatically rose at the same time from 3.5 to 4.3 pounds. It does not follow, however, that an increase in body size inevitably brings an accompanying increase in egg size. This is shown in Fig. 85 by the data for the last 3 years. In that period, body size was raised even more rapidly than earlier, but without any appreciable change in egg weight. This seeming inconsistency probably results from the fact that in larger birds of a breed, just as in those of a species, family, or order, egg size is related to body size less closely than in the smaller ones. Rhode Island Reds lay eggs little bigger, if any, than those of Leghorns. This is partly because market prices and other considerations do not encourage the poultryman to produce eggs exceeding 2 ounces in weight. It is probable also that, even if this limitation did not apply, breeders would find it more difficult to make 2,700-gm. Rhode Island Reds lay 3-ounce eggs than it is to make 1,800-gm. Leghorns produce eggs of 2 ounces, even though the relative egg weight is the same in both cases.

Because larger birds require more room and more feed for maintenance, it would probably be advantageous, from the economic standpoint (but not biologically), if egg size could be raised without a corresponding increase in body size. However, to do this would seem a difficult task, if not an impossible one. The reverse operation, to reduce egg size without lowering body size, should be much easier. So far as the author is aware, neither experiment has been attempted, but the parasitic cuckoos have demonstrated the efficacy of natural selection in reducing egg size without sacrifice of body size.

The association between body weight and egg weight is emphasized by the fact that during the first laying year, at least, a loss of body weight is accompanied by a reduction in size of egg. Conversely, when part of the weight lost is regained, there is a concomitant increase in egg weight. This is nicely illustrated by the record of Hays (1939) for a large number of Rhode Island Red pullets (Fig. 86).

Relation between Egg Size and Age at First Egg. As would be expected from the fact that the smaller birds tend to lay small eggs, pullets showing precocious sexual maturity (as indicated by laying at an early age) start off with smaller eggs than those which begin at a later age and hence with larger body size. This was apparently first pointed out by

Curtis (1914), who took weight of the first yolk as a measure of egg size. This increased consistently from 6.2 gm. for a pullet laying at 3 months to 15.1 gm. for another, not laying till 9 months of age. The close relationship is shown by the high correlation between age at first egg and weight of the first 10 eggs. This was found to be +.714 by Lippincott (1921) in White Leghorns, +.845 by Jull (1924a) in Barred Plymouth Rocks, +.517 by Axelsson (1934) in various crossbreds.

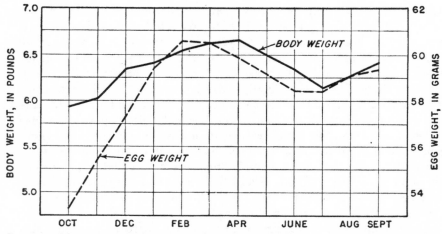

Fig. 86. Changes in egg weight associated with changes in body weight of 267 Rhode Island Reds during the first year of laying. (*From data of Hays, 1939.*)

Pullets beginning to lay at an early age are smaller at that time than those not maturing sexually until somewhat older. Thus the correlation between age at first egg and weight at first egg was found to be +.468 in Rhode Island Reds, by Hays (1933), and +.615 in White Plymouth Rocks, by Funk (1935). It follows that the weight of the first eggs laid will be related not only to age of the pullet but also to her body weight (Parkhurst, 1926; Upp and Thompson, 1927; and others). The question arises, therefore, whether the first eggs are small because the pullet began early or merely because she herself was small at the time. When the influence of age at first egg is eliminated by measuring partial correlation, a highly significant relationship is still found between egg weight and body weight at first egg (Funk, 1935) as would be expected from the other evidence that these two variables are closely related in fully mature birds.

While age at first egg and body weight at that time have a marked effect on the size of the first eggs laid, they have much less to do with the final egg size attained by the birds when full-grown or (usually) with the average size of all eggs laid. This seems to apply both in Leghorns (Marble, 1931) and in heavy breeds. In Rhode Island Reds, Hays (1939) found that average egg weight for the year is closely correlated with body weight at 11 to 12 months of age ($r = +.399$, correlation ratio $= +.466$) but (1944) is only slightly dependent on body weight at first egg ($r = +.109$). A similar situation is indicated by data of Funk and Kempster (1934) for a flock of White Plymouth Rocks (Fig. 87). Olsen

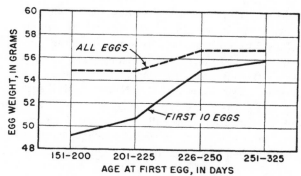

Fig. 87. The mean weight of all eggs for the year is less dependent upon age at first egg than is the weight of the first 10 eggs laid. (*From data of Funk and Kempster.*)

and Knox (1940) were able to increase average egg weight for the year without raising the age at first egg.

On the other hand, various workers have claimed that the mean egg weight for the first year of laying is significantly related to the age at first egg, the earlier layers producing smaller eggs for the year than the later ones. It is obvious that this could be so in any flock in which the birds are slow in attaining their maximum egg size. In such cases, as Maw and Maw (1932) have shown, the small eggs laid before reaching the definitive egg weight would comprise a sufficient proportion of the total number to reduce the average weight considerably.

While the average weight of all eggs laid by a hen in her first laying year is important, in actual practice no poultryman could afford to measure it. A more practical consideration is the length of time required by a pullet to get her eggs from a modest initial weight up to the standard 2-ounce egg that the market demands. Concerning this question Maw and Maw (1932) found that in their White Leghorns the younger the age at first egg the longer the time required to attain an egg weight of 2 ounces. This applies also in heavy breeds, according to Hays (1934), who studied this point in a large flock of Rhode Island Reds. In these, the correlation between age at first egg and the number of days to standard egg was —.642, and the correlation between the latter variable and body weight at first egg was only —.331. This means that a pullet maturing too early lays more small eggs than one maturing late. Birds beginning to lay when small are also handicapped, but not so much as those which begin too early.

Altogether, the interrelationship of age at first egg, body weight, and early attainment of large egg size are well illustrated by the actual experience at the Mount Hope Farm (Goodale, 1935–1936). In five generations of selection, mean weight of the fiftieth to sixtieth eggs was raised from 48.7 to 58.2 gm., but at the same time the age at first egg was retarded from 185 to 199 days and, concomitantly, weight of the pullets at first egg rose from 3.4 to 4.2 pounds.

Relation between Egg Size and the Number of Eggs Laid. The general tendency is for the more prolific layers to lay smaller eggs, but there are enough exceptions to the rule to account for some of the disagreement among those who have studied the relationship. More of it is attributable to conclusions based on flocks too small to contain many high producers. Furthermore, as Marble (1930) has shown, the relationship is curvilinear, both prolific layers and very poor ones usually laying smaller eggs than those between the extremes.

This tendency for the better layers to produce smaller eggs is demonstrated (albeit in reverse order) in the summary by Jull (1930) of data from the fourth Scottish egg-laying trial. This showed that, in each of three breeds, hens with egg size above the median for the breed laid fewer eggs than those for which the eggs were below the median weight. It should be noted that these large-egg birds all had mean egg size exceeding 60 gm. This may explain why Bennion and Warren (1933a) found no relationship between egg size and number of eggs laid in a flock of White Leghorns with mean egg size ranging only from 50.3 to 52.3 gm. in poor, medium, and high producers. There is no reason why a hen should hesitate about laying eggs of that size in quantity, but there is ample justification for some slowing down by hens producing a quality product 10 gm. heavier. This discrepancy is discussed later along with the effects of temperature on egg size.

The tendency for high egg production to be associated with smaller eggs is indicated by the fact (Hays, 1934) that pullets with longer cycles of daily laying take longer to attain standard egg weight than those having shorter cycles. Hays (1944a) also found that pullets with longer cycles in winter lay smaller eggs at that time but that the egg production and the egg size for the whole year showed a positive, though non-linear.

correlation. Since the mean weight of his birds' eggs was 58.5 gm., his finding is difficult to reconcile with that of Jull, though in agreement with that of Bennion and Warren. Unfortunately, all three used different methods of analysis.

Variations in Consecutive Eggs of a Cycle. Hens usually lay for a number of days in succession, then miss a day or two and repeat the process. Such a series of consecutive eggs has been referred to as a "cycle" and as a "clutch." The former term seems preferable because a clutch means a brood or hatch and is more correctly applied to the number of eggs laid by a bird before starting to incubate them. Cycles of laying vary from two eggs to several dozen, those of two to four being most common.

It was observed by Curtis (1914) that in such cycles the first egg is the largest and subsequent eggs are successively smaller. This has been confirmed by Atwood (1926), Bennion and Warren (1933a), and others. An interesting point, first noted by Atwood, is that the decline in size of successive eggs is less during periods of heavy production than when the birds are laying fewer eggs, and somewhat less in the better layers than in the poor ones. Since the better layers are characterized by longer cycles, it would be expected from this that the decline in weight of successive eggs would be less in longer cycles than in short ones. This has been proved by Funk and Kempster (1934), whose data are given in part in Table 47.

TABLE 47. DATA SHOWING THE DECLINE IN WEIGHT OF SUCCESSIVE EGGS IN CYCLES AND THAT THIS IS LESS IN LONG CYCLES THAN IN SHORT ONES*

Eggs in cycle, number	Cycles analyzed, number	Mean weight of first egg, grams	Decrease in successive eggs, grams				Decrease in weight, grams	
			Second	Third	Fourth	Fifth	From first to last	Per egg
2	856	57.3	−2.6	.....	.....	...	2.6	2.6
3	178	57.5	−1.7	−1.2	.....	...	2.9	1.45
4	232	56.2	−1.6	−0.7	−0.2	...	2.5	0.83
5	104	54.7	−1.1	−0.6	−0.3	0	2.0	0.50

* From Funk and Kempster (1934).

In smaller eggs than those considered by Funk and Kempster, the trend is identical with that shown, but, as Bennion and Warren (1933a) found in the White Leghorns studied by them, the decreases in successive eggs were somewhat smaller than those shown in Table 47. In their 45 clutches of eight eggs each, the weight declined from 53.96 to 52.1 gm., a mean decrease of only 0.26 gm. per egg. An additional point noted by Bennion and Warren is that at the start of the laying year, a period when egg size is steadily increasing, the decline in weight of successive eggs in three-egg cycles was less than half of that in similar eggs from the same hens in March, when maximum egg size had been attained.

Related to this subject is the effect upon egg size of a temporary cessation of egg laying, or "pause." It was shown by Féré (1898) that, following such a period of rest, the first egg is considerably smaller than later ones. After pauses varying from 8 to 30 days, Bennion and Warren (1933a) found the mean weight of the first egg to be lower than that of comparable eggs before the pause by 4.14 gm. in birds laying regularly eggs of about 57 gm. and by 2.32 gm. in Leghorns laying normally 54-gm. eggs. However, full egg size was recovered by the time two or three eggs had been laid.

With pauses or intervals of short duration, the effect is the opposite of that just discussed. Eggs laid 2 to 4 days after the preceding one are larger than those following an interval of only 1 day, according to Axelsson (1934). The exact number of days without laying that are necessary to reduce the size of the next egg has not been determined and is probably variable. The underlying principle is possibly that in long periods of non-laying the oviduct shrinks, while in short intervals between eggs it does not.

Relation between Egg Size and Age of the Hen. It has been reported by several investigators that the mean weight of eggs laid in the second year of laying is 4 to 8 per cent greater than that of eggs laid during the first year. While this is correct, the statement by itself conveys an erroneous impression. It is obvious that the mean for first-year eggs is lowered by all the small eggs laid before maximum egg size is attained. The fundamental principle is that once maximum size is reached it remains comparatively constant (apart from the environmental influences discussed later) during the first 2 years of laying. The fact that second-year eggs are bigger than the average for first-year eggs is therefore merely a mathematical inevitability and has no biological significance.

A slight decline in egg size in the third year is evident in the data of Hadley and Caldwell (1920), Atwood and Clarke (1930), Clark (1940), and Hays (1944). It is so small that none of these investigators considered it significant, but their results are consistent. Clark's valuable record of egg size up to the tenth laying year shows a steady decrease in egg size after the second year, with more abrupt changes after the fourth year (Fig. 88). Since the original flock numbered 188 and there were 26 survivors with records for the tenth year, the data are quite significant. They do not exclude the possibility that layers of big eggs die early, while layers of small eggs survive. However, the smoothness of the curves and the fact that about 70 per cent of the original flock were included in the 5-year group, which showed a marked decline, leave little doubt of the general trend. It will be noted that there was a correspond-

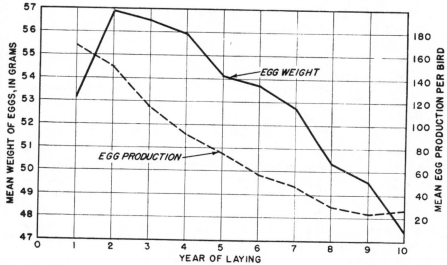

FIG. 88. The decline in mean egg weight and in numbers of eggs laid with advancing age. (*From data of Clark.*)

ing decline in the number of eggs laid. Both effects may be considered as indications of senescence.

Relation of Air Temperatures to Egg Size. In the Northern Hemisphere there is usually a decline in size of egg during the spring and summer months similar to that shown in Fig. 89. The work of Bennion and Warren (1933) showed that this is caused to a large extent by hot weather. In their experiments, temperatures above 85°F. lowered egg size by 15 to 20 per cent. Later studies by Warren (1939) of seasonal fluctuations in different latitudes indicated that, after the daily maximum temperature rose above 70°F. for a few days or longer, variations in egg size were closely related to those in temperature. Lorenz and Almquist (1936) even found a decrease in egg weight proportional to any increase in temperature between 40 and 90°F. The increase in size of egg when temperatures fall toward the end of the summer (Fig. 89) suggests that the earlier decline is attributable to the influence of temperature rather than ·

to any physiological exhaustion resulting from a long period of egg laying.

It follows inevitably from this that the rating of fowls in laying tests (and in national schemes for evaluating flocks) according to an index combining the number of eggs laid and their weight automatically handicaps the southern birds exposed to more hot weather than those in the north. This could be overcome by making allowances for this environmental influence that could vary according to latitude, altitude, or mean summer temperature at different points.

Similarly the influence of temperature should be considered in attempts to reconcile differing conclusions about egg size based on data from different latitudes. The evidence of Jull (1930) from the Scottish laying trials that the best layers produce smaller eggs was in direct contrast to the failure of Bennion and Warren (1933a) to find any such relation in their birds at Manhattan, Kansas. However, the records of Warren (1939) show that birds there are exposed to mean maximum temperatures above 70°F. for about half the year, while at Roslin, in Scotland, the source of Jull's data, that figure was reached only in one half-month period. This may explain in part why the mean weight of eggs at Roslin exceeded 60 gm. during 10 months of the year, while those at Manhattan never got up to 56 gm. It is not unlikely that the true physiological relationship between number of eggs and their size could have been completely obscured by the environmental influence at Kansas but more fully revealed at Roslin, where that influence is much less.

Relation between Size of Egg and the Thyroid Gland. There is considerable evidence that the seasonal changes in egg size may not be related entirely to air temperatures but may be influenced by seasonal fluctuations in the activity of the thyroid gland. The curves of Warren (1939), for egg size at Roslin, Scotland, show a marked decline in weight beginning in March before the mean maximum temperatures had risen above 50°F. Furthermore, the egg weight rose in July and August when temperatures were higher than in any other 2 months of the year. Much closer than any relationship at Roslin between egg size and air temperature is that found at Edinburgh, only 15 miles away, by Galpin (1937–1938) between egg size and size of the thyroid gland. Her extensive data are shown graphically in Fig. 89. During the period of maximum egg production from March to June, both size of egg and weight of thyroid declined steadily to reach their low points in July. Thereafter both rose rather abruptly during August and September.

Galpin suggested that the functional activity of the fowl's thyroid may be inversely related to its mass. In that case, the decline in size of egg would be accompanied, not by a decrease in the amount of thyroxine produced, as one might at first suppose from the reduction in size of the gland, but actually by an increase in the amount of that hormone. There is excellent evidence in support of this theory in the findings of Asmundson (1931a), Asmundson and Pinsky (1935), and Larionov (1936) that, when the hen's own production of thyroxine is supplemented by the feeding of additional thyroid substance, a significant decline in the size of the eggs follows.

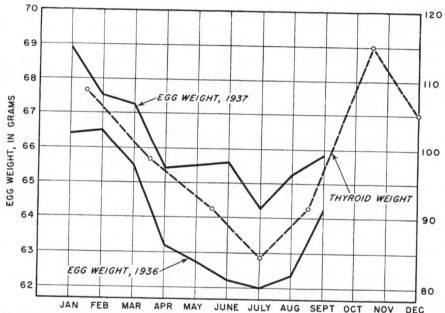

Fig. 89. The associated seasonal changes in the size of eggs and of the thyroid gland. (*From data of Galpin.*)

It was shown by Cruickshank (1929) that during the winter the fowl's thyroid is not only larger than in the spring and summer but also higher in total and proportional amount of thyroxine. If this be taken to mean, not that the larger gland is producing more thyroxine, but merely that it is storing what it does produce and actually liberating more of it in spring and summer, her findings are quite in accord with the theory just given. Further support is given by the histological studies of Podhradsky (1935), showing that in October and January the fowl's thyroid contains much colloid and looks more like a storage organ, while in May it is more active and in July most active.

Returning to Fig. 86, it will be seen that changes in egg size are roughly parallel to those in body weight. The dosage of desiccated thyroid found by Asmundson to reduce egg size was 1 mg. thyroid iodine daily per 1,750 gm. of body weight. This had previously been determined by Hutt (1930) to be about the minimum necessary to cause a loss in body weight. Considering all the evidence, it seems probable that some of the seasonal changes, both in body size and in egg size, are caused by corresponding changes in the functional activity of the thyroid gland. The decline of egg size in spring and summer may, indeed, be greater because of the combined action of high temperatures and thyroid activity than it would be from either influence alone, for Bennion and Warren (1933) found heat to reduce the albumen and shell proportionately more than the yolk, while Asmundson and Pinsky (1935) showed that extra thyroid lowers the amount of yolk proportionately more than it does the other two parts of the egg.

Variations in Size with the Hour of Laying. Eggs laid before 9 A.M. are the largest of the day. Collections at hourly intervals by Atwood (1927) showed a consistent decline in weight up to 11 A.M. with little change thereafter (Fig. 90). However, Funk and Kempster (1934) found the decline to continue, so that eggs laid after 2 P.M. were half a gram smaller than those laid between noon and 2 P.M. This discrepancy may be related to the fact that their period of study included many short winter days, while Atwood's eggs were taken in the long days of the summer.

The question arises whether the early morning eggs are biggest because they were laid early or merely because they include a high proportion of eggs that are the first in the cycles to which they belong. As was seen earlier, these are larger than later eggs of the cycle. After an interval of 1 or 2 days without laying, the next egg is usually laid early in the morning and subsequent eggs slightly later on successive days of the cycle. Eggs laid in the afternoon are likely to include a high proportion of eggs that terminate cycles. These are usually smaller than those which precede them in the cycle, and that may be why they are smaller than those laid earlier in the day.

Measures of Egg Weight in Mature Birds. Perhaps because of the egg-laying tests, in which egg size is important right from the beginning of the year to its end, poultrymen have long been unduly obsessed with the significance of the mean weight of all first-year eggs as a measure of the hen's genetically determined egg size. For most practical purposes it would suffice to know the maximum egg size and when it is attained or, better still, the egg size after some 4 or 5 months of laying, by which time the producers of big and little eggs can be easily differentiated.

It was shown by Jull (1930) that, if eggs were weighed on only 1 fixed day of the week throughout the year, the mean egg weight thus determined differed by only 0.06 gm. from that for all eggs. Similarly, the correlation between the mean for eggs of one hen laid on Fridays and that for all her eggs throughout the year was found by Dudley (1931) to be +.95. Exactly the same high correlation applied when the sample weighed consisted of all eggs laid in 4 consecutive days at the middle of

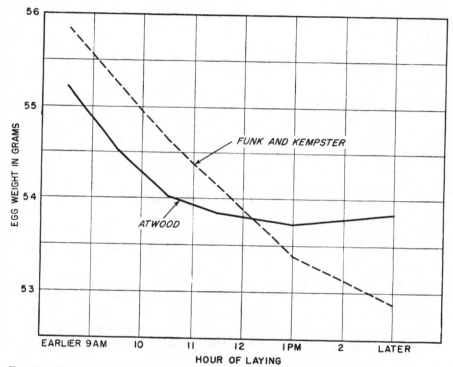

Fig. 90. Mean weight of the eggs is heaviest in those laid earlier in the morning and declines fairly consistently in those laid later in the day.

each lunar month. It is not surprising that the two coefficients should be identical, as the samples contained the same number of weighing days per lunar month by either method. It would be interesting to calculate how much time has been wasted in weighing all eggs at laying tests on 7 days a week instead of 1 since 1931, when Dudley's data, based on 198 birds, were published. The samples used by him were also found adequate by Godfrey (1933).

Even smaller samples give a fair estimate of the average weight of eggs for the year if they be taken at the right time. Maw and Maw (1932) considered that the first 10 eggs laid in the fifth month of laying gave a reliable method for the year. In practice, the use of such a sample would be difficult, as it would necessitate separate weighing periods for each bird and much calculation of which eggs to weigh. The feasibility of using the first 10 eggs in March as a measure has been examined by Jull (1930), Godfrey (1933), and Jeffrey (1938) with widely different procedures and equally divergent conclusions. Hays (1937) found that egg weight in February or March is highly correlated with that for the year and recommended its use.

Much of this sort of investigation has been directed toward determining with great accuracy the mean egg size for all eggs laid by individual birds in the first year. This may be desirable for laying tests or in national plans for testing birds, but in practical breeding to raise egg size the important consideration is not so much the record of the individual as the mean egg weight for all daughters of one dam or of one sire. If there are several pullets in a family, it is not necessary to have so many eggs per pullet to determine the level of genetic egg size that the dam or sire is transmitting. This is particularly so because in good progeny testing what counts is not so much the actual weight (or number) of the eggs but the rank, or standing, of the parent in comparison with the other dams or sires.

The author has found that adequate differentiation of sires and dams with respect to the egg size of their progeny can be made by weighing only the eggs laid by the daughters in one 7-day period about the middle of March. The mean number of eggs weighed runs about 4.7 per daughter, from 25 to 50 per dam, and several times that per sire. These are enough to differentiate the families and even the pullets within those families. Together with a weighing of eggs in the late fall, as mentioned below, this measure has made possible the raising of egg size by breeding (even though that was incidental to other objectives) to a point beyond which further increase was hardly warranted. Proof of this is shown in Fig. 85.

Early Measure of Egg Weight in Immature Pullets. Egg weights taken, as these are, after mature body size and maximum egg weight are attained should be the chief guide to selection of breeding stock. However, most poultrymen will want some earlier indication of egg size to help in the selection of breeders in December or January, which is the season when breeding pens are usually made up, in latitudes higher than about 35°N. Apart from that, it is desirable to eliminate early from any commercial flock the pullets capable of laying only small eggs.

To that end, Maw and Maw (1932) calculated that, if the pullet is to attain standard egg size (56.7 gm.) during the first year, her first 10 eggs should have an average weight of 47.5 gm. Wilson and Warren (1934) put the figure at 46, 50, and 52 gm. for pullets starting in October, November, or December, respectively. Similarly Jull and Godrey (1933) considered 48.8 gm. for the first 10 eggs necessary to indicate that mean weight for the year would be up to standard or better. Hays (1937) concluded that, in order to lay standard eggs in February and March, pullets should have a mean egg weight of 53 gm. for all eggs up to Jan. 1.

While such early measures of ultimate egg size are of considerable value to the commercial poultryman seeking to eliminate his small-egg birds, the up-to-date breeder should be somewhat more concerned with averages for families than with records of individuals. To know which sires and dams from the breeding pens of the previous spring may profitably be used again, his best guide is the average egg size for all daughters or for enough of them to constitute a fair sample. The actual mean weight in grams may vary considerably depending upon the length of time the birds have been laying before it is taken, but, with pullets of comparable ages, one can make at any time a comparison of all the sires under test or of all the dams mated with one sire. The important consideration is not so much the actual egg weight for the progeny as the rating of the sire or dam in comparison with others.

To do this, the author has found that families can be adequately differentiated in the fall by weighing all the eggs laid in 1 week. Preferably that week should be put off till late November or early December to give the pullets the maximum possible period of laying before eggs are weighed. By this method, recognition of sires and dams that transmit undesirably small eggs and detection of big-egg families are easy, but estimating the ultimate egg size for individual pullets is less so.

The feasibility of doing this is shown in Table 48, which gives December and March egg weights for daughters of 16 unselected sires in one line of White Leghorns in 1941 and for 16 others, also unselected, in 1936. In the former year, the ratings were remarkably consistent. Not only were the best 8 sires in December the best 8 when final weights were determined in March, but with only 2 exceptions those ranking in any quartile in December also ranked in that quartile in March. Results in 1936 were not so accurate, but 6 of the 8 males rated above average in December were found above average in the final returns, and the same degree of accuracy applied to those rated below average in December.

Other advantages of the system of ranking the sires according to the means for their daughters rather than setting merely arbitrary standards (of egg size, egg production, or other objectives) are considered in the chapter on Genetics in Practice.

Effects of Diet and Drugs on Egg Size. It has been proved by Heuser (1936) that diets containing only 12 per cent of protein cause the

TABLE 48. MEAN EGG WEIGHTS SHOWING THAT THE MEAN DETERMINED FROM 7 DAYS' EGGS IN DECEMBER GIVES A FAIRLY ACCURATE RATING OF THE SIRE'S TRANSMISSIBLE EGG SIZE AS FINALLY MEASURED IN MARCH

16 sires used in 1941, mean egg weights				16 sires used in 1936, mean egg weights			
December		March		December		March	
Grams	Rank	Rank	Grams	Grams	Rank	Rank	Grams
56.2	1	1	58.4	55.1	1	1	60.4
54.6	2	2	58.3	54.8	2	3	58.3
54.6	3	3	57.5	54.3	3	2	58.8
54.0	4	4	57.1	53.7	4	6	54.9
53.8	5	8	56.6	53.0	5	5	55.3
53.5	6⎱	5⎱	56.8	52.8	6	12	52.9
53.5	7⎰	6⎰	56.8	52.6	7	4	56.4
53.1	8	7	56.7	52.1	8	13	52.3
52.7	9	12	55.9	51.5	9	9	54.2
52.6	10	13	55.8	51.0	10	7	54.9
52.5	11	9	56.5	50.4	11	10	53.7
52.3	12	10	56.2	50.2	12	8	54.3
52.1	13	15	54.8	49.9	13	14	52.3
52.0	14	11	56.0	49.4	14	11	53.2
51.5	15	16	54.7	49.1	15	15	51.9
50.1	16	14	54.9	48.2	16	16	51.7
Mean 53.0			Mean 56.4	Mean 51.6			Mean 54.9

production of fewer and smaller eggs than diets containing 16 per cent of protein. One would expect vitamin D to have some influence, at least on eggshell, and evidence has been adduced by Graham (1932) to show that birds getting cod-liver oil lay heavier eggs than those without it.

The anthelminthic drug, kamala, when given at its effective dosage of 1 gm. per bird, causes a drop in egg production and reduces the size of eggs from mature birds by as much as 4 gm. (Atwood and Clark, 1929). A similar effect, but less severe, was noted by Maw (1934) in pullets just beginning to lay. Apparently the decrease in size of egg is not merely incidental to the drop in egg production, for some of his birds continued to lay at the same rate as before treatment but produced smaller eggs.

The decrease is proportionately smaller in the yolk than in the albumen and shell.

Undoubtedly other drugs may have similar effects, and it will be surprising if further modifications of egg size by the diet are not brought to light.

Genetic Basis for Variations in Egg Size. Although several attempts have been made to specify the number of genes affecting the size of eggs, none of these has been particularly successful, and one can only say that, as with most other quantitative characters, an unknown number of multiple factors is involved. The preceding discussion of variation in egg size should have made clear the difficulty of distinguishing between any genes directly affecting egg size and those doing so indirectly by influencing body size, age at first egg, rate of egg production, and other functions. Apart from this there is some question about when the genetic egg weight (*i.e.*, the phenotype) is best measured.

The ease with which egg size may be raised by breeding, when compared with the difficulty of improving some other quantitative characters, suggests that the genes affecting egg size are fewer in number than those determining fecundity, viability, and other physiological characters. On the other hand, the quick success in breeding for big eggs may, perhaps, depend more on the fact that breeders are satisfied with eggs of about 58 to 60 gm. Larger ones do not bring correspondingly higher prices, do not hatch so well, and are less desirable for shipping in standard egg cases. Consequently there is no effort to continue selection for large eggs to the utmost biological limits, as there is in breeding for viability or for egg production.

Results of crosses between breeds differing in size of egg, as reported by Benjamin (1920), Hurst (1921), Kopeć (1924), and Lauth (1935) agree in finding the F_1 population intermediate but closer to the small-egg parents than to the others. This indicates that genes for small eggs may be dominant, or epistatic, to those for large ones, as Hays (1937) has suggested. If that be so, it is not surprising that mass selection by Hadley (as reported by Waters and Weldin, 1929) was effective in breeding a strain of hens to lay smaller eggs, but not so in a parallel attempt to make another strain lay bigger ones. The possibility that dams influence egg weight more than sires do was examined and rejected by Hays (1941), whose data showed no indication of either sex-limited or sex-linked inheritance. This was confirmed by Hutt and Bozivich (1946).

Attempts to find differences among breeds with respect to egg weight are somewhat futile because of the difficulty of making any allowances for the amount of selection for large eggs in the particular samples tested.

Corrections should also be made for differences in size. It is recognized that Leghorns laying eggs of 58 gm. are producing relatively bigger ones than Rhode Island Reds that lay eggs of that same size. Presumably the difference is attributable to selection, forced by market demands, to get the Leghorn eggs up to the standard size.

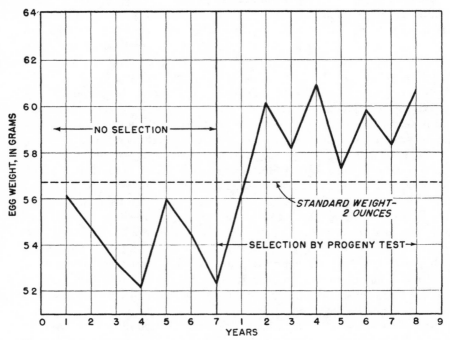

Fig. 91. Rapid increase in egg size by selection, and its maintenance. From data of Snyder for February egg size of Barred Rock pullets over a 15-year period at the Ontario Agricultural College.

Increasing Size of Egg by Breeding. The feasibility of doing this, and of doing so rapidly, was demonstrated with White Leghorns at the Mount Hope Farm (Goodale, 1935–1936) where, by five generations of selection, the mean weight for 10 eggs beginning with a pullet's fiftieth egg was raised from 48.7 to 58.2 gm. In ounces per dozen, this increase is from 20.6 to 24.3 ounces, which is slightly over standard weight. This was done not by mass selection but by careful progeny testing. Similar success was achieved by Olsen and Knox (1940), who raised average egg weight from 54.7 to 59.7 gm. in 4 years.

For results over a longer period of time the record of Snyder (1945) shown in Fig. 91 is of unusual interest. During 7 years without selection, egg size in February of Barred Plymouth Rock pullets varied considerably and got down to about 52 gm. Selection by progeny test, begun at that point, quickly raised egg size to 60 gm. in 2 years and thereafter maintained it for 6 years more at weights varying slightly above or below 59 gm.

Results like these show the ease with which egg size may be raised by breeding to the level required by present market standards. Most poultrymen cannot concentrate on breeding for egg size alone to the exclusion of other desiderata, but the author's data in Fig. 85 show that considerable improvement can be made by the right kind of selection even when egg size is incidental to other more important objectives.

VARIATIONS IN SHAPE

Causes of Shape. Just why a bird's egg should have its characteristic shape is a problem that has intrigued biologists for many years. The theories of Ryder, Szielasko, Pearl, and Curtis were reviewed by Asmundson (1931), whose own contribution was to emphasize the importance of the isthmian region of the oviduct in determining egg shape. Removal of a portion of the isthmus in such a way as to shorten it or to narrow it and temporary ligation of the isthmus both caused a modification in the shape of eggs laid after the operation. He concluded that egg shape is determined by (1) the amount of albumen secreted in the albumen-secreting region, (2) the size of the lumen of that part and of the isthmus, and (3) the muscular activity of the walls in these regions, together with (4) some possible alteration in the uterus. The fact that one end is somewhat pointed and the other comparatively blunt he attributed to the fact that the isthmus is narrower than the rest of the tract and hence would tend to force the albumen toward the anterior end, and the elongated ovate form thus established would be retained by the shell membranes laid over it in the isthmus.

The fact that a pullet's first egg is sometimes long and narrow, while later ones approach successively to the normal shape of an egg (Pearl, 1909) suggests that the small lumen of the newly functioning oviduct may have an especially important influence on the shape of the first eggs laid.

From later studies in which 16 hens laid eggs after resection of portions of the uterus, Asmundson and Jervis (1933) concluded that shape of the egg is determined while in the isthmus and that the uterus has little effect, if any. The same concept was extended to the turkey by Asmundson (1939). Harper and Marble (1945), who took eggs from the isthmus, immersed them in water till plump, and then compared the shape with that of eggs laid previously by the same hens, came to the same conclusion as did Asmundson.

Measures. Egg shape is usually measured by the index, breadth/ length × 100. The narrower the egg, the lower the index. In 5,887 eggs of White Leghorns for which the distribution of such indices was given by Axelsson (1938), there were 12 between 60 and 62, and 2 over 82, with a mean for the whole lot of 71.8. While this index is convenient, it does not measure the differing degrees of pointedness, *i.e.*, such differences as that between eggs of a hen and a guillemot or of a robin and a killdeer. Axelsson recorded these by comparison with a series of 10 eggs showing different gradations of pointedness, and Hutt (1938) did so by measuring the diameters at a fixed point (13 mm.) from each end. This was done by fitting the ends into holes of known diameter in a thin brass plate fixed 13 mm. above a base plate.

Variability. Pearl and Surface (1914) and Asmundson (1931) agree that shape of the egg is more variable than either length or breadth but less so than weight. Among 85 pullets for which all eggs were measured for over 5 months, Marble (1943) found that some females were much more variable in the shape of their eggs than others and that the coefficients of variability ranged from 1.97 to 5.46 per cent, with a mean of 3.33 for all the birds. He saw no evidence of any seasonal change in the shape of eggs but proved clearly that the first egg of a cycle is slightly longer or narrower than succeeding eggs in the same cycle. Similarly, the first egg laid after a pause of 7 days or more is longer or narrower than the last one preceding it. These facts are especially interesting because, as we have seen earlier, the first eggs of a cycle are larger than average, while the first eggs after a pause are smaller than average. Since both classes are changed in shape, being either elongated or narrowed down or both, the independence of forces influencing shape from those influencing size is demonstrated.

Genetic Influence. Differences in the shape of eggs are hereditary, but the number of genes concerned is unknown. In two generations of selection Marble established two strains of Barred Plymouth Rocks, one producing rather long eggs with indices a little over 69, and the other laying rounder eggs with indices about 76 (Fig. 92). When these were crossed, the F_1 generation produced eggs intermediate in shape between the parental types. Backcrossing to the "long" line yielded birds laying eggs with a mean index 71.1, and backcrossing to the "round" line produced pullets with a mean egg index of 75.9. Clearly, multiple factors are responsible for genetic variations in egg shape.

Axelsson's extensive data showed highly significant differences between breeds in egg shape, the mean indices being 71.8, 73.1, and 74.0 for

White Leghorns, Rhode Island Reds, and Barnevelders, respectively. However, remembering that in eggs of Barred Plymouth Rocks Pearl and Surface found an index of 74.5 and Marble one of 71.9, the question arises, as in most attempts to compare breeds, whether the differences observed by Axelsson were characteristic of breeds or of the particular

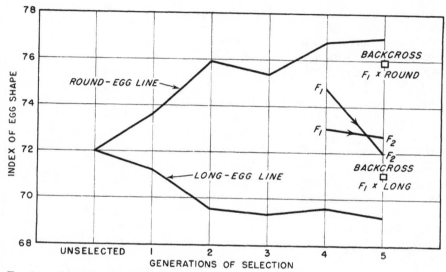

FIG. 92. The differentiation in two generations of two lines of Barred Rock pullets, one producing round eggs, the other long ones. Crosses between the two after three generations yielded two F_1 populations, both intermediate, as were the F_2 birds. Backcrosses of F_1 to both strains yielded daughters intermediate between the F_1 and the parental strain concerned. (*From data of Marble.*)

flocks from which he drew his samples. Crosses of his breeds yielded results similar to those of Marble.

It must not be supposed, however, that the genotype is the only source of differences in egg shape. Sometimes the eggs laid by one hen differ much more among themselves than those of the two lines bred by Marble. Atwood (1922) found that, over a 3-month period, one such hen laid 26 eggs with shape indices from 60 to 68 and 16 with indices from 71 to 77. This bimodal distribution led him to believe that the hen had two functional oviducts, but Professor Atwood later advised the author that at autopsy only one was found.

VARIATIONS IN THE SHELL

Variations in Thickness

Thin-shelled eggs are undesirable not only because they are easily broken in the nests, in collecting pails, in egg-grading machines, and in transit to market but also because they usually do not hatch so well as eggs with thicker shells. For these reasons, factors affecting thickness of shell have received considerable study.

Measures. Using a micrometer caliper, Romanoff (1929) found the thickness of shell in 3,998 eggs (of the domestic fowl) to vary from 0.244 to 0.373 mm., the average for all being 0.311. The corresponding figure of Olsson (1936), determined in the same way, was 0.345 mm. His eggs were thicker at the pointed end than at the round end, but Romanoff's were not. Following Romanoff's demonstration that there is a relation between thickness of shell and its breaking strength, or ability to withstand crushing, the correlation between these two variables was found to be about +.51 by Stewart (1936) and +.63 by Lund, Heiman, and Wilhelm (1938). A similar correlation exists between breaking strength and the proportion of shell (by dry weight) in the whole egg (Morgan, 1932). Thickness of shell may be measured just as accurately by the weight per unit of area as by the actual thickness (Warren and Schnepel, 1940), but the method is a laborious one.

However, measurement of the actual thickness, in millimetres, or of the weight required to crush the egg has the disadvantage that eggs thus assayed cannot be used for reproduction. This limitation does not apply to the ingenious method devised by Olsson (1934). He determined (1) that the specific gravity of the shell is more than twice as high as that of other parts of the egg and (2) that, even though the air-dried shell comprises only a small proportion of the total weight of the egg, it does affect the specific gravity of the fresh, whole egg. In three lots totalling 1,405 eggs, the correlations between specific gravity of the fresh egg and the proportion of shell were all above +.93. In one of these lots, eggs from hens inadequately supplied with vitamin D ranged in proportion of air-dried shell from under 5 to over 11 per cent, but the correlation between this variable and the specific gravity of the whole egg was +.98. This means that variations in specific gravity of the egg are determined almost entirely by variations in the shell. Olsson proposed that in practice the specific gravity of eggs could be determined by testing their ability to float in a series of solutions of sodium chloride. Acting on this suggestion, Munro (1940) was able to demonstrate a relation between low specific gravity (*i.e.*, thin shells) and low hatching power and to devise a simple means for detecting by flotation the thin-shelled eggs least likely to hatch. Many of these can be recognized by inspection.

With another method, utilized by Axelsson (1932), one determines the loss of weight in eggs during some fixed period under standardized conditions of temperature and humidity. It is probably a better measure of permeability of the shell than of its thickness and is open to the criticism that corrections are necessary for differences in the surface areas if large and small eggs are to be compared. Nevertheless it has proved a satisfactory general measure of that combination of shell thickness and permeability sometimes referred to as the "quality" of the shell. Axelsson found that even the loss of weight in 24 hours at room temperature was some indication of the hatchability of the eggs. Quinn, Gordon, and Godfrey (1945) used the loss in weight during 14 days of incubation as a guide for evaluating breeding stock when breeding for better eggshells.

Sources of Variation. According to correlations worked out by Kopeć (1924) for eggs of Buff Orpingtons, the shells tend to be thicker in the shorter, rounder eggs than in the longer ones. This was shown by a positive correlation of thickness with the index of egg shape (+.349) and a negative one with length of egg (−.353). Correlation of thickness with breadth was +.162 and with weight of shell, +.633. In these eggs, thickness also increased with intensity of brown color ($r = +.398$).

Differences in the amount of shell depend upon various environmental and genetic influences. Hens not getting enough calcium or vitamin D eventually cease production but lay thin-shelled eggs before doing so. Diets very low in manganese have a similar effect, but it is doubtful that the amount of this element is likely to be low enough to cause trouble except in experiments for which such a diet is deliberately prepared.

The tendency for eggshells to become thinner during the summer is well known. In controlled experiments, Warren and Schnepel (1940) proved that, when temperature of the circumambient air is raised from 70 to about 90°F., shells are reduced in weight by about 25 to 30 per cent, a decrease associated with a proportionate reduction of the blood calcium (Conrad, 1939). They suggested that high temperatures are responsible for the decline in shell strength during the summer. This is probably correct, at least in part, but it is worth noting that the same summer weakness of shells with increasing strength in the fall was noted by Baskett, Dryden, and Hale (1937) in Northern Ireland at lat. 54°N., where high temperatures are unusual.

Good metabolism of calcium is not the only essential for the formation of shell, which is about 94 per cent calcium carbonate. The shell is formed by the action of an enzyme, carbonic anhydrase, which catalyzes the hydration of carbon dioxide to form calcium carbonate. This enzyme is more concentrated in the uteri of laying fowls than in those of non-layers (Common, 1941). Following the discovery that sulphanilamide inhibits the action of carbonic anhydrase, it was shown that administration of this drug causes the fowls to lay soft-shelled eggs (Benesch *et al.*, 1944; Gutowska and Mitchell, 1945; Genest and Bernard, 1945). This inhibitory effect of sulphanilamide on the formation of eggshells (Fig. 93) had been noted earlier by Hinshaw and McNeil (1943) and by Scott,

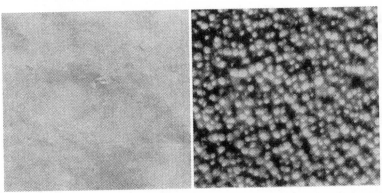

FIG. 93. Faulty formation of shell induced by feeding sulphanilamide. *Left,* normal; *right,* soft, rough shell of an egg laid about 27 hours after a single dose of sulphanilamide. Both shells ×30.

Jungherr, and Matterson (1944) in tests made to determine the feasibility of using the drug for control of disease.

Some indication that shells are thinner in eggs of the best layers is seen in the fact that the correlation between the number of eggs laid and their breaking strength was consistently negative in seven different groups of fowls studied by Van Wagenen, Hall, and Wilgus (1937). Because the coefficients ranged only from −.071 to −.244, any effect of productivity on thickness of shell cannot be very great. Similarly, the hens of Wilhelm (1940) which laid over 200 eggs produced thinner shells than those which laid fewer, although the difference was not significant in the numbers that he had.

Another source of variation in thickness of the shell is revealed by the extensive study of Berg (1945) showing that in cycles of 3 to 7 eggs the first and last have thicker shells than those intervening. In all these cycles, the second egg is thinner than the first; but, in cycles of 2 eggs only, the second egg is also the last egg, and it has a thicker shell than the first. These same conditions exist in the cycles of 2, 3 and 4 eggs for which Wilhelm (1940) gives shell thickness. The reason is that, regardless of the length of the cycle, the interval of time between the laying of the last egg and its predecessor is longer than the interval between any other two eggs in the cycle (Atwood, 1929, and others). Since such differences (Table 40) in the intervals between eggs result from variations in the length of time the egg is retained in the uterus, and since shell formation goes on continuously while the egg is in the uterus (Burmester *et al.*, 1939), it is not surprising that the last egg of a cycle should have a thicker shell than all those preceding it, except the first one of the cycle.

Genetic Variations in Shell Thickness. As is known to any poultryman who has compared the eggs laid by different birds in the same environment, there are great differences among hens in the thickness of their shells. These differences are more accurately revealed by measurements of the actual thickness and of the proportion of shell in the egg, such as those of Willard and Shaw (1909) and others. Variations of this sort are hereditary, and it is comparatively easy to improve the shells in thickness by selective breeding.

In just one selected generation, Taylor and Lerner (1939) differentiated two lines of White Leghorns, one laying eggs with shells comprising about 9.8 per cent of egg weight, the other, 9.14 per cent. Selection for three more generations was ineffective in raising the proportion of shell in the one line or lowering it in the other, but the original difference was maintained. While its significance might be questioned because (1) eggs of the thick-shell line were 1 to 4 gm. heavier than the others and (2) the proportion of shell increases with size of egg, the correlations in their material ranging from +.280 to +.875, this criticism does not apply to the actual measurements of thickness of shell, which were consistently lower in the thin-shell line. Hens of this last-named group were less able to maintain shell thickness in the second egg of a cycle than were the birds that produced the thicker shells.

Taking as a measure of shell quality the proportion of initial weight lost during 14 days of incubation at 99.5°F. and 60 per cent relative humidity (*i.e.*, normal conditions for incubating eggs), Quinn, Gordon, and Godfrey (1945) differentiated two lines of White Leghorns differing markedly in this respect (Fig. 94). Starting with unselected stock, the eggs from which lost 7.2 per cent, in seven generations this figure was reduced to 5.9 per cent in the line with good shells and raised to 9.5 per cent in the other. It should be emphasized that this was accomplished, not by mass selection each year of the eggs with lowest losses, but by evaluating the breeders according to the results for the families to which they belonged. With the measure of shell quality used in this experiment considerable error may be entailed if the eggs under test differ much in size.

That is because the loss in weight is dependent upon surface area of the egg, which decreases in relation to volume (or weight) of contents as the size of the egg increases. Any possible error from this source was eliminated by Quinn *et al.* in the seventh generation of their experiment by specially designed matings which reduced the difference between the lines in egg size to a negligible figure.

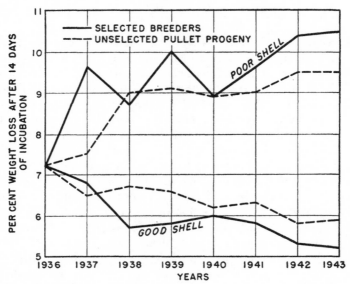

Fig. 94. The differentiation by breeding of two lines of White Leghorns that differed in quality of the shell as indicated by loss of weight during incubation. (*From Quinn et al. in Poultry Sci.*)

Whether the differences in loss of weight depend on thickness of shell, its texture, porosity, or cuticle is not yet clear, but the general value of the measure is indicated by the fact that, in the routine handling of the eggs prior to incubation, the proportion cracked in the "good-shell" line was only 1.8 per cent, in contrast with 5.9 per cent in the other one. It would seem that this is a very satisfactory and practical procedure for improving the quality of shell. It is one which any breeder doing pedigree hatching could easily use, with a minimum loss of valuable eggs.

Differences among Breeds in Shell Thickness. Evidence of various kinds from several sources showing a general tendency for the shells of White Leghorn eggs to be thicker than those of heavier breeds is summarized in Table 49.

TABLE 49. COMPARISONS INDICATING GREATER SHELL STRENGTH IN EGGS OF WHITE LEGHORNS THAN IN EGGS OF HEAVY BREEDS

Measure and source	White Leghorns	Heavy breed
Proportion of shell in fresh egg, per cent:		
Taylor and Martin (1928).............	9.13	8.66—Barred Plymouth Rocks
Morgan (1932)......................	9.72	9.31—Barred Plymouth Rocks
Weight to crush, grams:		
At side, Morgan (1932)..............	3,787	3,498—Barred Plymouth Rocks
At ends, Van Wagenen *et al.* (1937)....	4,140	3,770—Barred Plymouth Rocks
		3,950—White Plymouth Rocks
Weight lost in 24 hours, grams:		
Data of 1930, Axelsson (1932).........	0.127	0.137—Rhode Island Reds
		0.143—Barnevelders
Data of 1931, Axelsson (1932)........	0.134	0.146—Rhode Island Reds
		0.160—Barnevelders
Weight lost, 14 days incubation, per cent:		
Fertile eggs, Godfrey and Olsen (1937)..	8.82	9.40—Rhode Island Reds
Infertile eggs, Godfrey and Olsen (1937)	8.42	9.52—Rhode Island Reds

In some of these comparisons weights of the eggs were not given, and the possibility was therefore not excluded that the apparent superiority of the Leghorns might have resulted merely from a difference in size of the eggs compared. If the Leghorns laid smaller eggs than heavy breeds, the former would have the advantage if absolute loss were the measure (as in Axelsson's comparisons) but would be at a disadvantage if the loss were measured as a percentage of the initial weight (as in the eggs of Godfrey and Olsen), because small eggs have proportionately more surface (*i.e.*, more evaporation) than large ones. Some correction for this was made by Axelsson.

Altogether, the uniform superiority of the Leghorns in all these comparisons suggests that the breed does tend to produce thicker or stronger shells. On the other hand, Van Wagenen *et al.* found this to be so at one laying test (data in Table 49) but not at another. Baskett *et al.* (1937) found little differences among breeds in this respect, but their eggs came from different farms. It is to be hoped that more data on this interesting breed difference in physiology will become available. It is desirable that comparisons based on measures of the evaporation of the egg's contents be supplemented by other tests to determine whether any differences found are related to thickness of the shell, its permeability or that of the shell membranes, the number of pores, or the amount of cuticle or the color of the shell. With respect to the last of these it will be noted that the lower losses in weight shown in Table 49 for Leghorn (white) eggs than for the Rhode Island Reds and Barnevelders are contrary to various reports (see Marshall and Cruickshank, 1938) that white-shelled eggs lose more weight than brown ones when incubated or otherwise tested for porosity.

Variations in Texture of the Shell

Anyone who has "candled" eggs knows that there are great differences in the translucency, porosity, and texture of the shells (Fig. 95). Some of these variations have been examined in detail, and one of them is

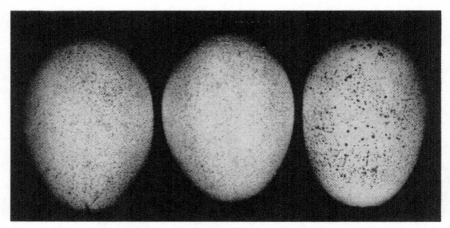

Fig. 95. Two strong, dense shells (*left*) and a weak, porous one. The differences can be seen by candling but are shown here by a dye which has worked through from the inside and revealed the larger pores of the shell on the right. (*From Snyder in Ontario Dept. Agr. Bull. 446.*)

known to be hereditary. For literature on the structure of the shell, the useful review by Stewart (1935) may be consulted.

Translucent spots in the shells are readily detected by candling but sometimes give the egg a mottled appearance even in reflected light. Experiments of Holst, Almquist, and Lorenz (1932) showed that they result from an uneven distribution of moisture in the shell. When mottled eggs with many translucent spots were dried at low temperatures, the spots disappeared and the shells assumed the appearance of normal ones; but when the eggs were immersed in water, the spots returned at their former locations. Storage of mottled eggs at low temperature and high humidity caused the number of translucent spots to increase, but in eggs held at high temperatures and low humidity the spots diminished.

The "glassy" shells studied by Almquist and Burmester (1934) differed from the mottled ones in having fewer and smaller areas of translucency. They were called glassy because when such eggs were tapped they emitted a musical clink, as does a glass vessel. Compared with normal shells, the glassy ones have fewer pores, less thickness, less

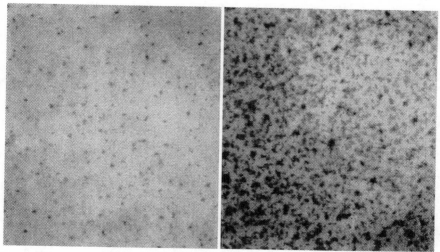

Fig. 96. Photomicrographs of a normal chalky shell (*left*) and a glossy one (*right*). Both have been stained with potassium permanganate. This has little effect on the normal shell but causes splotchy stains on the glossy one because of differences in the amount and distribution of the cuticle. (*From Taylor and Lerner in J. Heredity.*)

calcium carbonate, and a lower proportion of shell membranes, but a higher content of protein. Presumably because of their comparatively few pores, but also because these may be more completely filled with organic matter, glassy eggs deteriorate less rapidly than normal ones at high temperatures. Conversely, they do not keep so well at cold-storage temperatures as do normal eggs because of undue retention of carbon dioxide and resultant changes in the albumen. Apparently some hens produce eggs of this type consistently, while others do so only occasionally.

Glossy Shells. Quite different from glassy eggs are the glossy ones, for which a genetic origin was established by Taylor and Lerner (1941). These are characterized by a sheen on the surface that causes much greater reflection of light than one gets from the chalky surface of normal eggs. Classification can be made by the presence of "high lights" on the glossy eggs and their absence from others. When stained with potassium permanganate, the surface (*i.e.*, the cuticle) of the glossy eggs appears more splotchy than that of normal chalky eggs (Fig. 96).

This character was observed in the white eggs of Hamburgs and Leghorns. In matings within the latter breed it was shown to be hereditary and incompletely recessive to the normal chalky type of shell, but in matings of other breeds it appeared to be dominant. Although an exact genetic basis was not determined, this variation is of considerable interest because the genes involved apparently influence the cuticle, a part of the shell concerning the formation of which little is known.

Variations in Color of the Shell

The brownish pigment which in varying degrees characterizes the shells of some birds' eggs is generally considered to be an oöporphyrin or protoporphyrin derived from the hemin of the blood (Fischer and Kogl, 1923). Although certain breeds lay generally pure white eggs, this does not mean that they cannot form protoporphyrin, for after periods of non-laying some representatives (if not all birds) of such breeds lay eggs of a darker tint (Fig. 98). Moreover, even in the white eggs of White Leghorns, the shell membranes contain a pigment which Klose and Almquist (1937) found to be very much like protoporphyrin and probably identical with it. This is responsible for the pinkish cast noticeable on the inside of freshly opened white eggs.

Although it is generally assumed that the brown pigment is deposited on the shell in the uterus, Asmundson (1931) showed experimentally that its deposition may be influenced also by the isthmus. By comparing eggs expelled prematurely by hand from the uteri of anaesthetized hens with those laid normally by the same birds, Warren and Conrad (1942) concluded that half to three-quarters of the pigment is added during the last 5 hours that the egg spends in the uterus, which is about a quarter of the usual stay there. Similarly, premature turkey eggs removed up to 12 hours after shell was first detected were still pure white, and others indicated that most of the pigment, including the speckles, was put on in the next 1 to 3 hours, or close to the time of laying.

Variations in Intensity of Brown. From studies of Kopeć (1924) with Orpingtons and of Axelsson (1932) with Rhode Island Reds and Barnevelders, there emerged no consistent evidence that color of the egg is related to its length, breadth, shape or weight. While some groups seemed to show relationships of this sort, others did not.

However, Kopeć (1926) has proved by a detailed study of all eggs laid by certain hens over a period of 27 months that color of the shell changes markedly with the seasons (Fig. 98). This applies both in breeds laying usually white eggs and in those producing brown ones.

Using a standard scale with 13 different tints from white to the darkest brown of Orpington eggs, Kopeć found that the shells are darkest in the fall and early winter. The intensity declines thereafter to a low point in spring and summer, but the shells again become darker in the fall. In Leghorns, the darkest eggs were laid following periods of 2 to 3 months in the late fall or early winter when no eggs were laid. Seasonal changes similar to those demonstrated by Kopeć were also found by Axelsson (1932) and Hall (1944) with Rhode Island Reds and other fowls laying brown or tinted eggs. A darkening of Leghorn eggs toward the end of the laying year had earlier been noted by Benjamin (1920). Shells are darker in the first 10 eggs laid after a moult than in the last 10 to be laid before it (Axelsson).

Presumably the decrease in intensity of color in the spring and summer is associated with continuous production. The effect of season is probably no greater than its influence on egg production, which, in turn, is accompanied by a gradual lightening of the eggs. For 28 of 36 fowls for which Kopeć (1926a) gave data, the correlation between the numbers of eggs laid in particular periods and their intensity of color was negative. In the birds observed by Hall (1944), which began laying in October and continued through the winter, the lightening of shell color proceeded more rapidly during December and January than in the warmer months that followed. Kopeć's hens, which did not lay well during the winter, showed progressive lightening of shells in spring and summer. From this, and from Axelsson's evidence, it would seem that the seasonal changes in intensity of shell color cannot be attributed to the influence of temperature or of other meteorological conditions.

Tinted White Shells. In some markets, white eggs are preferred, while in others brown ones command a premium. Similar likes and dislikes were probably responsible for the fact that breeds developed in the Mediterranean area are characterized by the laying of white-shelled eggs, while most of those originating elsewhere lay brown ones. These preferences seem quite illogical because until very recently (see page 393) there has never been any indication that eggs of either color might excel the other in food value, provided that both are equally fresh. Nevertheless, the producer must cater to customer's whims. The Leghorn breeder meticulously discards the hens that lay eggs with the least tint or cream color and by so doing usually has little difficulty in maintaining a stock that lays chalk-white eggs. It seems probable that the Leghorn that lays tinted eggs may do so because of a mutation in one of many genes affecting shell color. Progeny testing and elimination of whole families may be necessary if many birds in the flock lay tinted eggs that cannot be accounted for merely by the periodic fluctuations in intensity of color.

Because most breeds laying brown-shelled eggs are characterized by red ear lobes, there is a common idea that Leghorns with a little red in the lobes are more likely to lay tinted eggs than those without. The fallacy of this belief has been shown by Warren (1928), who could find no relation between the two variables in crossbred chickens with earlobes ranging from red to white. These results were later confirmed by Axelsson (1932).

Genetic Basis for Shades of Brown. It is well known that when white-egg breeds are crossed with brown-egg breeds the F_1 generation lays eggs of various shades but in general intermediate between the two parental types. This indication that shell color is determined by multiple factors was confirmed by Punnett and Bailey (1920; reviewed by Punnett, 1923), who found that the variability in the F_2 generation was greater than that in the F_1 but that the results varied considerably in different crosses. In one of these, a bimodal distribution in the F_2 suggested the action of a gene with major effects. In the F_2 from Hamburg $\times$ Langshan, the mean color was near that of the F_1, and this applied also to the cross Leghorn $\male$ $\times$ Langshan $\female$. However, in the reciprocal mating Langshan $\male$ $\times$ Leghorn $\female$, the F_1 generation laid lighter eggs than those of the other crosses, and the F_2 did the same. This suggested that the Brown Leghorn females used might carry an inhibitor of brown-shell pigment.

These results are of special interest because they differ from those obtained with other breeds. In the F_1 generations from reciprocal crosses between White Leghorns and Orpingtons, Kopeć (1926a) found that daughters of the Leghorn sire laid paler eggs than daughters of the Orpington sire and concluded therefrom that "it is the breed of the male and not that of the female which decides the intensity of color in eggs of the first generation." This rule of patroclinous inheritance has since been confirmed in crosses of Leghorns with Rhode Island Reds by Axelsson (1932) and by Hall (1944). Axelsson found it to apply also when Barnevelders are crossed with Leghorns or with Rhode Island Reds. The obvious inference is that among the genes influencing shell color some are located in the sex chromosome.

There are considerable differences among the brown-shell breeds in the intensity of the color. Eggs of White Wyandottes are not so dark as those of Rhode Island Reds, but these, in turn, are almost pale in comparison with the dark brown eggs of Barnevelders and Welsummers. The results of Kopeć (1922) with Polish Greenlegs (which lay a cream-colored egg) and of Axelsson with Rhode Island Reds and Barnevelders show that, when a brown-shell breed is crossed with a white-shell one, the mean for the F_1 population is paler than the mid-point between the two parental breeds. In other words, white shell tends to be dominant.

In contrast, when Rhode Island Reds are crossed with Barnevelders, the F_1 and F_2 lay eggs almost as dark as those of Barnevelders, thus making dark brown predominant over the modest shade of the Reds. Axelsson's

Fig. 97. Stefan Kopeć. Eminent Polish biologist, whose career was unhappily terminated during the occupation of his country. (*Courtesy of Dr. Laura Kaufman.*)

TABLE 50. MEAN GRADES OF SHELL COLOR IN THREE CROSSES SHOWING DIFFERENCSE IN THE APPARENT DOMINANCE OF WHITE OR BROWN *

(Intensity of brown increases with the numerical grade)

Population	White Leghorns × Rhode Island Reds	White Leghorns × Barne- velders	Rhode Island Reds × Barne- velders
Mid-point between parental means.....	3.88	5.24	8.78
Mean for F_1 generation..............	2.90	3.63	10.18
Mean for F_2 generation..............	2.54	4.96	11.59

* From Axelsson (1932).

data given in Table 50 show this nicely for crosses involving White Leghorns, Rhode Island Reds, and Barnevelders. These breeds had mean color grades on his scale of 0.36, 7.40, and 10.11, respectively.

These results suggest that when trying to get darker shells one might well introduce some genes from these Dutch breeds, which not only lay very dark eggs themselves but are able to transmit the quality to their offspring. Presumably this indicates a great deal of selection for dark eggs when these breeds were being formed. However, if the producer of brown-shelled eggs does not wish to cross his breed with any other, he can still make considerable improvement by selection. In a series of four matings in each of which light-shell dams and dark-shell dams were mated to the same sire, Axelsson showed that, regardless of the influence of the sire, the dams laying the darker eggs produced daughters that laid darker eggs than did those from the light-shell dams (Table 51).

TABLE 51. MEAN GRADES OF SHELL COLOR FOR DAMS AND DAUGHTERS SHOWING THE INFLUENCE OF THE DAM'S SHELL COLOR ON THAT OF HER DAUGHTERS REGARDLESS OF THE INFLUENCE OF THE SIRE *

(Intensity of brown increases with the numerical grade)

	Dams with light shells	Their daughters	Dams with dark shells	Their daughters
White Leghorn ♂ × Rhode Island Red ♀ ♀	6.49	2.06	9.12	2.66
White Leghorn ♂ × Barnevelder ♀ ♀	6.60	2.60	11.12	4.05
Barnevelder ♂ × Rhode Island Red ♀ ♀	5.62	9.70	9.59	11.98
Rhode Island Red ♂ × Barnevelder ♀ ♀	8.22	9.00	10.30	10.20

* From Axelsson (1932).

Tests for Xenia. An immediate effect of the male gametes upon some cytoplasmic character of the fertilized egg is called "xenia." Although it is a normal event in maize, its occurrence in animals is doubtful. However, there are reports in the literature that hens laying white eggs produced darker ones after being mated with cocks of brown-shell breeds and, conversely, that hens laying brown-shelled eggs produced paler ones when mated with males of white-shell breeds. These supposed cases of xenia were reviewed by Kopeć (1926), who tested the matter in carefully controlled experiments. Neither when White Leghorn hens were mated with Buff Orpingtons nor in the reciprocal cross could he find any change in color of the eggs, except the variations at different seasons of the year, and those affected eggs of the unmated control hens as well as those of the mated birds (Fig. 98). In addition to these two groups, some Leghorn hens were injected six times with ground-up testes of Orpingtons, and vice versa, but no change in color of shell resulted that was not found also in controls. This was done

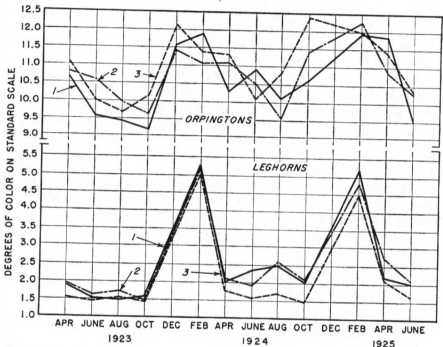

Fig. 98. Changes in the intensity of shell color over 27 months and absence of xenia. The points shown give the mean colors for bimonthly periods and mid-points of those periods. 1, eggs of hens without males; 2, eggs of hens of breed given but mated with males of the other breed; 3, eggs of hens injected with testicles of the other breed. (*From Kopeć in J. Genetics.*)

in May and June of 1923, which, as Fig. 98 shows, was a period when the brown eggs were normally becoming lighter. Had there been no controls this might have been attributed to xenia.

Kopeć's studies permitted him to show the unreliability of the previous reports. He concluded that xenia does not occur and that claims to the contrary had arisen from failure to recognize that there is a normal periodical variation in shell color. This has been confirmed by Axelsson (1932), who mated various kinds of brown-shell females with Leghorn males and found no differences in shell color before, during, or after the breeding season that were inconsistent with the seasonal changes.

Blue Eggs; *O*. In South and Central America there are fowls that lay eggs of various shades of blue or green. Some of these have been called Araucanas after a district in Chile from which they have been taken to Europe and to North America. They have been tested genetically by Punnett (1933), who found that blue is an autosomal dominant mutation which segregates sharply from white shell, without any doubtful intergrades. This is the only simple mutation affecting the egg that has been demonstrated thus far. The symbol *O* has been used to designate it. The gene is closely linked with the one for pea comb.

An interesting point brought out by Punnett's studies is that, when the blue mutation is combined with genes for brown shells, the result is olive or green depending on the intensity of brown. He showed also that the polychromatism normally found in eggs of the ring-necked pheasant and its geographic races could probably be accounted for by brown and blue, or lack of the latter, in combinations similar to the series that he had demonstrated in the fowl.

While brown pigment is deposited mostly if not entirely on the outer surface of the shell, the blue pervades the whole shell structure and shows on the inner surface of the shell an intensity of color little different, if any, from that on the outside. The exact chemical nature of the blue pigment is not yet clear, but Dr. Rudolf Lemberg, who analyzed some of the eggs at Punnett's request, considered that it was not identical with the oöcyan found in shells of some other birds but was more probably a "banded oöcyan."

VARIATIONS IN THE ALBUMEN AND YOLK

Proportion of Firm Albumen. The white of newly laid egg includes the following four layers of albumen: (1) the chalazae, or whitish twisted strands of dense albumen, continuous with a thin layer of the same material surrounding the yolk; (2) a small amount of thin albumen, inside (3) a layer of firm albumen standing up around the yolk when the egg is opened into a dish; and (4) an outer layer of rather watery, or "thin," albumen. If the second of these layers is really derived from the third, as some investigators think, the number of original layers should be reduced to three.

Eggs with a high proportion of firm albumen are preferred in the market because they look better when broken out and are better for poaching than eggs with "watery whites." The latter are commonly associated with undesirable changes in the yolk whereby it accumulates an excessive amount of water, with consequent weakening of the vitelline membrane and greater chance of the yolk's rupturing when the egg is broken out of the shell. Most eggs do not have excessively watery whites when laid, but they deteriorate if held in unsatisfactory conditions because of liquefaction of the firm albumen. There is some indication that eggs with an initially high proportion of firm albumen are less subject to such deterioration. For all these reasons it is desirable that newly laid eggs have a high proportion of firm albumen.

It was shown by Holst and Almquist (1931) that hens differ greatly in the ability to produce eggs of this desirable type. In 150 eggs the proportion of firm albumen varied from 45 to 90 per cent (of the total albumen), the average being 62 per cent. The proportion is remarkably constant in the eggs of any one hen. For example, one of their birds laid eggs with 47 to 49 per cent, another with 62 to 65 per cent, and one with 75 to 82 per cent firm albumen. By selective breeding, Lorenz *et al.* (1934) and Lorenz and Taylor (1940) differentiated (in some breed not stated) two lines that differed consistently in this respect. Their results are shown graphically in Fig. 99. The improvement in their "high-line" birds of 1932, when compared with the unselected stock of 1931, cannot be attributed entirely to one generation of selection, since the breeding birds of that year were evaluated from family records for several years previously. The significant thing is that over a period of 5 years a remarkable difference was maintained between the lines with respect to the proportion of firm albumen in their eggs. As the illustration shows, crosses between the two lines yielded F_1 generations intermediate between the parents. Backcrosses of these F_1 birds produced progeny intermediate between the F_1 and the particular parental strain involved. These studies show that the proportion of firm albumen is an inherited character, apparently influenced by multiple genes. A somewhat similar differentiation of strains was made by Knox and Godfrey (1940) in Rhode Island Reds.

Thus far no one breed has proved superior to others in this respect. Van Wagenen *et al.* (1937), who examined adequate samples of White Leghorns, Barred and White Plymouth Rocks, Rhode Island Reds, and New Hampshires at two laying tests, were unable to find any significant differences between them in the proportion that the firm albumen comprised of the whole. The mean figure for 1,273 birds was 64.5 per cent. According to Knox and Godfrey (1934, 1938) the character is not influenced by the number of eggs laid, nor is it related to the size of egg. This last was confirmed by Lorenz and Almquist (1936).

Apart from the genetic constitution of the hen that lays the egg, the only thing thus far shown to affect the proportion of firm albumen is the season of the year. Knox and Godfrey (1938) found that in eggs from pullets the proportion declined steadily from a high point in October and

November to a low one in June and then rose slightly from July to October. A similar seasonal change in "interior egg quality" as measured by various other criteria had been noted earlier by Hunter *et al.* (1936). Lorenz and Almquist (1936) showed experimentally that the proportion of firm white decreased rapidly when fresh eggs were held

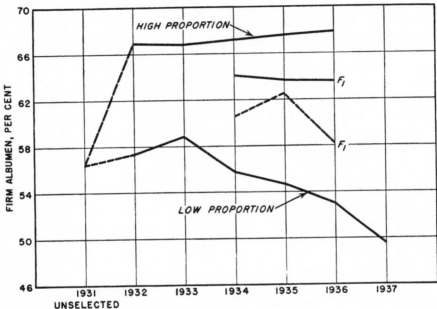

Fig. 99. The differentiation and maintenance by breeding of two lines differing in the proportion of firm albumen in their eggs, and the record for F_1 generations from crosses of the two lines. The broken line is for the F_1 from high ♀ × low ♂; the other is from the reciprocal cross. (*From data of Lorenz and Taylor.*)

for 24 hours at 86°F. and suggested that the apparent seasonal influence is really attributable to hot weather. This may be so in part, but it still leaves unsolved the question why the proportion of firm albumen in the eggs studied by Knox and Godfrey was slightly higher during the hot months of July and August than during the comparatively cool months of May and June and why it declined steadily from November to May. Another interesting and still unexplained point in their data is that the proportion of firm albumen was consistently higher in the eggs of older hens than in those of pullets. The seasonal changes were much the same in both groups.

Anatomical and Physiological Basis. Considerably more is known about the nature of the cellular activities responsible for differing proportions of firm albumen than is the case with other physiological genetic characters. It was first noted by Surface (1912) that epithelium of the albumen-secreting portion of the oviduct is characterized by the presence of non-ciliated unicellular glands (later called "goblet cells"), which seemed to be secreting something different from the product of the ciliated cells. These goblet cells he found in all regions of the oviduct, but nowhere were they so large or so active as in the albumen tube. This was confirmed and extended by Bradley (1928), who determined from its staining reactions that the material secreted by the goblet cells is mucin. These cells he found to be the largest and most numerous in the posterior part of the albumen-secreting region, near its junction with the isthmus. Here the goblet cells are so full of secretion that their nuclei are crowded by it to the ends of the cells.

Resection of a portion of the oviduct in this region causes a marked reduction in the amount and proportion of firm albumen in eggs laid subsequently (Asmundson and Burmester, 1936), whereas removal of a similar portion from the middle of the albumen tube has less effect, and from the anterior portion none at all, so far as the firm albumen is concerned. Obviously the posterior end of the albumen tube, which Bradley described as being practically a continuous mucin-secreting surface, is the region in which the firm albumen is produced. It is not surprising, therefore, that McNally (1933) should find the amount of mucin in firm albumen to be about nine times as great as in thin albumen. Finally, Cole (1938) showed histologically that firm albumen of good consistency contains many closely packed fibres of mucin and that hens producing eggs with such albumen have bigger goblet cells in the albumen tube than have hens laying eggs with less firm albumen.

His measurements showed the average height of these cells to increase from about 11 microns at the anterior end of the albumen tube to a maximum of about 34 microns at the junction of that tube with the isthmus. This agrees well with Bradley's findings. Cole demonstrated also (Fig. 100) a direct continuity between the mucin in the goblet cells and the mucin fibre formed in a fold, or crypt, of the oviduct by the contributions from many such cells.

From all these studies it would seem that the genes causing the formation of eggs with a high proportion of firm albumen do so by inducing a maximum secretion of mucin by the goblet cells in the distal portion of the albumen-secreting section of the oviduct. This may also be the basis for variations in the "score of the condition of the firm albumen" studied by Van Wagenen and Hall (1936), which appear to be related to the consistency of the firm albumen rather than to its proportionate amount. The high correlations between daughters and dams in this respect indicate that these variations have a genetic basis. Cole's studies of eggs differing in "condition" suggest that the physiological basis for such differences may be the same as for differences in the proportion of firm albumen.

Variations in the Yolk. Although the eggs laid by different hens may vary considerably in the relative weight of the yolk (Curtis, 1914), little evidence has been adduced to show that any of that variation is

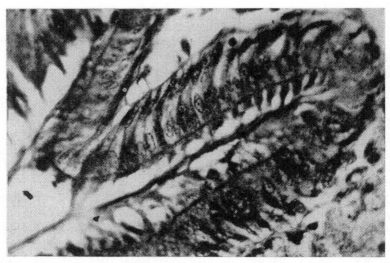

Fig. 100. Photomicrograph of a section through a crypt in the albumen-secreting region of the oviduct, showing the derivation of the mucin fibre in the lumen of the crypt from the adjacent goblet cells. ×440. (*From Cole in Anat. Record.*)

hereditary. Such evidence will be difficult to get because, as has been shown in the earlier part of this chapter, many things affect egg size (and hence size of yolk), some of which influence the yolk more than other parts of the egg. Kaufman and Baczkowska (1938) present some evidence that in eggs of Polish Greenleg fowls the proportion of yolk is lower than in those of White Leghorns and Rhode Island Reds, but one might question, as in any such comparison, whether or not the samples were adequate to represent the breeds compared.

Among hens receiving the same diet there can be marked differences in the color of the yolk (Parker *et al.*, 1926, and others), but it has not yet been proved that such differences are genetic in origin. Kaufman and Baczkowska (1938a) had some evidence that breeds may differ in yolk color when the birds have access to an abundance of green feed. Most of the variation commonly seen in yolk color is apparently attributable to differences in the diet. The yolks may be made colorless by diets lacking carotinoid pigments, differing shades of yellow and orange by different kinds of green feed, bronzed or olive by acorns, by rape and some other plants of the family Cruciferae, or reddish in color by the pigments of pimiento peppers. Dyes taken up by fats, such as Sudan III, are deposited in the yolk. That its color may be influenced by carotinoids from animals as well as by those from plants was shown by Vecchi (1935), who induced the formation of dark yellow and orange yolks by feeding various crustaceans.

From the fact that yellow pigments fade from the shanks, beak, and skin of laying birds, one might expect the yolks to get paler in color as more eggs are laid. According to Radeff (1935) this is not the case. Among 10 hens the average amount of carotinoid pigment in the yolks of several eggs varied from 4.8 to 8.9 mg. per 100 mg. yolk, but it was not related to the antecedent egg production of the hen. This applied to birds getting a diet apparently rich in carotinoid pigments. Eggs laid after a pause contained more pigment than those preceding it.

VARIATIONS IN THE CHEMICAL COMPOSITION

It is now well known that the amounts of various chemical entities in eggs may be greatly increased or decreased by feeding diets high or low in those substances or in their precursors. Iodine and vitamin A are good examples. With respect to vitamin D, the amount of it in eggs may be influenced by the diet, by the amount of available ultra-violet light, or by both together. However, there are at least two cases on record which show that the amount of a substance in the egg can be influenced by the genetic constitution of the hen that lays it, apart entirely from any effect of the diet.

"Fishy" Eggs. Vondell (1932) gives a brief account of eggs with a distinctly bad flavor and odor which he called "fishy" eggs. These were produced only by Rhode Island Reds. Among 150 White Leghorns and 150 Barred Rocks on the same diet as that of the Reds, not a single one was found to lay the peculiar eggs, although all were tested periodically. Studies of 26 Rhode Island Reds that produced fishy eggs showed that some did so continuously, others intermittently and with varying intensities of odor. In another flock of 700 Rhode Island Reds, 24 were found to lay fishy eggs, and the pedigrees of these birds showed a familial basis for the peculiarity. Unfortunately the study was not continued. While the exact nature of the substance responsible for the bad taste and smell is unknown, the condition obviously indicates an abnormal metabolism that leaves in the egg some end product not normally found there. The author has heard reports of this same abnormality in other flocks of Rhode Island Reds, in one of which the prevalence of it was so high as to affect seriously the sale of the eggs. Further studies of the condition are desirable.

Thiamine Content. Another genetic variation in chemical composition of the egg results from the fact that White Leghorns are apparently able to utilize the thiamine (vitamin B_1) in their diet more efficiently than Rhode Island Reds and Barred Rocks. At any rate, as Scrimshaw, Hutt, and Scrimshaw (1945) have shown, when all three breeds are getting exactly the same feed, the Leghorns put 60 to 66 per cent more thiamine in their eggs than do the heavy breeds (Table 52).

TABLE 52. SHOWING THAT EGGS OF WHITE LEGHORNS CONTAIN MORE THIAMINE THAN THOSE OF TWO OTHER BREEDS

Breed	Hens, number	Thiamine, micrograms		
		Mean per egg	Per 100 gm. yolk	
			Mean	Range
White Leghorns..........	23	49.0 ± 5.9	279	214–360
Rhode Island Reds.......	11	34.3 ± 6.3	167	125–187
Barred Plymouth Rocks..	11	33.4 ± 6.4	175	127–235

Since all the thiamine is in the yolk, the amount of it per 100 gm. of yolk is probably the best basis for comparison, as it removes variations that might be caused by yolks of different sizes. It is worth noting that only 1 egg of the 22 assayed from the two heavy breeds had a thiamine content higher than 200 micrograms per 100 gm. of yolk, while in the Leghorn eggs none was lower than 214. The differences shown in Table 52 between the Leghorns and the other breeds are all highly significant.

This can hardly be attributed to differences in food consumption, as the Leghorns are known to eat less than the heavy breeds. It seems more likely that this difference in utilization of thiamine is another manifestation of fundamental differences in metabolism which are responsible for several important differences between Leghorns and heavy breeds in physiological characters (Hutt, 1941). Since these variations in function are characteristics of the breed, even though not deliberately incorporated when the breeds were being formed, they are genetic variations just the same as the more obvious deviations of form and color by which the breeds were differentiated.

It is probably a coincidence that the Leghorn eggs should have white shells and the most thiamine, while Barred Rocks and Rhode Island Reds lay eggs with brown shells and less thiamine. However, if further studies should show a constant relationship between color of shell and content of thiamine, that would be, so far as the author is aware, the first evidence that there might be any justification from the standpoint of food value for preferring white eggs to brown ones, as some consumers and markets seem to do.

ABNORMAL EGGS

The literature on biology, ornithology, and poultry contains almost innumerable reports of abnormal eggs of various kinds. Since none of these has been shown to have a genetic basis except the blood spots considered later, it is impossible within the scope of this book to give any more than a brief discussion of the chief types of abnormalities. For reviews of the literature up to 1860, the monographs of Davaine and of Panum, both published in that year, are useful. The recent review by Romanoff and Romanoff (1949) should also be consulted.

Double- and Triple-yolked Eggs. Double-yolked eggs are common, particularly among the first eggs laid by pullets. Some hens seem to lay more of them than others, but none does so continuously. Curtis (1914a) found that only about 20 per cent of the flock produce them, the remainder never doing so. In 87 per cent of her double-yolked eggs, the two yolks had a common envelope of thick albumen, thus indicating that they had traversed the albumen-secreting region of the oviduct close together. This is quite consistent with the later conclusion of Conrad and Warren (1940) that 90 per cent of these double-yolkers result from the simultaneous ovulation of two ova (Fig. 101). In 65 per cent the two yolks were believed to have developed to full size together, but for 25 per cent it was calculated that one of the two had been released a day earlier than it should have been in the normal sequence of maturing ova. In 13 per cent of double-yolked eggs Curtis (1915) found each yolk to have its own separate envelope of thick albumen, although both had common shell membranes and shell. These may correspond to the 10 per cent which Conrad and Warren attributed in part to the oviduct's picking up, along with some freshly ovulated ovum, another which had been released a day earlier but had lain in the body cavity.

Triple-yolked eggs are much scarcer. Curtis (1914a) found only three during 6 years, among the eggs from about 3,000 hens altogether. As she and her associates were studying abnormal eggs, it is unlikely that any were overlooked.

The study by Pearl (1910) of eggs with 0, 1, 2, or 3 yolks showed

FIG. 101. Photograph of an ovary taken 3 hours after the simultaneous release of ova from the two lower follicles. A double-yolked egg was found in the isthmus of the oviduct. A whitish follicle that had discharged its ovum on the previous day is seen above the lower two. The apparent pairing with respect to size of the four largest ova remaining suggests that the hen might have laid more double-yolked eggs. (*From Conrad and Warren in Poultry Sci.*)

that the relation between the number of yolks and weight of the egg is described by a parabola. In other words, the double-yolked eggs are less than twice the weight of normal eggs, and eggs with 3 yolks are not 50 per cent heavier than eggs with 2.

Dwarf Eggs. Down through the ages the diminutive eggs occasionally laid by hens have given rise to many peculiar superstitions and beliefs, some of which still persist. Variously called "wind eggs," "cock's eggs," and other names indicating a lack of knowledge about them, they have been supposed to be laid by cocks and to hatch a deadly serpent, the basilisk or cockatrice.

The mystery surrounding such eggs was dispelled by Pearl and

Curtis (1916), who made a detailed study of 298 of them. The ratio of dwarf eggs to normal ones was 1:1,158, and about 5 per cent of the females laid at least 1. Contrary to popular belief, a dwarf egg does not mark the end of a period of laying, and such an egg may come at any time during a cycle of eggs on successive days. About 65 per cent contained yolk, and the rest did not. A clue to their origin is given by the fact that 55 per cent of these dwarf eggs contained free yolk not enclosed in a vitelline membrane, and only 10 per cent had yolks so enclosed. Pearl and Curtis concluded that such eggs often result (65 per cent) from the stimulus to secretion of albumen provided by bits of yolk but that something other than yolk might have the same effect. They considered that yolks broken before or after ovulation, in the body cavity or in the oviduct, provided the stimulating fragment, a conclusion in which Asmundson (1931) concurred.

These investigators concluded that dwarf eggs are produced only when the ovary is in fully active condition. While this may be true for such eggs that contain yolk, it is not necessarily so for dwarf eggs lacking yolk. This was shown by the remarkable hen studied by Benoit and Courrier (1933), which laid 50 dwarf eggs and no normal ones at all. At autopsy the left ovary was atrophic; the right one contained only immature follicles, and the oviduct was only partially developed. Stimulus to the secretion of albumen was apparently provided in this case by a small aggregation of spermatozoa, no bigger than the head of a pin, which was found regularly in the dwarf eggs.

Such cases are very unusual. Of 200 birds that laid dwarf eggs for Pearl and Curtis, only 3.5 per cent did so more than once, and the highest number for any one hen was 17.

Eggs Enclosed in Others. The various kinds of double eggs were conveniently classified by Curtis (1916) in two main groups: (1) double eggs in which the enclosing one is complete, with a yolk as well as the enclosed egg; and (2) those in which the enclosing egg lacks a yolk but is otherwise complete. Each of these classes may again be subdivided according to whether the enclosed egg is (a) complete with shell and yolk or (b) a dwarf egg. It is now generally agreed that such eggs are caused, as Davaine (1860) suggested, by return of the enclosed egg from the uterus to the albumen tube, either by antiperistalsis or otherwise, and its subsequent return to the uterus, sometimes with a yolk, but always with additional albumen and membranes, to acquire a new shell and be laid as a double egg.

The evidence for this interpretation and against the contrary opinions of some writers on the subject is reviewed by Asmundson (1933) and by Romanoff and Hutt (1945). These last found, in 10 such double eggs laid by one hen, that the enclosed egg was larger than eggs laid singly by the same bird and had thicker shells. From this and other evidence they concluded that the enclosed egg had been retained unduly long in the uterus and that its return to the albumen tube had been caused by the excitation of the oviduct following the engulfing of the succeeding ovum. These double eggs weighed 170 to 193 gm. each (Fig. 102).

Fig. 102. A double egg containing a normal yolk and another egg complete with shell. One hen laid 10 eggs like this one. (*From Romanoff and Hutt in Anat. Record.*)

Among the most remarkable eggs on record for the domestic fowl are the 8-ounce ones (227 gm.) reported by Brown (1939) from a Rhode Island Red in Scotland. These contained not only a complete, shelled egg but two free yolks as well.

Intrafollicular Ova and Ovarian Fragments. The range of variations in eggs includes not only eggs containing no yolks but also those containing yolks and little else. These last are apparently rare, but occasionally a follicle containing an ovum is torn, unruptured, from the ovary and carried down the oviduct. It may be laid before acquiring membranes and shell (Hutt, 1939). It may be included with a normal yolk in an egg (Hutt, 1946), in which case the stalk of the follicle protrudes through the large end and prevents formation of shell in that area. Sometimes, as in the case reported by Parker and Kempster (1940), a piece of the ovary is torn loose and partially enclosed in an egg. Cole (1946) found an egg containing a large intrafollicular ovum with three small ova attached to its stalk.

Inclusions within Eggs. The voluminous literature on abnormal eggs includes reports of eggs that contained peculiar bodies ranging from intestinal parasites to grass. The intestinal parasite *Ascaridia lineata*, is occasionally found within the egg or in the shell, but the trematode *Prosthogonimus* is somewhat more common.

Blood Spots and Meat Spots. Clots or streaks of blood and little flesh-like masses referred to by the poultry world as "meat spots" are common in eggs. Because consumers are squeamish about such things, it is the established practice to "candle" eggs before marketing them so that those containing these undesirable inclusions can be eliminated. Since the proportion of eggs in which blood clots and meat spots are recognizable by candling is of the order of 2 to 5 per cent, they cause considerable economic loss. Nor is the candling fully effective, for many of these inclusions escape detection, especially in brown-shelled eggs.

Following the discovery by Burmester and Card (1938) that the so-called meat spots are really degenerated blood clots, various studies have extended somewhat our knowledge of these undesirable defects. Blood clots result from haemorrhage in the follicle at some time prior to ovulation. Nalbandov and Card (1943) found that their transformation to what the trade calls meat spots is rapid and that blood spots in new-laid eggs indicate haemorrhages within 2 days before ovulation. Their frequency declined rapidly when confined hens were turned out of doors on free range, but the reason for this is not yet known. Attempts to lessen the incidence of blood spots by feeding vitamins A, C, D, E, K, and P were unsuccessful. The common belief that blood spots result from the hen's being frightened was disproved experimentally by Jeffrey and Pino (1943).

Evidence of a genetic basis for these inclusions was provided by Van Wagenen, Hall, and Wilgus (1937), who opened the eggs of 1,273 hens at two laying tests and found the frequency of meat spots to be about 10 per cent in eggs of White Leghorns but approximately four times as great in those of Plymouth Rocks, Rhode Island Reds, and New Hampshires. An even greater difference between Leghorns and heavy breeds was observed by Jeffrey (1945). It is curious that both studies should reveal such a marked breed difference in meat spots but little or none in blood spots. The frequency of these was about 8 to 9 per cent at the laying tests and 3 to 7 per cent in Jeffrey's birds. If blood spots represent recent haemorrhages, and meat spots earlier ones, it is difficult to see why the latter class should be so much more frequent in the heavy breeds, but not the former one.

Most investigators have found that certain hens produce more of these abnormalities than others. Some evidence has been adduced that sires may differ in the propensities of their daughters for laying eggs with such inclusions, but genetic investigations have not yet gone very far.

Literature Cited

Almquist, H. J., and B. R. Burmester. 1934. Characteristics of an abnormal type of egg shell. *Poultry Sci.*, **13**:116–122.

Asmundson, V. S. 1921. The relation of the keel bone to egg production. *Sci. Agr.*, **1**:30–33, 63–67.

———. 1931. The formation of the hen's egg. *Sci. Agr.*, **11**:590–606, 662–680, 775–778.

———. 1931a. Effect of hormones on the formation of the hen's egg. *Poultry Sci.*, **10**:157–165.

———. 1933. The formation of eggs within eggs. *Zool. Anz.*, **104**:209–217.

———. 1939. The formation of the egg in the oviduct of the turkey (*Meleagris gallopavo*). *J. Exptl. Zoöl.*, **82**:287–304.

——— and B. R. Burmester. 1936. The secretory activity of the parts of the hen's oviduct. *J. Exptl. Zoöl.*, **72**:225–246.

——— and J. G. Jervis. 1933. The effect of resection of different parts of the oviduct on the formation of the hen's egg. *J. Exptl. Zoöl.*, **65**:395–420.

——— and P. Pinsky. 1935. The effect of the thyroid on the formation of the hen's egg. *Poultry Sci.*, **14**:99–104.

Atwood, H. 1922. A hen with two ovaries? *Poultry Sci.*, **2**:59–61.

———. 1923. Certain correlations in the weight and number of eggs and the weight of fowls. *West Virginia Agr. Expt. Sta. Bull.*, **182**:1–16.

———. 1926. Some factors affecting the weight of eggs. *West Virginia Agr. Expt. Sta. Bull.*, **201**:1–30.

———. 1927. The weight of eggs in connection with the time of day when they are laid. *Poultry Sci.*, **6**:108–109.

———. 1929. A study of the time factor in egg production. *West Virginia Agr. Expt. Sta. Bull.*, **233**:1–11.

——— and T. Clark. 1929. Further studies on factors influencing the weight of eggs. *Poultry Sci.*, **8**:193–197.

——— and ———. 1930. The relationship between the number and weight of eggs and body weight of Leghorn fowls during the first three years of production. *West Virginia Agr. Expt. Sta. Bull.*, **233**:1–20.

Axelsson, J. 1932. Variation and heredity of some characters in White Leghorns, Rhode Island Reds and Barnevelders. I. *Lunds Univ. Arsskrift. N.F. Avd 2.*, **28**:1–196.

———. 1934. Continued research upon variation and heredity of some characters in White Leghorns, Rhode Island Reds and Barnevelders. *Lantbruks-Högskol. Ann. (Uppsala)*, **1**:69–207.

———. 1938. Variation und Erblichkeit der Form der Hühnereier. *Züchtungskunde*, **13**:414–428.

Baskett, R. G., W. H. Dryden, and R. W. Hale. 1937. Investigations on the shell strength of hen eggs. *J. Ministry Agr. Northern Ireland,* **5**:132–142.

Benesch, R., N. S. Barron, and C. A. Mawson. 1944. Carbonic anhydrase, sulphonamides and shell formation in the domestic fowl. *Nature,* **153**:138–139.

Benjamin, E. W. 1920. A study of selections for the size, shape, and color of hens' eggs. *Cornell Univ. Agr. Expt. Sta. Mem.,* **31**:191–312.

Bennion, N. L., and D. C. Warren. 1933. Temperature and its effect on egg size in the domestic fowl. *Poultry Sci.,* **12**:69–82.

—— and ——. 1933a. Some factors affecting egg size in the domestic fowl. *Poultry Sci.,* **12**:362–367.

Benoit, J., and R. Courrier. 1933. Sur le cas d'une poule de race bédouine, qui pondit exclusivement des oeufs nains, privés de jaune. *Compt. rend. soc. biol.,* **114**:1335–1337.

Berg, L. R. 1945. The relationship of clutch position and time interval between eggs to eggshell quality. *Poultry Sci.,* **24**:555–563.

Bradley, O. C. 1928. Notes on the histology of the oviduct of the domestic hen. *J. Anat.,* **62**:339–345.

Brown, J. M. 1939. Scotland claims a world egg record. *Farmer and Stock-Breeder,* **53**:746.

Burmester, B. R., and L. E. Card. 1938. On the nature of "meat spots" in eggs. *Poultry Sci.,* **17**:235–239.

——, H. M. Scott, and L. E. Card. 1939. Rate of egg-shell formation in the hen. *Proc. World's Poultry Congr. 7th Congr., Cleveland:* 99–101.

Clark, T. B. 1940. The relation of production and egg weight to age in White Leghorn fowls. *Poultry Sci.,* **19**:61–66.

Cole, R. K. 1938. Histology of the oviduct of the fowl in relation to variations in the condition of the firm albumen. *Anat. Record,* **71**:349–361.

——. 1946. Stimulation of the avian oviduct by an ovarian fragment. *Poultry Sci.,* **25**:472–475.

Common, R. H. 1941. The carbonic anhydrase activity of the hen's oviduct. *J. Agr. Sci.,* **31**:412–414.

Conrad, R. M. 1939. The effect of high temperature on the blood calcium of the laying hen. *Poultry Sci.,* **18**:327–329.

—— and D. C. Warren. 1940. The production of double yolked eggs in the fowl. *Poultry Sci.,* **19**:9–17.

Cruickshank, E. M. 1929. Observations on the iodine content of the thyroid and ovary of the fowl during the growth, laying, and moulting periods. *Biochem. J.,* **23**:1044–1049.

Curtis, M. R. 1914. A biometrical study of egg production in the domestic fowl. IV. Factors influencing the size, shape and physical constitution of eggs. *Arch. Entwicklungsmech. Organ.,* **39**:217–327.

——. 1914a. Studies on the physiology of reproduction in the domestic fowl. VI. Double- and triple-yolked eggs. *Biol. Bull.,* **26**:55–83.

——. 1915. Relation of simultaneous ovulation to the production of double yolked eggs. *J. Agr. Research,* **3**:375–386.

——. 1916. Studies on the physiology of reproduction in the domestic fowl. XVI. Double eggs. *Biol. Bull.,* **31**:181–213.

Davaine, C. 1860. Mémoire sur les anomalies de l'oeuf. *Compt. rend. mém. soc. biol. Paris* (ser. 3), **2**:183–269.

Dudley, F. J. 1931. Short period trapnesting as a means of estimating annual egg production and average annual egg weight. *Harper Adams Util. Poultry J.,* **16**:557–562.

Féré, C. 1898. Note sur le poids de l'oeuf de poule et sur ses variations dans les pontes successives. *J. anat. physiol. norm. pathol.,* **34**:123–127.

Fischer, H., and F. Kogl. 1923. Zur Kenntnis der natürlichen Porphyrine. IV. Über das Ooporphyrin. *Z. physiol. Chem.,* **131**:241–261.

Funk, E. M. 1935. Relation of body weight and egg weight in the domestic fowl. *Poultry Sci.,* **14**:232–236.

———. 1937. The size and shape of turkey eggs. *Poultry Sci.,* **16**:398–399.

——— and H. L. Kempster. 1934. Egg weight in the domestic fowl. *Missouri Agr. Expt. Sta. Bull.,* **332**:1–15.

Galpin, N. 1937–1938. Factors affecting the hatching weight of Brown Leghorn chickens. *Proc. Roy. Soc. Edinburgh,* **58** (pt. 2): 98–113.

Genest, P., and R. Bernard. 1945. Étude de l'action des sulfamides sur la formation de la coquille de l'oeuf chez la poule. *Rev. can. biol.,* **4**:172–192.

Godfrey, A. B. 1933. Methods of estimating the mean egg weight per bird for the first year production. *Poultry Sci.,* **12**:368–372.

——— and M. W. Olsen. 1937. Individual hen and breed difference in egg weight losses during incubation. *Poultry Sci.,* **16**:216–218.

[Goodale, H. D.] 1935–1936. "Early Egg Size." Williamstown, Mass.: Mount Hope Farm.

Graham, W. R. 1932. Some factors affecting the weight of egg in domestic fowl. *Sci. Agr.,* **12**:427–446.

Grossfeld, J. 1938. "Handbuch der Eierkunde." Berlin: Verlag Julius Springer.

Gutowska, M. S., and C. A. Mitchell. 1945. Carbonic anhydrase in the calcification of the egg shell. *Poultry Sci.,* **24**:159–167.

Hadley, P., and D. Caldwell. 1920. Studies on the inheritance of egg weight. I. Normal distribution of egg weight. *Rhode Island Agr. Expt. Sta. Bull.,* **181**:1–64.

Hall, G. O. 1944. Egg shell color in crosses between white and brown egg breeds. *Poultry Sci.,* **23**:259–265.

Harper, J. A., and D. R. Marble. 1945. Egg shape II. Muscular and other oviducal influences. *Poultry Sci.,* **24**:61–65.

Hays, F. A. 1933. Relation between body weight and age at sexual maturity. *Poultry Sci.,* **12**:23–25.

———. 1934. Time interval from first egg to standard egg weight in Rhode Island Red pullets. *Massachusetts Agr. Expt. Sta. Bull.,* **313**:1–11.

———. 1937. Inheritance of egg size and egg character. *Massachusetts Agr. Expt. Sta. Bull.,* **344**:1–28.

———. 1939. The significance of body weight in breeding for egg production. *Massachusetts Agr. Expt. Sta. Bull.,* **364**:1–16.

———. 1941. Transmitting ability in males of genes for egg size. *Poultry Sci.,* **20**:217–220.

———. 1944. Variability in egg weight in Rhode Island Reds. *Massachusetts Agr. Expt. Sta. Bull.,* **411**:1–16.

———. 1944a. Relation of intensity to egg weight and egg production. *Massachusetts Agr. Expt. Sta. Bull.,* **416**:1–12.

Heinroth, O. 1922. Die Beziehungen zwischen Vogelgewicht, Eigewicht, Gelegegewicht und Brutdauer., *J. Ornithol.,* **70**:172–285.

Heuser, G. F. 1936. The protein requirements of laying hens. *Wiss. Ber. Welt-gefügelk. 6th Congr., Berlin and Leipzig:* 276–279.

Hinshaw, W. R., and E. McNeil. 1943. Experiments with sulfanilamide for turkeys. *Poultry Sci.,* **22**:291–294.

Holst, W. F., and H. J. Almquist. 1931. Measurement of deterioration in the stored hen's egg. *Hilgardia,* **6**:49–60.

———, H. J. Almquist, and F. W. Lorenz. 1932. A study of shell texture of the hen's egg. *Poultry Sci.,* **11**:144–149.

Hunter, J. A., A. Van Wagenen, and G. O. Hall. 1936. Seasonal changes in interior egg quality of Single Comb White Leghorn hens. *Poultry Sci.,* **15**:115–118.

Hurst, C. C. 1921. The genetics of egg production in White Leghorns and White Wyandottes, and its application to poultry breeding. *Trans. World's Poultry Congr. 1st Congr., The Hague–Schevenigen:* 3–20.

Hutt, F. B. 1930. A note on the effects of different doses of thyroid on the fowl. *J. Exptl. Biol.,* **7**:1–6.

———. 1938. Embryonic mortality in the fowl. VII. On the relation of malpositions to the size and shape of eggs. *Poultry Sci.,* **17**:345–352.

———. 1939. An intrafollicular ovum laid by a fowl. *Poultry Sci.,* **18**:276–278.

———. 1941. The association of physiological traits with breed characteristics in the fowl. *Proc. Intern. Genetic. Congr. 7th Congr., Edinburgh:* 156–157.

———. 1946. A pedunculate, double-yolked hen's egg containing an intrafollicular ovum. *Auk,* **63**:172–175.

——— and H. Bozivich. 1946. On the supposed matroclinous inheritance of egg size in the fowl. *Poultry Sci.,* **25**:554–561.

Huxley, J. S. 1927. On the relation between egg-weight and body-weight in birds. *J. Linnean Soc. London,* **36**:457–466.

Jeffrey, F. P. 1938. The measurement of egg weight. *Poultry Sci.,* **17**:179–184.

———. 1945. Blood and meat spots in chicken eggs. *Poultry Sci.,* **24**:363–374.

——— and J. Pino. 1943. The effects of heredity and of certain environmental factors on the incidence of blood spots in chicken eggs. *Poultry Sci.,* **22**:230–234.

Jull, M. A. 1924. Egg weight in relation to production. I. The relationship of the weights of the parts of the egg to the total egg weight. *Poultry Sci.,* **3**:77–88.

———. 1924a. Egg weight in relation to production. II. The nature and causes of changes in egg weight in relation to annual production in pullets. *Poultry Sci.,* **3**:153–172.

———. 1930. Problems in egg weighing in relation to production. *Poultry Sci.,* **9**:207–218.

——— and A. B. Godfrey. 1933. Mean annual egg weight in relation to mean weight of first ten eggs laid. *Poultry Sci.,* **12**:310–312.

Kaufman, L., and H. Baczkowska. 1938. The weight of yolk, white and shell in the eggs of Polish Greenleg, Leghorn and Rhode-Island fowls. *Mém. inst. nat. polon. écon. rurale Pulawy,* **17**:57–80.

——— and ———. 1938a. Yolk colour in Greenleg, Leghorn and Rhode-Island fowls. *Mém. inst. nat. polon. écon. rurale Pulawy,* **17**:176–187.

Klose, A. A., and H. J. Almquist. 1937. The pigment of egg shell membranes. *Poultry Sci.,* **16**:173–174.

Knox, C. W., and A. B. Godfrey. 1934. Variability of thick albumen in fresh-laid eggs. *Poultry Sci.,* **13**:18–22.

Knox, C. W., and A. B. Godfrey. 1938. Factors influencing the percentage of thick albumen of hens' eggs. *Poultry Sci.*, **17**:159–162.

────── and ──────. 1940. Five years of breeding for high and low percentage of thick albumen in the eggs of Rhode Island Reds. *Poultry Sci.*, **19**:291–294.

Kopeć, S. 1922. Quelques observations sur l'hérédité de la couleur des oeufs de poules. *Mém. inst. nat. polon. écon. rurale Pulawy*, **3**:328–342.

──────. 1924. Some data referring to size, shape and weight of eggs in the domestic fowl. *Mém. inst. nat. polon. écon. rurale Pulawy*, **5**:1–34.

──────. 1926. An experimental study on xenia in the domestic fowl. *J. Genetics*, **16**:269–286.

──────. 1926a. Nouvelles observations sur l'hérédité et sur la variabilité périodique de la couleur des oeufs de poule. *Mém. inst. nat. polon. écon. rurale Pulawy*, **7**:158–179.

Larionov, W. T. 1936. Experimentelle Analyse der Wechselbeziehung zwischen Mauser und Legeleistung beim Huhn. *Z. Zücht. Reihe B. Z. Tierzücht. Züchtungsbiol.*, **36**:377–385.

Lauth, H. 1935. Vererbung von Körper und Eigewicht bei Haushuhnrassen. Ein Beitrag zur Genetik quantitativer Eigenschaften. *Z. Zücht. Reihe B. Z. Tierzücht. Züchtungsbiol.*, **31**:271–310.

Lippincott, W. A. 1921. Preliminary note on the correlation between age at first laying and size of first eggs in pullets. *J. Am. Assoc. Instr. Invest. Poultry Husb.*, **7**:73–74.

Lorenz, F. W., and H. J. Almquist. 1936. Seasonal variations in egg quality. *Poultry Sci.*, **15**:14–18.

────── and L. W. Taylor. 1940. The inheritance of albumen quality characteristic of chicken eggs. *J. Agr. Research*, **61**:293–301.

──────, ──────, and H. J. Almquist. 1934. Firmness of albumen as an inherited characteristic. *Poultry Sci.*, **13**:14–17.

Lund, W. A., V. Heiman, and L. A. Wilhelm. 1938. The relationship between egg shell thickness and strength. *Poultry Sci.*, **17**:372–376.

Marble, D. R. 1930. The non-linear relationship of egg weight and annual production. *Poultry Sci.*, **9**:257–265.

──────. 1931. A statistical study of factors affecting egg weight in the domestic fowl. *Poultry Sci.*, **10**:84–92.

──────. 1931a. The non-linear relationship between mean egg weight and mean annual body weight. *Proc. 22nd Ann. Meet. Poultry Sci. Assoc.*: 55–59.

──────. 1943. Genetics of egg shape. *Poultry Sci.*, **22**:61–71.

Marshall, W., and D. B. Cruickshank. 1938. The function of the cuticle in relation to the porosity of eggs. *J. Agr. Sci.*, **28**:24–42.

Maw, A. J. G. 1934. The effect of kamala on egg production and egg weight. *Poultry Sci.*, **13**:131–134.

────── and W. A. Maw. 1932. A method of estimating the mean annual egg weight. *Sci. Agr.*, **12**:281–286.

McNally, E. 1933. Relative amount of mucin in thick and thin white. *Proc. Soc. Exptl. Biol. Med.*, **30**:1254–1255.

Morgan, C. L. 1932. Relationship between breaking strength and the percent of egg shell. *Poultry Sci.*, **11**:172–175.

Munro, S. S. 1940. The relation of specific gravity to hatching power in eggs of the domestic fowl. *Sci. Agr.*, **21**:53–62.

Nalbandov, A. V., and L. E. Card. 1943. The problem of blood clots and meat spots in chicken eggs. *Poultry Sci.*, **23**:170–180.

Needham, J. 1931. "Chemical Embryology." New York, The Macmillan Company.

Olsen, M. W., and C. W. Knox. 1940. Breeding for egg weight and related characters. *Poultry Sci.*, **19**:254–257.

Olsson, N. 1934. "Studies on Specific Gravity of Hens' Eggs." Leipzig: Otto Harrassowitz.

———. 1936. Studies on some physical and physiological characters in hens' eggs. *Wiss. Ber. Weltgeflügelk. 6th Congr., Berlin and Leipzig:* 310–320.

Panum, P. L. 1860. "Untersuchungen über die Entstehung des Missbildungen zunächst in den Eiern der Vögel." Berlin: Geo. Reimer.

Parker, S. L., S. S. Gossman, and W. A. Lippincott. 1926. Studies on egg quality. I. Introductory note on variations in yolk color. *Poultry Sci.*, **5**:131–145.

Parker, J. E., and H. L. Kempster. 1940. Partial ovarian ablation concurrent with egg formation. *Poultry Sci.*, **19**:157–158.

Parkhurst, R. T. 1926. Certain factors in relation to production and egg weight in White Leghorns. *Poultry Sci.*, **5**:121–126.

Pearl, R. 1909. Studies on the physiology of reproduction in the domestic fowl. I. Regulation in the morphogenetic activity of the oviduct. *J. Exptl. Zoöl.*, **6**:339–359.

———. 1910. A triple-yolked egg. *Zool. Anz.*, **35**:417–423.

——— and M. R. Curtis. 1916. Studies on the physiology of reproduction in the domestic fowl. XV. Dwarf eggs. *J. Agr. Research*, **6**:977–1042.

——— and F. M. Surface. 1914. A biometrical study of egg production in the domestic fowl. III. Variation and correlation in the physical characters of the egg. *U.S. Dept. Agr. Bull.*, **110** (III): 171–241.

Podhradsky, J. 1935. Die Veranderungen der inkretorischen Drüsen und einiger innerer Organe bei der Legeleistung. *Z. Zücht. Reihe B. Z. Tierzücht. Züchtungsbiol.*, **33**:77–103.

Punnett, R. C. 1923. "Heredity in Poultry." London: Macmillan & Co., Ltd.

———. 1933. Genetic studies in poultry. IX. The blue egg. *J. Genetics*, **27**:465–470.

——— and P. G. Bailey. 1920. Genetic studies in poultry. II. Inheritance of egg colour and broodiness. *J. Genetics*, **10**:277–292.

Quinn, J. P., C. D. Gordon, and A. B. Godfrey. 1945. Breeding for egg shell quality as indicated by egg weight loss. *Poultry Sci.*, **24**:399–403.

Radeff, T. 1935. Beitrag zum Studium der Schwankungen des Farbstoffgehaltes im Huhnereigelb. *Arch. Geflügelk.*, **9**:111–114.

Romanoff, A. L. 1929. Studies in the physical properties of the hen's eggshell in relation to the function of shell-secretory glands. *Biol. Bull.*, **56**:351–356.

——— and F. B. Hutt. 1945. New data on the origin of double avian eggs. *Anat. Record*, **91**:143–154.

——— and A. Romanoff. 1949. "The Avian Egg." New York: John Wiley & Sons, Inc.

Scott, H. M., E. Jungherr, and L. D. Matterson. 1944. The effect of feeding sulfanilamide to the laying fowl. *Poultry Sci.*, **23**:446–453.

Scrimshaw, N. S., F. B. Hutt, and M. Scrimshaw. 1945. The effect of genetic variation in the fowl on the thiamine content of the egg. *J. Nutrition*, **30**:375–383.

Snyder, E. S. 1945. Eggs. The production, identification and retention of quality in eggs. *Ontario Dept. Agr. Bull.*, **446**:1–47.

Stewart, G. F. 1935. The structure of the hen's egg shell. *Poultry Sci.,* **14**:24–32.

———. 1936. Shell characteristics and their relationship to the breaking strength. *Poultry Sci.,* **15**:119–124.

Surface, F. M. 1912. The histology of the oviduct of the domestic hen. *Maine Agr. Expt. Sta. Bull.,* **206**:395–430.

Taylor, L. W., and I. M. Lerner. 1939. Inheritance of eggshell thickness in White Leghorn pullets. *J. Agr. Research,* **58**:383–396.

——— and ———. 1941. Inheritance of shell finish in single-comb White Leghorns. *J. Heredity,* **32**:33–36.

——— and J. H. Martin. 1928. Factors influencing thickness of egg shell. *Poultry Sci.,* **8**:39–44.

Upp, C. W., and R. B. Thompson. 1927. Influence of time of hatch on hatchability of the eggs, rate of growth of the chicks, and characteristics of the adult female. *Oklahoma Agr. Expt. Sta. Bull.,* **167**:1–36.

Van Wagenen, A., and G. O. Hall. 1936. The inheritance of certain characters affecting egg quality. *Poultry Sci.,* **15**:405–410.

———, G. O. Hall, and H. S. Wilgus, Jr. 1937. Variations in egg-quality characters in certain breeds, varieties and strains of chickens. *J. Agr. Research,* **54**:767–777.

Vecchi, A. 1935. I carotinoidi dei crostacei per la colorazione dei tuorli d'uova di gallina. *Nuovi ann. agricoltura,* **15**:473–502.

Vondell, J. H. 1932. Is the production of "off-flavor" eggs an individual characteristic? *Poultry Sci.,* **11**:375.

Warren, D. C. 1928. Inheritance of earlobe color in poultry. *Genetics,* **13**:470–487.

———. 1939. Effect of temperature on size of eggs from pullets in different latitudes. *J. Agr. Research,* **59**:441–452.

——— and R. M. Conrad. 1942. Time of pigment deposition in brown shelled hen eggs and in turkey eggs. *Poultry Sci.,* **21**:515–520.

——— and R. L. Schnepel. 1940. The effect of air temperatures on egg shell thickness in the fowl. *Poultry Sci.,* **19**:67–72.

Waters, N. F., and J. C. Weldin. 1929. Studies on the inheritance of egg-weight. II. The effect of selection on egg-weight. *Rhode Island Agr. Expt. Sta. Bull.,* **218**:1–26.

Wilhelm, L. A. 1940. Some factors affecting variations in egg shell quality. *Poultry Sci.,* **19**:246–253.

Willard, J. T., and R. H. Shaw. 1909. Analyses of eggs. *Kansas Agr. Expt. Sta. Bull.,* **159**:143–177.

Wilson, W., and D. C. Warren. 1934. Initial egg weight as a basis of prediction of maximum egg size. *Poultry Sci.,* **13**:52–55.

CHAPTER 12

GENETIC RESISTANCE TO DISEASE

Although poultrymen formerly considered the number of eggs laid and their size to be the chief factors determining the profits in their enterprises, it became increasingly apparent in the 1930's and 1940's that excessively high mortality in growing stock and in adult birds had become one of the chief worries of the poultry industry, and perhaps its major problem. Because evidence is increasing to show that genetic resistance to disease is an important factor in reducing losses, and because further research in this field is highly desirable, it seems pertinent to review briefly our present knowledge of that subject. This is done, after some general considerations of (1) genetic aspects of mortality, by considering in turn genetic differences (2) in resistance to bacterial infections, (3) to neoplasms, (4) to parasites, (5) in tolerance of extreme heat, and (6) in nutritional requirements. Finally the relation of these to (7) transfers of stock is considered.

GENETIC ASPECTS OF MORTALITY

The high death rates now prevailing in poultry flocks during growth and in the first year of laying have been so thoroughly discussed in the poultry press that further emphasis on that problem is unnecessary in this book. It is pertinent to point out, however, that most of the estimates of the extent of mortality on which these discussions are based are far too low. This is merely because, being compiled by agricultural economists and others from surveys and questionnaires, they do not include the hens that would have died if their experienced owners had given them a chance to do so. Most good poultrymen cull their flocks regularly throughout the year and send the less thrifty birds to market while they are still in marketable condition. This has proved to be one of the easiest and least expensive ways to reduce the mortality rate. The extent to which it may do so was shown by the data of Marble (1939) for the 6-year period 1927 to 1932 at the Pennsylvania Experiment Station. Here the proportion of the pullets that died in their first laying year was only 23 per cent in White Leghorns and 19 per cent in Barred Plymouth Rocks. However, when to these figures were added the numbers removed "for health" (but not, apparently, merely for low egg production), the total reduction of the flock was 40 per cent for the Leghorns and 49 per cent for the Barred Rocks. It is only fair to add that these birds were removed in this case not so that they could be sold but rather so that their presence would not imperil the healthy members of the flock.

Most good poultrymen cull out not only the unthrifty birds but also the poor layers. Since many of these are laying poorly or not at all because of the incipient stages of disease (page 288), their elimination automatically reduces the proportion of the flock that will be recorded as having died. Figures on mortality in the laying tests are accurate because the birds there are not culled, but since they pertain to highly selected hens kept in small groups of 13 birds or so, such figures may not reveal adequately the death rates prevailing in the flocks of several hundred that are more usual on large poultry farms. Data for large flocks not culled are unavailable, with the exception of records from experiments in which no culling was done so that selection for viability could be practised. Some of these are given in Table 53.

Reduction of Mortality by Breeding. Some years ago it was pointed out (Hutt, 1938) that, among 1,922 deaths of hens at two laying tests in 6 years, 87 per cent were caused by conditions not preventable by the usual orthodox procedures of sanitation, immunization, and elimination of carriers and exposed birds. General recognition of this situation and of the fact that families of pullets differ greatly in viability has resulted in attempts to reduce mortality by breeding better stock. The results obtained in some of these experiments are summarized, in very condensed form, in Table 53.

Any reader appalled by the high mortality rates shown in the penultimate column of this table and comparing them with the modest 18.4 per cent given by the Bureau of Agricultural Economics of the U.S. Department of Agriculture for farm poultry in the period 1939 to 1944 would conclude that chickens have much better chances of surviving on farms than in the flocks of agricultural colleges. This is true, to some extent, because all pathogenic organisms, whether travelling on diseased birds or on the poultrymen who bring those birds for diagnosis, eventually find their way to the colleges. The greater part of the difference in mortality is attributable to the fact that the college flocks cited in Table 53 were not culled and hence provided accurate figures on mortality. This situation does not apply to many farm flocks.

The results in this table show that, in every case, the high mortality prevailing in the unselected population before selection began was significantly reduced in a comparatively short period of selection. It is true

TABLE 53. SOME RESULTS IN EXPERIMENTS DEMONSTRATING THE FEASIBILITY OF REDUCING MORTALITY BY BREEDING

Investigator	Breed	Period of selection	Length of test period	Mortality, per cent, in	
				Original unselected population	Latest generation reported
Marble (1939)........	Barred Rock	1933–1937	150 to 515 days *	48.7 †	24.6
Marble (1939)........	White Leghorn	1933–1937	150 to 515 days *	39.8 †	20.1
Sturkie (1943)........	White Leghorn	1935–1940	365 days from first egg	89.0	27.0
Bostian and Dearstyne (1944)..............	White Leghorn	1939–1941	30 to 360 days *	23.3	11.2
Bryant (1946).........	White Leghorn	1940–1944	140 to 525 days *	25.0	17.1
Hutt and Cole (1947)..	White Leghorn C	1936–1945	42 to 500 days *	66.8	22.4
Hutt and Cole (1947)..	White Leghorn K	1936–1945	42 to 500 days *	66.8	19.9

* Days of age.
† Includes those removed "for health."

that mortality in any one year, whether for the original unselected population or for the resistant stock, may be misleading by itself, but the consistency of these results is highly significant. Comparisons of the efficiency of the selection in the different experiments are both unnecessary and impossible because of differences in environment, in severity of exposure to disease, and in duration of the periods in which mortality was determined. For example, mortality was apparently lowest in the flocks studied by Bostian and Dearstyne, but since it was recorded only to 12 months of age, which is about half the normal first year of laying, these data are not comparable with those for longer test periods. Similarly, the comparatively low mortality in Bryant's birds for 2 years before selection was begun suggests that their exposure to disease was somewhat less severe than in the other flocks. The really important thing is that in every case the prevailing mortality, whatever it was, declined as a result of selection.

Hopeful breeders must not jump to the conclusion that a few years of selection will solve their problem. In some cases, particularly when no strain susceptible to disease has been maintained concurrently with that selected for high viability, investigators have found in later years that the reduction of mortality hopefully ascribed to genetic selection had resulted merely from lessened exposure to disease. This is particularly the case in so far as lymphomatosis is concerned. Another limitation arises because mere viability is not enough. When the breeder seeks also to improve or maintain the egg production, body size, egg size, reproduction, and other characters of economic value, he may make slow progress. A common limiting factor is the difficulty of getting enough proven sires that are sufficently good in all these objectives. This is indicated by the results shown in Fig. 103 for two strains of disease-resistant

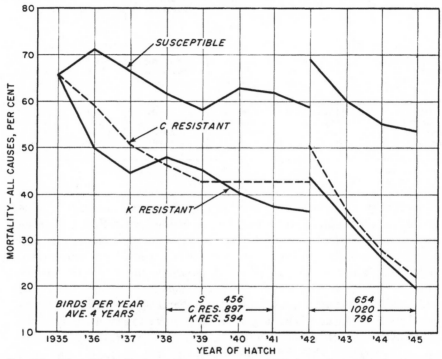

FIG. 103. Mortality in Leghorn females from 42 to 500 days of age, showing how it was reduced by selective breeding in two lines and maintained in a third. The accelerated improvement after 1942 resulted from testing more sires, which intensified the selection. The higher points for 1942 apply to birds severely exposed, the lower points to the whole population. (*From Hutt and Cole in Science.*)

White Leghorns studied at Cornell University (Hutt and Cole, 1947). In this case, the high mortality of the unselected population was considerably reduced in the first two selected generations, but thereafter improvement was very slow from 1938 to 1942. When ways were found to test two and three times as many cockerels each year, thus providing plenty of good proven sires, the rate of improvement was greatly accelerated from 1942 to 1945. Another factor contributing to that result was an increased exposure to lymphomatosis, which permitted better differentiation of the resistant families. This is discussed on pages 523–525, and the procedure for testing more cockerels each year is given in Chap. 15.

Relation of Mortality to Egg Production. It is sometimes said that the rise in mortality from 1920 on is merely the result of breeding and feeding domestic fowls so that they lay eggs in excess of the natural

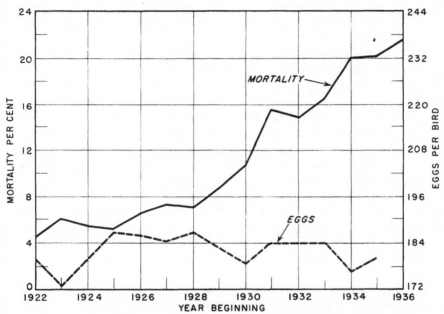

Fig. 104. Data from the laying trials at Harper Adams Agricultural College, showing that the mortality rose steadily during 14 years while the average egg production remained unchanged. (*From Hutt in Amer. Naturalist, 1938.*)

limits for the species. No evidence to support that thesis has thus far been adduced. On the contrary, there is plenty of evidence that productivity is reduced by disease. Figure 104 shows that mortality during the first laying year at the laying trials at Harper Adams Agricultural College, Newport, Salop, England, rose steadily from 5.2 per cent in 1922 to more than four times that figure 15 years later. At the same time the average egg production per bird changed little, being actually lower from 1929 to 1935 than in the 4 years preceding 1929. These data show not only that the rise in mortality has occurred independently of any change in production but also that it is a phenomenon not restricted to North America. Similarly, at the Vineland egg-laying contests, Platt (1935) found that mortality was more than tripled in the decade from 1918 to

1928, while egg production remained unchanged. In the next 5 years, productivity increased slightly, but mortality remained unchanged.

In comparisons of hens which died with those which survived, Munro (1936) and Lerner *et al.* (1939) found that the poorer layers are more likely to die than the good ones. This means, not that they die because they are poor layers, but, more likely, that incipient stages of disease or low physiological efficiency will lower the egg production for some weeks or months before death. The earlier evidence of Harris on this point was considered in Chap. 10.

Breed Differences in Mortality. Popular opinions that some one breed is more susceptible (or more resistant) to disease are plentiful, but critical evidence on this point is very limited. The opinions would be significant if they were unanimous, or even in general agreement, but this they are not. Even within one state or province, opinions on this score differ at any one time, as do the opinions of many poultrymen at different times over a quarter century. There is somewhat better ground for the varying preferences that prevail in different parts of the world. This is because breeds differ in important physiological characters (Hutt, 1941), some of which might affect their viability in one latitude, but not in another. A good example of such a character is the superior ability of the Leghorns to tolerate high temperatures, which is discussed later in this chapter.

Differential viability of breeds could result from any of the following causes.

1. Linkage of lethal or semi-lethal genes, or genes causing physiological deficiencies, with those determining breed characters, *e.g.*, Dunn's lethal linked with recessive white. Some of these might reduce the heterozygote's viability.

2. Genes for physiological characters incorporated, either deliberately or unwittingly, as determiners of the breed, *e.g.*, rapid feathering, nonbroodiness, and low requirement of thiamine and manganese in Leghorns.

3. Disproportion or abnormality of structure, *e.g.*, extremely short legs in Dark Cornish, abnormally large crests or combs, frizzled plumage.

4. Effects in the heterozygote of lethal genes unwittingly adopted as breed characters, *e.g.*, the creeper mutation in the fowl and crest in the duck.

To determine whether or not breeds differ in viability it would be necessary to maintain under uniform environmental conditions adequate samples of the breeds to be compared and to do so without any culling. These conditions are most nearly met in laying trials, but even there the conditions are not entirely satisfactory because the environment during growth is different for each entry. As is now well known, susceptibility of adults to some diseases (*e.g.*, lymphomatosis, Newcastle disease) depends to a large extent upon whether or not the birds were exposed as chicks.

From records of the Storrs (Connecticut) laying contest for the decade 1911 to 1922, Harris and Boughton (1928) concluded that mortality in White Leghorns was significantly lower than in Rhode Island Reds and Wyandottes. However, Dudley (1928) could find no significant differences in mortality among any of these three breeds at the Harper Adams laying trials during the period 1912 to 1927. As it happened, the Leghorns experienced, in this case, slightly higher mortality than the Rhode Island Reds and Wyandottes. Dudley also showed that when the Storrs records analyzed by Harris and Boughton were considered year by year, and not lumped together, no significant difference between breeds was evident.

Both these studies pertained to periods when mortality was much lower than at present, and before lymphomatosis, now the most important single cause of mortality in adults, was prevalent. It is therefore possible that studies of more recent data similar to those cited might now reveal significant differences in viability among the more common breeds.

Differential Susceptibility of the Sexes. Sex is an important genetic factor influencing susceptibility to some pathological conditions. This is most obvious if one merely recalls that tumors of the ovary and peritonitis resulting from intra-abdominal yolk concretions are restricted to females. Apart from such associations with anatomical differences between the sexes, there is evidence that in some cases one sex is much more susceptible than the other to infection.

The most remarkable difference of this sort is that between male and female turkeys in susceptibility to *Erysipelothrix rhusiopathiae*, the organism causing swine erysipelas. Although all reports agree that it affects chiefly males, quantitative data are limited. From the account by Madsen (1937) of an outbreak that killed 325 birds in one flock, it can be calculated that the erysipelas killed about 46 per cent of the males but only 4 per cent of the females, or less. It is possible that the males are more susceptible because of lacerations inflicted in the course of their normal belligerent activities. The remarkable immunity or resistance of the females suggests that losses in the males might be prevented, in flocks likely to experience the disease, by temporarily feminizing them at the critical period with diethylstilbestrol, dienestrol, or some other synthetic estrogen. This should serve the double purpose of preventing the disease and improving the finish of the carcass. Males thus feminized should be kept apart from any others not treated.

In the fowl, male hormones greatly increase the degree of resistance to lymphomatosis (Marine and Rosen, 1940, 1941). This is nicely shown by the data of Burmester and Nelson (1945) for eight lots of males, half of them caponized, and some given testosterone propionate (male hormone), others diethylstilbestrol (female hormone), with results as shown in Table 54. The number of birds was 33 to 37 in each lot.

TABLE 54. INCIDENCE OF LYMPHOMATOSIS, PER CENT, IN DIFFERENT GROUPS SHOWING THAT RESISTANCE TO IT WAS RAISED BY MALE HORMONES, WHETHER NATURAL OR SYNTHETIC *

Exposure to lymphomatosis	Hormone	Lymphomatosis in	
		Males	Capons
Natural..............	None supplied	38.3	84.8
Inoculated............	None supplied	64.7	88.4
Inoculated............	Testosterone propionate	40.2	42.0
Inoculated............	Diethylstilbestrol	77.8	60.0

* Data of Burmester and Nelson (1945).

Apart from such experiments, the incidence of lymphomatosis in normal birds naturally exposed is about twice as high in females as in males (Burmester, 1945). While some of this difference may result from the fact that the ovary is more frequently affected than the testes, the high incidence in capons shown in Table 54, its reduction by treatment with testosterone, and the higher level in males given diethylstilbestrol all show the role of the hormones in causing the greater resistance of the males to this disease.

In at least one case the differential susceptibility of the sexes seems to be associated with differences in the rate of feathering. Males are much more susceptible than females to the formation during growth of cysts or bursae in the skin overlying the keel (Hodgson and Gutteridge, 1941). According to experiments by Kondra and Cavers (1947) the females of heavy breeds are less affected (as are both sexes in Mediterranean breeds) because they feather out more rapidly and thus have greater protection over the skin where the keel meets the roost.

RESISTANCE TO BACTERIAL INFECTIONS

Avian Diphtheria

The study of resistance to this disease by Frateur (1924) was apparently the first attempt to determine experimentally whether or not fowls differed genetically in their capacity to withstand infection. Considering as resistant those birds in which lesions were confined to the site of inoculation, he observed the following segregations:

Parents	Progeny	
	Resistant	Susceptible
Resistant × susceptible...........	17	0
F₁ birds *inter se*.................	7	2
Backcross of F₁ to susceptible.....	10	13
Susceptible × susceptible........	1 (?)	8

These results suggest that susceptibility in this case was a simple recessive character, but, as Frateur himself recognized, more extensive data are desirable. The data are recorded here because they provided the first evidence from controlled experiments of the possibility of increasing resistance of fowls to disease by breeding.

Pullorum Disease

Breed Differences. Leghorns are so highly resistant to natural infection by *Salmonella pullorum* that it is not likely to cause much loss in chicks of that breed unless they are chilled or otherwise mismanaged. Evidence of this superior resistance was early seen in records for the first state-wide campaigns for testing flocks to eliminate reactors. These were summarized by Hutt and Scholes (1941). The data for Connecticut and New Jersey are typical (Table 55).

TABLE 55. PROPORTION OF REACTORS (PERCENTAGE OF FEMALES TESTED) TO TESTS FOR *Salmonella pullorum* IN THE FIRST 2 YEARS OF TESTING IN CONNECTICUT AND THE FIRST 3 YEARS IN NEW JERSEY

Breed	Connecticut		New Jersey		
	1914–1915	1915–1916	1924–1925	1925–1926	1926–1927
White Leghorns..........	4.5	3.4	3.0	2.4	3.4
Rhode Island Reds.......	12.9	11.9	15.7	20.4	18.1
White Wyandottes........	25.5	10.3	17.9	19.6	15.4
Plymouth Rocks.........	14.2	11.7	14.0	14.4	15.2

That the comparatively low proportion of reactors in the Leghorns is a true breed characteristic and not merely a local phenomenon was shown by similar records from Massachusetts, North Carolina, and British Columbia. In Massachusetts, the incidence of reactors was gradually reduced over a 13-year period, but in all that time the proportion in the Leghorns was consistently lower than in Reds and Plymouth Rocks (Fig. 105).

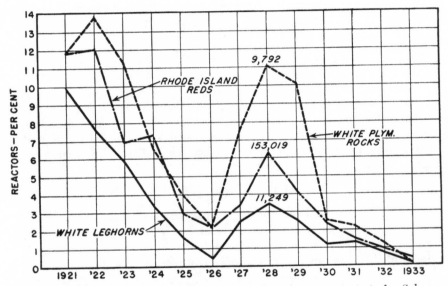

Fig. 105. Showing the consistently lower proportion of reactors to tests for *Salmonella pullorum* among White Leghorns in comparison with two heavy breeds. The data are from annual reports of such tests in Massachusetts for the years shown. The figures for 1928 give some idea of the numbers tested annually.

This evidence was confirmed experimentally when White Leghorn chicks were proved more resistant than Reds and Rocks both to inoculation with *S. pullorum* and to exposure by contact (Hutt and Scholes, 1941). The question whether the superiority of the White Leghorns in this respect depends upon their being white or being Leghorns was answered (in part) by backcrossing white males heterozygous for dominant white (Ii) to black ii females and testing their progeny. These showed no difference between Ii and ii birds in resistance to *S. pullorum*. It seems probable, therefore, that dominant white, which is the distinguishing character of the White Leghorn, is not responsible and that the resistance of Leghorns is a characteristic of the breed rather than of the variety.

In other comparisons of breeds by inoculation of chicks, Roberts and

Card (1935) found White Leghorns to be more resistant than four different Chinese breeds, but one of these, the small Chia Gi, found near Peiping, proved highly resistant when samples from it were tested in China and in the United States.

These references to the resistance of the White Leghorns should not leave the impression that other breeds are hopelessly susceptible. The author has found some Rhode Island Red chicks completely indifferent to dosage with millions of pullorum bacteria, although this was less common with highly virulent strains. Tests by De Volt *et al.* (1941) of Rhode Island Reds that had been selected during several years for viability in the presence of pullorum infection showed them to be almost as resistant as the resistant Leghorns of Roberts and Card, which were tested concurrently. In these two stocks, survival of chicks inoculated subcutaneously with severe doses was 28 and 33 per cent, whereas among chicks from flocks kept free of pullorum for several years only 11 per cent survived. Unfortunately the three types were not tested in any way that might indicate their resistance to natural infection. As Severens *et al.* (1944) pointed out, the difference between resistant and susceptible stocks is less evident with subcutaneous inoculations than with oral ones. One would expect, therefore, that if these three types of chicks had been exposed to natural infection, or even exposed orally, the superior resistance of the selected Rhode Island Reds and Leghorns would have been even more pronounced.

Resistant Strains. That this natural resistance can be enhanced by selection was proved by Roberts and Card (1935). In three different resistant strains of White Leghorns, one selected for 9 years, the other two for 4, the proportions of chicks surviving a standard oral dose of the organism were 74, 61, and 70 per cent, while of control chicks given the same dosage only 28 per cent survived.

Crosses of the resistant strains with unselected controls yielded progeny fully as resistant as the better parent. This is important information, for it suggests that such resistant strains can be utilized to full advantage by crossing them with flocks unimproved in this respect. Further evidence that resistance is dominant was provided by diallel matings in which certain sires were mated with dams from both susceptible and resistant stocks. The results, when all progeny were tested with a standard dose of the organism, were as shown at the top of page 416.

Although resistance to *S. pullorum* is clearly dominant, there is no evidence that it has a simple genetic basis. The reciprocal crosses between the resistant and susceptible strains show that no sex-linked genes are affecting resistance in this case.

Parents	Progeny	
	Number tested	Survived, per cent
5 susceptible ♂♂ × susceptible ♀♀	398	46
5 susceptible ♂♂ × resistant ♀♀	450	74
10 resistant ♂♂ × susceptible ♀♀	512	79
10 resistant ♂♂ × resistant ♀♀	357	80

Physiological Basis of Resistance. The classical demonstration by Pasteur, Joubert, and Chamberland (1878) that the fowl's immunity to anthrax is attributable to its high temperature suggested that this same factor might influence resistance to *S. pullorum*. It was then proved that in White Leghorn chicks the body temperature rises more rapidly in the

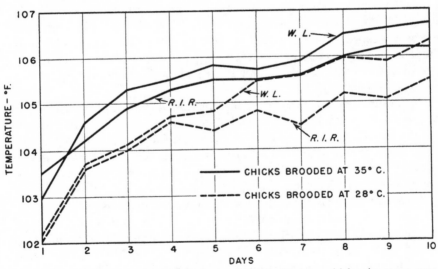

FIG. 106. Showing that body temperatures of White Leghorn chicks rise more rapidly than those of Rhode Island Reds during the first 10 days after hatching. (*From Scholes and Hutt.*)

first 10 days after hatching than it does in Rhode Island Reds (Hutt, 1935; Lamoreux and Hutt, 1939; Scholes and Hutt, 1942). This association of higher temperature with the more resistant breed (Fig. 106) is not in itself proof that the one causes the other. Its significance is enhanced by the well-known fact that infected chicks will suffer severe losses if chilled but comparatively little if brooded at high temperatures. Moreover, the resistance of the chick to infection by the pullorum organism increases rapidly during the first 5 days after hatching, as does the temperature.

Further evidence of the relation of body temperature to resistance was found by Scholes and Hutt (1942), who used Rhode Island Red chicks for several types of experiments bearing on the problem. The following results are significant:

1. Inoculated chicks in which body temperature was lowered by 0.7 to 1.4° F. by brooding them at 28° C. were consistently more susceptible than inoculated controls brooded at 35°C. in which body temperatures were normal.

2. Chicks in which the temperature was temporarily lowered by 8.4°F. following injection of sodium amytal were more susceptible than controls.

3. Chicks in which artificial fever (from 0.6 to 2.1°F.) was temporarily induced by the use of a carbon-filament lamp were consistently more resistant than controls.

4. Following inoculation with *S. pullorum,* 48 per cent of the chicks developed abnormally high temperatures for their age (107° F. in the first 8 days), but others did not, and in controls not inoculated only 4 per cent did so. Mortality was lower in those that developed fever than in the inoculated chicks that did not do so.

5. Among chicks inoculated when 1 day old and brooded at 28°C., the mean body temperatures from 1 to 8 days of age were consistently higher for survivors than for those that died.

6. In chicks not inoculated until 2 and 3 days of age, the body temperatures of those that subsequently died were significantly lower, even before inoculation, than the temperatures of those that survived (Fig. 107).

7. Among families of sibling chicks from different dams, those characterized by high familial temperatures, as determined in uninfected chicks, subsequently proved more resistant when adequate representative samples of each family were inoculated.

From all this evidence, it seems reasonably certain that high temperatures and resistance to *S. pullorum* are not associated merely by chance but that either the high temperatures or the greater adaptability of the temperature-controlling mechanism that they indicate, or both together, are responsible for the increased resistance to the infection which accompanies them. This effect is not necessarily attributable to the direct action of high temperatures upon *S. pullorum.* It could result from their acceleration of such defensive processes as phagocytosis and the production of antibodies.

A contrary view was advanced by Severens *et al.* (1944), who attributed resistance to the greater number of lymphocytes found by them in chicks of a resistant strain than in chicks of a susceptible one, the difference being significant during the first 5 days after hatching. However, since their resistant strain was in White Leghorns and the susceptible one a Rhode Island Red, it is questionable whether the extra lymphocytes of

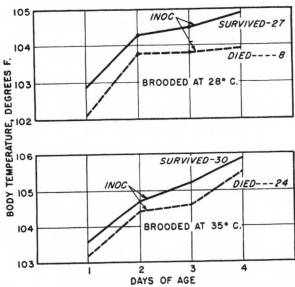

FIG. 107. Showing that mean body temperatures of chicks that died following inoculation with *Salmonella pullorum* were significantly lower than those of survivors, both before and after the inoculation. (*From Scholes and Hutt.*)

the Leghorns have any more significance than their higher temperatures, so far as resistance to *S. pullorum* is concerned. The same applies to their larger spleens, an interesting difference, also noted by Severens *et al.* They considered significant the fact that treatment with X rays reduced both lymphocytes and resistance, but, as Scholes (1942) found with even lighter dosage, such treatment also lowers the temperature for several days thereafter and, equally important, causes lesions in the intestine and liver that might account for any lowered resistance to the pullorum organism.

These comments are not intended to belittle the possible role of the lymphocytes in resisting infection, though further proof is necessary before assuming that they are primarily responsible. It is possible that both temperature and lymphocytes are involved, especially since the rate of phagocytosis is accelerated at higher body temperatures and retarded at low ones (Fenn, 1922). Moreover, while many chicks respond to inoculation by developing a fever (Scholes and Hutt, 1942), there are significant concurrent changes in the blood (Kelly and Dearstyne, 1935).

Relation of Genetic Resistance to Control. It seems unfortunate that the innate resistance of White Leghorns has been completely ignored in state and national programs for control of pullorum disease. Perhaps that is because such programs are still based, as were the first ones, on the recommendations of the bacteriologists and veterinarians whose sole idea was to eradicate the disease, to eliminate all birds that carried the organism. While this may be possible in a small state like Connecticut or Massachusetts, the feasibility of eradicating *S. pullorum* from the hens of North America (without even considering the quail, pheasants, and other wild species that carry it) seems somewhat remote. In the attempt to accomplish it, one envisions little armies of blood testers struggling on to the millennium, while, as a result of their labors, the poultry population, in the absence of any natural selection, becomes more and more susceptible. The fact that the same thing is happening with respect to tuberculosis in man and in cattle does not necessarily justify the program for pullorum disease in poultry.

From this geneticist's point of view, a more desirable approach, if one is to consider the future and not merely this year's chicks, would be to find what the Leghorns have (*i.e.*, the basis of their resistance) and then to incorporate it in the heavy breeds. With natural selection operating up to the time of the first state-wide tests in Connecticut and New Jersey, the proportion of reactors in White Leghorn flocks was only 2.4 to 4.5 per cent (Table 55). With some additional selection by breeders it could be reduced still further. During the past 14 years the author has raised annually several thousand White Leghorn chicks from breeding flocks that contained in every year but one a few reactors. There have been no serious losses except when, through accidents or otherwise, the chicks got chilled. Unfortunately, in the fourteenth year, in spite of all efforts to maintain a few infected birds in the population, no reactors could be found among about 300 birds used for breeding.

At the present time, while any Leghorn breeder interested only in raising his own stock could do the same, no hatcheryman could do so and remain in business. This is merely because, under the present moral code imposed upon him by the poultry specialists who indoctrinate his customers, by the veterinarians who examine their dead chicks, and by the pullorum-controlling officials who list him as clean or unclean, the hatcheryman gets the blame for all chicks that die of pullorum disease. Since he must pay compensation for such losses or go out of business, or both, his only defence is to eliminate all reactors from his supply flocks. This is particularly necessary under present conditions because the risk of chicks being chilled in transit between the hatcheryman's incubator and the customer's brooder is added to the usual risk of being chilled after they get there. This situation is not likely to be changed so long as immediate profits and losses take precedence over the longer view. The author's views are given here merely in the hope that they may catch the eye of some discouraged poultryman still battling pullorum disease in the year 2100 A.D. and, mayhap, give him cause to think, between curses of the agglutination test that begot his highly susceptible stock, of the possibility of genetic control.

Fowl Typhoid

The feasibility of breeding birds with high resistance to *Salmonella gallinarum,* the organism causing fowl typhoid, was demonstrated by Lambert (1932). Starting with half-grown White Leghorns that had

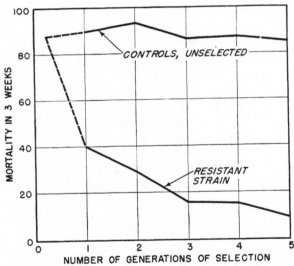

Fig. 108. Mortality in chicks inoculated with *Salmonella gallinarum,* showing increase in resistance in five generations of selection. Since the original unselected stock was not given the standard test, the starting point is taken as the 5-year average of the controls, or 88 per cent. (*From data of Lambert.*)

withstood large doses of *S. gallinarum,* he subjected five generations of their descendants at 7 days of age to a standard dose of this organism and made selection on the basis of familial resistance and progeny tests. The results (Fig. 108) showed that even in the first selected generation mortality was less than half that of controls. By the fifth generation only 9.4 per cent succumbed to a dose that was fatal to 85 per cent of the unselected controls. One of the problems in this kind of work is to maintain the virulence of the organism and to ensure a constant dosage. The uniformly high mortality of the control chicks throughout the experiment shows that this factor was unusually well controlled in this experiment. This, in turn, accentuates the remarkable difference brought about in five generations of selection. The greater resistance of the selected stock was shown, not only by its lower mortality, but also by the fact that few of the chicks died within five days of inoculation, while most of the controls did.

Any possibility that the marked resistance of the selected stock might have resulted from passive immunity transmitted by surviving hens through the egg to their chicks was removed by the results of reciprocal crosses between the resistant stock and unselected (susceptible) controls. These showed little difference between the contributions of dams and sires to the resistance of their offspring. Moreover, dams still carrying the infection produced chicks that were no more resistant than those of resistant dams not carrying the infection (Lambert, 1932, part II). Some differences among breeds in resistance to *S. gallinarum* were noted (1932, part III), but since differences almost as great occurred between strains within a breed, their significance was doubtful.

RESISTANCE TO NEOPLASMS

If one includes among neoplasms the various manifestations of what is sometimes called "avian leukosis," "fowl paralysis" (Fig. 109), or "lymphomatosis," that group now constitutes a more serious cause of death in growing stock and in the first year of life than any other disease. Recognition of this fact has led to much study of avian tumors in recent years.

Lymphomatosis

Although some pathologists do not consider the lymphoid tumors characteristic of this disease to be true neoplasms, it is here considered under that heading for convenience—and not (as readers of the previous section may suppose) because of any innate heterodoxy of the author. Lymphomatosis results from genetic susceptibility to a virus that is remarkable for its ubiquity and the diversity of its effects. There is good evidence that more than one virus may be involved. The characteristic lymphoid tumors are commonly found in the sciatic and brachial nerves, but apparently almost any nerve in the body may be affected (Fig. 110). Visceral organs and the iris are commonly involved, and even osteope-

FIG. 109. A pullet showing typical symptoms of fowl paralysis.

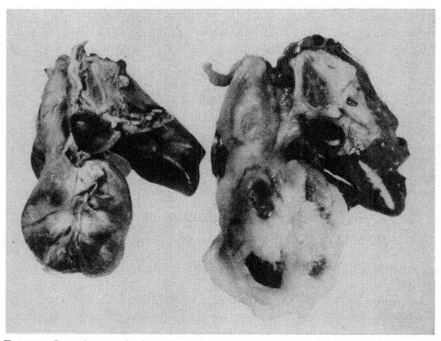

FIG. 110. Lymphomatosis shown by enlargement of the anterior splanchnic nerve in the specimen on the left. This nerve is seen in the picture as a whitish cord running vertically upward from the left side of the spleen. The normal specimen on the right shows more fat but no enlargement of this nerve.

trosis is included by some pathologists among other manifestations of the disease.

Early attempts to control the disease by practising the orthodox procedures of sanitation proved futile. It was soon found that chicks from flocks free of the disease were subject to greater losses when raised on infected premises than were chicks from infected flocks. However, when chicks are reared in complete isolation until about 5 months of age, they are then almost completely resistant to subsequent exposure. This method of control, though effective, is difficult and expensive in practice. Moreover, breeders maintaining their own stock free of disease by this method find it unusually susceptible in the hands of some of their customers.

Evidence of Genetic Resistance. That families differ in susceptibility to the disease was first shown by Asmundson and Biely (1932). This has been confirmed by many others and can be readily seen in the records of any well-exposed flock. Some idea of the variation among sires in this respect is given by the records for 86 White Leghorn cockerels tested in 3 years by Hutt and Cole (1947). Of these, 65 belonged to lines bred for resistance to lymphomatosis, the remainder to a susceptible line. These records (Table 56) illustrate the important points that (1) strains differ in susceptibility, (2) sires differ greatly within strains, and (3) many cockerels must be tested, particularly in susceptible (or unselected) stock to get one or two worth using a second year. Although the general term "neoplasms" is used in Table 56, over 90 per cent of them were cases of lymphomatosis.

In flocks subject to natural infection and selection but not otherwise bred for resistance to lymphomatosis, hens that have survived for at least 2 years produce chicks more resistant to neurolymphomatosis than do pullets that have lived only about a year (Table 57).

Such differences are to be expected only in populations undergoing natural selection, not in those bred for resistance by progeny testing and family selection. In these latter, the pullets are often superior to their dams because they represent one more generation of selection and should, therefore, have more genes for resistance.

Resistant Strains. The feasibility of controlling lymphomatosis genetically was demonstrated by Hutt and Cole (1947, 1948), who developed, by 10 years of selection, two strains of White Leghorns comparatively resistant to it. The experiment differed from other selections for resistance to disease cited earlier in this chapter in that the birds were not inoculated with pathogenic material but were subjected to exposure by natural infection. As Heisdorf et al. (1947) have shown, the difference is important with this disease (and probably with others also) be-

TABLE 56. DISTRIBUTION OF 86 COCKERELS ACCORDING TO MORTALITY IN THEIR DAUGHTERS, (1) FROM NEOPLASMS AND (2) FROM ALL CAUSES, BETWEEN 42 AND 500 DAYS OF AGE

(1) Mortality from neoplasms among daughters, per cent	Sires in		(2) Mortality from all causes among daughters, per cent	Sires in	
	Resistant lines, number	Susceptible line, number		Resistant lines, number	Susceptible line, number
0	5				
0.1–3	12	..	5 –10	1	
3.1–6	13	..	10.1–15	6	
6.1–9	19	1	15.1–20	8	
9.1–12	9	..	20.1–25	13	
12.1–15	3	1	25.1–30	11	1
15.1–18	2	2	30.1–35	8	1
18.1–21	1	3	35.1–40	7	1
21.1–24	1	2	40.1–45	8	2
24.1–27	..	1	45.1–50	2	6
27.1–30	..	3	50.1–55	..	4
30.1–33	..	2	55.1–60	1	1
33.1–36	..	2	60.1–65		
36.1–39	..	1	65.1–70	..	2
39.1–42	..	1	70.1–75	..	3
42.1–45	..	2			
Total.......	65	21	....	65	21

TABLE 57. DIFFERENCES BETWEEN HENS AND PULLETS IN THE SUSCEPTIBILITY OF THEIR OFFSPRING TO FOWL PARALYSIS

Investigator	Paralysis, per cent, in offspring of	
	Hen breeders	Pullet breeders
Kennard (1933), 1931–1932........	12.5	20
Kennard (1933), 1932–1933........	16.0	30
Gildow et al. (1940), series I.......	27.4	34.7
Gildow et al. (1940), series II......	17.0	24.6

cause the genetic resistance is not so well revealed by unnatural infections as by those approaching more nearly the natural method. Adequate exposure was attested by the high incidence of lymphomatosis in a susceptible strain maintained concurrently with the resistant ones. The experiment also differed in that the egg production, size of egg, and body

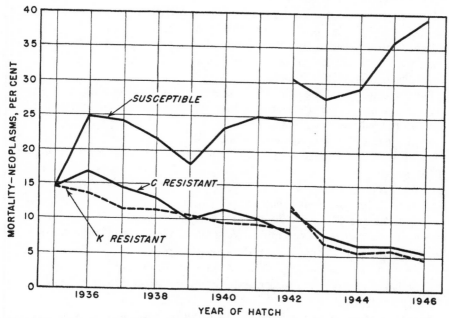

FIG. 111. Differentiation of lines resistant or susceptible to neoplasms as a result of selective breeding during 11 years. The graphs are smoothed by using a 3-year moving average (except for terminal points). Exposure to lymphomatosis was more severe after 1942. (*From Hutt and Cole in Proc. World's Poultry Congr., 8th Congr.*)

weight of the birds were improved at the same time as was their resistance to disease.

Deaths from neoplasms (over 90 per cent of which were cases of lymphomatosis) declined steadily (Fig. 111). The improvement was even more significant than the lines in Fig. 111 suggest because the exposure was much more severe in the last four generations (after the breaks in the lines) than in the earlier ones. Moreover, diagnoses improved, so that obscure manifestations of the disease in some of the smaller nerves (Fig. 110), which had been overlooked in the earlier years, were detected in the later ones. In spite of these factors, deaths from neoplasms in the ninth generation were only 5.4 and 6.3 per cent in the two resistant lines from 42 to 500 days of age. In the daughters of proven sires, they were only 2.0 and 4.4 per cent. At the same time, proven sires in the susceptible strain lost 34 per cent of their daughters from this cause. Deaths from neoplasms were slightly higher in the tenth generation than in the ninth, presumably because of a more severe exposure affecting all three lines.

In the resistant strains even the birds that did die were more resistant than their opposite numbers in the susceptible line, as was indicated by differences in the mean age at death. For the two resistant lines the means were 272 and 304 days, whereas in the susceptible line the mean age at death was only 233 days.

The superior resistance to lymphomatosis of the selected strains was largely responsible for the remarkable decrease in mortality from all causes in these lines (Fig. 103).

Strains can differ, not only in susceptibility to lymphomatosis, but also in the form that is most frequently manifested. Waters and Prickett (1946) found some inbred lines of Leghorns to be more subject to neuro-lymphomatosis and others to show a high incidence of visceral lympho-matosis, with few cases of the neural form, or none. There is some evi-dence that Barred Plymouth Rocks are more likely to show tumors of the viscera and White Leghorns more likely to develop neurolymphomatosis (Davis et al., 1947), but further data on this point and on the general question of differential susceptibility of breeds are desirable. The physi-ological basis of genetic resistance to lymphomatosis has not been ex-tensively studied.

Relation of Genetic Resistance to Control. Some attempts to breed strains resistant to lymphomatosis have reduced losses in a few years almost to the vanishing point, only to be followed by a return of the disease just when success seemed assured. In these cases, the lack of a susceptible strain made it impossible to know whether the chicks were exposed or not, but the reappearance of the disease with full effects sug-gested that its temporary suppression had resulted merely from inade-quate exposure of the chicks. In one case, reduction by breeding of losses from paralysis was later followed by high mortality from visceral lymphomatosis. Since few breeders can afford to maintain a susceptible strain merely to measure the degree of exposure of the flock, the question arises as to what procedure a practical poultry breeder can follow to im-prove the resistance of his flock.

In any infected premises there is little difficulty in ensuring adequate exposure so long as the chicks are brooded in close proximity to adult birds for the first few weeks after hatching. Chicks brooded within 40 feet of older birds for only the first 2 weeks may be exposed more than twice as severely as their full siblings brooded 100 feet from the older birds, even though both lots go to the rearing range at 2 weeks of age (Hutt *et al.*, 1944). In this case attendants going from hen pens to brooder pens may have helped to ensure exposure, but some evidence suggests that the virus may be carried through the air.

The difficulty is not so much to ensure exposure of this sort as, rather, to minimize the financial losses likely to result if the breeder's whole flock of chicks be severely exposed each year. The practical solution may be to expose only two or three of each season's weekly hatches of pedigreed chicks (or enough to provide progeny tests for all unproven cockerels used as breeders) and then to rear the remainder of the chicks in isolation as complete as may be feasible, in order to keep them comparatively free from infection. At any rate, good breeders are now finding that some losses from lymphomatosis in their own flocks are less expensive than sending chicks from unexposed and unselected stock to the infected premises of a customer. The feasibility of increasing genetic resistance while at the same time improving other characteristics of economic value (Fig. 112) has been demonstrated (Hutt et al., 1945; Hutt and Cole, 1947, 1948).

Other Neoplasms

Osteopetrosis gallinarum. This condition, which is characterized by extreme thickening and hardening of the diaphysis in the long bones and also by similar involvements in other parts of the skeleton, has been described in detail by Jungherr and Landauer (1938). It resembles the osteopetrosis, or marble bones, of man. Because it can be transmitted, and apparently caused, by agents inducing lymphoid tumors (Jungherr and Landauer; Burmester *et al.*, 1946), it has been considered as one of the manifestations of avian lymphomatosis. The complexity of the problem is shown by the fact that even in flocks so susceptible that 30 to 50 per cent of the females die from that disease, with every conceivable variation of neural, visceral, or ocular lymphomatosis, there may be not a single case of osteopetrosis in a decade. This has been true of the susceptible strain of White Leghorns at Cornell University to which reference was made in the previous section.

Prior to the studies mentioned above, the author had noted that the only two cases of this abnormality found in a large flock were full brothers and had suggested (1932) that the condition is hereditary. More extensive evidence to that effect was found by Coles and Bronkhorst (1946), who found osteopetrosis occurring spontaneously in White Leghorns. In the year of its greatest frequency (before its complete disappearance 5 years after the first cases were seen) the incidence of the abnormality in different families showed that susceptibility to it is genetic (Table 58).

It is clear from these data that sires and dams differ greatly in the degree of susceptibility or resistance to osteopetrosis transmitted to their offspring. Altogether the available information suggests that the abnor-

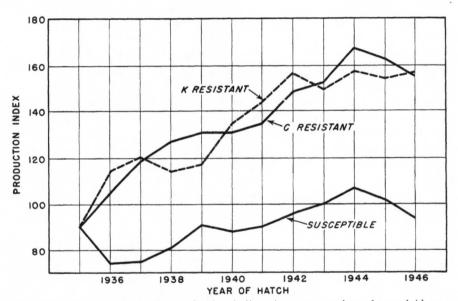

FIG. 112. Showing rise in the production indices (average number of eggs laid per pullet housed) to 500 days of age as a result of the reduction in mortality from lymphomatosis in the two resistant strains and concurrent selection for higher egg production. The lines are smoothed by using a 3-year moving average. Attempts to improve egg production in the susceptible line by selection have had little effect on the index. (*From Hutt and Cole in Proc. World's Poultry Congr., 8th Congr.*)

mality results from specific genetic susceptibility to some agent that may or may not also cause lymphoid tumors. It would appear to be different from some forms of the virus causing the more common manifestations of lymphomatosis.

Sarcomata. Fowls differ genetically in susceptibility to various kinds of sarcomata. These are not spread by contact, and susceptibility is measured by response to inoculation. Resistant birds prevent or retard growth of such tumors, and susceptible fowls do not. Rous and Lange (1914) found Barred Plymouth Rocks more susceptible to a spindle-cell sarcoma (No. 18) than Brown Leghorns, the breed in which it had originated. On the other hand, a sarcoma induced with a chemical carcinogen

TABLE 58. FAMILIAL INCIDENCE OF OSTEOPETROSIS IN 1 YEAR *

Sires	Dams	Progeny	
		Total number	With osteopetrosis, number
13 different sires......	129 different	1,154	0
♂ 2,572.............	8 different	55	0
	E 223	12	3
♂ 2,788.............	10 different	61	0
	E 903	12	1
	E 985	14	2
♂ 2,899.............	6 different	72	0
	E 69	9	4
	E 153	18	7
	E 268	14	4
	E 406	4	1
	E 440	2	1

* Data of Coles and Bronkhorst (1946).

in Brown Leghorns by Greenwood and Peacock (1945) grew better in that breed than did another one derived from Barred Plymouth Rocks. These investigators also observed consistent differences among four in-bred lines of Brown Leghorns in susceptibility to both these tumors. In a different kind of experiment, Cole (1941) differentiated by a few gener-ations of selection two lines of White Leghorns, one highly resistant to a transmissible sarcoma resembling the Rous No. 1, the other highly sus-ceptible (Fig. 113). In the third generation only 12.5 per cent of the resistant line proved susceptible, while the proportion of susceptible chicks was over five times as high in the other line.

RESISTANCE TO PARASITES

Little is known about genetic variations in resistance to parasites apart from some remarkable differences in this respect among species.

A good example of these is provided, within the order Galliformes, by the very high resistance of the domestic fowl and the marked susceptibil-ity of the turkey to the flagellate, *Histomonas meleagridis*, which causes the disease commonly called "blackhead," "enterohepatitis," or "histo-moniasis." In this case the resistance of the fowl might better be called tolerance, because after infection the organism is not repelled or eliminated but is retained in large numbers without causing any visible signs of disease. According to Tyzzer (1932), pheasants are also highly resistant to this protozoon, but several species of North American grouse are susceptible. The fact that some chickens do die of histomoniasis in

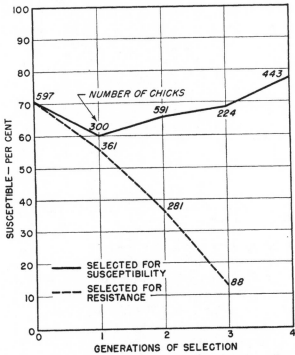

Fig. 113. Differentiation by selection of two lines of White Leghorns, one highly resistant to a transmissible sarcoma, the other highly susceptible. (*From Cole in Cancer Research.*)

flocks of which 99 per cent are resistant suggests that the high resistance of the fowl and the pheasant may have been developed by many centuries of natural selection in Europe and Asia. It seems probable that the susceptibility of the North American gallinaceous birds could be attributed to the fact that they have been exposed to such selection for a comparatively short time. As Tyzzer pointed out, blackhead was apparently responsible, in part at least, for the extinction of the heath hen, a grouse of which the last survivor died on Martha's Vineyard Island in 1935. It is not surprising that the natives of North America, both avian and human, should have proved susceptible to diseases that were quite innocuous to the invaders who brought them from Europe.

Fowls are more resistant than ducks to the fluke *Prosthogonimus macrorchis.* In this case resistance is shown, not, as in the previous instance, by tolerance of the parasite, but by its elimination in 3 to 5 weeks after infection (Macy, 1934). Conversely, chickens are susceptible to the gapeworm Syngamus, which does not survive in the duck. Other cases of host specificity include the complete immunity of the domestic fowl to infection with coccidia of the genus Isospora, for which the natural host is the house (English) sparrow. Conversely, the latter bird is not infected with coccidia of the genus Eimeria, which are commonly found in the fowl (Boughton, 1929).

After infecting representatives of five different breeds of the fowl with embryonated eggs of the nematode *Ascaridia lineata,* Ackert *et al.* (1935) concluded that the White Leghorn is more susceptible to this parasite than other breeds. Susceptibility was measured by the average number and length of worms present 3 weeks after infection. The heavier breeds, Rhode Island Reds and Plymouth Rocks, seemed comparatively resistant. Similarly, Morgan and Wilson (1939) found differences among breeds (all maintained at one laying test) in susceptibility to the caecal worm *Heterakis gallinae,* as measured by the average numbers found at autopsy in birds that had been infected by natural means. These were 217 for White Leghorns, 189 for Rhode Island Reds, and 119 for White Wyandottes.

Evidence recently provided by Ritcher and Insko (1948) suggests that White Leghorns may be less resistant than Rhode Island Reds to infestation with lice, particularly to *Gonioctes gigas,* the large body louse. Among birds originally free of lice that were equally exposed to natural infestation for five months, the mean number of these parasites per bird was found to be in one house about twice as high in the Leghorns as in the Rhode Island Reds, and in another house four times as high.

TOLERANCE OF EXTREME HEAT

It is recognized by experienced poultrymen in North America that during unusually hot weather White Leghorns seem to be less affected than the heavier breeds. In one heat wave at Ithaca, New York, during which maximum temperatures for 3 consecutive days were higher than in the 11 years preceding, it was found that the deaths from heat were only 1.8 per cent in White Leghorns, but about three times as high in Rhode Island Reds and Barred Plymouth Rocks (Hutt, 1938a). On the hottest days, deaths in the heavy breeds were five times as high as in the Leghorns. There was no great difference between the Reds and the Rocks in this respect, but both proved significantly more susceptible than the White Leghorns.

It is quite possible that this genetic difference might not be evident in other parts of the world where annual exposure to severe heat has regularly eliminated susceptible stock. In such places, one would expect all indigenous stocks to be highly resistant. In the case mentioned above, the maximum temperature on the hottest day was only 103° F. in the shade, a figure at which the hardy hens of Aden and Massaua might well turn up their beaks in disdain. As Yeates *et al.* (1942) showed, the degree of discomfort depends, not on temperature alone, but also on the relative humidity. In their experiments, White Leghorns were consistently more resistant to high temperatures and high humidities than Australorps. After 7 hours at 95°F., rectal temperatures of the Australorps were 0.8 to 3.9° higher than in White Leghorns, when the humidity ranged from 45 to 95 per cent. With humidity of 75 and 85 per cent, some Australorps could not stand exposure to 100° F. for 7 hours, but all the Leghorns that were tested could do so.

Physiological Basis. The greater resistance of the Leghorns is apparently not related to their smaller size. Contrary to common belief, laying hens are no more susceptible than non-layers, provided that they are not unduly confined in hot trap nests (Hutt, 1938a). Hens dying from the heat did not differ from controls in current or antecedent egg production. Birds over 2 years old were more susceptible than younger ones. Apart from these facts, the basis for the greater resistance of the White Leghorn to heat is unknown. It may be related to their color, but it seems more likely that the underlying reason may be the same superior control over its thermoregulatory mechanism that is responsible for the comparatively rapid rise of the Leghorn chick's temperature in the first 10 days after hatching.

In turkeys, a somewhat indirect effect of extreme heat is shown by the birds genetically susceptible to the development of pendulous crops (page 240). That abnormality is associated, in susceptible birds, with excessive consumption of water when a combination of high temperature and low humidity causes intense thirst (Asmundson and Hinshaw, 1938).

Genetic differences in ability to tolerate extreme heat deserve further study. The resistance that characterizes the White Leghorn should be of value in hot climates throughout the world. This does not necessarily mean that Leghorns would be more valuable than native breeds in such places. On the contrary, they are likely to be susceptible to any diseases to which they have not been exposed. It is possible, however, that the superior heat tolerance of the Leghorn could be utilized by crossing with other breeds, just as the same thing has been introduced from zebus to cattle of European origin in the southern part of the United States, in India, and in Brazil. One must also recognize that the indigenous breeds of fowls in the hot areas are likely to be already highly resistant to extreme heat (and to prevailing diseases) as a result of natural selection. It might, therefore, be good policy in such places to improve those breeds with respect to economic characters and thus retain what has been established by natural selection.

NUTRITIONAL REQUIREMENTS

It is convenient to consider genetic variations in nutritional requirements in this chapter because one of them, at least, causes a pathological condition, even in what might be considered a normal environment, while others are revealed only by deficient diets.

Perosis and Manganese. The abnormality known as slipped tendon, or perosis, is characterized by enlargement of the tarso-metatarsal joint, often unilateral, and appears at 3 to 8 weeks of age (Fig. 114).

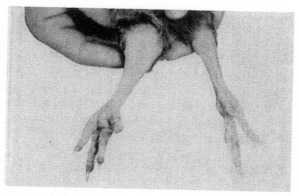

FIG. 114. Slipped tendon, or perosis. (*Courtesy of L. C. Norris.*)

The tibia and tarso-metatarsus become curved, frequently causing the tendon from the gastrocnemius muscle to slip from the intercondylar groove. In extreme cases, the leg cannot be flexed and is extended rigidly, often rotated to one side. Bone ash and blood calcium are normal. The discovery by Wilgus *et al.* (1937) that most cases are prevented by adding manganese to the diet showed that an unusually high requirement of that element is largely responsible for the abnormality.

Prior to that discovery, Serfontein and Payne (1934), noting that the frequency of perosis was 14 per cent in their Rhode Island Reds but only 0.7 per cent in White Leghorns, had shown that susceptibility to it was genetic. When Rhode Island Red chicks were raised on a diet inducing perosis, the following difference was evident between those from two types of parents:

Parents	Progeny	
	Number	With perosis, per cent
Normal when chicks.......	102	18.6
Showing perosis as chicks, but recovered..........	112	50.0

So far as the author is aware, this was the first experimental evidence that by selection strains could be made to differ in response to an inadequate diet. It was later found that, while 30 parts of manganese per million prevented perosis in all Leghorns and 50 p.p.m. did so in most New Hampshires, some of the latter showed the abnormality even when getting 100 p.p.m. (Gallup and Norris, 1939). It is now known that some birds need, not only more manganese than others for normal osteogenesis, but also more choline, and that all require biotin. The fact that perosis is rare in Leghorns but still occurs in some chicks of the heavier breeds, even on supposedly optimum diets, shows that these cases result from abnormal requirements for which the basis is genetic.

Thiamine (Vitamin B_1). On diets deficient in thiamine, fowls develop polyneuritis, which is characterized by unsteady gait, diarrhoea, trembling, tetanic spasms, and opisthotonos. In the last-named state, the head and tail are brought almost together over the back, and the legs are extended and held rigid (Fig. 115). Paralysis of muscles of the alimentary tract may cause death from choking with food returned to the mouth. Recovery follows rapidly when thiamine is supplied (Fig. 116).

It was found by Nichita et al. (1934) that Rhode Island Reds, 10 months old, when put on diets lacking vitamin B_1, showed the onset of polyneuritis at 7 to 19 days, and those not fed yeast died at 9 to 21 days. At the same time (Nichita and Iftimesco, 1934) White Leghorns showed no sign of polyneuritis until 41 and 107 days, and another bird was unaffected at 78 days. Further evidence of the lower requirement

FIG. 115. Polyneuritis and opisthotonos developed by a White Wyandotte cockerel after 24 days on a diet of degerminated white corn, grit, and water. (*Courtesy of C. W. Carrick.*)

FIG. 116. The bird shown in Fig. 115, recovered after 1 week on a diet of white corn germs, grit, and water. (*Courtesy of C. W. Carrick.*)

of thiamine by White Leghorns was provided by Lamoreux and Hutt (1939*a*) in a series of four experiments with chicks. When these were given a diet deficient in thiamine, the mean ages at death in the two breeds compared were as follows:

Regimen	White Leghorns	Rhode Island Reds
On deficient diet from hatching..............	12.9	10.9
Same, except for normal diet on third day only..	22.1	17.0
Normal diet to 2 weeks, deficient one thereafter..	34.2	29.0

When other chicks were placed at 3 weeks of age on the diet deficient in thiamine, the proportion of survivors was consistently higher in White Leghorns than in Rhode Island Reds and Barred Rocks (Fig. 117). It seems probable, therefore, that the White Leghorns differ, not merely from Rhode Island Reds, but from the heavy breeds as a class in their resistance to a deficiency of thiamine.

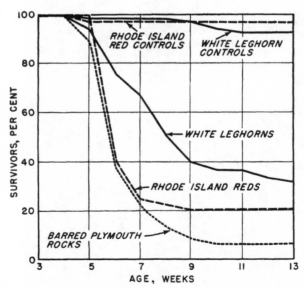

FIG. 117. White Leghorn chicks withstand a deficiency of thiamine better than those of some heavy breeds. This is shown by the higher proportion of survivors among the Leghorns when all three breeds were put on a diet deficient in thiamine at 3 weeks of age. (*From Lamoreux and Hutt in J. Agr. Research.*)

The genetic and physiological bases for this difference are not known, but it is clear that their remarkable ability to withstand a deficiency of thiamine is just as much a breed characteristic of the White Leghorn as are the dominant white, the lopping single comb, and other distinguishing features. As with other physiological differences between the White Leghorns and the heavy breeds, it seems probable that the ability to tolerate diets low in thiamine is a characteristic of Leghorns as a class, rather than of white ones as a color variety (Hutt, 1941). Chicks of the F_1 generation from the cross Rhode Island Red ♀ ♀ × White Leghorn ♂ were apparently intermediate between the two parental breeds in requirement of thiamine, a situation that would be expected if multiple factors were responsible for the difference between the breeds.

It is doubtful that the ability to tolerate diets low in thiamine has any great value for domestic fowls receiving modern diets. Most of these apparently contain thiamine in excess of the requirements. It is quite possible that a low requirement of thiamine might permit survival under some conditions less favorable. One recalls that the classical experiments of Eijkman showing the relation of a diet of polished rice to beriberi were prompted by his observation that fowls fed on the garbage of his prison hospital in Java developed symptoms of paralysis and of polyneuritis much like those of his patients with beriberi.

A more important expression of this genetically low requirement of thiamine is the ability of White Leghorns to deposit 60 to 66 per cent more of it in their eggs (page 392) than do Rhode Island Reds and Barred Plymouth Rocks when all three are maintained on the same diet (Scrimshaw et al., 1945). This suggests that the fundamental character in the Leghorns is some peculiar physiological trait that permits them to utilize thiamine more efficiently than can the heavy breeds.

Riboflavin. Evidence of genetic differences among White Leghorns in the utilization of riboflavin was found by Davis et al. (1938) in five families (each containing three full sisters) that were maintained on a diet deficient in riboflavin. The hatchability of fertile eggs (which is an indication either of the reserve maintained by the hen or the requirement of the embryo, or both) ranged in these families from 2 to 63 per cent.

Subsequently, Lamoreux and Hutt (1948) differentiated by selection two strains of Leghorns, one of which was comparatively resistant to a deficiency of riboflavin and the other relatively susceptible. Chicks of the resistant strain, when reared on a diet deficient in riboflavin, survived better and grew faster than did controls and chicks of the susceptible strain. Since these differences between the strains disappeared when chicks were raised on a diet containing ample riboflavin, it was clear that the resistant and susceptible strains did not differ in growth and viability when on normal feed but specifically in ability to tolerate a diet deficient in riboflavin.

Vitamin D. The amount of this vitamin needed in the feed for normal calcification of the long bones by Rhode Island Red chicks was found by Olsson in two series of thorough tests (1941, 1948) to be 2.6 and 2.75 times the amount required by White Leghorns. In still another experiment, when no vitamin D was supplied in the feed, the period of irradiation with ultraviolet light necessary to induce a given degree of calcification was found to be 3.6 times as long for Rhode Island Reds as for White Leghorns. These highly significant differences were consistent in all comparisons of the two breeds, and were evident at 7 to 28 days of age. At that time these two breeds do not ordinarily differ in rate of growth, and Olsson's Rhode Island Reds actually weighed less than the Leghorns. For that reason, the higher requirement of the Rhode Island Reds at that age cannot be attributed to more rapid growth, as could a similar difference at 8 to 10 weeks of age. It results from genetic differences between the breeds. This interpretation may not apply to the Light Sussex chicks, which Olsson (1948) found to require 1.6 times as much vitamin D as White Leghorns, for they grew more rapidly than the Leghorns, even at 7 to 21 days of age when the comparisons were made.

Apart from differences between breeds, it seems probable that there are also remarkable genetic differences within breeds with respect to requirement of vitamin D. In northern latitudes, a supplement of this vitamin is considered indispensable in winter, and, for birds not receiving direct sunlight, in summer also. Olsson (1936) found that even as far north as southern Sweden some White Leghorn hens are able to maintain satisfactory egg production and hatchability without any supplement of vitamin D whatever, while others cannot do so. Although such differences within a breed have not yet been shown to be of genetic origin, it seems probable that individuals, like breeds, may differ genetically in their requirement of vitamin D. In that case, as Olsson aptly pointed out, the selection of breeders should be made from flocks on diets with minimal levels of vitamin D rather than with optimal ones.

Dysgenic Nutrition. Poultrymen have failed thus far to grasp the significance of the fact that diets for domestic fowls of all ages are now so formulated as to provide protection against shortage of every constituent known to be essential. This is done without any consideration of the extreme variation among individuals with respect to their requirements of those constituents. In other words, the diet is made to protect the weakest, least fit bird in the flock. This enhances the usual tendency of domestication to permit much greater variation in a domesticated animal than is possible for the same species in nature.

The case may be illustrated by the conclusion of Ringrose and Norris (1936) that the minimum requirement of vitamin A for Leghorn chicks during the first 8 weeks of life is about 150 U.S.P. units per 100 gm. of feed. In their tests, 50 chicks receiving only two-thirds of that amount were slightly lower in weight than those getting 150 units (though not significantly so), but only one out of 50 exhibited any sign of deficiency of vitamin A. The protection of the weakest 2 per cent may be desirable from the standpoint of the feed manufacturer and may even appear so to the poultryman. Obviously, it is preferable from the standpoint of future generations of domestic fowls to set the level of vitamin A at only 100 units, to eliminate the abnormal chicks and to pass along to posterity strains of fowls from which the extreme variants in the direction of unfitness have been systematically eliminated. Selection of that sort is not necessary for birds that are all to be marketed, but it is highly desirable for any flocks from which breeders are to be selected.

This is especially so in the case of expensive supplements like vitamin A, and perhaps vitamin D. It probably costs the Leghorn raiser little to feed his birds the extra manganese which they do not need but which now goes into all mashes in order to protect the heavy breeds. One of the important steps in educating the poultryman about genetic differences in nutritional requirements is to convince him that the feed manufacturer should not be blamed if 5 per cent of the chicks on his feed are diagnosed by some nutritionist or veterinarian as having dermatitis, encephalomalacia, or any other condition that can be attributed to deficiency of some vitamin or mineral. So long as the diet is adequate for 95 per cent of the flock, it is far better to have the weaklings eliminated than to save them. An ideal situation would be to have for broilers a diet replete with maximum levels of everything needed but to provide for potential breeding stock mashes with something less than the levels now used to protect the weaklings.

SUSCEPTIBILITY OF TRANSFERRED STOCK

As with other species of domestic animals, breeds and strains of fowls that have been bred to a point of excellent performance in one part of the world often prove quite unsuitable when transferred to another. This is particularly the case with birds imported to tropical countries from Europe and North America. In most cases the imported stock is susceptible to diseases and parasites to which it had not previously been exposed. By contrast the native fowls are much hardier.

Exact data on the viability of imported and native stocks are not easy to obtain because the two kinds are not always kept under identical conditions. Morcos *et al.* (1946) report that spirochaetosis causes much greater losses among imported breeds than in the native Egyptian fowls. It is not clear whether this is because of genetic differences only or whether the native birds acquire some immunity because of different environment during rearing. The author is indebted to Mr. Henry Hirst, of the Department of Agriculture, Malta, for records of three imported breeds and of native stock that were all hatched in the same incubators and reared under identical conditions. Among these, the mortality during the first month after hatching was as follows:

Breed	Chicks, number	Died, per cent
White Leghorns.............	589	26
Rhode Island Reds..........	1,201	21
Buff Plymouth Rocks........	639	32
Maltese Blacks.............	626	7

In this case the high mortality among chicks of the imported breeds could not be ascribed to any specific cause. Similar reports, but with less quantitative data, have been made from India, Africa, the Malay Peninsula, and the West Indies. In most such cases, the breeders have sought to produce suitable poultry by crossing the native stock with the imported to combine the good features of both. It is important to recognize that the native stocks, though sometimes described in disparaging terms as unimproved stock, have really been developed by natural selection to a point at which their genes for resistance to disease make a contribution to the crossbred that is just as important as are the imported genes for egg production and size of body. It would be interesting to determine how quickly the native stocks could be improved in size and egg production by selection, without any crossing, but using progeny tests on an extensive scale.

One must not suppose that the problem, in these transfers of stock, is limited merely to the susceptibility of birds raised in temperate zones to new diseases encountered in the tropics. For some years the author maintained at Cornell University a stock of the Red Jungle Fowl that came originally from Indo-China. These suffered much higher mortality during the period of growth than did the other birds reared on the same range at the same time. While no one particular cause seemed responsible for the difference, it was evident that the Jungle Fowls were more susceptible to blackhead (histomoniasis) than the other birds. Similarly, Cambar chicks hatched at Cornell from birds imported from England, though fine and vigorous to 6 weeks of age, subsequently suffered losses in the next 4 months that were three times as high as in chickens of North American stock reared with them on the same range. This is no reflection on the Cambars as a breed. Mr. Michael Pease, who kindly supplied the stock, stated that losses to the extent suffered at Cornell were unheard of in the related stock at Cambridge. It is quite probable that highly viable strains from Cornell might prove similarly susceptible, even in other temperate parts of the world.

Literature Cited

Ackert, J. E., L. L. Eisenbrandt, J. H. Wilmoth, B. Glading, and I. Pratt. 1935. Comparative resistance of five breeds of chickens to the nematode *Ascaridia lineata* (Schneider). *J. Agr. Research,* **50**:607–624.

Asmundson, V. S., and J. Biely. 1932. Inheritance of resistance to fowl paralysis (*Neurolymphomatosis gallinarum*). I. Differences in susceptibility. *Can. J. Research,* **6**:171–175.

———— and W. R. Hinshaw. 1938. On the inheritance of pendulous crop in turkeys (*Meleagris gallopavo*). *Poultry Sci.,* **17**:276–285.

Bostian, C. H., and R. S. Dearstyne. 1944. The influence of breeding on the livability of poultry. *North Carolina Agr. Expt. Sta. Tech. Bull.* **791**.

Boughton, D. C. 1929. A note on coccidiosis in sparrows and poultry. *Poultry Sci.,* **8**:184–188.

Bryant, R. L. 1946. Breeding Leghorn chickens to increase the life span. *Virginia Agr. Expt. Sta. Tech. Bull.* **99**.

Burmester, B. R. 1945. The incidence of lymphomatosis among male and female chickens. *Poultry Sci.,* **24**:469–472.

———— and N. M. Nelson. 1945. The effect of castration and sex hormones upon the incidence of lymphomatosis in chickens. *Poultry Sci.,* **24**:509–515.

————, C. O. Prickett, and T. C. Belding. 1946. A filtrable agent producing lymphoid tumors and osteopetrosis in chickens. *Cancer Research,* **6**:189–196.

Cole, R. K. 1941. Genetic resistance to a transmissible sarcoma in the fowl. *Cancer Research,* **1**:714–720.

Coles, J. D. W. A., and J. J. Bronkhorst. 1946. The familial incidence of spontaneous *Osteopetrosis gallinarum. Onderstepoort J. Vet. Sci. Animal Indust.,* **21**:79–98.

Davis, H. J., L. C. Norris, and G. F. Heuser. 1938. Further evidence of the amount of vitamin G required for reproduction in poultry. *Poultry Sci.,* **17**:87–93.

Davis, O. S., L. P. Doyle, F. L. Walkey, and L. K. Cenker. 1947. Studies in avian leukosis III. The incidence of avian leukosis in various breeds of chickens. *Poultry Sci.,* **26**:499–507.

DeVolt, H. M., G. D. Quigley, and T. C. Byerly. 1941. Studies of resistance to pullorum disease in chickens. *Poultry Sci.,* **20**:339–341.

Dudley, F. J. 1928. The death rate of three standard breeds of fowl during the pullet year. *Poultry Sci.,* **7**:245–253.

442 GENETICS OF THE FOWL

Fenn, W. O. 1922. The temperature coefficient of phagocytosis. *J. Gen. Physiol.*, **4**:331–345.

Frateur, J. L. 1924. The hereditary resistance of the fowl to the bacillus of diphtheria. *Proc. World's Poultry Congr. 2d Congr., Barcelona:* 68–71.

Gallup, W. D., and L. C. Norris. 1939. The amount of manganese required to prevent perosis in the chick. *Poultry Sci.*, **18**:76–82.

Gildow, E. M., J. K. Williams, and C. E. Lampman. 1940. The transmission of and resistance to fowl paralysis (lymphomatosis). *Idaho Agr. Expt. Sta. Bull.* 235.

Greenwood, A. W., and P. R. Peacock. 1945. The influence of genetic factors on the transmissibility of fowl sarcomas. *Brit. J. Exptl. Pathol.*, **26**:357–361.

Harris, J. A., and D. C. Boughton. 1928. The death rates of three standard breeds of fowl. *Poultry Sci.*, **7**:120–131.

Heisdorf, A. J., N. R. Brewer, and W. F. Lamoreux. 1947. The genetic relationship between mortality from induced and spontaneous lymphomatosis. *Poultry Sci.*, **26**:67–73.

Hodgson, G. C., and H. S. Gutteridge. 1941. A progress report from Canada of research on breast blisters. *U.S. Egg Poultry Mag.*, **47**:150–155.

Hutt, F. B. 1932. Eight new mutations in the domestic fowl. *Proc. Intern. Genetic. Congr. 6th Congr.*, **2**:96–97.

——. 1935. On the physiological basis of genetic resistance to *Salmonella pullorum* in the fowl. *Am. Naturalist,* **69**:66–67.

——. 1938. The geneticist's objectives in poultry improvement. *Am. Naturalist,* **72**:268–284.

——. 1938a. Genetics of the fowl. VII. Breed differences in susceptibility to extreme heat. *Poultry Sci.*, **17**:454–462.

——. 1941. The association of physiological traits with breed characteristics in the fowl. *Proc. Intern. Genetic. Congr. 7th Congr., Edinburgh, 1939:*156–157.

——, R. K. Cole, M. Ball, J. H. Bruckner, and R. F. Ball. 1944. A relation between environment to two weeks of age and mortality from lymphomatosis in adult fowls. *Poultry Sci.*, **23**:396–404.

——, ——, and J. H. Bruckner. 1945. A test of fowls bred for resistance to lymphomatosis. *Poultry Sci.*, **24**:564–571.

—— and ——. 1947. Genetic control of lymphomatosis in the fowl. *Science,* **106**:379–384.

—— and ——. 1948. The development of strains genetically resistant to avian lymphomatosis. *Proc. World's Poultry Congr. 8th Congr., Copenhagen,* **1**:719–725.

—— and J. C. Scholes. 1941. Genetics of the fowl. XIII. Breed differences in susceptibility to *Salmonella pullorum*. *Poultry Sci.*, **20**:342–352.

Jungherr, E., and W. Landauer. 1938. Studies on fowl paralysis. 3. A condition resembling osteopetrosis (marble bone) in the common fowl. *Storrs (Conn.) Agr. Expt. Sta. Bull.* 222.

Kelly, J. W., and R. S. Dearstyne. 1935. Hematology of the fowl: A. Studies on normal chick and normal adult blood. B. Studies on the hematology of chicks suffering from pullorum infection and on adult carriers of pullorum disease. *North Carolina Agr. Expt. Sta. Tech. Bull.* 50.

Kennard, D. C. 1933. Pullet mortality. *Poultry Sci.*, **12**:335–336.

Kondra, P. A., and J. R. Cavers. 1947. Relation of the rate of feathering to the development of keel bursae. *Poultry Sci.*, **26**:83–85.

Lambert, W. V. 1932. Natural resistance to disease in the chicken: I. The effect of selective breeding on natural resistance to fowl typhoid. *J. Immunol.* **23**:229-240. II. Bacteriological studies upon surviving birds of resistant stock in relation to progeny resistance. III. The comparative resistance of different breeds. *J. Immunol.*, 241-251, 253-260.

Lamoreux, W. F., and F. B. Hutt. 1939. Variability of body temperature in the normal chick. *Poultry Sci.*, **18**:70-75.

—— and ——. 1939a. Breed differences in resistance to a deficiency of vitamin B_1 in the fowl. *J. Agr. Research*, **58**:307-316.

—— and ——. 1948. Genetic resistance to deficiency of riboflavin in the chick. *Poultry Sci.*, **27**:334-341.

Lerner, I. M., L. W. Taylor, and R. E. Lubbehusen. 1939. The relation of winter production to subsequent mortality from various causes. *Poultry Sci.*, **18**:457-463.

Macy, R. W. 1934. Studies on the taxonomy, morphology, and biology of *Prosthogonimus macrorchis* Macy, a common oviduct fluke of domestic fowls in North America. *Minnesota Agr. Expt. Sta. Tech. Bull.* 98.

Madsen, D. E. 1937. An erysipelas outbreak in turkeys. *J. Am. Vet. Med. Assoc.*, **91**:206-208.

Marble, D. R. 1939. Breeding poultry for viability. *Pennsylvania Agr. Expt. Sta. Bull.* 377.

Marine, D., and S. H. Rosen. 1940. Increase in the incidence of lymphomatosis in male fowls by castration. *Am. J. Cancer*, **39**:315-318.

—— and ——. 1941. Sex hormones and lymphomatosis in fowls. *Proc. Soc. Exptl. Biol. Med.*, **47**:61-62.

Morcos, Z., O. A. Zaki, and R. Zaki. 1946. A concise investigation of fowl spirochetosis in Egypt. *J. Am. Vet. Med. Assoc.*, **109**:112-116.

Morgan, D. O., and J. E. Wilson. 1939. The occurrence of *Heterakis gallinae* in poultry and its relation to disease, breed, and to other helminths. *J. Helminthol.*, **17**:177-182.

Munro, S. S. 1936. The relation of production to mortality in the domestic fowl. *J. Agr. Sci.*, **26**:101-113.

Nichita, G., and G. Iftimesco. 1934. Recherches sur l'avitaminose du complexe B chez les poules Leghorn Blanches. *Ann. inst. nat. zootech. Roumanie*, **3**:79-109.

——, N. Tuschak, and C. Calcef. 1934. Recherches sur l'avitaminose du complexe B chez les poules Rhode Island Red. *Ann. inst. nat. zootech. Roumanie*, **3**:35-78.

Olsson, N. 1936. Några synpunkter på hönsens D-vitaminbehov och i samband därmed stående faktorer. *Nord. Jordbrugsforskning*, **17-18**:185-218.

——. 1941. "Studien über die Verwendbarkeit wachsender Küken zur Bestimmung des antirhachitischen Effekts von Vitamin D und ultra-violettem Licht." Lund. Gleerupska Universitetsbokhandeln.

——. 1948. Investigation on the vitamin D requirements of chicks, poults, ducklings and goslings. Lantbruks-Högskol. Ann. (Uppsala), **16**:1-38.

Pasteur, Joubert, and Chamberland. 1878. Sur le charbon des poules. *Compt. rend. acad. sci.*, **87**:47-48.

Platt, C. S. 1935. Egg production and mortality in White Leghorn pullets in the Vineland contests. *Poultry Sci.*, **14**:294-295.

Ringrose, R. C., and L. C. Norris. 1936. A study of the vitamin A requirement of the chick during early life. *Poultry Sci.*, **15**:390-396.

Ritcher, P. O., and W. M. Insko, Jr. 1948. External parasites of chickens and their control. *Kentucky Agr. Expt. Sta. Bull.* 517.

Roberts, E., and L. E. Card. 1935. Inheritance of resistance to bacterial infection in animals. A genetic study of pullorum disease. *Illinois Agr. Expt. Sta. Bull.* 419.

Rous, P., and L. B. Lange. 1914. On the greater susceptibility of an alien variety of host to an avian tumor. *J. Exptl. Med.,* **20**:413–418.

Scholes, J. C. 1942. Experiments with X-rays on the roles of lymphocytes and body temperatures in the resistance of chicks to *Salmonella pullorum. Poultry Sci.,* **21**:561–565.

—— and F. B. Hutt. 1942. The relationship between body temperature and genetic resistance to *Salmonella pullorum* in the fowl. *Cornell Univ. Agr. Expt. Sta. Mem.* 244.

Scrimshaw, N. S., F. B. Hutt, and M. Scrimshaw. 1945. The effect of genetic variation in the fowl on the thiamine content of the egg. *J. Nutrition,* **30**:375–383.

Serfontein, P. J., and L. F. Payne. 1934. Inheritance of abnormal anatomical condition in the tibial metatarsal joints. *Poultry Sci.,* **13**:61–63.

Severens, J. M., E. Roberts, and L. E. Card. 1944. A study of the defense mechanism involved in hereditary resistance to pullorum disease of the domestic fowl. *J. Infectious Diseases,* **75**:33–46.

Sturkie, P. D. 1943. Five years of selection for viability in White Leghorn chickens. *Poultry Sci.,* **22**:155–160.

Tyzzer, E. E. 1932. Problems and observations concerning the transmission of blackhead infection in turkeys. *Am. Phil. Soc. Proc.,* **71**:407–410.

Waters, N. F., and C. O. Prickett. 1946. Types of lymphomatosis among different inbred lines of chickens. *Poultry Sci.,* **25**:501–508.

Wilgus, H. S., Jr., L. C. Norris, and G. F. Heuser. 1937. The role of manganese and certain other trace elements in the prevention of perosis. *J. Nutrition,* **14**:155–167.

Yeates, N. T. M., D. H. K. Lee, and H. J. G. Hines. 1942. Reactions of domestic fowls to hot atmospheres. *Proc. Royal Soc. Queensland,* **53**:105–128.

CHAPTER 13

GENETIC ASPECTS OF REPRODUCTION

Although a separate, detailed account of the physiology of avian reproduction and the endocrinology pertinent thereto is beyond the scope of this book, these subjects have already been treated to some extent wherever consideration of them was relevant to the subject under discussion, particularly in the chapter on Egg Production. The present chapter will deal only with certain aspects of reproduction which cannot be excluded from any complete account of the action of genes in the fowl but which have not thus far been mentioned. These include (1) physiology of reproduction in the male, (2) fertility, (3) embryonic mortality, (4) sex ratios, (5) sex dimorphism, (6) sex reversal, and (7) gynandromorphs and mosaics.

PHYSIOLOGY OF REPRODUCTION IN THE MALE

The Reproductive System. Formation of the gonads and the earlier stages of gametogenesis were considered in Chap. 2, and the formation of eggs was reviewed in Chap. 10, together with some account of factors influencing that process. It is in order now to consider briefly the homologous process in the male, *i.e.*, the production of spermatozoa. The male reproductive tract, which is paired throughout, consists of the testis, epididymis, and vas deferens. Seminal vesicles are lacking, unless the dilated distal ends of the vasa deferentia be considered as such, and accessory glands corresponding to those of mammals have not been demonstrated in the fowl. The testis consists of many seminiferous tubules. One may see in properly prepared sections of active tubules successive stages of spermatogenesis from primary spermatocytes near the wall of the tubule to free spermatozoa in the lumen (Fig. 118). These spermatozoa are collected in the epididymis and thence conveyed in the convoluted vas deferens to the cloaca. According to Burrows and Quinn (1937), the vasa deferentia empty into ducts in walls of the large intestine, and these, in turn, pass into the dorsal quadrants of the internal sphincter muscle. From that they emerge as two elongated papillae overlying the rudimentary copulatory organ on the ventral surface of the cloaca.

In chicks, as in other birds, the left testis is usually slightly larger
at hatching than the right one, but the difference is lost as the bird gets
older. Mimura (1928) found that after a year the right was the larger
in 43 per cent of his males. He also noted that the melanic pigment
commonly seen in chick testes is more abundant in the left one than in
the right. Although several theories have been advanced to account for
the asymmetrical development of the gonads in birds, particularly in the

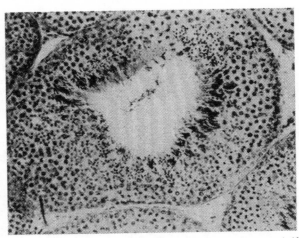

Fig. 118. Photomicrograph of a section through an active seminiferous tubule,
showing cells in successive stages of spermatogenesis from primary spermatocytes
near the outer wall to free spermatozoa in the lumen. (*From Miller in Anat.
Record.*)

female, none seems to meet with universal acceptance. Reviews of the
problem will be found in the papers by Witschi (1935) and Stanley and
Witschi (1940).

Spermatozoa of gallinaceous birds have a short sharp acrosome at the
tip, a slender curved head which contains the nucleus, a middle piece
below the head, and a long flagellum, or tail. The latter comprises about
75 per cent of the total length of the spermatozoon (Fig. 119), which
is not likely to exceed 0.095 mm. The minute size of these cells is indicated by the fact that their number was found to range from 825,000
to over 7,000,000 per cubic millimetre of semen, with an average of
4,015,088 for 36 samples (Hutt, 1929). Wheeler and Andrews (1943)
observed a similar range, with a maximum count of 10,200,000, and an
average of 3,200,000 for 2,697 samples. From studies of the internal
structure of the head by reactions to different stains, Adamstone and

Card (1934) concluded that it contains globules of fatty materials which serve as food material after the spermatozoon is released.

It was shown by Munro (1938) that spermatozoa taken from the testis and the epididymis are immature, less motile, and less able to effect fertility than those from the vas deferens. Apparently a maturing or ripening stage is necessary, but it must be short, for spermatozoa were shown to pass from the testis to the cloacal end of the vas deferens in 24 hours. This applied in active males; in others, the process took three to

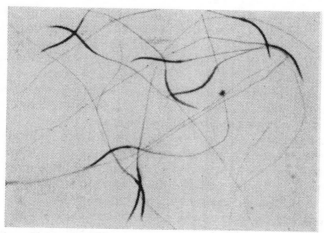

Fig. 119. Photomicrograph of spermatozoa of the turkey, which are indistinguishable from those of the fowl.

four times as long. It was also found (Munro, 1938a) that the male hormone is apparently not a factor in ripening the spermatozoa.

Semen. The introduction of new techniques for artificial insemination as a useful practice in poultry breeding (Burrows and Quinn, 1935, 1939) led to study of various factors influencing the production of semen. Burrows and Titus (1939) found this process to be just beginning at 222 days of age in crossbred males and that in mature males the amount produced (about 1 cc. daily) was not related to the degree of sexual activity or to the size of the comb and wattles. Their finding that it is highly correlated with the size of the testes was confirmed by Lamoreux (1943), who showed that both the size of the testes and the yield of semen were greatly increased by exposure of the males to 12 hours or more of light daily. Maximum response was obtained about 1 month after treatment with light began. According to Wheeler and Andrews (1943) the largest volumes of semen are produced between November and March, but the density of spermatozoa was highest, in their birds, between May and August. The average number of spermatozoa per sample of semen (which at 0.41 cc. was much smaller than the average yield obtained by Burrows and Titus), was about 1.3 billion,. and the maximum number was in excess of 10 billion.

A genetic influence on the production of semen was demonstrated by Jones and Lamoreux (1942), who compared males of two strains of Leghorns, one characterized by early maturity and high egg production of the females, the other by late maturity and extremely low fecundity. Although the males of the two strains did not differ in size of testes, those of the high-fecundity strain produced a significantly greater volume of semen than the others. This was evident at 12 weeks of age, when the first samples were obtained, and the difference was consistently maintained at later ages. Sections of the testes showed that spermatogenesis was proceeding more actively in males of the high-fecundity strain than in the other. This interesting study indicates that, although egg production is a sex-limited character, the genes accelerating that process in females have a corresponding effect in the males. These genes might perhaps be considered, not merely as genes for egg production, but rather as genes affecting gametogenesis in general.

An interesting point brought out in this study by the comparisons at 12 and 26 weeks is that genetically determined early maturity, though most easily recognized in females by the laying of their first egg, has its counterpart in early activity of the gonads in the males. This was confirmed by Lorenz and Lerner (1946), who found significant differences in this respect among families of cockerels (and of male turkeys) from different sires.

Although dubbing (cutting of the comb and wattles) has no effect on the size of testes or yield of semen (Lamoreux and Jones, 1942; Searcy and Andrews, 1943), this does not necessarily refute the opinion of some poultrymen that dubbed males are more fertile than others.

FERTILITY

Site of Fertilization. The former belief that spermatozoa travelled up the oviduct by rheotaxis, *i.e.*, by orienting their heads toward an outward oviducal current, was disproved experimentally by Parker (1932). He concluded that in birds the spermatozoa are carried to the isthmus of the oviduct by muscular contraction in an antiperistaltic direction and thence to the infundibulum by a current set up by cilia beating in the direction of the ovary (Parker, 1930). These pro-ovarian cilia were found in a band covering about one-quarter of the circumference of the oviduct. Abovarian cilia, beating toward the cloaca, characterize the remainder of the albumen-secreting part of the oviduct, the uterus, and the vagina. On the other hand, Mimura (1939), who found that spermatozoa traverse the entire oviduct in 26 minutes, unless temporarily delayed by an egg in the albumen-secreting portion, considered that such rapid transit must be induced by muscular activity of the oviduct.

The general opinion that fertilization occurs either in the body cavity or soon after the ovum is engulfed by the infundibulum was brought into question by the demonstration by Ivanov (1924) that it is possible to obtain fertile eggs up to 3 weeks after the entire oviduct and body cavity have been thoroughly douched with a spermicidal solution. Ivanov's conclusion that the spermatozoa penetrate the follicle and thus fertilize ripe and unripe ova before their release from the ovary was tested by Walton and Whetham (1933), who repeated his experiments. Although they confirmed his results, they considered that it was possible for fertilization to be effected, even after thorough irrigation with spermicidal solutions, by spermatozoa that were buried in the folds and inaccessible crypts of the oviduct and thus protected against the treatment.

Exactly such concentrations, or "sperm nests," have since been found in crypts of the chalaziferous region at the anterior end of the oviduct by Van Drimmelen (1946). Spermatozoa thus apparently buried could easily be brought to the lumen of the oviduct by the distention, the muscular activity, and the heightened secretion that follow the engulfing of an ovum. These facts are consistent with the cytological studies by Olsen (1942), showing that the egg is normally fertilized in the infundibulum within 15 minutes after ovulation. Since one of Olsen's specimens taken from the body cavity carried a male pronucleus, it would appear that in some cases, at least, spermatozoa may enter the ovum before it is engulfed by the infundibulum. Fertilization of eggs in the body cavity was accomplished experimentally by Van Drimmelen (1945), who injected semen intraperitoneally with a syringe to the region of the ovary. Of 23 hens thus inseminated, 21 laid fertile eggs.

Onset and Duration of Fertility. It is doubtful that any phase of the physiology of avian reproduction has been more extensively investigated than (1) the length of time required after mating to get fertile eggs and (2) the duration of fertility after removal of the male. For reviews of the earlier literature in this field, the contributions to it by Crew (1926), Fronda (1926), Curtis and Lambert (1929), and Nicolaides (1934) should be consulted. After single matings that yielded fertile eggs, the average time elapsing before laying of the first fertile egg was found to be 57.1 hours by Curtis and Lambert and 66 hours by Nicolaides. Fronda's record of getting a fertile egg in 20 hours stood for 8 years but was finally wrested from him by Nicolaides, who, in 68 trials, got one fertile egg only 19.5 hours after mating. Since the earliest fertile egg obtained by Van Drimmelen (1945) after putting semen directly in the abdominal cavity came through 19 hours later, and since it takes 26 minutes for spermatozoa to traverse the oviduct (Mimura, 1939), no one is likely to lower by more than 4 minutes this record for natural matings now held by Nicolaides. More important, perhaps, is the fact that fertility for a whole pen of females is likely to be sufficiently established by 6 or 7 days to warrant saving the eggs for hatching. With old males and with young ones not adequately exposed to light a longer time may be necessary.

After removal of the male, the average duration of fertility was found to be 10.7 days by Curtis and Lambert, 14.8 days by Nicolaides. The high records here are 29 and 32 days recorded by Nicolaides and Crew, respectively. In practice, poultrymen recognize that, a week after removal of the male, fertility is declining so rapidly that only special circumstances warrant saving eggs longer than 12 or 14 days.

It is important to know how soon after one male is replaced by another the influence of the first will be lost so that all or most of the fertile eggs can be attributed to the second sire. This has a special significance for breeders who are testing two or three consecutive series of cockerels in the same pens in one breeding season, as it is desirable to reduce to a minimum the number of eggs that must be discarded between series because paternity of chicks hatched from them would be in doubt. It was found by Crew (1926) and by Warren and Kilpatrick (1929) that in such cases the influence of the first male is lost in 7 to 10 days and frequently in as little as 3 to 5 days. Furthermore, once the second male's sperm begin to fertilize eggs of any one hen, few of them, if any, are subsequently fertilized by the first male. However, there is apparently some variation among males in the persistence of their spermatozoa in competition with those of a replacing sire. Altogether, it seems clear that 7 to 10 days are ample as an interim when one male replaces another. The procedure followed by the author with such "double shifts" and "triple shifts" of males is given in Chap. 15. Warren and Gish (1943) have shown that, when two different males are used successively for artificial insemination, the time lost between them is much less than with pen matings. The influence of the first male persists in all eggs laid on the first day following insemination (at 2 to 3 P.M.) by the second. However, on the second day the greater majority of the chicks can be assigned to the second male. The error entailed by following this rule varied from 4 to 13 per cent.

Density of Sperm Suspension and Fertility. The numbers of spermatozoa transferred in natural matings are normally far in excess of the number needed to effect good fertility. With suspensions varying in density from 825,000 to over 7,000,000 sperm per cubic millimetre, no relation could be found between the concentration of sperm and resultant fertility (Hutt, 1929). Similar results were obtained by Parker *et al.* (1942) except that in their tests semen containing less than 1,000,000 sperm per cubic millimetre did not induce good fertility. With artificial insemination, Burrows and Quinn (1938) found that as little as 0.05 cc. of semen once a week resulted in fertility of 87 per cent but considered 0.1 cc. a safer amount to use because of the variation among different matings.

The feasibility of diluting semen without reducing fertility was shown by Munro (1938b). Bonnier and Trulsson (1939) found that dilutions with Ringer's solution to a concentration of only 10 per cent semen yielded as good fertility as did the undiluted sample. Several different diluents were evaluated by Grodzinski and Marchlewski (1935) according to their ability to maintain motility of the spermatozoa at different temperatures. Blood serum proved to be best in this respect. For most samples the optimum temperature for holding was 2°C., but egg albumen preserved motility best at 16°C. One must not assume, however, that the fertilizing capacity of spermatozoa is directly related to their motility. It may be indicated by the proportion of abnormal sperm (Parker *et al.*, 1942), and this possibility merits further study.

Selective Fertilization. There were indications in the experiments of Crew (1926) and Dunn (1927) that in natural matings the spermatozoa of one male may effect fertilization better than those of another when both types are in competition. The possibility that such selective fertilization does occur has been reexamined on a somewhat more accurate basis since the introduction of easy methods for artificial insemination.

Bonnier and Trulsson (1939a), who inseminated Rhode Island Red hens alternately with semen from a Rhode Island Red male and a White Leghorn, found that more chicks were sired by the Red male than by the other. Samples of semen from the two males seemed equal in vitality, but when the two kinds were mixed in equal parts and used together, there was still an excess of chicks sired by the Red male. One hen produced none at all by the White Leghorn. Similar results were obtained with a second group of Rhode Island Red hens and two (other) males as before, but in this trial the mixed semen resulted in no chicks being sired by the White Leghorn male. Since this semen appeared to contain abnormal spermatozoa, that result was not surprising. However, the results with the first group did show selective fertilization by the sperm of the Rhode Island Red male when in apparently equal competition with sperm of the White Leghorn. The difference was not solely in the spermatozoa, for the hens also reacted differently to the two types.

In similar experiments, Parker *et al.* (1942) inseminated New Hampshire hens with a mixture of equal volumes of semen from a White Leghorn, a Barred Rock, and a New Hampshire. Of 15 hens thus treated that subsequently produced two chicks or more, 5 had offspring by all three sires, and all had chicks by at least two sires. The remarkable

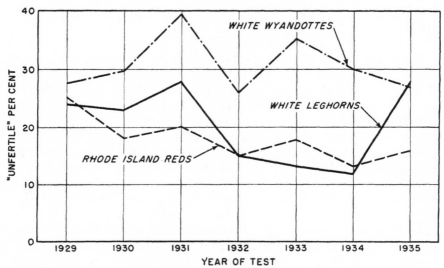

FIG. 120. Incidence of "unfertile" eggs in three breeds at the Lancashire Official Pedigree Breeding Station over 7 years.

thing was that among 89 chicks thus engendered, there were 40 by New Hampshire sires, 42 by the Barred Rocks, but only 7 sired by the White Leghorns. The basis for such selective fertilization is unknown.

Infertility of White Wyandottes. About the only evidence (other than that from selective fertilization) of a genetic basis for infertility that has been adduced thus far is found in the fact that at least one breed of fowls, the White Wyandotte, is characterized by lower fertility than others. Proof of this was found (Hutt, 1940) in the records for several years of official pedigree breeding stations in Lancashire and in Northern Ireland. At both of these the proportion of "unfertile" eggs was higher in White Wyandottes than in Rhode Island Reds and White Leghorns by highly significant differences ranging from 9.7 to 13.2 per cent (Fig. 120). The eggs classified as unfertile at the Lancashire station included those in which embryos had died during the first 2 weeks of incubation, and hence the data from there could not by themselves show whether low fertility or high embryonic mortality was responsible for the poor showing of the Wyandottes.

This does not mean that all White Wyandottes exhibit low fertility. On the contrary, as every lover of the breed will testify, many of them produce only fertile eggs. On this point the data of Hindhaugh (1932) are informative. They concern 582 individual matings of White Wyandottes involving 65 males and 448 females, with an average of 30 eggs incubated from each mating (Table 59).

TABLE 59. DISTRIBUTION OF FERTILITY IN 582 MATINGS OF WHITE WYANDOTTES
(DATA FROM HINDHAUGH)

Proportion of eggs fertile	Matings	
	Number	Proportion of total, per cent
0	46	7.9
0.1– 20	46	7.9
20 – 40	37	6.4
40 – 60	48	8.2
60 – 80	67	11.5
80 – 90	74	12.7
90 – 95	76	13.0
95 – 99.9	91	15.6
100	97	16.7

The average fertility for these matings (in over 17,000 eggs) was 70 per cent, a figure matching remarkably well the average infertility of 31.4 per cent for the White Wyandottes at the Lancashire station over a period of 7 years (Fig. 120). It should be noted, however, that 16.7 per cent of these matings yielded no infertile eggs whatever and that in 45 per cent the proportion of fertile eggs was higher than 90 per cent. Similarly, Munro (1946) has reported fertility in White Wyandottes better than 98 per cent, although the numbers of females, males, eggs, and days yielding those results were not given. Altogether, it would seem that the infertility characteristic of this breed results from an unusually high proportion of birds that produce few fertile eggs or none at all.

Miscellanea. While some birds of both sexes maintain good fertility for several years, the average figure tends to decline slightly even in the second breeding season and more markedly in later ones. Variation among individuals in this respect is great. Attempts by Crew (1925) to rejuvenate senile cocks by unilateral ligation of the vas deferens (Steinach operation) were unsuccessful. Attempts have been made to overcome incipient senility by endocrine therapy during the breeding season, but more and better experiments along these lines are desirable. The claim of McCartney (1923) that hens can be temporarily sterilized by spermotoxins induced by subcutaneous injection of cocks' sperm was thoroughly investigated and refuted by Lamoreux (1940). The feasibility of sterilizing male birds with X rays was shown by Benoit (1929) and by Mirskaia and Crew (1931). Males can also be sterilized eventually if maintained for 2 years on a diet deficient in vitamin E (Adamstone and Card, 1934a), but all five males tested were still fertilizing eggs after a whole year on the deficient diet. Sterility of cocks has also been ascribed to lack of the diminutive copulatory organ in the cloaca (Dove, 1928) and to cystic testes (Gowen, 1926). The reduced fertility of rumpless fowls is discussed in Chap. 3.

Fertility of the male is lowered when the comb or wattles are frozen; hence most breeders of Leghorns or other large-combed breeds in northern latitudes guard against that risk by dubbing the cockerels while they are still small. According to Payne and Ingram (1927) the reduction of fertility after freezing does not persist more than 11 days in Kansas, but it is conceivable that matters might be more serious at Murmansk. Apart from freezing, Lamoreux (1942) found that the degree of fertility shown by hens kept in unheated houses was not related to outdoor mean weekly temperatures within a range from 22.9 to 50.1°F. Fertility of males is also reduced by inanition (Chirife, 1933; Parker and McSpadden, 1943). It is possible to have males and females (of different breeds) with such disparity in size that fertility from natural matings is impossible. According to Quinn and Burrows (1936) fertility is reduced when the larger mate exceeds the smaller one by more than 70 per cent, and in their experiments no fertility whatever resulted when the larger bird was four times the size of the smaller one. As they showed, fertility of 97 per cent can be obtained in such cases by artificial insemination. With this practice, best results are obtained when the hens are inseminated right after laying (Moore and Byerly, 1942) or in the afternoon (Gracewski and Scott, 1943; Parker, 1945); fertility is poor when hens are inseminated that have a hard-shelled egg in the uterus.

This does not mean that good layers, which carry such eggs more often than poor layers, are likely to have lower fertility than the latter in natural matings. On the contrary, as Lamoreux (1940a) found in the records of 1,084 hens over a 5-year period, the best layers show the highest fertility (Fig. 121). For hens laying only 1 egg a week the proportion infertile among those eggs was 31.2 per cent, while for hens laying every day of the week the corresponding figure was only 11.8 per cent. The same principle applied to longer periods. For hens laying in 6 weeks only 13 to 22 eggs the proportion of these infertile was 24.4

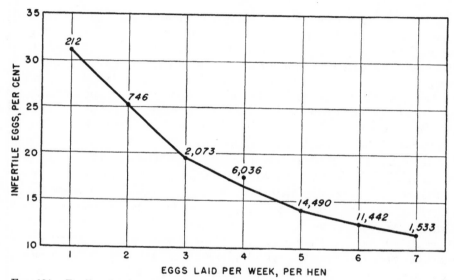

FIG. 121. Decline in the proportion of infertile eggs as the number laid per week per hen increases from 1 to 7. Numbers above the curve are those in which the proportion of infertile eggs was determined. (*From data of Lamoreux.*)

per cent, but for hens laying 32 to 40 in the same period the proportion of infertile eggs was only 13 per cent. Lamoreux attributed the low fertility of the poorer layers to the fact that they copulate less frequently than the good layers. This is undoubtedly one of the factors underlying the so-called "preferential mating" (Upp, 1928).

Although both Lamoreux (1940a) and Funk (1939) showed that eggs laid in cycles of four consecutive daily eggs or more have higher fertility than those in cycles of three or less, neither of them could find any relation between fertility and the position of the egg in the cycle.

In unincubated eggs the fertile ones can be distinguished from infertile ones by differences between the disintegrating blastodisc of the infertile egg and the rapidly developing blastoderm of the fertile one. This is possible because development of the latter has progressed almost to the completion of gastrulation by the time the egg is laid. Differences between the two types were described by Barfurth (1895). More recently Kosin (1944, 1945) has found that by staining with alum cochineal the differentiation is facilitated and that with practice fertility may be determined as accurately in opened fresh eggs as in those which are incubated.

EMBRYONIC MORTALITY

Reproduction depends, not only upon the numbers of eggs laid and their fertility, but also upon the amount of embryonic mortality during incubation or before it. Although some investigators have written in the past of "genes for hatchability," it is now recognized that hatchability of fertile eggs is influenced by too many different conditions to permit of its being considered as any one specific genetic trait. Some of these conditions are environmental, others are genetic, and the question whether or not the embryo becomes a hatched chick is answered by the sum total of the interactions of all such forces.

Of the 21 lethal genes known to date in the fowl (page 231), at least 16 are fatal to some or all homozygotes during incubation, and the other 5 exert their effects after hatching. It seems probable, from what is known of the high proportion of lethal genes in other species (such as Drosophila), which are genetically better explored than the fowl, that these 21 lethal genes thus far identified constitute only a fraction of the total number extant in the fowl. While most of the known lethal genes cause some abnormality that is not lethal until the later stages of incubation (or after hatching), there must be many others that are undetected thus far merely because the homozygotes die at stages too early to permit recognition of their abnormality without microscopic examination. For a discussion of lethal genes and their effects on hatchability, the reader is referred to Chap. 8.

Apart from the direct action of lethal and semi-lethal genes in the genotype of the embryo, hatchability of the eggs may be influenced by the genotype of the hen that lays them. To illustrate such an indirect genetic influence, the relation between size of egg and hatchability will serve as an example. As is well known, eggs weighing from 45 to 60 gm. hatch better than smaller or larger ones. Since size of egg is determined almost entirely by the genetic constitution of the hen and is influenced comparatively little by environment, it is clear that for any embryonic mortality related to egg size the genotype of the dam is indirectly responsible. One recognizes that in such cases the direct cause of death may be some disturbance of embryonic development resulting from disproportions of albumen, yolk, and surface area. Other similar indirect genetic influences of the dam on hatchability are associated with differences in the type of shell, in the deposition of essential nutrients in the egg, and in egg production.

Apart from lethal genes, a discussion of all the factors affecting hatchability is beyond the scope of this book. For full information, the excellent review of the literature in this field by Landauer (1948) should be consulted.

SEX RATIOS

Because the fowl is a prolific species, and because it differs from mammals in having heterogametic females, it has been a useful animal for satisfying the perennial curiosity of biologists concerning the mechanism of sex determination and variations in the sex ratio. Many studies of the latter have been made.

It is usual to say that sex is determined at the time of fertilization. While this is true for species in which the male is heterogametic, it does not apply to groups like the birds, in which all spermatozoa are equipotential with respect to sex determination but two kinds of eggs are produced. For any chick, its sex is determined about 15 minutes prior to fertilization when the first polar body is extruded from the oöcyte. This occurs just before the follicle ruptures to release the oöcyte from the ovary (see Chap. 2). If the oöcyte retains its sex chromosome, the egg is destined to produce a male, but if that chromosome be extruded in the polar body, the egg will give rise to a female. It is probable that in birds, as in other species, sex is determined, not simply by the presence or absence of a sex chromosome, but by the balance between its male-determining potencies and forces in the autosomes that favor the other sex.

Primary Sex Ratio. Although the primary sex ratio (*i.e.*, the proportions of the sexes at fertilization) is not known for any mammal, the available evidence indicates that there must be a considerable excess of males. This is not the case with the fowl, a species in which it is possible to determine the primary sex ratio with a high degree of accuracy. This is found in the chicks hatched from hens with complete and perfect records of reproduction, *i.e.*, every egg fertile and every one hatched. Among 870 such chicks from 39 Rhode Island Red hens, Hays (1945) found the sex ratio to be 432 ♂ ♂ :438 ♀ ♀, or 49.7 per cent males.[1] This is as close to a 1:1 ratio as could be expected. It showed that, in

---

[1] It is an old custom of biologists to talk of sex ratios but to give proportions instead of ratios, thus using one figure instead of two. The author follows suit in this section.

these females at least, male-determining and female-determining gametes were produced in equal numbers.

Secondary Sex Ratio. The secondary sex ratio, which is that prevailing in chicks at hatching, has been determined by many different investigators. It should be the same as the primary sex ratio except in so far as one sex may experience higher mortality than the other during incubation.

So far as the author is aware, the first published statement based on numbers sufficient to be informative was the record by Darwin (1871) for Mr. Stretch's 1,001 Cochins, among which the proportion of males was 48.65 per cent. Since this apparently pertained to birds that were reared, it may not be a true secondary sex ratio, but it is worth citing, partly as a matter of history, but also because the sex ratios since determined by others do not differ greatly from it. In fact, Landauer and Landauer (1931), who combined all the figures available from 14 different reports, emerged with 48.77 per cent males among 67,993 chicks. Some of these figures and others published since are given in Table 60, but records based on embryos as well as hatched chicks have been excluded therefrom in order to restrict the data to the secondary sex ratio.

TABLE 60. PROPORTIONS OF MALES AMONG CHICKS AT HATCHING AS REPORTED BY VARIOUS INVESTIGATORS

Investigator	Year	Total chicks, number	Males, per cent
Darwin.......................	1871	1,001	48.65
Field........................	1901	2,105	44.63
Pearl *......................	1917	20,037	48.57
Mussehl.....................	1924	1,514	52.24
Lambert and Knox...........	1926	1,862	50.97
Callenbach..................	1929	7,850	49.41
Dunn (cited by the Landauers)..	1931	5,421	48.57
Crew †......................	1938	515,976	50.34
Crew ‡......................	1938	2,216,051	51.38
Dudley and Hindhaugh........	1939	6,030	51.77
Asmundson..................	1941	5,590	49.46
Hazel and Lamoreux ‡........	1946	8,355	49.79

* In families containing 10 chicks or more.
† In sex-linked crosses between breeds.
‡ Sex determined by examination of the cloaca.

Apart from these records for chicks that hatched, many investigators have determined the sex ratio in chick embryos. This has a special interest because of its bearing on the theory that the higher prenatal and postnatal mortality of males in mammals might be attributable to the effects of sex-linked lethal genes upon the less protected heterogametic sex. If this were so, one would expect a correspondingly higher mortality of females in birds and other species in which that sex is heterogametic. Various data contributed to this question are given in Table 61.

TABLE 61. PROPORTION OF MALES AMONG EMBRYOS DYING LATE ENOUGH IN INCUBATION TO PERMIT IDENTIFICATION OF SEX

Investigators	Year	Dead embryos, number	Males, per cent
Various, as summarized by Byerly and Jull.........	1911–1932	6,864	48.59
New data of Byerly and Jull	1935	17,989	47.56
Crew (in sex-linked crosses)	1938	8,565	51.03
Asmundson..............	1941	2,095	49.21

Were it not for Crew's data, it would appear from inspection of Tables 60 and 61 that among chicks that hatch and embryos that do not there is a slight excess of females. The very extensive data of Crew for chicks sexed by color of the down in sex-linked crosses show equal numbers of the sexes, and these must be significant because of the accuracy with which sex can be thus identified. It seems probable that some of the discrepancies among the sex ratios found by different investigators may be attributable to differences between breeds in this respect. Thus, Callenbach (1929), Byerly and Jull (1935), and Crew (1938) all reported the proportion of males to be higher in Rhode Island Reds than in White Leghorns. Even if Crew's data be excluded (because of any error inherent in sexing by examination of the cloaca), the difference in the extensive data of Byerly and Jull was highly significant.

Considering embryos that died, one can conclude only that there is no evidence of differential mortality consistently affecting one sex more than the other. Some opinions to the contrary have been based on differences that were apparently significant between the proportion of males among the dead and the 50 per cent assumed to be expected by chance. Actually the sex ratio in the dead should be compared with that in the living embryos or in the hatched chicks of the same material. When this is done, as in the case of Crew's data for sex-linked crosses (Tables 60 and 61), no difference is found. In turkeys, Asmundson (1941) found the proportion of males at hatching to be 49.2 per cent, but among dead embryos it was significantly higher.

It should be clearly understood that, while there is no evidence of differential mortality of the sexes in several thousand embryos that have died from many different causes, there may be such a difference with respect to any one specific abnormality. For example, among 465 chondrodystrophic embryos in which sexes were determined by Dunn (1927a), Hutt and Greenwood (1929), Munro (1932), and Byerly and Jull (1935), the number of males was 263, or 56.6 per cent. This condition, to which males are apparently more susceptible than females, is the so-called "sporadic" type of chondrodystrophy in which the diaphysis of the tibia is bent. In the simple recessive type described by Lamoreux (1942a) both sexes are equally susceptible. Presumably there may be other conditions to which females are more susceptible, a situation inevitable whenever any sex-linked lethal gene is involved.

Tertiary Sex Ratio. This term refers to the proportions of the sexes at any stated age after hatching. A difference between the secondary and tertiary ratio is to be expected only if the postnatal mortality has fallen more heavily on one sex than the other. Unfortunately, while some data have been reported concerning the actual proportions of the sexes alive at various ages after hatching, the complementary figures for those which died in the same populations are not available. Conversely, the data of Landauer and Landauer (1931) showing an excess of males (52.7 per cent) among 5,683 chickens that died within 2 months of hatching are difficult to evaluate because the proportion of males among the chicks that did not die was not given. If among these there were equal numbers of both sexes, the difference would be significant.

Byerly and Jull (1935) found the proportion of males among 28,015 chickens of various breeds alive at 10 weeks of age to be 50.1 per cent. This figure and the similar one given by Hays (1941) for 23,273 Rhode Island Reds alive at 8 weeks (50.8 per cent males) do not preclude the possibility of a higher mortality of males up to these ages, although they do suggest that any such difference must have been a slight one. This point is illustrated by the record of MacArthur and Baillie (1932) for 1,030 chicks among which the proportion of males was 51.16 per cent at hatching, 50.06 per cent in survivors to 120 days, but 54.21 per cent in the 273 that died. Although these differences were not significant in the comparatively small number of chicks concerned, they show that an equality of sexes at some time after hatching does not preclude, *ipso facto,* any differential mortality in chicks that died. However, Byerly and Jull found that families in which no chicks had died did not differ significantly in proportion of males from those in which losses had occurred. They concluded from this and other evidence that the males had experienced no higher mortality than the females.

On the other hand, Dudley and Hindhaugh (1939) found that, after losses from weak chicks killed at hatching and mortality prior to 16 weeks of age, the proportion of chicks reared to 16 weeks of age was lower in males than in females. For White Leghorns, Rhode Island Reds, and crosses between them the proportions reared were 80.3 and 83.7 per cent (in 6,030 chicks hatched), while for White Wyandottes (6,908 chicks) the proportions reared were 72.8 and 75.4 per cent in males and females, respectively.

It is well to remember that, while any difference between the sexes may be slight in so far as mortality from all causes is concerned, there can be marked differences between males and females in susceptibility to certain specific diseases. Some of these, like lymphomatosis in the fowl or erysipelas in turkeys, could greatly influence any tertiary sex ratio in affected flocks.

Factors not Influencing Sex Ratios. Although several attempts have been made to find conditions that might influence the secondary sex ratio in the fowl, none has been successful. Data of Jull (1924) showing an apparent decline in the proportion of males in eggs laid from the fall months through the year to the following October led to the belief that it was related to antecedent egg production of the dam. This has since been disproved by Lambert and Curtis (1929), Callenbach (1929), Christie and Wriedt (1930), and Jull (1931), and no significant relation of season to sex ratio has been found. Age of the dam has apparently no influence (Lambert and Curtis; Christie and Wriedt).

Many investigators have noted wide variations in the sex ratio in different families, but it seems probable that most of these, if not all, were the result of chance fluctuations. One must not jump to the conclusion that a ratio of 2 ♂ ♂ :1 ♀ seen in some family is evidence that a sex-linked lethal gene is reducing the proportion of females. In a statistical examination of sex ratios in 464 families of full siblings, with an average of 18 chicks per family, Hazel and Lamoreux (1946) could find no indication that any factors other than chance were affecting the sex ratio. Jull (1932) sought evidence of hereditary tendencies to produce an excess of either sex but found none.

Contrary to misbeliefs still prevalent, there is no relation between physical characteristics of the egg and sex of the chick hatched from it. This has been tested with respect to weight of egg, weight of yolk, water content of the yolk, and shape of the shell (Jull, 1924; Jull and Quinn, 1924, 1925).

SEX DIMORPHISM

Differences between males and females are sometimes classified as either primary or secondary sex characters. The latter term refers to differences effected by the action of sex hormones and hence subject to considerable variation, depending upon the kind of endocrine milieu by which the characters are influenced. Familiar examples of secondary sex characters are the comb and the structure of the feathers in the neck, back, saddle, and wing bow. Primary sex characters are usually considered to include anatomical differences, particularly those in the reproductive systems. The arbitrary nature of the classification is shown by the fact that even in mature birds the reproductive tract can be greatly altered by changes in the endocrine secretions.

Differences between the sexes have been discussed in almost every chapter of this book, and it is hardly necessary to make a summary of them here. Apart from the more obvious differences in size, rate of growth, development of spurs, structure and color of plumage, etc., there are differences so minute that they are recognizable only after statistical study of many birds. A good example is the relative size of the thyroid gland, which is slightly heavier in females than in males (Aberle and Landauer, 1935). Male fowls have a higher content of the enzyme, arginase (in the kidney), than females (Chaudhuri, 1927).

The erythrocyte count is higher in males than in females (Blacher, 1926). Chaudhuri (1927a) showed that this difference is found only in mature fowls, not in immature chickens, and that in hens which have undergone partial sex reversal and assumed male characteristics the number of erythrocytes is closer to the normal range for males than to that for females. Further evidence that the erythrocyte count varies with the sex hormones was provided by Juhn and Domm (1930) and Domm and Taber (1946). This applies also to the level of glutathione in the blood, which is normally higher in males than in females but can be raised in females or lowered in males by appropriate changes in the sex hormones (Chanton, 1932, 1932a).

These few examples suffice to indicate that, in addition to the more obvious differences between the sexes in form, their contrasting endocrine systems are responsible for diverse associated differences in physiology. Undoubtedly, many of these have yet to be discovered, but enough are known to show that with respect to any phase of avian physiology equality of the sexes should not be assumed until proved.

From Aristotle to Willier, and from Chicago to Strasbourg, the chick embryo has been the favorite animal of the embryologists. For an introduction to the extensive literature on its sexual differentiation, the reviews by Willier (1939, 1942) will prove useful. Similarly, the sex dimorphism in structure of the plumage and in the comb of the fowl have made its secondary sex characters subjects for much study by endocrinologists. For their purposes, the Brown Leghorn has been a favorite breed because its cocks and hens differ, not only in the structure of the plumage, but also in the color. Some of the relations of endocrine secretions to the development of combs, spurs, feathers, colors, and egg production have already been discussed in sections of this book concerned with variations in those items. Others are considered in the portion of this chapter dealing with Sex Reversal. The voluminous literature on variations in the secondary sexual characters of birds was reviewed by Domm (1939), and that on sex dimorphism in the plumage of the fowl by Greenwood and Blyth (1938). For a recent survey of present knowledge of the "biological actions of the sex hormones" the book bearing that title by Burrows (1945) should be consulted.

Identification of Sex at Hatching. One difference between the sexes that has proved to be of considerable economic importance is the dimorphism in the cloaca by which males can be distinguished from females at hatching. The feasibility of this practice was demonstrated by Masui and Hashimoto (1933), but it was in extensive use in Japan and China long before the first English translation of their report. The method of Masui and Hashimoto has also been explained by Hertwig (1927), Jull (1934), Gibbs (1935), and others.

The difference is in the genital papilla on the ventral surface of the cloaca. In males this persists as a rudimentary copulatory organ, but in females the papilla is either absent at hatching or sufficiently different in size and shape from that of males to permit identification of the two sexes with a high degree of accuracy. In a thorough study of the basis for the difference, Macdonald and Taylor (1933) found that the "phallic knob," or papilla, is equally developed in the two sexes at 12 days of incubation. Thereafter it diminishes in size in females, so that by the time of hatching it has disappeared or is comparatively undeveloped; it is completely gone by 12 weeks of age. During this same time the papilla enlarges in males.

Unfortunately, the distinction between the sexes in this respect is not always clearly defined at hatching. A valuable study of the various gradations in size and shape of the rudimentary organ and of their frequencies was made by Canfield (1940, 1941). These are illustrated in Fig. 122. Canfield's observations and those of experienced sexers reporting to him indicated that the proportions of the several types vary in different breeds and strains. The female types designated as c, c′, and

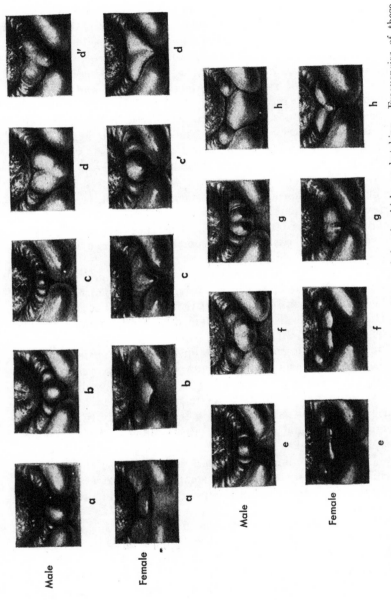

FIG. 122. Various types of cloacal papillae seen in male and female chicks at hatching. Frequencies of these types (per cent) in 10,000 White Leghorns were as follows: In ♂ ♂: *a* and *b*, 64.3; *c*, 7.9; *d* and *d'*, 0.6; *e* and *f*, 20.5; *g*, 3.3; *h*, 3.4. In ♀ ♀: *a* and *b*, 57.2; *c*, *c'*, and *d*, 17.0; *e* and *f*, 24.5; *g* and *h*, 1.3. *(From Canfield in Poultry Sci., 1941; drawings by Jean Hirsch.)*

d in his illustration are those most likely to be wrongly classified as males. Conversely, types *c* and *e* of the male are more likely to cause confusion than any of the others.

Efficient use of this method of distinguishing sex in chicks at hatching comes only after long practice. Much of the art depends upon learning how to handle the chicks and to expose the cloaca for examination. Methods for doing this are described in the reports cited above. An interesting observation of Jull (1934) was that for four novices in the art accuracy of identification increased steadily with practice, reaching about 91 per cent after 2,500 had been done. Experienced professional sexers can do about 800 chicks per hour, with an accuracy of 98 per cent or better.

Synthetic Estrogens for Fattening. One very practical application of the knowledge that has resulted from endocrinological studies of sex dimorphism is the use of synthetic estrogens for fattening. Following his earlier studies of the relation of sex hormones to the level of blood lipides in the fowl, it was shown by Lorenz (1945, 1945a) that it was possible to increase greatly the amount of subcutaneous, muscular, and abdominal fat in male chickens by implanting a pellet of diethylstilbestrol under the skin. Similar effects from oral administration of other estrogens have been described by Jaap (1945), Thayer *et al.* (1945), and Lorenz and Bachman (1947). The effect of all these substances is to convert the male to a female type of metabolism, which entails a higher level of fat in the blood and resultant deposition of fat in the tissues. This persists only as long as supply of the hormone is maintained. Search for the most efficient estrogens and for methods of administering them is now being made, but already it seems clear that the procedure has remarkable commercial value. While it is likely to be used most extensively for fattening broilers and roasters, it is also effective in making the flesh of old cockbirds tender like that of young ones. The feminizing influence of one of the synthetic estrogens, dienestrol diacetate, is indicated by the White Leghorn males shown in Fig. 123.

SEX REVERSAL

Reversals Experimentally Induced. Since explanations of the cases of intersexuality and sex reversal that occur spontaneously in the fowl depend upon corresponding variations that have been produced experimentally in various ways, it is convenient to consider these latter first. In so doing, experiments pertaining to genetically hen-feathered males are excluded, as the genetic and physiological bases for that type of plumage have already been explained in Chap. 5.

Castration of male fowls is not followed by any regeneration of testes, and the capon ordinarily remains a capon. It can be so feminized by ovarian grafts as to be indistinguishable from females (Fig. 124) except by its larger size (Goodale, 1916, 1918; Finlay, 1925; and others). The only case known to the author in which a capon has spontaneously assumed female characters was the Brown Leghorn described by Greenwood

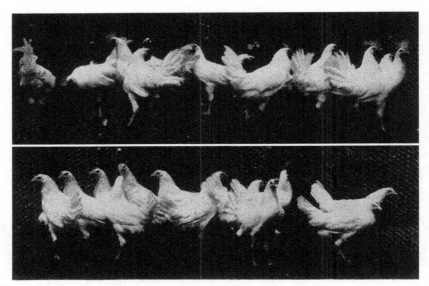

Fig. 123. The feminizing influence of a synthetic estrogen. *Above,* normal White Leghorn males at 14 weeks of age; *below,* their brothers of the same age that had received dienestrol diacetate in their feed from the age of 2 weeks onward.

and Blyth (1932), which did so at about 15 months. A small tumor near the normal site of the right gonad was considered responsible.

The sequence of events following gonadectomy in the female is more complicated. Studies by Goodale (1916a, 1916b), Finlay (1925), Pezard (1928), Benoit (1932), and others showed that removal of the (left) ovary makes the female a poularde, a bird with the same shrunken comb, spurs, and long male-type feathers as are seen in the capon (Fig. 124). Both sexes are thus reduced by complete gonadectomy to the same neutral state; but while the capon remains in that condition, many of the poulardes do not. Domm (1927) found that some of them lose their male feathers and replace them with plumage of the female type. At the same time, the combs and wattles of these birds enlarge to the state normally found in males. These changes result from the regeneration of a sex gland at the site of the right gonad.

Somewhat as the removal of the left testis causes a compensatory hypertrophy of the right one, so does removal of the left gonad in females induce new development of the vestiges of the right gonad. As Brode (1928) has shown, these persist after hatching. The regenerated gland is not an ovary, but either a somewhat atypical testis or, less often, an

FIG. 124. The modification of secondary sex characters by hormones in Brown Leghorns. (*From Finlay in Brit. J. Exptl. Biol.*)

1. Normal male.
2. Castrated male.
3. Male castrated and with ovary engrafted.
4. Male with both ovary and testis.

5. Female ovariotomized and with testes engrafted.
6. Ovariotomized female.
7. Normal female.
8. Female with both ovary and testis.

ovotestis. There is some evidence that if the female be ovariotomized soon after hatching the resultant right gonad is more likely to contain ovarian structures than when the operation is done in older birds. Although this right gonad consists of tubules, in most cases there is no sign of active spermatogenesis; but exceptions to this rule were found by Benoit, Zawadowsky, and Domm (see Domm, 1929). Apparently, it produces both male and female hormones, the former causing development of the comb and wattles, and the latter responsible for the female plumage. Proof of this dual function of the right gonad is found in the fact that, following its removal, the bird reverts to the neutral state of the poularde (Domm, 1929a). Poulardes that retain the male plumage or an intermediate type not entirely henny presumably do not have enough female hormone produced by the right gonad to influence the structure of the plumage.

Confirming the evidence from gonadectomy of the relation of sex hormones to secondary sex characters, there are various other experiments in which normal males and females have been given grafts of gonads from the opposite sex. These simulate more closely the conditions causing spontaneous sex reversal in fowls. From the experiments of Finlay (1925), Caridroit (1926), Greenwood and Blyth (1930), and others, it seems clear that in such experimental hermaphrodites the plumage becomes female in type because of the ovarian hormone, while the comb and wattles enlarge as in normal males because of the endocrine secretions of the testis (Fig. 124). This confirms the evidence from gonadectomized birds. Additional evidence of the relation of the sex hormones to the type of plumage is provided by grafts of skin from males to females, and vice versa (Danforth and Foster, 1929).

Spontaneous Reversal of Sex. The simplest forms of abnormal sexuality in the fowl are seen in developmental capons and poulardes. These are males and females in which the gonads fail to function, so that the secondary sex characters are not expressed, and to all appearances the birds are indistinguishable from capons and poulardes produced by gonadectomy. One of these is illustrated in Fig. 125. A series of 11 such birds, comprising 8 capons, 2 poulardes, and 1 with no gonads at all, was described by Greenwood and Crew (1927). In these cases the abnormality persisted throughout the life of the birds.

In other, rarer instances, a hen may temporarily be reduced to the neutral state of the poularde but subsequently revert to her normal condition as a female. It sometimes happens that at the time of moulting, when activity of the reproductive system is normally at its lowest ebb, the ovary is apparently so inactive that it does not secrete enough female hormone to cause the new feathers to be of the female type. In such cases the bird's plumage after the moult is that of the poularde and hence indistinguishable by most persons from that of the male. If the bird's ovary is subsequently restored to its normal state, the hen will function as a female and may even lay eggs. Since the plumage cannot be changed until the next moult, such a bird becomes notorious as a laying cock. In olden times, this was a serious business for the unhappy fowl, as in at least one case (at Basel, in 1474) the offending "cock" was burned at the stake "for the heinous and unnatural crime of laying an egg." At one time it was well known that the egg laid by such a perverted parent would hatch into a dreadful serpent, the deadly cockatrice, or basilisk. Unfortunately, several such eggs from a "laying rooster" that were incubated by Cole (1927) produced only Leghorns, no cockatrices. In one of these hens, described by Parkes and Brambell (1926), plumage after the moult was again of the male type, but Crew (1927) kept one for 5 years in which the plumage at successive annual moults was in turn

Fig. 125. A developmental capon at 10 months of age. A rudimentary spur is evident. When this bird died, 2 months after this photograph was taken, the testes were no bigger than in a chick of 3 weeks.

male, female, male, male, and female. Throughout these years the hen laid regularly and well.

In the more common type of reversal, apparently normal females, including hens that have laid eggs, develop (in varying degrees) the large head furnishings and spurs of the male. They usually retain female plumage, even after a moult, but in some cases it is a mixture of male and female feathers or, more rarely, entirely like that of the male. These birds will crow and usually exhibit various degrees of male sexual behavior. In nearly every case that has been carefully examined, some pathological condition of the ovary has been found. Frequently it is invaded by a tumor. In most cases, some kind of right gonad has been regenerated.

Many such birds have been reported in the literature. Some of them were reviewed by Boring and Pearl (1918), who added eight cases, and by Crew (1923) who described eight more. Earlier records, and superstitions about such birds were reviewed by Forbes (1947). The extreme limit of sex reversal thus far reported was shown by the Buff Orpington of Crew (1923, 1923a), which, although she had once been a good layer

FIG. 126. F. A. E. Crew, of the University of Edinburgh.

and a mother, began at $3\frac{1}{2}$ years to assume the characters of a male and climaxed the performance over a year later by becoming the sire of two chicks. One of these was a male, the other a female, but unfortunately they were not enough to test the expectation in such a mating of $2\ ♀♀ : 1\ ♂$. When it died, the bird was found to have not only two large testes and vasa deferentia but also an ovary, almost entirely destroyed by disease, and a small oviduct on the left side. A similar sex-reversed female reported by Arnsdorf (1947) apparently became the sire of two chicks.

All these cases of sex reversal, whether laying hens with male plumage or crowing hens with female plumage and male characteristics, are found only in birds that are genetically females. The reverse situation, the spontaneous assumption of female characteristics by genetic males, has been reported only once, so far as this author is aware. That case was found in a Dorking cock that became hen-feathered when 2 years old, a condition attributed by Buchanan (1926) to hypofunction of the thyroid, associated with abnormal testes. Her explanation can be questioned because thyroidectomy tends to induce plumage of the male type (Green-wood and Blyth, 1929; Parkes and Selye, 1937), whereas hen feathering is caused in males by feeding extra thyroid substance (Torrey and Horning, 1922; Cole and Hutt, 1928). Another possibility is that Buchanan's bird might have been genetically hen-feathered, as this mutation is known to occur in other breeds than the Sebrights and Campines, for which it is normal.

GYNANDROMORPHS AND MOSAICS

A gynandromorph is an animal in which one section of the body is genetically male and the remainder female. Either sex may have the larger portion of the combination, or, as frequently happens, there may be equal amounts of the two. A gynandromorph is thus distinctly different from an intersex, which (in higher vertebrates) is genetically either all male or all female but, because of hormonal modifications, appears to show characteristics of both sexes. It is intermediate. The hens that undergo spontaneous sex reversal, as described in the foregoing section, are intersexes.

In birds, most of the gynandromorphs reported to date have had the two sexes about equally represented, so that the birds showed lateral asymmetry, being larger and male-like on one side, but smaller and resembling a female on the other. This does not mean that all birds showing a difference in size between the two sides of the body are gynandromorphs. Some of them are merely autosomal mosaics. Both these kinds of abnormality may apparently result from the same general cause, *i.e.*, some kind of maldistribution of chromosomes, so that some cells have more or fewer chromosomes than the normal complement of the zygote at fertilization. It is therefore convenient to consider both gynandromorphs and mosaics in this section, even though the latter may often have nothing to do with sex.

Gynandromorphs. Since experts still disagree on the exact basis for the origin of avian gynandromorphs, discussion of them will here be limited to description of a few typical cases in the fowl and a representative sample of the various interpretations that have been offered.

In the gynandromorphic Barred Plymouth Rock of Macklin (1923) the plumage was predominantly of the female type, but the comb and wattles were like those of a male. The big difference between this bird and an intersex was that the bones on the left side were smaller than those on the right. From Macklin's measurements, it was later calculated that the difference between the two sides was the same as that between normal males and females (Hutt, 1929a). The bird had an ovotestis on the left side, a testis on the right. Its condition was ascribed to the elimination of a sex chromosome during the first cleavage division of a male zygote, thus leaving one cell and its descendants with two such chromosomes (*i.e.*, male) and the other with only one.

An amazing specimen described by Vecchi (1936) was apparently a hybrid between a Leghorn and a Transylvanian Naked-neck. Its right side was larger, with naked neck, feathered foot, red ear lobe, larger wattle, dark plumage, and a normal male reproductive system. The left side was smaller, with feathered neck, unfeathered foot, white ear lobe, mostly white plumage, an ovotestis, but no oviduct. No satisfactory interpretation of this case has yet been given.

A gyandromorphic Barred Plymouth Rock very similar to Macklin's was reported by Hutt (1937). The right side exceeded the left in size by approximately the usual difference between males and females (Fig. 127). Evidence that this arose from loss of a sex chromosome in a zygote originally male was provided by the plumage and the shanks, both of which were lighter in color on the larger (male) side than on the other. This is exactly the normal difference between males homozygous for the sex-linked barring gene, *B*, and females. The latter can carry that gene only in the hemizygous condition. It seemed clear, therefore, that one side of this bird had two sex chromosomes and the other side only one. On autopsy, a testis and vas deferens were found on the larger side; an ovary, oviduct, and rudimentary vas on the left side.

This case refutes the theory of Lillie (1931) that gynandromorphism is caused in birds by lateral hemihypertrophy in females with subnormal ovarian activity. That interpretation could not account for the difference in color of plumage and shanks on the two sides of the bird, whereas the other basis for its origin does do so.

In a good review of gynandromorphism and lateral asymmetry in birds, Crew and Munro (1938) described two new cases of gynandromorphism in the fowl. One of these differed from the others mentioned above in that the left side was not only about 13 per cent smaller than the right but also showed white skin, whereas the larger side had yellow skin. At autopsy the bird was found to have a left ovary and a right testis. From this and other evidence, Crew and Munro concluded that some gynandromorphs result from non-disjunction of a pair of autosomes, so that both sides are aneuploid, the larger being trisomic $(2n + 1)$ and the smaller one monosomic $(2n - 1)$, with respect to the particular auto-some involved. This interpretation was considered to account for all gynandromorphs showing in their two sides the disparity in size of about 10 to 15 per cent that represents normal sex dimorphism in the skeleton of the fowl.

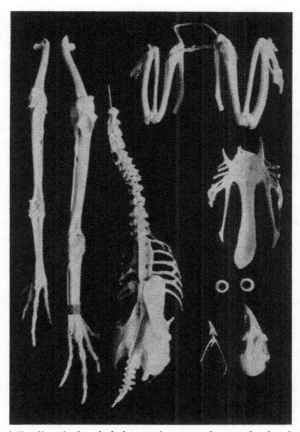

Fig. 127. Partially disarticulated skeleton of a gynandromorph, showing discrepancy in size between the right and left sides and resultant curvature of every bone in which the two sides are fused.

Crew and Munro considered that this interpretation accounted, not only for their two cases, but also for those of Macklin, Vecchi, and Hutt, mentioned earlier. While it is plausible that non-disjunction of autosomes carrying W or w (for white or yellow skin) could cause differences in skin color and in size, it is not clear that any autosome could cause the differences between the light and dark sides of Hutt's gynandromorph, whereas a difference in the sex chromosomes could do so. Similarly, if non-disjunction of an autosome carrying *Na* (naked neck) were responsible for Vecchi's bird, it must presumably have caused both the naked neck and the feathered foot on the right side. This seems unlikely because these two characters are apparently not linked (Warren, 1933). While it is to be expected that non-disjunction occurs in the fowl, as in other species, no case of it has yet been incontrovertibly proved. In the light of later knowledge of the sex chromosome, it seems probable that for the aberrant inheritance of sex-linked characters attributed by Crew (1933) to non-disjunction some other interpretation is possible. In the fruit fly, Drosophila, in which gynandromorphs have been more extensively studied than in any other animal, most of such cases result from loss of a sex chromosome.

For the laterally asymmetrical mosaic of unknown sex described by Roberts and Quisenberry (1935) no satisfactory explanation has yet been advanced. It was evidently a hybrid from a Light Brahma δ × Barred Plymouth Rock ♀. The left side resembled the sire, with large size, feathered shank, and Columbian restriction (*ee*) in the plumage. The other side was smaller, barred, and with clean shank. To various interpretations of Roberts and Quisenberry were added the possibility of double fertilization of a binucleate ovum (Castle, 1935) and non-disjunction (Munro, 1938*c*), but the mystery remains unsolved.

The Rhode Island Red gynandromorph described by Moszkowicz and Kolmer (1931) was evidently female on the left side and male on the right, with corresponding disparity in size, a testis on the right, and an ovotestis on the left. Its uniform color provided no genetic clue to its origin. As with some other gynandromorphs, it had some feathers of the male type (structure) on the male side and also a spur that was unmatched on the female side.

Pseudogynandromorphism. Some reports of gynandromorphs in the fowl are really concerned with hormonal intersexes of the type considered earlier. It is easy to produce a bird showing some characteristics of both sexes merely by allowing some of the feathers to develop under the influence of male hormones, as occurs in any normal male, and then causing other parts of the plumage to develop under the influence of female hormones. This is well illustrated by the pseudogynandromorph thus made to order by Lamoreux (1939). It was a male hybrid from the cross Barred Plymouth Rock δ × Silver-Spangled Hamburg ♀. After it had acquired its definitive male plumage, the right side was plucked and the bird treated with Progynon B (female hormone) while new feathers were grown on that side. The result was a bird which, so far as the plumage was concerned, was typically male on one side but female on the other (Fig. 128).

Mosaics. The simplest type of genetic mosaic in the fowl is probably that in which one feather or even a small part of one feather shows a color or pattern that differs from that prevailing in the remainder of the plumage. The non-barred, black feathers found in Barred Plymouth Rock females will serve as examples (see page 208). For a general discussion

Fig. 128. Right and left sides of a pseudogynandromorph artificially produced as explained in the text. On one side the plumage is that of a normal female, while on the other it is typically male. The spangling, for which the bird is heterozygous, is manifested more clearly in the plumage of the male type than on the other side, where the black is more fully extended. (*From Lamoreux in J. Heredity, 1939.*)

of mosaics in birds the review by Hollander (1944) should be consulted. Consideration of mosaics in the fowl will here be restricted to the peculiar group in which one part of the bird differs from the remainder in color of the skin.

These cases are most often recognizable by differences in the color of the shanks, one being white, the other yellow. In some of them the atypical part is only a small portion, but in others the bird is sharply divided in the median line, with one side showing white skin, the other yellow. In some of these last (Lambert, 1929; Crew, 1932) there is apparently no difference in size between the two halves, but in others (Crew, 1928; Crew and Munro, 1938, case *D;* Warren, 1945) one side is much smaller than the other. Lambert attributed the origin of his mosaic to non-disjunction (at an early cleavage) of the chromosomes carrying W (white skin) and w (yellow skin) in a bird of the genotype Ww. However, it was pointed out by Hutt (1929b) that non-disjunction was likely to be manifested by disparity in size as well as in color and that, when no such difference in size was observed, the mosaic was more likely to have arisen from gene mutation. He suggested that birds showing lateral asymmetry in both size and skin color resulted from early elimination of the autosome carrying W and genes for size in a Ww zygote, thus leaving one side (or part) yellow and smaller than the other. This situation is exemplified by the bird described by Crew (1928).

Complications arise in the interpretation of these skin-color mosaics because in some of them there are apparently disturbances in the reproductive systems associated with differences in size. Thus, in case D of Crew and Munro (1938) and in the specimen observed by Warren (1945), the left gonad resembled an ovary, the right one a testis. Crew and Munro concluded that, when the difference in size of the two sides amounts to 10 to 15 per cent, the cause lies in non-disjunction of one pair of autosomes. In these skin-color mosaics, this would be the pair carrying W and w. The resultant heteroploid condition, with trisomic cells on one side and monosomic cells on the other, was considered responsible for the gynandromorphism shown by such birds and by others in which the two sides do not differ in skin color. However, the bird described by Crew (1928) had his two sides different in skin color and in size, but not in sex. He was apparently a normal male. Difficulties in applying this hypothesis to the Vecchi and Hutt gynandromorphs were given earlier. Another is presented by the specimen observed by Warren (1945). In the five gynandromorphs attributed to non-disjunction by Crew and Munro the larger side was on the right, had a testis, and was considered to be male because of being trisomic. The smaller and supposedly monosomic side had an ovotestis in all five birds and was presumably female. However, in Warren's case, the larger side was on the left, had apparently an ovotestis, and was therefore more likely to be female. While it is conceivable that the larger side in any laterally asymmetrical gynandromorph might be larger because of a trisomic condition, it is difficult to see how that trisomic condition could cause maleness in some birds but the female state in another, particularly when the same autosome is involved as in Warren's bird and in case D of Crew and Munro.

Apart from gynandromorphs, Crew and Munro (1938, 1939) considered that mosaics showing lateral asymmetry not exceeding 4 per cent resulted from early elimination of a chromosome and not from non-disjunction. Regardless of the difficulties besetting attempts to explain these anomalies, it is remarkable that so many mosaics show differences in the color of the skin. It would appear that the W and w locus is particularly subject to mutation, or that the chromosome carrying it is subject to irregular behavior during cell division, or that both occur. Crew and Munro (1939) reported several cases of mosaicism involving these genes, together with evidence that the tendency to produce such irregularities may be hereditary.

After all this discussion of aberrant behavior of chromosomes, it is desirable to remind the reader that mosaics of various kinds, whether in the plumage or in the skin, can result from nothing more serious than

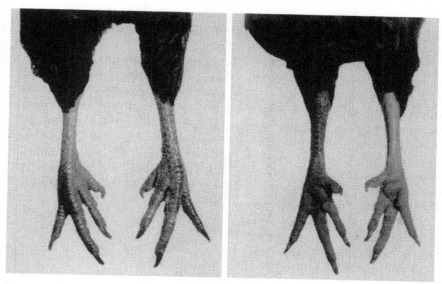

FIG. 129. Legs of a skin-color mosaic, the left one green and the right one yellow; the result of a mutation at the locus of the sex-linked gene *Id*, as explained in the text.

a simple mutation in one gene. The black feathers of barred females are the most familiar examples, but not the only ones. Fowls with white or yellow shanks frequently show a few scales with the typical bluish black that indicates melanin in the dermis. These spots are more likely to represent somatic mutations than anything else. The dominant allele of the gene concerned, *Id*, suppresses dermal melanin, but in any area descended from a cell in which that gene has mutated to its recessive allele a bluish-black spot will appear.

A hen with the left leg yellow and the right one green was described by Knox (1931). A similar pair of shanks, but with the colors reversed, is shown in Fig. 129. In this case there was some yellow on the tips of digits II and III of the green foot and on the web between them. The hen thus distinguished was a pure and respectable Rhode Island Red with an immaculate pedigree of yellow-shanked ancestry. Neither she nor

Knox's hen showed any asymmetry in size. To explain both these cases, it is unnecessary to consider non-disjunction, loss of a chromosome, or anything more serious than a simple mutation of the gene *Id*. Green shank color results merely from the presence of dermal melanin in combination with yellow. The mosaics are easily explained because (1) they were both females and (2) *Id* is sex linked. Having only one sex chromosome, they must have been at fertilization either *Id– ww* (yellow), or *id– ww* (green). The former genotype is more likely, but in either case they could have acquired the alternate form in some cells—and thus become mosaics—only by mutation.

These mosaics with respect to sex-linked genes support the explanation suggested earlier (Hutt, 1929) for similar mosaics in which autosomal genes are involved, *i.e.*, that, when no discrepancies in size are evident in the two differing parts, the mosaic is more likely to have resulted from gene mutation than from elimination or non-disjunction of chromosomes. Since both the cases just described occurred in normal females, there could not have been any non-disjunction of the single sex chromosome. Had it been eliminated, the bird was not likely to be a normal viable female. With other interpretations thus eliminated, gene mutation remains as the only possible explanation.

Literature Cited

Aberle, S. D., and W. Landauer. 1935. Thyroid weight and sex in newly hatched chicks. *Anat. Record*, **62**:331–335.

Adamstone, F. B., and L. E. Card. 1934. A study of the spermatozoon of the fowl, with particular reference to osmiophilic bodies in the sperm head. *J. Morphol.*, **56**:325–337.

―――― and ――――. 1934a. The effects of vitamin E deficiency on the testis of the male fowl (*Gallus domesticus*). *J. Morphol.*, **56**:339–359.

Arnsdorf, R. E. 1947. Hen into rooster. *J. Heredity*, **38**:320.

Asmundson, V. S. 1941. Note on the sex ratio and mortality in turkeys. *Am. Naturalist* **75**:389–393.

Barfurth, D. 1895. Versuche über die parthenogenetische Furchung des Hühnereies. *Arch. Entwicklungsmech. Organ.*, **2**:303-351.

Benoit, J. 1929. Le déterminisme des caractères sexuels secondaires du coq domestique. Etude physiologique et histophysiologique. *Arch. zool. exptl. gén.*, **69**:217–499.

――――. 1932. Etude physiologique, histologique et histophysiologique de l'inversion sexuelle de la poule déterminée par l'ablation de l'ovaire gauche. *Arch. zool. exptl. gén.*, **73**:1–112.

Blacher, L. J. 1926. On the influence of sexual hormones upon the number of erythrocytes and percentage quantity of haemoglobin by fowl. *Biol. Generalis*, **2**:435–441.

Bonnier, G., and S. Trulsson. 1939. Artificial insemination of chickens with semen diluted in Ringer solution. *Proc. World's Poultry Congr., 7th Congr., Cleveland:* 76–79.

―――― and ――――. 1939a. Selective fertilization in poultry. *Hereditas*, **25**:65–76.

Boring, A. M., and R. Pearl. 1918. Sex studies XI. Hermaphrodite birds. *J. Exptl. Zoöl.*, **25**:1–47.

Brode, M. D. 1928. The significance of the asymmetry of the ovaries of the fowl. *J. Morphol. Physiol.*, **46**:1–41.

Buchanan, G. 1926. The testis and thyroid in a hen-feathered Silver-grey Dorking cock. *Brit. J. Exptl. Biol.*, **4**:73–80.

Burrows, H. 1945. "Biological Actions of Sex Hormones." Cambridge: Cambridge University Press.

Burrows, W. H., and J. P. Quinn. 1935. Demonstration of (*a*) the ejaculatory reflex in the cock and (*b*) artificial insemination in the hen. *Poultry Sci.*, **14**:306.

———— and ————. 1937. The collection of spermatozoa from the domestic fowl and turkey. *Poultry Sci.*, **16**:19–24.

———— and ————. 1938. Effective dosages of undiluted semen in artificial insemination of chickens. *Poultry Sci.*, **17**:131-135.

———— and ————. 1939. Artificial insemination of chickens and turkeys. *U.S. Dept. Agr. Circ.* 525.

———— and H. W. Titus. 1939. Some observations on the semen production of the male fowl. *Poultry Sci.*, **18**:8–10.

Byerly, T. C., and M. A. Jull. 1935. Sex ratio and embryonic mortality in the domestic fowl. *Poultry Sci.*, **14**:217–220.

Callenbach, E. W. 1929. The relation of antecedent egg production to the sex ratio. *Poultry Sci.*, **8**:230–234.

Canfield, T. H. 1940. Sex determination of day-old chicks. *Poultry Sci.*, **19**:235–238.

————. 1941. Sex determination of day-old chicks. *Poultry Sci.*, **20**:327–328.

Caridroit, F. 1926. Etude histo-physiologique de la transplantation testiculaire et ovarienne chez les Gallinacés. *Bull. biol. France Belg.*, **60**:135–312.

Castle, W. E. 1935. The Brahma-Plymouth Rock mosaic. *J. Heredity*, **26**:66.

Chanton, L. R. 1932. Teneur en glutathion réduit du sang du coq et de la poule domestique adultes normaux. *Compt. rend. soc. biol.*, **110**:556–558.

————. 1932a. Teneur en glutathion réduit du sang des coqs féminisés, des poules masculinisées et des intersexués. *Compt. rend. soc. biol.*, **110**:757–759.

Chaudhuri, A. C. 1927. A study of arginase content in the fowl with special reference to sex. *Brit. J. Exptl. Biol.*, **5**:97–101.

————. 1927a. The erythrocyte count in sexually normal and abnormal fowls. *Proc. Roy. Phys. Soc. (Edinburgh)*, **21**:109–113.

Chirife, A. 1933. Effetti dell'inanizione grave e prolungate sui caratteri e funzioni sessuali del gallo. *Arch. fisiol.*, **31**:250–260.

Christie, W., and C. Wriedt. 1930. Seasonal effects on Mendelian segregations and sex ratios. *Hereditas*, **14**:173–196.

Cole, L. J. 1927. The lay of the "rooster." *J. Heredity*, **18**:96–106.

———— and F. B. Hutt. 1928. Further experiments in feeding thyroid to fowls. *Poultry Sci.*, **7**:60–66.

Crew, F. A. E. 1923. Studies in intersexuality. II. Sex reversal in the fowl. *Proc. Roy. Soc. (London)* B, **95**:256–278.

————. 1923a. Complete sex-transformation in the domestic fowl. *J. Heredity* **14**:360–362.

————. 1925. Unilateral vasoligation on the senile male of the domestic fowl. *Proc. Roy. Soc. Edinburgh*, **45** (pt. **3**):249–251.

————. 1926. On fertility in the domestic fowl. *Proc. Roy. Soc. Edinburgh*, **46** (pt. **2**):230–238.

Crew, F. A. E. 1927. Studies on the relation of gonadic structure to plumage characterization in the domestic fowl. III. The laying hen with cock's plumage. *Proc. Roy. Soc. (London)* B, **101**:514–518.

———. 1928. A case of lateral asymmetry in the domestic fowl. *J. Genetics*, **20**:179–186.

———. 1932. A case of leg-colour asymmetry in the fowl. *J. Genetics*, **25**:359–365.

———. 1933. A case of non-disjunction in the fowl. *Proc. Roy. Soc. Edinburgh*, **53** (pt. **2**):89–100.

———. 1938. The sex ratio of the domestic fowl and its bearing upon the sex-linked lethal theory of differential mortality. *Proc. Roy. Soc. Edinburgh*, **58** (pt. **1**):73–79.

——— and S. S. Munro. 1938. Gynandromorphism and lateral asymmetry in birds. *Proc. Roy. Soc. Edinburgh*, **58** (pt. **2**):114–134.

——— and ———. 1939. Lateral asymmetry in the fowl. *Proc. World's Poultry Congr., 7th Congr., Cleveland:* 61–64.

Curtis, V., and W. V. Lambert. 1929. A study of fertility in poultry. *Poultry Sci.*, **8**:142–150.

Danforth, C. H., and F. Foster. 1929. Skin transplantation as a means of studying genetic and endocrine factors in the fowl. *J. Exptl. Zoöl.*, **52**:443–470.

Darwin, C. 1871. "The Descent of Man." Vol. I. New York: D. Appleton & Company, Inc.

Domm, L. V. 1927. New experiments on ovariotomy and the problem of sex inversion in the fowl. *J. Exptl. Zoöl.*, **48**:31–173.

———. 1929. Spermatogenesis following early ovariotomy in the Brown Leghorn fowl. *Arch. Entwicklungsmech. Organ.*, **119**:171–187.

———. 1929a. The effects of bilateral ovariotomy in the Brown Leghorn fowl. *Biol. Bull.*, **56**:459–497.

———. 1939. Modifications in sex and secondary sexual characters in birds. Chap. V in "Sex and Internal Secretions," 2d ed. Baltimore: The Williams & Wilkins Company.

——— and E. Taber. 1946. Endocrine factors controlling erythrocyte concentration in the blood of the domestic fowl. *Physiol. Zoöl.*, **19**:258–281.

Dove, W. F. 1928. Sex sterility and the diminutive copulatory organ in the domestic fowl. *Science*, **68**:327–328.

Dudley, F. J., and W. L. S. Hindhaugh. 1939. Sex ratios and comparative rearability of the sexes in the cross-breeding experiments (1934–7) at the Northern Breeding Station of the National Poultry Institute, Reaseheath. *J. Genetics*, **37**:491–497.

Dunn, L. C. 1927. Selective fertilization in fowls. *Poultry Sci.*, **6**:201–214.

———. 1927a. The occurrence of chondrodystrophy in chick embryos. II. The genetic evidence. *Arch. Entwicklungsmech. Organ.*, **110**:341–365.

Field, G. W. 1901. Experiments on modifying the normal proportion of the sexes in the domestic fowl. *Biol. Bull.*, **2**:360–361.

Finlay, G. F. 1925. Studies on sex differentiation in fowls. *Brit. J. Exptl. Biol.*, **2**:439–468.

Forbes, T. R. 1947. The crowing hen: early observations on spontaneous sex reversal in birds. *Yale J. Biol. Med.*, **19**:955–970.

Fronda, F. M. 1926. Studies on the fertility of the hen's egg. *Philippine Agr.*, **15**:349–360.

Funk, E. M. 1939. The relation of size of clutch and position of the egg in the clutch to hatching results. *Poultry Sci.*, **18**:350–353.

Gibbs, C. S. 1935. "A Guide to Sexing Chicks." New York: Orange Judd Publishing Co., Inc.

Goodale, H. D. 1916. A feminized cockerel. *J. Exptl. Zoöl.*, **20**:421–428.

———. 1916a. Gonadectomy in relation to the secondary sexual characters of some domestic birds. *Carnegie Inst. Wash.* Pub. 243.

———. 1916b. Further developments in ovariotomized fowl. *Biol. Bull.*, **30**:286–293.

———. 1918. Feminized male birds. *Genetics*, **3**:276–299.

Gowen, J. W. 1926. Cystic testes, a cause of male sterility in the domestic fowl. *Poultry Sci.*, **5**:146–148.

Gracewski, J. J., and H. M. Scott. 1943. The influence of time of mating on fertility. *Poultry Sci.*, **22**:264–265.

Greenwood, A. W., and J. S. S. Blyth. 1929. An experimental analysis of the plumage of the Brown Leghorn Fowl. *Proc. Roy. Soc. Edinburgh*, **49** (pt. **4**): 313–355.

——— and ———. 1930. The results of testicular transplantation in Brown Leghorn hens. *Proc. Roy. Soc. (London)* B, **106**:189–202.

——— and ———. 1932. Reversal of the secondary sexual characters in the fowl. A castrated Brown Leghorn male which assumed female characters. *J. Genetics*, **20**:199–213.

——— and ———. 1938. Sex dimorphism in the plumage of the domestic fowl. *J. Genetics*, **36**:53–72.

——— and F. A. E. Crew. 1927. Studies on the relation of gonadic structure to plumage characterisation in the domestic fowl. II. The developmental capon and poularde. *Proc. Roy. Soc. (London)* B, **101**:450–462.

Grodzinski, Z., and J. Marchlewski. 1935. Studies on the motility of spermatozoa of the domestic cock outside the organism. *Bull. intern. acad. polon. sci. lettres, Classes sci. math. nat.* B, **II**:347–361.

Hays, F. A. 1941. Sex ratio in domestic chickens. *Am. Naturalist*, **75**:187–188.

———. 1945. The primary sex ratio in domestic chickens. *Am. Naturalist*, **79**: 184–186.

Hazel, L. N., and W. F. Lamoreux. 1946. Family sex ratios in the fowl. *J. Heredity*, **37**:333–334.

Hertwig, P. 1927. Über eine Möglichkeit, bei frisch geschlüpften Küken das Geschlecht zu erkennen. *Arch. Geflügelk.*, **1**:23–27.

Hindhaugh, W. L. S. 1932. Some observations on fertility in White Wyandottes. *Harper Adams Util. Poultry J.*, **17**:555–560.

Hollander, W. F. 1944. Mosaic effects in domestic birds. *Quart. Rev. Biol.*, **19**: 285–307.

Hutt, F. B. 1929. On the relation of fertility in fowls to the amount of testicular material and density of sperm suspension. *Proc. Roy. Soc. Edinburgh*, **49**:102–117.

———. 1929a. Sex dimorphism and variability in the appendicular skeleton of the Leghorn fowl. *Poultry Sci.*, **8**:202–218.

———. 1929b. A note on Lambert's mosaic in the fowl. *J. Heredity*, **20**:323–324.

———. 1937. Gynandromorphism in the fowl. *Poultry Sci.*, **16**:354–355.

———. 1940. A relation between breed characteristics and poor reproduction in White Wyandotte fowls. *Am. Naturalist*, **74**:148–156.

Hutt, F. B. and A. W. Greenwood. 1929. Studies in embryonic mortality in the fowl. II. Chondrodystrophy in the chick. *Proc. Roy. Soc. Edinburgh,* **49**:131–144.

Ivanov, E. I. 1924. Recherches expérimentales à propos du processus de la fécondation chez les poules. *Compt. rend. soc. biol.,* **91**:54–56.

Jaap, R. G. 1945. Activity of synthetic estrogens on oral administration in the domestic fowl and turkey. *Endocrinology,* **37**:369–376.

Jones, D. G., and W. F. Lamoreux. 1942. Semen production of White Leghorn males from strains selected for high and low fecundity. *Poultry Sci.,* **21**:173–184.

Juhn, M., and L. V. Domm. 1930. The relation of gonadal condition to erythrocyte number in fowls. *Am. J. Physiol.,* **94**:656–661.

Jull, M. A. 1924. The relation of antecedent egg production to the sex ratio of the domestic fowl. *J. Agr. Research,* **28**:199–224.

———. 1931. The sex ratio in the domestic fowl in relation to antecedent egg production and inbreeding. *Biol. Bull.,* **60**:124–131.

———. 1932. Is the tendency to produce an excess of either sex in the domestic fowl inherited? *Poultry Sci.,* **11**:20–22.

———. 1934. The feasibility of sex segregation in day-old chicks. *Poultry Sci.,* **13**:250–254.

——— and J. P. Quinn. 1924. The shape and weight of eggs in relation to the sex of chicks in the domestic fowl. *J. Agr. Research,* **29**:195–201.

——— and ———. 1925. The relationship between the weight of eggs and the weight of chicks according to sex. *J. Agr. Research,* **31**:223–226.

Knox, C. W. 1931. Color chimeras in the domestic fowl. *J. Heredity,* **22**:133–134.

Kosin, I. L. 1944. Macro- and microscopic methods of detecting fertility in unincubated hen's eggs. *Poultry Sci.,* **23**:266–269.

———. 1945. The accuracy of the macroscopic method in identifying fertile unincubated germ discs. *Poultry Sci.,* **24**:281–283.

Lambert, W. V. 1929. A "half and half" skin color mosaic in the chicken. *J. Heredity,* **20**:167–169.

——— and V. Curtis. 1929. Further studies on the sex ratio in the chicken. *Biol. Bull.,* **56**:226–233.

——— and C. W. Knox. 1926. Genetic studies in poultry. I. The sex ratio in the domestic fowl. *Biol. Bull.,* **51**:225–236.

Lamoreux, W. F. 1939. A pseudogynandromorph in the fowl. *J. Heredity,* **30**:78–80.

———. 1940. Spermatozoal antibodies and infertility in the fowl. *J. Exptl. Zoöl.,* **85**:419–430.

———. 1940a. The influence of intensity of egg production upon infertility in the domestic fowl. *J. Agr. Research,* **61**:191–206.

———. 1942. Environmental temperature and infertility in White Leghorns. *Poultry Sci.,* **21**:18–22.

———. 1942a. Hereditary chondrodystrophy in the fowl. *J. Heredity,* **33**:275–283.

———. 1943. The influence of different amounts of illumination upon the production of semen in the fowl. *J. Exptl. Zoöl.,* **94**:73–95.

——— and D. G. Jones. 1942. The effects of dubbing White Leghorn males. *Poultry Sci.,* **21**:437–444.

Landauer, W. 1948. The hatchability of chicken eggs as influenced by environment and heredity. *Storrs (Conn.) Agr. Expt. Sta. Bull.* 262.

Landauer, W. and A. B. Landauer. 1931. Chick mortality and sex-ratio in the domestic fowl. *Am. Naturalist,* **65**:492–501.

Lillie, F. R. 1931. Bilateral gynandromorphism and lateral hemihypertrophy in birds. *Science,* **74**:387–390.

Lorenz, F. W. 1945. The influence of diethylstilbestrol on fat deposition and meat quality in chickens. *Poultry Sci.,* **24**:128–134.

———. 1945a. The fattening action of orally administered synthetic estrogens as compared with diethylstilbestrol pellet implants. *Poultry Sci.,* **24**:91–92.

——— and G. H. Bachman. 1947. Lipemia and fat deposition in response to oral administration of synthetic estrogens. *Poultry Sci.,* **26**:419–431.

——— and I. M. Lerner. 1946. Inheritance of sexual maturity in male chickens and turkeys. *Poultry Sci.,* **25**:188–189.

McCartney, J. L. 1923. Studies on the mechanism of sterilization of the female by spermatoxin. *Am. J. Physiol.,* **63**:207–217.

MacArthur, J. W., and W. H. T. Baillie. 1932. Sex differences in mortality in Abraxas-type species. *Quart. Rev. Biol.,* **7**:313–325.

Macdonald, E., and L. W. Taylor. 1933. The rudimentary copulatory organ of the domestic fowl. *J. Morphol.,* **54**:429–449.

Macklin, M. T. 1923. A description of material from a gynandromorph fowl. *J. Exptl. Zoöl.,* **38**:355–375.

Masui, K., and J. Hashimoto. 1933. "Sexing Baby Chicks." Vancouver: Journal Printing Co.

Miller, R. A. 1938. Spermatogenesis in a sex-reversed female and in normal males of the domestic fowl, *Gallus domesticus. Anat. Record,* **70**:155–189.

Mimura, H. 1928. On the asymmetrical development of the right and left testes in the domestic fowls. *Japan J. Zootech. Sci.,* **3**:1–10.

———. 1939. On the mechanism of travel of spermatozoa through the oviduct in the domestic fowl, with special reference to the artificial insemination. *Okajimas folia anat. japon.,* **17**:459–476.

Mirskaia, L., and F. A. E. Crew. 1931. The effect of destruction of the spermatogenic tissue by X-rays upon certain secondary gonadic characters of the cock. *Quart. J. Exptl. Physiol.,* **21**:135–138.

Moore, O. K., and T. C. Byerly. 1942. Relation of time of insemination to per cent fertility. *Poultry Sci.,* **21**:253–255.

Moszkowicz, L., and W. Kolmer. 1931. Ein gynandromorphes Huhn. *Virchow's Arch. path. Anat.,* **279**:768–779.

Munro, S. S. 1932. Chondrodystrophy in fowl embryos. *Sci. Agr.,* **13**:97–109.

———. 1938. Functional changes in fowl sperm during their passage through the excurrent ducts of the male. *J. Exptl. Zoöl.,* **79**:71–92.

———. 1938a. The effect of testis hormone on the preservation of sperm life in the vas deferens of the fowl. *J. Exptl. Biol.,* **15**:186–196.

———. 1938b. The effect of dilution and density on the fertilizing capacity of fowl sperm suspensions. *Can. J. Research D,* **16**:281–299.

———. 1938c. A single chromosome explanation of Roberts and Quisenberry's Brahma × Barred Rock mosaic. *J. Heredity,* **29**:389–391.

———. 1946. Relative influence of heredity and environment on fertility and hatchability in Wyandottes. *Empire J. Exptl. Agr.,* **14**:25–30.

Mussehl, F. E. 1924. Sex ratios in poultry. *Poultry Sci.,* **3**:72–73.

Nicolaides, C. 1934. Fertility studies in poultry. *Poultry Sci.,* **13**:178–183.

Olsen, M. W. 1942. Maturation, fertilization, and early cleavage in the hen's egg. *J. Morphol.*, **70**:513–533.

Parker, G. H. 1930. The ciliary systems in the oviduct of the pigeon. *Proc. Soc. Exptl. Biol. Med.*, **27**:704–706.

———. 1932. The passage of sperm and of egg through the oviducts in terrestrial vertebrates. *Phil. Trans. Roy. Soc. (London)* B, **219**:381–419.

Parker, J. E. 1945. Relation of time of day of artificial insemination to fertility and hatchability of hens' eggs. *Poultry Sci.*, **24**:314–317.

———, F. F. McKenzie, and H. L. Kempster. 1942. Fertility in the male domestic fowl. *Missouri Agr. Expt. Sta. Research Bull.* 347.

——— and B. J. McSpadden. 1943. Influence of feed restriction on fertility in male domestic fowls. *Poultry Sci.*, **22**:170–177.

Parkes, A. S., and F. W. R. Brambell. 1926. The anomalous appearance of male sexual characters in female fowls. *J. Genetics*, **17**:69–76.

——— and H. Selye. 1937. The endocrine system and plumage types. I. Some effects of hypothyroidism. *J. Genetics*, **34**:297–306.

Payne, L. F., and C. Ingram. 1927. The effects of freezing the combs of breeding males. *Poultry Sci.*, **6**:99–107.

Pearl, R. 1917. The sex ratio in the domestic fowl. *Proc. Am. Phil. Soc.*, **56**:416–436.

Pezard, A. 1928. Die Bestimmung der Geschlechtsfunktion bei den Hühnern. *Ergeb. Physiol.*, **27**:552–656; also published separately as "La détermination de la fonction sexuelle chez les Gallinacés." Paris: Masson et Cie. 1930.

Quinn, J. P., and W. H. Burrows. 1936. Artificial insemination in fowls. *J. Heredity*, **27**:31–37.

Roberts, E., and J. H. Quisenberry. 1935. A Brahma–Plymouth Rock mosaic. *J. Heredity*, **26**:11–14.

Sampson, F. R., and D. C. Warren. 1939. Density of suspension and morphology of sperm in relation to fertility in the fowl. *Poultry Sci.*, **18**:301–307.

Searcy, G. L., and F. N. Andrews. 1943. The effect of comb and wattle removal upon testicular activity in the domestic fowl. *Poultry Sci.*, **22**:235–241.

Stanley, A. J., and E. Witschi. 1940. Germ cell migration in relation to asymmetry in the sex glands of hawks. *Anat. Record*, **76**:329–342.

Thayer, R. H., R. G. Jaap, and R. Penquite. 1945. Fattening chickens by feeding estrogens. *Poultry Sci.*, **24**:483–495.

Torrey, H. B., and B. Horning. 1922. Hen-feathering induced in the male fowl by feeding thyroid. *Proc. Soc. Exptl. Biol. Med.*, **19**:275–279.

Upp, C. W. 1928. Preferential mating of fowls. *Poultry Sci.*, **7**:225–232.

Van Drimmelen, G. C. 1945. Intraperitoneal insemination of birds. *J. S. African Vet. Med. Assoc.*, **16**:1–6.

———. 1946. "Spermnests" in the oviduct of the domestic hen. *J. S. African Vet. Med. Assoc.*, **17**:42–52.

Vecchi, A. 1936. Un caso di ginandromorfismo bipartito con mosaico somatico nel pollo. *Arch. zool. italiano*, **23**:377–395.

Walton, A., and E. O. Whetham. 1933. The survival of the spermatozoon in the domesticated fowl. *J. Exptl. Biol.*, **10**:204–211.

Warren, D. C. 1933. Nine independently inherited autosomal factors in the domestic fowl. *Genetics*, **18**:68–81.

———. 1945. A case of lateral asymmetry in the fowl. *J. Heredity*, **36**:226–231.

Warren, D. C. and C. L. Gish. 1943. The value of artificial insemination in poultry breeding work. *Poultry Sci.,* **22**:108–117.

—— and L. Kilpatrick. 1929. Fertilization in the domestic fowl. *Poultry Sci.,* **8**:237–256.

Wheeler, N. C., and F. N. Andrews. 1943. The influence of season on semen production in the domestic fowl. *Poultry Sci.,* **22**:361–367.

Willier, B. H. 1939. The embryonic development of sex. Chap. III in "Sex and Internal Secretions," 2d ed. Baltimore: The Williams & Wilkins Company.

——. 1942. Hormonal control of embryonic differentiation in birds. *Cold Spring Harbor Symposia Quant. Biol.,* **10**:135–144.

Witschi, E. 1935. Origin of asymmetry in the reproductive system of birds. *Am. J. Anat.,* **56**:119–141.

CHAPTER 14

LINKAGE

Historical Notes. Since any sex-linked gene is automatically assigned to its proper chromosome as soon as its mode of inheritance is known, one might say that the mapping of the fowl's chromosomes began in 1908, when Spillman showed the genetic basis for barring. Actually the position of B in relation to some gene in the sex chromosome was not measured quantitatively until 13 years later, when Haldane (1921) reported 34.6 per cent crossing over between B and S. (That figure has since been raised by later investigators.) During the next two decades five additional genes were assigned to tentative positions in the sex chromosome, and three others are now known to belong somewhere in it.

The first case of autosomal linkage, that between Cp (creeper) and R (rose comb), was reported by Serebrovsky and Petrov in 1928. Others soon followed, and 8 years later the first chromosome map (Hutt, 1936) showed the relative positions of 7 genes in the sex chromosome and 11 more in four autosomal linkage groups. Four years later Hutt and Lamoreux (1940) were able to assign 14 autosomal genes to their positions in five different linkage groups, and one more was marked for the F I Cr chromosome, with its position not definitely established. Since that time only one other autosomal mutation, polydactyly, has been added to the map, and sex-linked blue has been located in the sex chromosome.

DIFFICULTIES AND SUGGESTIONS

It is evident from this brief survey that the mapping of the fowl's chromosomes will be a slow process and that the addition of a new linkage group or even of a new gene to existing groups is a real achievement. Presumably, one of the difficulties is that with 39 or 40 chromosomes (haploid number) the chance of testing two mutations for linkage and finding it is rather remote. The number of genes located on the map of the sex chromosome is comparatively large, but this results merely from the ease with which sex-linked genes can be assigned to their proper chromosome. Nevertheless, there are at least six autosomes large enough to warrant some hope that they may carry the majority of the fowl's genes. If they do, the present sparsely dotted maps for five autosomes should be considerably extended over the course of a hundred years. To facilitate this work, it is desirable, not merely that linkage tests be made by those in a position to do so, but also, because of the time and expense involved, that repetition of clearly negative tests made by previous investigators be avoided. To that end, it is important that those reporting trials of this sort should publish, not only their data that may indicate linkage, but also any results that show what genes are apparently independent of established linkage groups or of each other.

Some mutations are much better than others for studies of linkage. The very best are those which can be classified with accuracy at hatching or before. They thus provide larger numbers than one can have with mutations not expressed until the bird is mature. Numbers are important, because, when loose linkages are concerned, extremely large numbers are necessary if one is to distinguish between true linkage and chance fluctuation from a 1:1 ratio of parental to new combinations. For example, in the sex chromosome, B and S are so far apart that they would doubtless be considered independent if it were not known that both must be in that chromosome. In contrast to the useful mutations that are visible in the newly hatched chick, sex-limited variations expressed only at maturity are poor material for linkage studies. This is merely because they are not likely to be measured in more than 40 per cent of the birds hatched for the test. The linkage of O (blue egg) with P (pea comb) might never have been detected in 35 females were it not that these two genes are so closely linked that only two crossovers were found in that number (Bruckner and Hutt, 1939).

Anyone preparing to carry out linkage tests should first be satisfied that the mutations to be used will segregate distinctly from their normal alleles. The difficulty of interpreting linkage data when one of the characters under test is frequently suppressed was illustrated by Hutt and Mueller (1943) in their studies with polydactyly. As is well known, that character is expressed in normal ratios in some matings but not in others. Such mutations can be used so long as one is not misled by their occasional erratic behavior. With the limited numbers necessitated in most linkage tests with the fowl, a backcross of heterozygotes to doubly recessive homozygotes is more likely to reveal linkage than is an F_2 population. Finally, it is suggested that anyone undertaking a search for linkage should first assure himself that the tests contemplated will supplement those already made by others and not duplicate them. Records of some of these tests are given in this chapter and others will be found in the references cited. The report by Warren (1949) should also be consulted.

THE CHROMOSOME MAP

A map showing the approximate positions of the genes that have thus far been located in the fowl's chromosomes is given in Fig. 130. It is a revised form of the map drawn up by Hutt and Lamoreux (1940). Detailed descriptions of all the mutations shown thereon have been given in earlier chapters of this book, except for the brown eye placed by Mac-Arthur (1933) in the sex chromosome. The chromosomes have not been labelled as I, II, III, etc., because it seems desirable to defer such designations until the linkage groups have been related to the particular chromosome concerned. The relative positions of the genes in any one chromosome are shown by the approximate crossover distances between them, rather than by their cumulative distance from one end of the chromosome, as is done in the more extensive maps of other species. The procedure followed seems preferable until the present rather sketchy maps for all six chromosomes have been filled in more completely. Moreover, it is possible that any two groups now apparently independent may subsequently be found to belong in the same chromosome.

To label a variation as a mutant automatically necessitates some definition of what is meant by the non-mutated, normal form. Following the usual convention of geneticists, the normal is considered as the "wild type," presumably exhibited in this species by the Red Jungle Fowl, *Gallus gallus* (Figs. 3 and 4). Students sometimes ask how one knows what the wild type is like. For this purpose it is convenient to have a few Jungle Fowls handy, but that is not necessary for anyone who can conjure up a mental image of one or of a Single-comb Brown Leghorn with blue or slaty shanks. None of the photographs of the normal, wild-type alleles shown in the map are from Jungle Fowls, but the type of comb, feather structure, color, and other characters of that bird are shown with reasonable accuracy.

The Sex Chromosome. A lone crossover between B and S observed by Goodale (1917) provided the first case of crossing over reported for the fowl, but data on the linkage relations of B and S were first obtained by Haldane (1921) and Agar (1924). After the sex-linked gene K (slow feathering) was discovered by Serebrovsky in 1922, considerable information concerning linkage of these three genes and also of Id (inhibitor of dermal melanin) was contributed by several other workers. The data of Serebrovsky and Wassina (1926), Warren (1928), Hertwig and Rittershaus (1929), Hertwig (1930), Serebrovsky and Petrov (1930), and MacArthur (1933) on crossing over between various pairs of B, S, K, and Id were summarized by Punnett (1940), who added extensive records of his own linkage tests with these genes. As a result, he was able to compute determinations of crossing over based on tested gametes numbering from 1,123 to 2,154 for five of the six possible combinations of these genes in pairs.

Linkages of these four genes with *Li* (light down) and *ko* (head streak) were reported by Hertwig and Rittershaus (1929) and Hertwig (1930). MacArthur (1933) added similar data for a dominant gene *Br*, which causes a light iris, ranging in color from yellow-orange to bay, in contrast to the brownish-black iris.

The data available in all these various reports were combined by Punnett (1940) to make the useful summary of crossover values shown in Table 62.

TABLE 62. AMOUNT OF CROSSING OVER, PER CENT, BETWEEN VARIOUS GENES IN THE SEX CHROMOSOME*

	K	*S*	*Li*	*Br*	*Id*	*B*	*Ko*
K							
S	15						
Li	24	16					
Br	42	44	—†				
Id	46	47	30	27			
B	46	48	40	—†	10		
Ko	47	50	47	—†	—†	13	

* Computed from all published data by Punnett (1940).
† Not yet tested.

A valuable contribution to this table was Punnett's own evidence confirming that of Serebrovsky and Petrov (1930) and proving that crossing over does occur between *B* and *Id*. The *Id* gene has been difficult to handle in linkage tests because it is closely linked with *B*, which eliminates melanin from the dermis just as does *Id*. For that reason earlier investigators were unable to tell with certainty whether or not any crossovers occurred between the two genes.

To overcome this difficulty, Serebrovsky and Petrov (1930) mated doubly heterozygous males with *b id* females, discarded the barred prog-

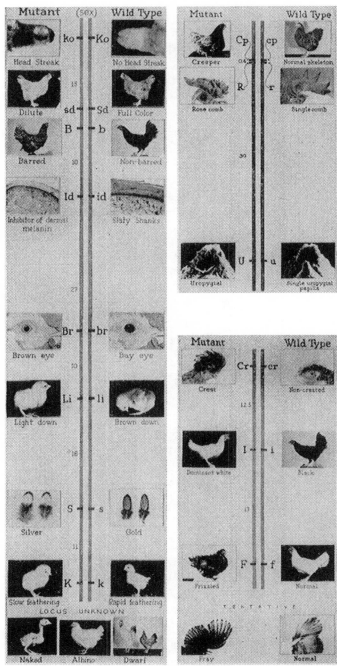

Fig. 130. A map of the sex-chromosome (*left*) and five auto-locations and relationships of 24 genes in these six linkage chromosome and one more assigned to the *Cr I F* group.

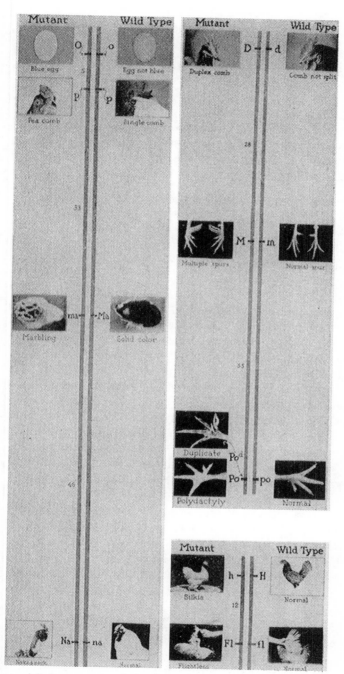

somal linkage groups of the fowl. It shows the approximate
groups, also three mutations yet to be located in the sex

eny, and measured the amount of crossing over in the non-barred birds. The method is useful but reduces the numbers of gametes tested. Punnett made similar crosses, $B\ id/b\ Id\ \male\ \male \times b\ id - \female\ \female$, but found that by classifying shank color of the chicks at hatching and again classifying both shank and plumage color when the birds were older he could differentiate all four types. That is possible because Id causes light shanks at hatching, while B does not do so, especially in heterozygotes, till later. The four classes can therefore be distinguished as follows:

Id B: Shanks light at hatching, also later; plumage barred.
Id b: Shanks light at hatching, also later; non-barred.
id B: Shanks dark at hatching, light later; barred.
id b: Shanks dark at hatching, also later; non-barred.

By differentiating the phenotypes in this way, Punnett found the amount of crossing over between B and Id to be 9.3 per cent in 107 gametes.

Sex-linked genes not represented in Table 62 include the blue dilution that Munro (1946) found to be so closely linked with B that no certain crossovers were found, although there were about 7 per cent of doubtful cases. Others not yet located are naked (Hutt and Sturkie, 1938), albinism (Mueller and Hutt, 1941), and dwarf.

Unfortunately, the seven genes considered in Table 62 cannot be located with accuracy on the map of the sex chromosome directly from the crossover values there given. This is merely because most of the 17 determinations are concerned with genes so far apart that the actual distances on the chromosome are not accurately revealed by the amounts of crossing over between them. It is possible, however, to determine the positions of these genes in relation to one another, and these are shown in Fig. 130.

There is some doubt whether K should go at the end of the chromosome or between S and Li. It is true that K appears to be slightly closer than S to Br, Id, B, and Ko, but these are all long distances. When K and S were tested for linkage with Li, a gene somewhat closer to both of them, the combined data of Hertwig and Rittershaus (1929) and Hertwig (1930) suggested (Table 62) that K was more remote than S from Li. Another reason for uncertainty is that identification of rapid feathering and slow feathering is not always easy, especially in crosses between the light and heavy breeds. As Punnett pointed out, there are some inconsistencies in the reports of linkage tests involving K, and the pooled data of all investigators may therefore be misleading. There is little point in debating the problem until linkage data are available for other genes that are close to K and S.

Although the sex chromosome has the longest map of any linkage group determined thus far, it ranks only fifth in size (Fig. 8). It would be interesting to know whether or not the two groups of genes at either end of its map are located in the two arms of this V-shaped chromosome. It is apparently long enough to permit considerable double crossing over, which has been observed in varying amounts by different investigators. Thus, with *B*, *Li*, *S*, and *K* involved, Hertwig and Rittershaus (1929) observed double crossing over to be 11.5 per cent and triple crossing over 2 per cent. A still higher figure was reported by MacArthur (18.4 per cent) for the distance between *Id* and *K*. Between *B* and *K*, Punnett (1940) found double crossing over to be 9.2 per cent in crosses involving *B*, *S*, and *K*. As he pointed out, his lower figure was to be expected because he was dealing with a three-point linkage, whereas the other investigators cited had four genes involved and hence were more likely to detect double crossovers.

The *Cp R U* Group. The announcement by Serebrovsky and Petrov (1928) that they had found *Cp* (creeper) and *r* (single comb) closely linked provided the first case of autosomal linkage to be discovered in the fowl. In a later report, these investigators (1930) were able to show that crossing over between *Cp* and *r* occurred in both sexes. In their combined data for tests with three heterozygous males, the amount of crossing over was 9.1 per cent in 297 gametes, and in the limited data from females tested the crossover value was twice as high.

In extensive investigations of this linkage, Landauer (1932, 1933) found crossing over to be only 0.39 per cent among 7,408 chicks and embryos. He concluded that the difference between this result and the much higher figure of the Russian investigators was attributable to genetic differences in the stocks. However, in similar tests, Taylor (1934) found only 0.5 per cent crossing over between *Cp* and *r* in 2,183 chicks and embryos. He found in his preliminary studies that some of the less affected creepers could be mistaken for normal chicks unless the leg were dissected and suggested that this might account for the much higher crossover value determined by Serebrovsky and Petrov.

The gene *U* (uropygial), causing in heterozygotes a bifurcation or complete division of the uropygial papilla, was found to show 29.6 per cent crossing over with *R* (Hutt, 1936).

The *Cr I F* Group. Tests by Dunn and Landauer (1930) indicated a close linkage between *I* (dominant white) and cerebral hernia but these investigators did not recognize that the latter character is merely one expression of the gene for crest, *Cr*. Linkage of *Cr* and *F* (frizzling), with 28 per cent crossing over between them, was found by Suttle and Sipe (1932), and the group began to take its present form when linkage of *F* and *I* was discovered (Hutt, 1933). With the accumulation of later data, the distance between these two genes is known to be about 17 crossover units. These linkages of *Cr* and *F* and of *F* and *I* were also discovered independently by Sungurov (1933), in whose limited data the crossover values were slightly higher than those just given. The three genes were finally assigned to their relative positions, as shown in the map, when Warren and Hutt (1936) found crossing over between *I* and *Cr* to be 12.5 per cent in 1,984 gametes. Their report reviewed all the available linkage data for this chromosome, added considerable new material confirming the relationships previously established, and clarified somewhat the once confused understanding of the identity of crest and cerebral hernia. In three-point linkage tests with *F*, *I*, and *Cr*, they found no double crossovers in 284 gametes tested.

Warren (1938) assigned the mutation, fray (affecting the plumage), to this chromosome, but did not give its position. He has since advised the author that fray shows 46 per cent crossing over with *Cr* and still more with *I*. The results of many investigations showing certain mutations to be independent of the genes in this linkage group were tabulated earlier (Hutt, 1933; Warren and Hutt, 1936). Since genes independent of the two terminal genes in this linkage group (*F* and *Cr*) must also be independent of *I*, tests of such genes with *I* are omitted from the following summary. Full details concerning them will be found in the two papers cited. Apart from them, the mutations that have been proved independent of one or more of the genes in this linkage group are as follows:

> *Independent of F and Cr:* Extended black, blue, duplex comb, rose comb, white skin, naked neck, muff, rumplessness, and polydactyly.
> *Independent of F:* Creeper, fibromelanosis.
> *Independent of I and Cr:* Silky, pea comb, feathered shanks, flightless.
> *Independent of I:* Creeper.

The *O P ma* Group. This linkage group was discovered by Hertwig (1933), who found 32.8 per cent crossovers between *P* (pea comb) and *ma* (marbled pattern in the down) among 839 gametes tested. She also found 45.6 per cent of crossing over between *ma* and *Na* (naked neck), and since the latter gene segregated independently of *P*, its position should be approximately as shown on the map.

Warren (1938) has since stated that *Na* belongs in the *h Fl* group; but, pending evidence to the contrary, one can hardly reject Hertwig's conclusion that it is linked with *ma*, since her determination of 45.6 per cent crossing over was based upon 1,141 gametes. It is quite possible that *Na* may be linked both with *ma* and with *Fl*, in which case these two apparently separate linkage groups would be joined to make a single large one.

Another gene added to this group is O (blue eggshell), which Bruckner and Hutt (1939) found to show only about 5 per cent of crossing over with P. It is not yet known on which side of the latter gene O belongs. Some evidence that Bl (blue) is linked with Na was found by Serebrovsky and Petrov (1930), but Warren (1938) has since reported that these genes showed independence in his data.

The h Fl Group. Linkage of h, the gene causing absence of hooks and scrolls on the barbules in feathers of the Silky, and Fl (flightless) was found by Warren (1935). His later data show the amount of crossing over between them to be 11.6 per cent (Warren, 1940). Warren (1938) has also placed Na in this group. Since the map in Fig. 130 was prepared he has informed the author that Na shows 43.3 per cent crossing over with h and 46.2 per cent with Fl. The possibility that Na may eventually link these genes with the O P ma group should not be forgotten.

The D M Po Group. This group, the latest one to be discovered, has its three genes rather widely separated and may represent one of the longer chromosomes. D (duplex comb) shows about 28 per cent of crossing over with the gene M for multiple spurs (Hutt, 1941). The latter is also loosely linked with Po (polydactyly), the amount of crossing over between them being 33 per cent (Hutt and Mueller, 1943). The relationships of the three genes were proved by tests that showed 42 per cent crossovers between D and Po, thus establishing the arrangement shown in the map. When all three genes were involved, the amount of double crossing over between D and Po was 9.3 per cent.

The locus of Po may be occupied by any of the three alleles in the series of multiple alleles to which it belongs. These are Po, Po^d (duplicate), and po. Warren (1944) showed that Po^d shows the same linkage relations with D and with M as does Po, and he also confirmed the positions of all three that were established by Hutt and Mueller.

The evidence from all published sources that could reveal what genes appear to be independent of this group was tabulated by Hutt and Mueller and is briefly summarized here. As before, when some mutation has been shown to be independent of both the terminal genes in the group, it is unnecessary to consider tests of that same gene with M. Otherwise, the following mutations have been excluded from the D M Po group:

Independent of D and Po: F and Cr; R and Cp (but not U); P (but not others of that group); also blue, extended black, fibromelanosis, muff, naked neck, white skin, and mottling.

Independent of D and M : Fl.
Independent of D: Recessive white.

Since future additions to this group are likely to necessitate tests involving *Po,* it is to be hoped that investigators will not be misled by its incomplete manifestation in some matings. Furthermore, as Hutt and Mueller found, genes suppressing polydactyly may also suppress multiple spurs. Usually the latter segregates sharply, but one male was found to contribute modifying genes that inhibited the manifestation of *Po* and *M* in 59 and 42 per cent, respectively, of those which should have shown these characters. The resultant distortion of ratios was much greater than that attributable to linkage. It is desirable, therefore, before estimating any crossing over or independence, to see whether or not these genes have segregated in clear 1:1 ratios in backcrosses. If they have not done so, the data should be corrected, discarded, or viewed with suspicion.

VARIATIONS IN CROSSING OVER

While most of the variations in crossover values for the fowl reported by different investigators may be attributed to chance fluctuations or to differences in classification, it is probable that differences among birds in the amount of crossing over in their gametes also contribute to the variability. Presumably, these are overcome as larger numbers are accumulated.

Because crossing over does not take place in the male of Drosophila or in the female silkworm and in rats and mice is somewhat lower in males than in females, it has been supposed that crossing over is generally less in the heterogametic sex than in the homogametic one. Early attempts to see whether this situation prevails in the fowl were not very informative because of variations arising from small numbers. A compilation of all the available data for some of the linkages for which large numbers are known was made by Warren (1940) to shed some light on this question. His total figures for five different linkages are given in Table 63. The data for the *R– Cp* pair are those of Landauer and of Taylor. Most of the others are Warren's own, together with some from Hutt and from Suttle and Sipe.

Of these five cases, only one shows a statistically significant difference, and that is the rose comb—creeper pair, in which crossing over is apparently more than twice as frequent in females as in males. In the other four instances, two show slightly more crossing over in females, and in the other two this situation is reversed. Apparently crossing over

TABLE 63. CROSSING OVER IN RELATION TO SEX *

Genes tested	Crossing over in females		Crossing over in males	
	Gametes tested, number	Cross-overs, per cent	Gametes tested, number	Cross-overs, per cent
Crest—dominant white....	1,303	12.4 ± 0.62	2,657	12.6 ± 0.43
Frizzling—dominant white.	563	19.2 ± 1.12	1,559	17.4 ± 0.64
Frizzling—crest..........	854	29.5 ± 1.05	1,248	27.8 ± 0.85
Silky—flightless..........	1,079	11.6 ± 0.66	580	12.2 ± 0.92
Rose comb—creeper.......	4,996	0.54 ± 0.70	4,595	0.24 ± 0.05

* Compiled by Warren (1940).

is influenced very little by sex in the fowl, at least so far as these figures for three different linkage groups can be any guide.

Some data obtained by Haldane and Crew (1925) suggested that crossing over between B and S, in the sex chromosome, increases with age. However, Punnett (1940) could find no evidence of such an effect on this linkage or on others in the sex chromosome. Similarly, Landauer (1933) found no significant change in crossing over with age in birds used for 3 successive years to test the linkage of Cp and R.

Literature Cited

Agar, W. E. 1924. Experiments with certain plumage colour and pattern factors in poultry. *J. Genetics,* **14**:265–272.

Bruckner, J. H., and F. B. Hutt. 1939. Linkage of pea comb and blue egg in the fowl. *Science,* **90**:88.

Dunn, L. C., and W. Landauer. 1930. Further data on a case of autosomal linkage in the domestic fowl. *J. Genetics,* **22**:95–101.

Goodale, H. D. 1917. Crossing over in the sex chromosome of the male fowl. *Science,* **46**:213.

Haldane, J. B. S. 1921. Linkage in poultry. *Science,* **54**:663.

—— and F. A. E. Crew. 1925. Change of linkage in poultry with age. *Nature,* **115**:641.

Hertwig, P. 1930. Die Erbfaktoren der Haushühner. 2. Beitrag: Die Ortsbestimmung von zwei weiteren Faktoren im X-Chromosom. *Biol. Zentr.,* 50: 333–341.

——. 1933. Geschlechtsgebundene und autosomale Koppelungen bei Hühnern. *Verhandl. deut. zool. Ges.:* 112–118.

—— and T. Rittershaus. 1929. Die Erbfaktoren der Haushühner. I. Beitrag: Die Ortsbestimmung von 4 Faktoren im X-Chromosom. *Z. ind. Abst. Vererb.,* **51**:354–372.

Hutt, F. B. 1933. Genetics of the fowl. II. A four-gene autosomal linkage group. *Genetics,* **18**:82–94.

––––––. 1936. Genetics of the fowl. VI. A tentative chromosome map. "Neue Forschungen Tierzucht und Abstammungslehre" (Duerst Festschrift): 105–112. Bern: Verbandsdruckerei AG.

––––––. 1941. Genetics of the fowl. 15. Multiple spurs, a mutation linked with duplex comb. *J. Heredity,* **32**:356–364.

–––––– and W. F. Lamoreux. 1940. Genetics of the fowl. 11. A linkage map for six chromosomes. *J. Heredity,* **31**:231–235.

–––––– and C. D. Mueller. 1943. The linkage of polydactyly with multiple spurs and duplex comb in the fowl. *Am. Naturalist,* **77**:70–78.

–––––– and P. D. Sturkie. 1938. Genetics of the fowl. IX. Naked, a new sex-linked mutation. *J. Heredity,* **29**:370–379.

Landauer, W. 1932. Studies on the Creeper fowl. V. The linkage of the genes for creeper and single-comb. *J. Genetics,* **20**:285–290.

––––––. 1933. Creeper and single-comb linkage in fowl. *Nature,* **132**:606.

MacArthur, J. W. 1933. Sex-linked genes in the fowl. *Genetics,* **18**:210–220.

Mueller, C. D., and F. B. Hutt. 1941. Genetics of the fowl. 12. Sex-linked, imperfect albinism. *J. Heredity,* **32**:71–80.

Munro, S. S. 1946. A sex-linked true-breeding blue plumage color. *Poultry Sci.,* **25**:408.

Punnett, R. C. 1940. Genetic studies in poultry. X. Linkage data for the sex chromosome. *J. Genetics,* **39**:335–342.

Serebrovsky, A. S. 1922. Crossing over involving three sex-linked genes in chickens. *Am. Naturalist,* **56**:571–572.

–––––– and S. G. Petrov. 1928. A case of close autosomal linkage in the fowl. *J. Heredity,* **19**:305–306.

–––––– and ––––––. 1930. On the composition of the plan of the chromosomes of the domestic hen. *J. Exptl. Biol.* (Russian), **6**:157–179 (from translation by Miss B. F. Glessing of the U.S. Department of Agriculture).

–––––– and E. T. Wassina. 1926. On the topography of the sex-chromosome in fowls. *J. Genetics,* **17**:211–216.

Sungurov, A. N. 1933. O plane chromosom kuricy. *Biol. Zhur.,* **2**:196–201 (quoted from *Animal Breeding Abstracts,* **2**:362–363).

Suttle, A. D., and G. R. Sipe. 1932. Linkage of genes for crest and frizzle in the domestic fowl. *J. Heredity,* **23**:135–142.

Taylor, L. W. 1934. Creeper and single-comb linkage in the fowl. *J. Heredity,* **25**:205–206.

Warren, D. C. 1928. Sex-linked characters of poultry. *Genetics,* **13**:421–433.

––––––. 1935. A new linkage group in the fowl (*Gallus domesticus*). *Am. Naturalist,* **69**:82.

––––––. 1938. Mapping the genes of the fowl. *Genetics,* **23**:174.

––––––. 1940. Crossing over and sex in the fowl. *Am. Naturalist,* **74**:93–95.

––––––. 1944. Inheritance of polydactylism in the fowl. *Genetics,* **29**:217–230.

––––––. 1949. Linkage relations of autosomal factors in the fowl. *Genetics,* **34**:333–350.

–––––– and F. B. Hutt. 1936. Linkage relations of crest, dominant white and frizzling in the fowl. *Am. Naturalist,* **70**:379–394.

CHAPTER 15

GENETICS IN PRACTICE

One of the author's former students confided (after he had safely graduated from the university) that, while genetics might have its good points, in his opinion it could be of practical value to the poultry breeder only if someone would separate the wheat from the chaff. Since some readers of this book may classify under that latter term most of the facts surveyed in the foregoing 14 chapters, it is perhaps desirable that a little wheat be put in this last one.

However, it should first be pointed out that in the previous pages it has been impossible to divorce facts from their applications. Consequently, any reader interested only in how to breed bigger and better chickens should at least glance through some of the other chapters for any kernels that may have been scattered, perhaps inadvertently, through them. This applies particularly to the discussion of egg production, in which the merits of various measures of productivity and periods for testing are reviewed, together with environmental influences that the breeder should consider and the relative importance of contributory variables that may influence the egg record for any hen and the flock to which she belongs. Similar reviews of many points that must be considered in breeding to increase body weight or size of egg are given in Chaps. 9 and 11. Procedures for eliminating lethal genes are outlined in Chap. 8, and some of the problems involved in breeding birds resistant to disease are reviewed in Chap. 12.

It is only with considerable misgiving that the author ventures to suggest how to improve our domestic fowls by breeding. One reason for his reluctance is that he knows from his own experience the inevitable disappointments, difficulties, and delays that will be encountered by the novice. Another is that many experienced poultry breeders have such firm convictions about methods to be followed that it is usually safer to listen to their expositions than to expound one's own ideas. Accordingly, the principles and practices given in that part of the ensuing discussion concerned with progeny testing are presented merely as a record of methods that the author has found to be successful. Others might be better.

For convenience, practical applications of genetics in poultry breeding will here be considered under the headings: (1) objectives and methods, (2) mass selection, (3) progeny testing, (4) inbreeding, and (5) utilization of hybrid vigor.

OBJECTIVES AND METHODS

From the viewpoint of the geneticist trying to simplify matters, there are two general classes of objectives and two general methods of seeking to attain them. These are outlined in Table 64. They do not consider inbreeding and hybrid vigor, which are treated as special cases later on.

TABLE 64. OBJECTIVES OF POULTRY BREEDERS AND METHODS BY WHICH THEIR ATTAINMENT MAY BE ATTEMPTED

Kind of objective	Examples	Method of breeding	Probable degree of success
Unifactorial characters	Rose comb Recessive white Any dominant allele of recessive lethal, or of other unifactorial defect	Mass selection	Complete for recessive characters; incomplete for dominant ones (see Fig. 131)
	fect Blue eggshell	Progeny test	Complete
Multifactorial characters	High egg production Size of egg, or of body Resistance to disease Conformation Non-broodiness	Mass selection	Effective up to a certain point, particularly in unimproved stock
		Progeny test	Permits progress beyond limits attained by mass selection

Unifactorial characters provide some of the distinguishing characteristics of breeds. Most of them show some variation because of multiple modifying genes such as those that cause the crest to range from the beautiful veil of the prize-winning Houdan down to the few stubby feathers of the geneticist's heterozygote. Similarly, barring is caused by a single gene in females, but variations in the width and straightness of the bars result from the action of an unknown number of modifiers. Other unifactorial characters are either present or not, with little evidence of modification, as, for example, recessive-white plumage or yellow skin.

Multifactorial characters generally show more variability, but their very elasticity is one of the things that intrigue the breeder and inspire him to see how far the species can be stretched. When, in 1913, Lady MacDuff was elevated to the peerage because she laid 303 eggs for James Dryden (1921), that first trap-nest record showing that a hen could lay over 300 eggs in a year provided for poultry breeders the world over an incentive by which they were literally egged on and on, until single records of that order became even too commonplace to advertise. (Hens not neglected in that respect include (1) the Barred Rock, Lady Victorine, that laid 358 eggs at Saskatoon in 1929; (2) the well-named "No Drone No. 5 H," a White Leghorn with 357 eggs at the Agassiz laying contest in 1930, both records in 365 days; and (3) the 13 White Leghorns, 12 of them full sisters, that turned in an average production of 312.1 eggs per bird in 51 weeks at the western New York egg-laying test in 1945.) If not inspired to manipulate these multifactorial characters by the urge to produce superior stock, the breeder is driven to do so by economic necessity, for most of the things to which he looks for income depend upon an undetermined number of multiple genes. The raising of the standard weight for Leghorns in the United States was forced on the breeders by their recognition of the fact that bigger Leghorns lay more and bigger eggs.

Mass selection consists in mating together individuals of the type desired or which the breeder hopes will produce the kind of stock that he wants. It is based on the dictum, more familiar than accurate, that "like begets like." So far as simple recessive characters are concerned, mass selection is completely satisfactory. To illustrate, matings of recessive whites *inter se* yield only recessive whites; the same applies to single combs. Mass selection is less effective when unifactorial dominant characters are concerned, as will be made clear in the next section. Finally, it has serious limitations as a method for improving the multifactorial characters that are the chief concern of the modern poultry industry. Good layers do not always beget good layers, and hens hatched from big eggs may lay small ones.

The effectiveness of mass selection is enhanced somewhat if the breeding birds be evaluated, not only by their own appearance or performance, but also by the performance of their ancestors, *i.e.* by their pedigree. Especially to be desired in such a pedigree are progeny tests of the ancestors. At best, there is no assurance that an unproven cockerel will beget offspring to equal his parents. Full brothers with identical pedigrees frequently yield disappointingly different results.

Progeny testing means merely the evaluation of breeders according to the performance of their offspring. It rejects the notion that fine feathers make fine birds, and adopts instead the proverb "Handsome is as handsome does." In practice, it incorporates mass selection but goes one step farther. The good breeder selects his cockerels for testing only after careful consideration of their appearance, weights, and pedigrees (if available), but that is only the preliminary stage. The final evaluation and the selection of males for re-use in subsequent seasons depend upon careful evaluation of what their daughters show in egg production, viability, egg size, or whatever the objectives may be.

Included in a progeny-testing program is sib-testing. A sib-tested cockerel is one that is evaluated according to the performance of his brothers or sisters, or both. In that process one should consider the performance not only of his full sisters but also of his half sisters. The former provide a progeny test for the cockerel's dam, the latter for his sire. This does not mean that the sib-tested cockerel is progeny tested; he does not attain that rank until his own daughters have turned in their records. The important thing is that, both in sib tests and in progeny tests, the evaluation of the breeding stock is determined first by the record of the families to which they belong and finally by record of the families which they produce.

In genetic parlance, mass selection is selection according to the phenotype. By contrast, progeny testing is selection based on the genotype, which, in turn, is estimated from the kinds of offspring produced.

MASS SELECTION

For Unifactorial Characters. It is axiomatic that simple recessive characters must "breed true," except for occasional matings. They are maintained merely by excluding from the breeding pen those which do not show the desired type. The ease with which some simple recessive type may be extracted from a heterogeneous stock and developed into a uniform flock was nicely demonstrated by Lippincott (1920). He mated White Orpington males to as fine a collection of mongrel hens as one could hope to see and apparently found in the F_1 generation no birds showing the recessive white of the Orpington. However, when some of the F_1 females were backcrossed to another White Orpington, a good proportion of the resultant offspring showed, not only recessive white, but also fair Orpington type. Some of these birds which most resembled their sire were again backcrossed to a White Orpington male, with the result that their offspring, though only the third selected population, were uniformly recessive white.

It is more difficult to "fix" a desired dominant character. It is probable that Lippincott's recessive whites would have bred true for that character but would have continued for some years to throw offspring with yellow shanks merely because Ww heterozygotes cannot be distinguished from the true-breeding homozygotes of the genotype WW.

This point is illustrated by a problem that plagued the Wyandotte breeders for years, *i.e.*, the continuous outcropping of the despised single comb. In spite of its being systematically excluded from the breeding pens, good respectable rose-combed Wyandottes with no bar sinister in their pedigrees continued to produce single-combed chicks. This happens merely because the desired homozygote is indistinguishable from the heterozygote. When two of the latter, Rr, are mated together, the proportion of single combs in their offspring is about 25 per cent, but among the rose-combed chicks the proportion of heterozygotes is two-thirds. This corresponds to an F_2 ratio. If one calculates the expectations in successive generations, assuming that all single combs are discarded but that all rose combs are mated at random and contribute equally to the next generation, it will be found that the proportions of the three genotypes in any ensuing generation, n, are given by the formula

$$F_n = (n-1)^2 RR + 2(n-1)Rr + 1rr$$

The rate at which the proportion of single combs decreases in successive generations, as calculated by this formula, is shown in Fig. 131. In the F_{10} generation, the proportions of the three genotypes are 81 RR:18 Rr:1 rr. Expressed otherwise, about one in every five or six rose-combed birds will still carry the gene for single comb even after 10 years of mass selection against it.

It is little wonder that mass selection is a slow method for eliminating undesirable recessives. The same persistence of the recessive allele would occur with any simple recessive character. With those which are lethal (*e.g.*, congenital loco, talpid, etc.) the recessive homozygote is self-eliminating, but the heterozygotes maintain the gene in the flock.

Multifactorial Characters. It is sometimes stated that the futility of mass selection was demonstrated in the Barred Rocks at the Maine Experiment Station, when 9 years of that practice failed to raise their mean winter egg production. This failure was accentuated by the remarkable increase achieved by Pearl (1911) in his first year of progeny testing in the same flock, an increase which was maintained thereafter (Fig. 132). When these findings were coupled with the earlier demonstration by Pearl and Surface (1909) that daughters of 200-egg dams laid no more eggs than pullets from dams with records of 150 to 200 eggs, no justification for mass selection could be seen at Orono, Maine.

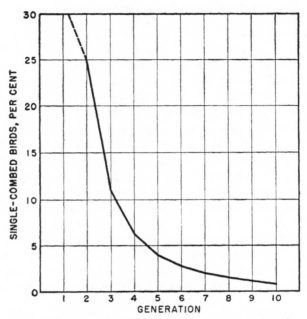

Fig. 131. Decrease of single-combed birds in successive generations from two hetero-zygous rose-combed parents, when only rose-combed birds are used for begetting the next generation. The rate of decrease is the same for any simple recessive, self-eliminating defect, such as a lethal gene.

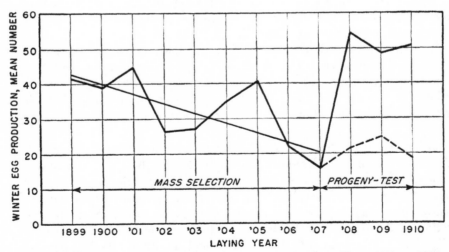

Fig. 132. Effect of progeny testing on winter egg production. From 1899 to 1907, mass selection for high fecundity was apparently ineffective, but when progeny-tested birds were used, the winter production was immediately raised to a higher figure than in the previous 9 years. (*From Pearl.*)

The fact remains that egg production can be raised by mass selection. At the very time when the spate of bulletins and reports deprecating that procedure was pouring from the Maine station, at the other side of the continent James Dryden (1921) was demonstrating at the Oregon Experiment Station, not only that egg production could be increased by mass selection, but also that it could be done quickly. This he did with no less than three different breeds, one of which, the Oregons, he himself

FIG. 133. Raymond Pearl, who contributed much to knowledge of the physiology of reproduction in the fowl and early stressed the importance of the progeny test. (*Courtesy of Mrs. Pearl.*)

originated. A summary of these results is shown in Fig. 134. Dryden selected breeding hens according to their individual trap-nest records and males on the basis of the records of their dams. In 10 years, the mean egg production was raised from 86 to 215 in Barred Rocks, from 135 to 231 in Oregons, and from 107 to 212 in White Leghorns.

The differing results shown in Figs. 132 and 134 are perhaps not so contradictory as they seem. It is evident from the graphs in Fig. 134 that Dryden's greatest progress was made in the earlier years of selection, and that no improvement (in the flock averages) was made after 1914 in the Leghorns or after 1915 in the Oregons. With the Barred Rocks, progress was slower than in the other two breeds but more consistent. Obviously, mass selection is most effective in an unimproved stock but less so after a certain level has been attained. In fowls that level may be around 200 to 220 eggs. It is not surprising, therefore, that Pearl should have found little merit in mass selection. The fact that Pearl and Surface (1909) were able to house in the fall of 1907 no less than

250 pullets from 200-egg hens (and 600 more from dams with records of 150 to 200 eggs) suggests that by that time their predecessor, Professor Gowell, had already improved the stock to the point beyond which little progress was likely to be made by mass selection.

This interpretation does not detract in any way from Pearl's valuable

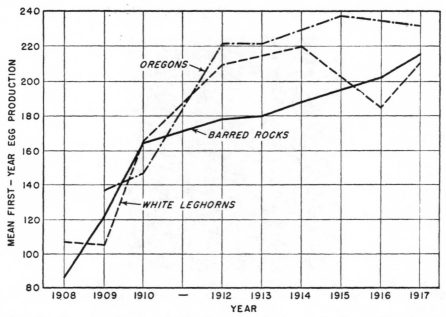

Fig. 134. Increase of egg production by mass selection at the Oregon Experiment Station. The report indicates that no birds were raised in 1911. (*From data of Dryden in Oregon Agr. Expt. Sta. Bull. 180.*)

demonstration that, when mass selection has ceased to be effective, remarkable progress can still be made by progeny testing. No one recognized this fact better than Dryden, who, without discarding mass selection as a useful procedure, wrote that "More rapid progress will be made by the breeder if he can test the breeding quality of his stock, and use for breeding those hens and males whose progeny has shown high production."

The limitations of mass selection and the efficacy of progeny testing have also been demonstrated at the other end of the scale of egg production. During the 22 years from 1913 to 1935, mass selection was practised at Cornell University to determine the feasibility of thus raising productivity in one strain of White Leghorns and of lowering it in another. Results in the low-fecundity line, as reviewed by Hall (1934) and by Lamoreux *et al.* (1943), showed no significant change in 22 years, at the end of which time mean egg production was approximately the same, 100 eggs per hen, that it had been in 1913. Beginning in 1935, mass selection was discarded, and by 5 years of progeny testing the egg production was lowered to 40 eggs per bird (Fig. 136).

FIG. 135. James Dryden, a leader in the demonstration of fundamental principles applicable in poultry breeding. (*Courtesy of Horace Dryden.*)

It should be noted in Fig. 136 that in the high-fecundity strain mean egg production was steadily increased to a little over 200 eggs in 1928, after which time it remained unchanged for the next 4 years. As Petrov (1935) pointed out, some of the increase in productivity during the long course of the mass selection must be attributed to improvements in management. The effect of one of these—provision of greater feeding space at the mash hoppers—is very obvious in Fig. 136. Nevertheless, this experiment tends to substantiate evidence from the other experiments cited above that mass selection will raise productivity of unimproved stock but has little efficacy in flocks with average production around 200 eggs.

Although this exposition of the possibilities and limitations of mass selection deals only with egg production, the principles apply equally well to other multifactorial characters, not only in the fowl, but also in other species. Obviously, mass selection will be more effective with characters in which the phenotype gives a good clue to the genotype than

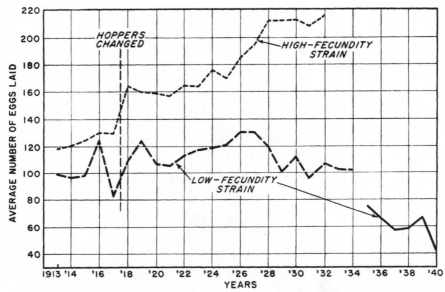

Fig. 136. Average egg production of two strains of White Leghorns selected for low or for high fecundity by mass selection at Cornell University from 1913 to 1934. In the high-fecundity strain, production was raised to a little over 200 eggs, after which point it remained fairly constant. In the low-fecundity line, production in 1934 remained about the same as in 1913, but it was significantly lowered thereafter by progeny testing, which was begun in 1935. (*From Lamoreux et al. in Poultry Sci.*)

when these two are less closely related. For that reason it should be more effective in selection for body size, or for conformation, than in selection for ability to lay eggs. Many questions remain unanswered. For example, if, after some years of using the best 30 per cent of the flock as breeders, one reaches a limit beyond which further progress seems unlikely, can that limit then be raised by using only the best 10 per cent? If so, by how much? For these questions, as for many others, the author would like to know the answers.

Special Value of Mass Selection in Grading. The consistent use of superior sires, a process known as "grading," is generally considered by breeders of the larger animals as one of the most effective ways of improving unimproved stock. It is both rapid and comparatively inexpensive. Grading has not found much favor with poultrymen in the United States, perhaps merely because it is so easy and cheap to obtain purebred stock. Nevertheless, for the many great areas of the world in which the native fowls have not been improved, grading is the most practicable method of improving egg production, egg size, and general uniformity. It is particularly to be recommended because the sup-

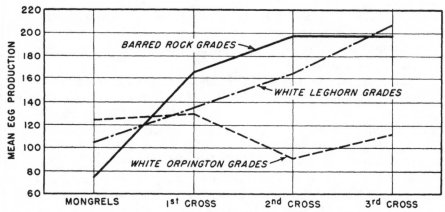

Fig. 137. The improvement of egg production in 3 years by grading. This was effective with males of two breeds, but not with those of a third, in which there had been less selection for egg production. (*From data of Lippincott.*)

posedly unimproved native fowls have in reality their own desirable contribution to make, *i.e.*, the resistance to disease bred in them by natural selection.

The demonstration by Lippincott (1920) of the remarkable improvement in egg production that can be made by grading, while considered in his own country to be of interest more academic than practical, has a special significance for anyone seeking to increase the productivity of native stocks anywhere. In this case, mongrel fowls and their offspring were backcrossed for 3 years to purebred males of three different breeds and all from strains bred for egg production. None of these males was a proven sire. The results (Fig. 137) are of special interest because during the 3 years the female breeders were selected merely to resemble the pure breed of their sires, and not with any consideration either of their own egg records or of the production of their dams. This was therefore mass selection with respect to the sires only. With the Barred Rock and Leghorn males, average production was raised in 3 years to

207 and 198 eggs, respectively. The failure of the Orpington males to effect any improvement was attributed to their having behind them less breeding for egg production than had the males of the other two breeds.

The effectiveness of grading in this way is well known to breeders who have used it in various parts of Africa, India, and the Malay Peninsula, but other records as complete as those of Lippincott are unknown to the author. Apart from egg production, it was clear from his illustration that continued backcrossing to one pure breed, coupled with some selection of the females for the desired type, will quickly convert any mongrel population into a flock with remarkable uniformity both in color and in conformation.

The Multiplying Million. In further justification of mass selection, it is well to remember that the progeny testers comprise only a small fraction of 1 per cent of the poultry breeders. In the United States over 90 per cent of the chickens raised each year come from the farm flocks supplying the commercial hatcheries. It is doubtful that one egg in a million passing through such hatcheries comes from proven dams or sires. Nevertheless, the quality of the chick has been steadily improving over the years, and it should continue to do so. This is partly because progressive hatcherymen ensure that their supplying flocks are headed by the best cockerels that they can get from the breeders who do the progeny testing. This process provides a steady distribution to the farm flocks of the desirable genes accumulated by the good breeders. The numerically insignificant progeny testers thus bear the responsibility for the uplifting of the masses, but they share it with the hatcheryman and with the multipliers, the farmers who supply in millions of eggs for hatching the genes upon which a profitable poultry industry depends. These multipliers have their own responsibility. It is concerned almost entirely with selection of the hens that produce the eggs. These must be regularly and thoroughly culled to ensure that only the most desirable females are used for reproduction. The undersized, the late-maturing, the early-moulting, and the low-producing hens all must go. So must the small or otherwise undesirable eggs, even if the hen that lays them cannot be detected. All this is mass selection. It is important, and its contribution should not be overlooked. Neither should that of natural selection, which does the chick buyer a good service when it removes from the supplying flock the females most susceptible to lymphomatosis, to blackhead, or to any other ailment.

PROGENY TESTING

The Unreliability of Pedigrees. After upholding thus the merits of mass selection, it is appropriate to turn again to consideration of its limitations. While these are fairly evident in Figs. 132, 134, and 136, they are made still clearer if illustrated by specific cases in which the pedigree of the breeding bird has proved a false guide to the inheritance transmitted by it. Examples of this situation are all too familiar to the poultryman who pays for breeding cockerels according to the egg records of their dams. Table 65, which gives the records for 15 White Leghorn males used in 1 year at Cornell, shows what often happens in such cases.

TABLE 65. PROGENY TESTS OF 15 WHITE LEGHORN MALES, SHOWING LACK OF RELATIONSHIP BETWEEN EGG PRODUCTION OF THE MALE'S DAM AND THAT OF HIS DAUGHTERS

Egg production of male's dam in 365 days	Males, number	Mean egg production of daughters to 500 days of age
218–224	2	141
244–250	3	169
250–260	2	176
264–265	3	144
277	3	177
296–299	2	132

These records *do not* show that sons of 296- and 299-egg dams produce poorer layers than sons of hens that lay only 218 or 224 eggs. They do show merely that, in dealing with records above 200 eggs for first-year production, the performance of the sire's dam does not give much assurance of how many eggs his daughters will lay. One should not expect differences of 20 to 40 eggs in the records for dams to be reflected in the transmitting abilities of their sons; but when larger differences than these are involved, the egg production of the sire's dam does indicate—in general terms—what may be expected in his progeny. As Hall (1935) has shown, this is evident when large numbers of sires are grouped according to differences of 50 eggs in the records of their dams. Most progressive breeders are concerned nowadays only with testing cockerels from hens that have laid upward of 200, 250, or even 300 eggs. In that range of egg production, cases in which the sire does not transmit fecundity proportional to his dam's record or to records of several ancestors

(Jull, 1934) are numerous enough to make mass selection unreliable and hence to necessitate progeny testing. Pride of pedigree is no guarantee that one may also take pride in the progeny.

Similarly, when only good dams of this type are concerned, any relationship between the record of dam and that of her daughters is not very conspicuous. This is too obvious in any breeder's records to need further amplification here, but it does not mean that selection is ineffective. It is fashionable, nowadays, to prove by abstruse statistical procedures that variations in egg production (and in other multifactorial characters of domestic animals) are influenced more by environment than by heredity. Breeders should not conclude therefrom that selection for the improvement of such characters is futile and that they should concentrate on the environment. While the environmental influences may completely outweigh genetic influences in any one year or in every year, the fact remains that the genetic variations can be accumulated by selection, whereas those caused by the environment cannot. Obviously, it is essential for the breeder to provide the environment most conducive to full manifestation of genetic differences in the stock.

The unreliability of pedigrees is perhaps best illustrated by the fact that full brothers (or full sisters) with identical pedigrees may produce families for which the records of performance are entirely different. Examples are given in the following section.

The Unreliability of Phenotypes. One desirable genetic character, for which the breeder is usually more willing to rely upon mass selection than upon progeny testing, is viability. It is true for hens, as for man, that the individuals which have demonstrated their fitness to survive are more likely to beget similarly disease-resistant offspring than are those which died early. The bearing of this fact on resistance to lymphomatosis was shown in Table 57. It is also demonstrated by the comparatively high resistance to different diseases developed by natural selection in various parts of the world. Because of the conviction common to many poultrymen that old fowls must produce highly resistant progeny, it seems desirable to show that this does not always happen. Expressed otherwise, the phenotype with respect to viability may be entirely different from the genotype.

Figure 138 shows two White Leghorn males that lived to be used for three consecutive breeding seasons, one of them for four. Obviously, both demonstrated remarkable fitness to survive the rather severe exposure to lymphomatosis that is routine treatment for most Leghorns at Cornell. From their appearances one might prefer K 3450. However, as the data in Table 66 show, this male lost annually for 4 years from 60 to 76 per cent of his daughters. Of those alive at 6 weeks, from 33 to 47 per cent died of neoplasms (mostly lymphomatosis) before 500 days of age. By contrast, daughters of the other male, K 3459, experienced comparatively low mortality (for unculled birds deliberately exposed to disease) and almost negligible losses from neoplasms. Offspring of both sires were reared together.

The remarkable difference in viability between the progenies of these two males resulted chiefly from the fact that one had been bred for

Fig. 138. K 3450 (*left*) and K 3459 (*right*), two hardy males that were used for four and three breeding seasons, respectively. One of them produced offspring resistant to lymphomatosis and subject to comparatively low mortality. The other lost annually 60 to 76 per cent of his daughters. Table 66 identifies each.

TABLE 66. COMPARISON OF THE TWO MALES SHOWN IN FIGURE 138 WITH RESPECT TO VIABILITY AND EGG PRODUCTION OF THEIR DAUGHTERS

Sire and year	Daughters alive at 42 days of age, number	Died 42–500 days, per cent		Eggs per bird,* number	Production index
		From all causes	From neoplasms		
K 3450 (susceptible):					
1943	55	60	32.7	163	102
1944	90	73	46.6	177	88
1945	216	64	41.2	151	93
1946	82	76	46.9	189	98
K 3459 (resistant):					
1943	56	27	3.6	210	191
1944	86	17	2.3	198	186
1945	69	25	11.6	213	186

* Average number laid to 500 days of age by those then alive.

susceptibility to lymphomatosis, the other for resistance to it. The genes contributed by susceptible dams in the one line and resistant dams in the other must also have influenced the viability of their daughters, but probably less than genes from the two sires. Both these were used for several consecutive years merely because they excelled contemporary males, the one in producing susceptible offspring, the other in begetting resistant stock. The important point is that, of two males surviving past 4 years of age, one may sire disease-resistant offspring and the other exactly the opposite. Only a progeny test can distinguish between the two.

The consistent performances of both these males with respect to fecundity, viability, and production index of their daughters in successive years should be noted. This is only one of many records available to show that sires proven good, bad, or mediocre in one breeding season will transmit the same capacities in subsequent ones, except for genetic differences in the females with which they may be mated and except for environmental influences.

K 3459 was one of four full brothers mated in 1943 to four groups of comparable females. For three of these the mean egg production of their daughters was 183, 193, and 210, but for the fourth male the figure was only 166. All had the same pedigree; only the progeny test revealed the difference of 44 eggs per daughter between the worst and best of the two brothers.

The impossibility of predicting the breeding performance of full brothers is also illustrated by the varying proportions of daughters with stubs (feathers on the feet) sired by 15 cockerels in one strain of White Leghorns at Cornell (Cole and Hutt, 1947). These comprised five trios of full brothers, and the members of each trio were used successively in the same breeding pen. None of these males had detectable stubs when used, nor had the 80 females in the five pens. All phenotypes were thus identical. So were the pedigrees of the brothers in any one pen, but remarkable differences in their genotypes were revealed by the progeny tests (Table 67).

Stubs are caused by an undetermined number of multiple genes. Only in one series, J 3, did all three brothers transmit similar inheritances. Since the maternal contribution was reasonably constant in each pen (being affected only in so far as some hens produced more chicks by one brother than by another), and since the incidence of stubs is presumably influenced little or not at all by the environment, the record in Table 67 is a useful indication of the extent to which full brothers may differ in the inheritance transmitted to their offspring.

TABLE 67. DIFFERENCES BETWEEN FULL BROTHERS MATED TO THE SAME HENS IN
THE PROPORTIONS, PER CENT, OF THEIR DAUGHTERS SHOWING STUBS

Breeding pen	First brother	Second brother	Third brother
J 1	17	29	8
J 2	44	4	54
J 3	34	29	29
J 4	28	20	38
J 5	36	7	45

Records for Progeny Testing. In its simplest form, the progeny test requires few records, or even none. Any mating of two Wyandottes that yields a single-combed chick is a progeny test revealing both parents to be heterozygous for rose comb. Any two birds producing any simple recessive lethal character have had their genotypes with respect to that character revealed by the progeny test in its simplest form.

With multifactorial characters that are not measurable until the birds are 6, 12, or 18 months old, the problem is more complicated. For a simple one, such as egg production, the following records are desirable, in addition to those necessary for pedigreeing all offspring and for maintaining trap-nest records in the laying pens:

1. *Individual record.* A cumulative record of the eggs laid by each daughter.
2. *Dam's summary.* A grouping of daughters by dams, with an average for the group, thus revealing the good, bad, and mediocre members in each family of full sisters.
3. *Sire's summary.* A grouping of all dams mated to any one sire, with averages for each dam's daughters and for all the sire's daughters, thus revealing which dams have raised the average for that sire and which have lowered it.
4. *Comparison of comparable sires.* A grouping of all sires, with averages for daughters of each, and with a grand average for all, so that sires which have produced superior daughters are easily recognized.

Such a system of records is fairly simple in so far as any one character is concerned. It becomes more complicated for the breeder who wants to consider, not merely egg production, but also hatchability, mortality during rearing, mortality after housing, age at first egg, weight of egg, weight of birds, and freedom from assorted real or imaginary defects. However, poultry breeders as a class take a special pride and delight in devising just such records. Their ingenuity in condensing indispensable data into the irreducible minimum of space is surpassed only by the zeal and enthusiasm with which the minutiae of the most complex system are described to anyone who will read or listen.

Since the time required for maintaining the necessary records is one of the chief deterrents that prevent some poultrymen from progeny testing, it is essential that the data recorded and the analyses required should be simplified as much as possible. The procedure of determining familial differences in size of egg by weighing for only one week in March, and perhaps for another in December (see Chap. 11), illustrates one way in which record keeping is simplified. It is also facilitated by measuring egg production only to 500 days of age (Chap. 10) rather than for 365 days from first egg. Using the median to determine familial differences in age at first egg (page 309) is a short cut that reduces by about one-half the record keeping necessary when that same variable is measured by the mean.

One of the big tasks is that of transferring the records for individual birds to those of the dams' families. Some breeders have greatly simplified this process by keeping the individual records on printed, punched cards. These can be quickly sorted according to sire families either by card-sorting machines, if the number of birds be large enough to warrant that expense, or manually, with the use of a sorting needle. Another simplification is to reduce to a minimum the number of times a year when the family averages are computed. The author does this four times, as follows:

1. *On Jan.* 1, in order to find which of the males and females used in the previous breeding season seem most worthy of being used in the next one and to find the best families from which to select cockerels for testing.

2. *On Apr.* 1, a reappraisal of families to determine from which breeders it would best pay to save cockerel chicks for the next year.

3. *On July* 1, another examination, primarily to decide which families and individuals to discard as soon as their 500-day test is completed. Since the birds hatched first reach that age about July 20, it is necessary to have the list of unwanted birds ready by that date.

4. *About Sept.* 20, a final appraisal to select the best families and (from them) the best individuals to keep for breeding. This is made as soon as the birds hatched latest have finished their 500-day test.

The second of these summaries might be eliminated, especially if enough proven sires and dams are used in the breeding pens to provide all the cockerels that are to be kept. Cumulative egg records of the pullets need not be added to the dam's summary from the individual records except when family averages are to be computed. Sometimes the quarterly summaries are begun on Dec. 1 instead of Jan. 1, but the longer test provided by the latter date permits a better evaluation of families.

The Use of Such Records. Poultry breeders like to set up standards for their breeding stock. The usual thing is to say that they breed only from birds of a certain body weight, with egg records not lower than 200, 230, or 250 eggs (according to available resources) and with egg size not smaller than 2 ounces. Standards are perhaps indispensable for national schemes for poultry improvement. A more flexible measuring stick sometimes has its advantages, as, for example, when an outbreak of coryza or of Newcastle disease lowers the average production of the flock some 20 eggs or so below that of previous years.

A flexible method of evaluation is provided simply by comparing the records of individuals and of families with the averages for the appropriate populations. A single daughter is compared with the average for her full sisters; a dam's record is compared with the average for all dams mated to the same sire; any one sire's record is compared with the average for all contemporary sires. This method has several advantages. It can be used before the progeny test has progressed further than 3 or 4 months or at any period that may be desired before the full test is completed. The success with which this method of ranking the families reveals differences between sires in the transmission of egg size, and does so long before definitive egg size is attained, is shown on page 366. The illustration is important because any breeder using progeny tests wishes to evaluate his families, to decide which sires to use again, and to pick his breeding cockerels by the time when breeding pens should be made up. In northern latitudes that time is usually early in January. This he can do with most multifactorial characters, even though his progeny tests are less than half completed by Jan. 1, by ranking his families in relation to the averages.

When evaluating the families according to their rank above or below the mean, one actually uses the same measure for egg production, egg size, viability, or any other objective, and it is somewhat easier, therefore, to detect the family that is superior in several different items. In other words, it is easier to think of a sire as ranking first in egg production, fifth in egg size, and second in viability than to remember that the average records to Jan. 1 for his daughters were 69.7 eggs, of 53.4 gm., with mortality 5 per cent since 6 weeks of age. Another reason for evaluating families according to their rank rather than by standards is that, when two or three "shifts" of males are used in one breeding season (page 520), the differing environments for the chickens hatched early, in mid-season, or late necessitate separate standards for each group. Comparisons within each series with the average for that series will solve the problem.

In selecting breeding stock by the use of such records, and considering for illustrative purposes only one objective, the first procedure is to exclude from consideration the sire families that are below average. Such sires should not be re-used, nor would their offspring be desirable, but one might well re-use any dams in such sire families that have clearly produced superior progeny in spite of the poor contribution of the sire. The next step, working only with the superior sire families, is to exclude from these the dam families showing less than average performance. One is thus left with the families that have both superior sires and superior dams. From these should come the cockerels and any pullets that are to be used for breeding. Obviously the sires and dams of such families should be re-used—if they are still available.

This does not mean that every above-average family is worth breeding from. The intensity of selection must be varied according to the number of breeding birds needed, the number of objectives, and their relative importance. Thus, if egg size is already fully satisfactory (and especially since beyond a certain point bigger eggs are undesirable), one may select families that are merely average in that respect, or even below it, in order thus to have more families, dams, sires, cockerels, or pullets among which to select for egg production, for viability, or for both. Similarly, if mortality should be no special problem, the breeder may be more concerned about numbers of eggs than anything else. In that case, he might use any families that are average or better in viability, but only the top 20 per cent with respect to egg production.

Another way of stating the basis for selection outlined above is that any cockerel selected for testing is evaluated by the performance (1) of his full sisters and also (2) of his half sisters. These two measures provide estimates of the genes contributed to the cockerel by his dam and his sire, respectively. The superiority of such an appraisal over one based only on contributions from the dam's side has been emphasized by Godfrey (1946).

Complications and Limitations. Lest any novice should assume from the foregoing paragraphs that science has reduced the esoteric art of poultry breeding to anything so commonplace as the law of averages, it is desirable to enumerate some of the difficulties that make progress slow in spite of the most assiduous efforts of the progeny tester. They can be summed up merely by saying that it is difficult to find many proven sires good enough to use for several years and to find them in time to do so.

These difficulties result chiefly from the fact that nowadays no breeder is satisfied with a single objective. If only egg production be considered, about half the sires are above average; but with each additional independent objective the chance of getting a sire superior in all is again halved. The chance that a sire will be superior with respect to the hatchability, egg production, egg size, and viability of his offspring is reduced to about 1 in 16. Even if such a sire be found, his superiority may not be recognized in time to ensure that he be used again in the second breeding season. By the third, he may be dead or reduced in fertility. Of 24 Leghorn cockerels tested by the author in 1943, 2 died early, and 7 of the remainder eventually proved superior both in egg production and in resistance to disease. Three of these were recognized in time to permit their use in 1944, but only 2 were still on hand for the breeding season of 1945.

This dismal record shows why progeny testing on a small scale is not likely to be very successful. Some breeders who have tried it with only half a dozen pens for single-male matings have become discouraged at their lack of progress. During eight generations, Hays (1940) was able to make no improvement in egg production by 8 years of selection in small flocks of 20 to 50 hens. Some breeders with ample breeding pens make little progress because they divide these resources among several strains or breeds and are therefore unable to test enough males in any one of them to find the outstanding sires upon which progress depends.

Another limitation may be lack of adequate laying pens in which to maintain the pullets that provide the tests. This applies particularly in breeding for resistance to disease. As Mueller and Hutt (1946) have shown, one needs more than 30 daughters to differentiate resistant and susceptible families when mortality is high (37 to 50 per cent) and at least 50 daughters when mortality is comparatively low. In such work, to test even 24 cockerels a year requires space for about 1,200 pullets in addition to the others hatched from proven sires and dams. Requirements of space and the task of the record keeping can be reduced by discarding

1. All daughters of any cockerels that die before housing time. There is no point in testing a cockerel that can never be used.

2. All daughters in sire families too small to provide an adequate test.

3. Surplus daughters above the 50 to 60 needed per sire. Since some families will have large surpluses and others small ones, or none, the pullets eliminated must be picked at random in order not to prejudice the sample that remains. It will not do to eliminate all late-hatched pullets in one family if such birds are retained in another. To reduce to families of 60, one could eliminate every third daughter from a family of 90, every fifth one from a family of 75.

4. Daughters of dams that have only one or two pullets, as long as

there are plenty of other daughters from at least six different dams. These small families tell nothing about the dam and add little to the test of the sire, but they do complicate the records.

Tests of dams for viability of their offspring are not so satisfactory as tests of sires. This is partly because most dam families are too small. Another reason may be that one dam's family by a single sire is a less reliable indicator of genotype than one sire's family from a dozen or more dams. This latter difficulty is removed by diallel or polyallel crosses in which one dam is mated at different times with two or more different sires.

Smaller families than these will suffice to determine the laying capacity transmitted by sires and dams. Mueller and Hutt obtained some evidence that as few as 6 daughters with complete egg records may be adequate to test a dam in this respect. However, to have 6 daughters survive to the end of the testing period, it may be necessary to start at least 10 or 12.

It has usually been considered that no culling should be practised in families under test, but Bird and Sinclair (1938) found that it is feasible to cull 15 to 25 per cent in comparatively large populations without disturbing the relationships among them of their means with respect to egg production. They considered that any culling in families under test should be no more than enough to eliminate the lowest producers, those which cause an abnormal "low tail" in the distribution curve. Obviously, any culling in families to be compared would have to be done at an equal rate in all of them. The feasibility of doing so in 12 different sire families without obscuring differences between them was shown by Lerner and Taylor (1940). They even considered that families thus culled could still be ranked with respect to viability, but the feasibility of doing this in flocks from which the birds are actually removed has yet to be demonstrated.

In addition to the complications considered in the foregoing paragraphs, others will occur to any breeder. Many of these are concerned with the environment, which is considered later. The limitations imposed by it are suggested by the fact that at least one breeder, after exhaustive analysis of his records and selection therefrom of the outstanding family of the year, found upon going to the rearing range to inspect the cockerels of that family that their superior merits had already been recognized by others, even without the records, and that the foxes had been there first.

Double Shifts, Triple Shifts, and Diallel Crosses. When, in the course of breeding for resistance to lymphomatosis at Cornell University, it became evident that the chief limiting factor was a scarcity of proven sires, a change in the system of breeding was adopted which quickly overcame that difficulty. It is called the "double shift," except when there are three shifts, in which case it is called the "triple shift."

The first of these terms means merely that, in all the pens available for cockerel testing, one series of males is used in the first half of the season and is then replaced by an entirely different lot for the last half of the season. In the first year of its use, the double shift proved so satisfactory that it was abandoned and replaced by the triple shift, which is still better. By its use, 30 cockerels are tested annually in 10 breeding pens, and there is no dearth of proven sires.

Transfers of the males are arranged to accommodate weekly settings of eggs in the incubators on Tuesday. To illustrate, shift I goes out of the breeding pens on Friday afternoon and is replaced on Sunday in the late afternoon. Eggs laid to Monday night are credited to shift I, but eggs from Tuesday to Saturday, when paternity is doubtful, are marketed. Beginning on the following Sunday, eggs are saved for incubation and credited to shift II, this being 7 days after the introduction of those cockerels and 9 days after the removal of shift I. In Chap. 13, evidence is cited to justify the assumption that the influence of the replacing male supplants that of the replaced male within 9 days. The details of working out a program of triple shifts are perhaps best understood by study of the actual records for a typical case, as presented in Table 68.

TABLE 68. DETAILS OF THE OPERATION OF TRIPLE SHIFTS FOR TESTING COCKERELS AT CORNELL UNIVERSITY IN 1947

Shift	Males introduced, date	Period of saving eggs		Days of lost eggs	Males removed, date	Daughters per male at 6 weeks	
		Dates	Days			Average	Range
I	Jan. 3	Jan. 29–Feb. 17	20	None	Feb. 14	39	26–49
II	Feb. 16	Feb. 23–Mar. 17	23	5	Mar. 14	58	33–90
III	Mar. 16	Mar. 23–Apr. 14	23	5	Immaterial	50	16–81

These data pertain to a hatching season of 10 weekly settings, beginning on Feb. 11, of which, because of the two intervals between shifts, only 8 included eggs from the cockerel-testing pens. Those were 2 settings from the first shift and 3 from each of the others. The breeding pens contained 16 females each. The comparatively small number of daughters per sire in shift I resulted from somewhat low fertility in the early settings and also because the period of saving eggs was 3 days shorter (*i.e.*, 48 hen-days) than for the other two shifts. Troubles with males of low fertility are inevitable but are less serious in a shift of 3 to 4 weeks than when one such male is used all season.

It will be noted that altogether 10 days' eggs were lost (marketed) because of the intervals between shifts. Anyone in a position to practise artificial insemination should note the evidence of Warren and Gish (page 450) that when that procedure is used little error in paternity is entailed if every egg is saved and none discarded. Most of those on the second day after use of the second male can safely be assigned to him. With such a program, and to get such results, it would be necessary to have the replacing males well trained prior to the date on which they are to be used.

While the primary purpose of the double and triple shifts is to provide progeny tests for a large number of cockerels in one season, another advantage lies in the fact that they permit better tests of the genotypes of the dams. If a hen produces superior offspring by one male, that result might be attributable to (1) her own good genes, or (2) his good genes, or (3) complementary action of genes from both. The last of these three possibilities is what the breeder calls "nicking." Individuals that nick with one mate might produce inferior offspring by another. It is desirable to find the hens with genotypes such that they will produce superior offspring with any male or with most of them. Obviously, such birds are more likely to be revealed by matings in turn with the two or three males that are used in the double or triple shifts than when mated all season with a single male.

In these cases, the value of the female is not determined merely by the performance of her own offspring by two or three sires. Each of the sires is first evaluated according to the average performance of his offspring from all the hens in the breeding pen. Each dam is then appraised by the record of her daughters by each sire in relation to the averages for each sire. Such an evaluation shows whether or not she excels the other hens in her breeding pen.

This method of determining a genotype with respect to multifactorial characters was devised by the distinguished Danish ichthyologist, Johannes Schmidt (1922), who designated it as diallel crossing. It should interest poultry breeders to know how he came to demonstrate the value of diallel crosses in poultry breeding. Schmidt will be best remembered for his studies with eels. In the course of tracing North American eels to rivers in that continent and European eels to rivers in Europe, both from their common breeding grounds in the western

Atlantic, he became interested in differences in the number of vertebrae by which these two types are distinguished. This interest was extended to other species, and Schmidt was able to prove experimentally in trout and in the fowl that differences in the genotype with respect to number of vertebrae could be accurately detected by diallel crosses. The procedure is equally valuable for any other multifactorial character.

Importance of the Environment. Most inherited characters of economic importance in the fowl can be modified by the environment. It is essential to progeny testing that differences caused by genes should not be obscured by variations induced by the environment. Clearly, the environment should be as uniform as possible for all birds under test, but it is easier to state that policy than to maintain it. It is easy to mix representatives of all families at random, to give all birds the same feed, to house them in flocks of comparable size, and to do all the other obvious things. It is not so easy to keep the late-hatched chicks from getting coccidia, to which their early-hatched sisters are better able to develop resistance. It is most convenient to vaccinate all birds for chicken pox or for Newcastle disease at one time, but some of them are much closer to laying than others when this is done. In addition to such complications there are others that may be entirely unsuspected.

A good example of unsuspected environmental modification was encountered by the author and his associates in breeding strains of White Leghorns resistant or susceptible to lymphomatosis. It was the custom each year to start the first hatch in one large brooder house, *F*, to start the second in another similar house, *B*, and thereafter to alternate the remaining eight weekly hatches in this way between the two houses. At 2 weeks of age, all chicks went to the rearing range, thus clearing the brooder houses for the next hatch of chicks. Not until this had gone on for 7 years was it discovered that chicks started in house *F* were annually exposed more severely to lymphomatosis than those started in house *B*. Moreover, that brief difference, though not evident at 2 weeks of age, was reflected in the mortality after the pullets became mature (Hutt *et al.*, 1944). Each year, as a result, pullets of the odd-numbered hatches (first, third, fifth, etc.) experienced higher losses from that disease than did their sisters of the even-numbered hatches. The 7-year averages for two strains shown in Fig. 139 reveal the remarkable influence of this brief difference in the environment. Because at that time there were no double or triple shifts, representatives of all families shared equally in the two kinds of exposure; hence familial differences were quite evident, although less so than they would have been had all the chicks been severely exposed. Once the difference was detected, all chicks were started in house *F;* all thus received the severe exposure, and selection became immediately more effective.

The extent to which such a difference in the environment can affect the appraisals of males being tested for viability of their offspring is illustrated in Table 69 by the records for 3 of 17 males so tested in one year. For each of those 17, one half the chicks were severely exposed (in house *F*); the other half (alternate hatches) went directly to the rearing range and hence were exposed only lightly.

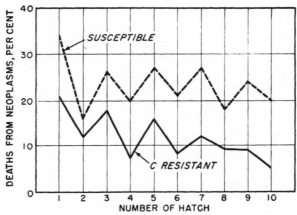

Fɪɢ. 139. Deaths from neoplasms in two strains of Leghorns, one resistant to lymphomatosis and the other susceptible, in birds of 10 weekly hatches between Mar. 1 and May 10. Each point is the unweighted average of 7 years' data. The graphs show the effect of the more severe exposure of the odd-numbered hatches. (*From Hutt et al. in Poultry Sci.*)

Daughters tested under one environment ranked ♂ *A* as best among 17; under the other environment he ranked next to the last. A similar reversal is shown for ♂ *C*. Clearly the breeding value of an individual, when measured by the progeny test, must depend greatly upon the environmental conditions under which that test is conducted.

One important environmental influence that must always be considered is the length of day or the amount of available light. The relation between variations in that factor and differences in age at first egg, in persistency, and in egg production are discussed at length in Chap. 10. It will suffice here to remind the reader that its influence makes it impossible to compare late-hatched chickens and early ones with respect to these three variables unless suitable corrections are first made in the records. This is particularly important when double or triple shifts of cockerels are tested. That direct comparisons between sires in these different

TABLE 69. INFLUENCE OF THE ENVIRONMENT ON THE RANKING OF 3 MALES AMONG 17 TESTED FOR VIABILITY OF THEIR OFFSPRING

Male	Lightly exposed daughters			Severely exposed daughters		
	Housed at 160 days, number	Died by 500 days, per cent	Rank among 17	Housed at 160 days, number	Died by 500 days, per cent	Rank among 17
A	33	12	1	38	58	16
B	73	16	2	82	39	7
C	36	19	6	41	61	17
Average for all 17.....	..	24.7	8.5	..	43.6	8.5

series are impossible is illustrated by the tests in 1 year for 15 cockerels of one strain, there being 5 of these in each shift. The females in the five pens were constant through the entire breeding season. For daughters of these males, three averages considered in December were as follows:

	First shift	Second shift	Third shift
Age at first egg, days.................	178	188	196
Eggs to Dec. 1, number..............	55	40	16
Mortality, 6 weeks to Dec. 1, per cent...	2.3	6.9	5.8

In addition to the expected differences in age at first egg and the inevitable one in egg production, it seems probable that the early-hatched chicks from the first shift had escaped some influences that caused higher mortality in their later hatched half sisters. Corrections could be made with respect to age at first egg, but not very satisfactorily in the other measures of desirability. Such corrections are unnecessary if comparisons are first made only among the five contemporary males of any one series. After that, one can estimate for the whole 15 males which ones excel in greatest degree the averages for their respective groups.

The Use of Proven Sires. Since this section on progeny testing has dealt mostly with the necessity of using proven sires and with methods for finding them, it is appropriate to include a few words about the use of such birds after they have been discovered. Although this is the most important part of the poultry breeder's program, it requires little comment. Obviously, one uses a superior sire to beget the greatest possible number of offspring. Moreover, such sires should be used as long as they will produce fertile eggs or until better ones are discovered by the progeny tests of later generations. Even if the fertility of a good old sire drops to 40 per cent in his fifth breeding season, the 30 offspring that he may then have are more valuable than 200 secured from some mediocre cockerel being tested for the first time. This is particularly so because the wise breeder will have mated the best proven sire to some of the best proven dams in the hope of thus preserving the desirable genes of both sides for transmission to future generations by their sons.

While 3 weeks' hatching eggs may suffice to provide a progeny test for a cockerel, the good proven sire should be used continuously throughout a breeding season as long as is compatible with the limitations of latitude and of good management. He should be mated with many hens. Sometimes such a male seems to maintain better fertility if his mates, to the number of 20 or 30, are divided in two pens, with the sire switched on alternate days from one pen to the other. A still larger number of hens might be used if artificial insemination be practised.

The proportions of the available breeding pens that should be devoted to cockerel testing and to proven sires will have to be decided annually by the breeder. They will vary according to his needs and the number of proven sires available. When these last are few, it may be desirable to devote 80 per cent of the available space to cockerels. Ten pens would thus permit testing 24 cockerels in three shifts and leave two pens for the use of the best proven sires throughout the season. Conversely, while few breeders are likely to be embarrassed by a surplus of superior proven sires, if that happy situation should ever arise it might be feasible to omit cockerel testing for one season.

Selection of Females. The emphasis here placed upon proven sires and the comparatively slight discussion of proving dams should not be interpreted as any indication that the genes from the dam are unimportant. Both sexes contribute equally to the inheritance, except for such sex-linked genes as females may receive from their sires. However, since a single sire may transmit his good or bad genes to the 130 offspring of 16 different dams, whereas any one of those dams is responsible for only 8 or 9 of that number, the old adage that "the sire is more than half the flock" should never be forgotten by the poultry breeder.

For the cockerel tests it is desirable to use as good females as are available in the numbers needed. They may be the next to the best hens left after the best ones have been allocated to the proven sires, or they may be pullets. The important thing is that each pen in the cockerel-testing program should have a random assortment of the available females. This is not hard to arrange when there are 16 birds, or thereabouts, per pen. Exceptions can be made as needed. For example, if one family from which cockerels are tested has all desired good points except body size, three brothers of that family may be used (in successive triple shifts) in the same breeding pen, and it can be made up to include females above average in size. Any such adjustment in January must not be forgotten in the following December when all the cockerels are being compared.

In addition to their main purpose, or perhaps as a part of it, the cockerel-testing pens will bring to light each year many females of superior merit. By utilizing annually the best of these, there should be no difficulty in maintaining at full strength the company of proven dams reserved for the breeding pens of the proven sires.

INBREEDING

Most poultry breeders become concerned about inbreeding as soon as their stock has been developed to the point at which they can view it with some pride of achievement. They would then like to maintain its good points, to improve it still further, perhaps with respect only to some minor character, but at all costs not to lose what they have gained by careful breeding. At that stage their problem is often whether to risk the dangers of inbreeding by continuing to use their own males or the other danger of bringing in undesirable inheritance if new blood be introduced from some other flock.

In the past many breeders of livestock have considered inbreeding as a word to be spoken only in whispers—its effects as abhorrent as the plague. Poultrymen, who have really less to worry about in this respect than have breeders of larger animals, have (in the past) been particularly prone to consider that anyone's temporary hard luck in the matter of fertility, hatchability, egg size, or body size has resulted from the stock's becoming too closely inbred. It now seems probable that this attitude may be abruptly changed and that, for some breeders at least, inbreeding may become an objective just as desirable as high records of egg production have been for years. This is happening merely because poultrymen know that suitable inbred strains of corn will give phenomenal yields when crossed. The same thing is now being demonstrated with poultry and with swine. For this reason, the future will probably see some poultrymen as anxious to prove that they have an inbred strain as they were to deny it in the past. It is to be hoped that the effort to be in the swim will not tempt any inexperienced swimmer to dive in waters beyond his depth.

Rates and Measures. The general effect of inbreeding is to increase the number of homozygous pairs of genes and to decrease the heterozygosity. It thus makes the inbred populations more uniform and differentiates families or lines. The unfortunate consequences that have caused its disrepute result from the inevitable lethal genes and others with undesirable effects. When such genes are made homozygous, death or reduced viability follows.

The closest kind of inbreeding possible in higher animals is the mating of brothers with sisters. With that system one does not attain as much homozygosity in 17 generations as can be brought about by 6 generations of self-fertilization in maize, a point worth remembering by anyone hoping to produce hybrid poultry that is as profitable as hybrid corn. On a theoretical basis, it would take over 20 generations of brother $\times$ sister matings to yield individuals that resemble each other as much as the two members of a pair of identical twins. In practice, even that is not likely to be attained, because of new mutations. Moreover, attempts thus far to get highly inbred strains of fowls by this most rapid method have been so unsuccessful as to suggest that a somewhat less intense degree of inbreeding may be preferable.

One such milder form of inbreeding is the mating of a male with his half sisters. Wright (1931) calculated that, whereas matings of full siblings reduce the residual heterozygosity by about 19 per cent in each generation, matings of a male with his half sisters reduce it only 11 per cent in each generation. Obviously, this is somewhat safer.

Contrary to common opinion, continued breeding within one flock does not result in rapid inbreeding, so long as the breeding stock is chosen at random and several different sires are used each year. When this is done, according to Wright, the heterozygosity is reduced in each generation by approximately $1/8N$, where N is the number of males used, provided that the number of females greatly exceeds the number of males. This formula has a special significance for poultry breeders because it is applicable to exactly the conditions that prevail in most sizable flocks to which new blood is not introduced. If 3 males be used per season, the remaining heterozygosity is reduced only about 4.2 per cent each year; if 10 be used, the figure is about 1.2 per cent. Such a slow approach to homozygosity is not likely to cause trouble in any flock. It is a system that has been successfully used in many.

It is customary to measure the amount of inbreeding in any individual by a formula devised for this purpose by Wright (1923). When X represents the inbred individual and A some ancestor common to X's sire and dam, the coefficient of inbreeding F_x is determined by the formula

$$F_x = \Sigma[(\tfrac{1}{2})^{n+n'+1}(1 + F_A)]$$

in which n is the number of generations from the sire of X back to the common ancestor, n' is the same for the dam of X, and F_A is the coefficient of inbreeding of the common ancestor A. If A be not inbred, that portion of the formula can be ignored, and if A be further back than four generations, its contribution is relatively unimportant. The sign Σ means merely that one must determine separately each different link in the pedigree by which the sire and dam are related and then add them up. The coefficient of inbreeding is a measure of the degree of relationship between the sire and dam, corrected, when necessary, for the inbreeding of a common ancestor A.

By way of illustration, and as a convenience to those who may wish to measure inbreeding, the component parts of the coefficient of inbreeding that are most frequently used are shown in Table 70. It is evident

TABLE 70. CONTRIBUTIONS OF SOME COMMON RELATIONSHIPS TO THE COEFFICIENT OF INBREEDING

Number of generations to the common ancestor		Contribution to the coefficient of inbreeding
Behind one parent	Behind the other parent	
0	1	$(\tfrac{1}{2})^2 = 0.25$
1	1	$(\tfrac{1}{2})^3 = 0.125$
1	2	$(\tfrac{1}{2})^4 = 0.0625$
2	2	$(\tfrac{1}{2})^5 = 0.0312$
2	3	$(\tfrac{1}{2})^6 = 0.0156$
3	3	$(\tfrac{1}{2})^7 = 0.0078$
3	4	$(\tfrac{1}{2})^8 = 0.0039$
4	4	$(\tfrac{1}{2})^9 = 0.0019$

from these that a common ancestor more than four generations back from the sire or dam of the individual under consideration can affect the coefficient of inbreeding very little.

Some pedigrees may show only one of these relationships. With those which have more than one, the contributions of each relationship must be added. To determine the amount of inbreeding in a flock, strain, or family, it is necessary to determine the average for a representative sample. A coefficient of 0.25 is said to show 25 per cent inbreeding.

A single brother $\times$ sister mating produces a chicken (or calf, or anything else) for which the coefficient is 25 per cent. With two and three generations of the same system, it becomes 37.5 and 50 per cent, respectively. For offspring from one mating of a male with his half sisters, the coefficient is 12.5 per cent. It was shown earlier that, according to one of Wright's formulae, the degree of inbreeding in a flock is slight when no new blood is added over several years, so long as several males are used each year and inbreeding is not deliberately sought. For two such strains at Cornell, in which no new blood was introduced during 11 years, the coefficients of inbreeding were found to be only 7 and 8 per cent. In a third strain, to which new blood had been added, inbreeding happened to be 13 per cent.

Line breeding refers to the continued mating back to descendants of some particular ancestor in order to increase the contribution of that animal to the inheritance. It is inbreeding, but of a degree less intense than that resulting from the mating of closer relatives.

Effects of Inbreeding in the Fowl. The effect of inbreeding that is most obvious, perhaps because it is soonest evident, is a marked decline in hatchability of the eggs. In one of the first attempts to produce highly inbred fowls, Cole and Halpin (1916) found that in three generations of brother $\times$ sister matings the hatchability of fertile eggs, which was originally 67 per cent, declined to 49, 41, and 18 per cent. In this experiment, hatchability was not considered in the selection of breeders, but in a later similar trial, in which such selection was practised in the hope of maintaining the stock, hatchability again declined so much that the inbred line could not be maintained (Cole and Halpin, 1922). Similar declines in hatchability, in varying degrees and resulting from different kinds of inbreeding, have been reported by Dunn (1923, 1928), Jull (1929, 1929a, 1933), Dumon (1930), Dunkerly (1930), Dudley (1934), and others.

The uniformity with which hatchability has been reduced in the different stocks studied by these investigators confirms the assumption that many lethal genes are widespread in *Gallus gallus* and assures the young graduating geneticist that there are still fields for him to conquer. For those who cannot forget the fields of waving hybrid corn, some encouragement is seen in the less frequent reports of those investigators who have been able to maintain a fair level of hatchability even in stock that is rather highly inbred. Waters and Lambert (1936, 1936a) developed a high degree of homozygosity in White Leghorns by degrees of inbreeding less intense than that of brother $\times$ sister matings and maintained careful selection for hatchability. As a result, the average hatchability was still well above 60 per cent when the coefficients of inbreeding ranged from 41 to 82 per cent. With other stock, Waters (1945) was able to raise four generations from brother $\times$ sister matings without any great decline in hatchability. Similarly Dumon (1938) developed by rigorous selection some inbred lines in which hatchability was even superior to that in birds not inbred at all.

From all these reports one must conclude that, while the closest inbreeding is likely to cause the extinction of most lines, if enough of them are started and if rigorous selection be practised, some of them will prove capable of adequate reproduction. The prospects for getting highly inbred lines with the least losses would seem to be best with inbreeding less intense than the continued mating of full brothers and sisters. Since this is a slower procedure, those preferring speed to safety will gamble on the more direct approach. They should be prepared to utilize a proportionately greater number of birds and also of bank notes.

Reports of the effects of inbreeding on egg production, fertility, body size, and other economic characters vary considerably. That is not surprising. There is little point in attempting to reconcile the irrefutable evidence of Dunn (1923), Jull (1933), Hays (1934), and others that inbreeding lowers egg production and raises age at first egg with the equally irrefutable evidence of Waters and Lambert (1936) that it does not do so in every case. It is to be expected that inbreeding will differentiate families, although tending to increase uniformity within families. Accordingly there should be, not only differences in the strains inbred by different investigators, but also equally great differences among the inbred families of any one of them.

While the differentiation of inbred families has been noticed by most investigators, the expected increase in uniformity is not always so evident. Dunn (1928a) found that eight inbred families of Leghorns differed in the length and proportions of certain bones of the limb and also in the shape of the cranium. Variability in these skeletons was slightly less than in outbred stock. In a flock brought in 9 years to an average coefficient of inbreeding of 60 per cent, Shoffner (1948) could see no consistent corresponding decline in variability. His inbred, later generations were more uniform than the earlier ones in egg production, age at first egg, and hatchability, but not in body weight or in size of egg.

Prepotent Sires. One of the objects of inbreeding is to get individuals that are homozygous with respect to desirable genes manifested by relatives. In such cases, inbreeding is risked in order to concentrate the blood (genes) of these outstanding relatives. The breeder hopes to get thus some sires that will pass desirable traits to a majority of their offspring.

Such a sire is said by the breeder to be prepotent and by the geneticist to be relatively homozygous. To get one without too great risk, it is sometimes good practice to mate a good proven sire or a promising cockerel (1) with some close relatives, such as sisters, daughters, or dam; (2) with more distant relatives; and (3) with unrelated females. Even if the first of these combinations should prove disastrous, some good genes may be salvaged by the others.

THE UTILIZATION OF HYBRID VIGOR

Another purpose for inbreeding is to develop highly inbred lines suitable for crossing with the hope of getting from such crosses enough hybrid vigor to cause greater productivity or viability (or both) than is already available in stock not inbred. As this type of inbreeding may be tried by quite a few breeders in the future, it is desirable to consider what happens when inbred lines are crossed. They may be utilized in three different ways, each of which is here considered separately.

Crosses of Inbred Lines of One Breed. In evaluating the performance by progeny of crosses between inbred birds, one must not conclude that merely because such progeny excel the inbred parents some special merit of such crosses has been demonstrated. From what is known of similar crosses in other species, it is to be expected that highly inbred birds will usually produce (when crossed) offspring superior to both parents The important question is whether or not the hybrids will excel improved stock that has not been deliberately inbred.

The data of Dunn (1928) and Jull (1930, 1933), showing that hatchability is improved when inbred strains are crossed, provide no evidence that it improved to the point of excelling stock not inbred. In fact, crossings by Jull (1933) yielded hatches 12 to 37 per cent lower than those of the original outbred stock. In four groups of his pullets from such crosses, the mean egg production was 35 to 72 eggs lower than in their outbred ancestors. Maw (1942) found that in some crosses between inbred lines of Iowa Leghorns the hybrids did excel controls not inbred, but since those controls laid only 73 eggs in 20 weeks, the significance of the difference might be questioned. Similarly, the data of Pease (as given by Maw) show that hybrids from two different strains of inbred Leghorns (one bred in Iowa and one at Reaseheath in England) excelled both the parental strains in egg production but barely equalled the record of Leghorns not inbred.

From these results it would seem that any advantage that might be gained merely by crossing two inbred lines of one breed has yet to be demonstrated. It it is to be expected that some of these might yield better results than have been reported to date.

Double Crosses of Four Inbred Lines. The negative results reviewed in the previous paragraphs have little or no bearing on the value of inbred lines for crossing. This is merely because anyone seeking hybrid vigor from the use of inbred strains is better advised to cross such strains from different breeds than to cross them within one breed. Over a period of several years, Knox (1946) found that females from inter-strain crosses of inbred Rhode Island Reds had an average production of 198 eggs, which differed little from that of similar females not inbred. However, when crosses were made between inbred Reds and inbred Leghorns, the mean production was 224 eggs. It is to be expected, from what is known about such crosses in maize, that the maximum benefits from hybrid vigor would result when the progeny from two inbred strains, *A* and *B*, are crossed with the progeny from two other inbred strains, *C* and *D*, to produce what is commonly called a "double-crossed hybrid." Experimental evidence of the value of such procedures in the fowl is still almost negligible. Dumon (1930) provided some evidence that hatchability is increased, and Maw (1942) cites a double cross in which mortality of chicks was apparently greatly reduced but egg production was nothing unusual.

Meanwhile, the production of double-crossed hybrid chickens on a commercial scale has begun and gives every promise of expanding as rapidly as inbred strains can be developed. The performance of such stock as is now available is good enough to create a tremendous demand for it, and this indicates that the double-crossed hybrid fowls have an assured future. Extensive studies are desirable to find out what kinds of inbred strains and what degrees of inbreeding are most suitable for such crosses. Because it is more difficult to get high homozygosity in the fowl than in maize, the poultry industry should not expect too much too soon from the hybrids.

Top-crosses on Outbred Stock. It seems probable that one of the most important benefits from highly inbred lines may be obtained by top-crossing the inbred males on flocks that are not inbred. The significant evidence from 5 years of such crosses presented by Waters (1938) shows an increase in hatchability and a decrease in mortality that are remarkable (Table 71).

Evidently the Leghorns that were not inbred were unusually low in fertility. At any rate, the apparent superiority of the other two groups in that respect is not significant. In hatchability, the top-cross progeny were consistently superior in every year regardless of which of the seven inbred families provided the males for crossing. (This refers to hatcha-

TABLE 71.   EFFECT OF TOP-CROSSING ON SOME ECONOMIC CHARACTERS IN LEGHORNS;
AVERAGES FOR 5 YEARS, PER CENT *

	Fertility	Hatch-ability of fertile eggs	Mortality	
			To 8 weeks	To 24 weeks
1. Leghorns, not inbred..	75.9	80.8	8.1	15.8
2. Leghorns, inbred.....	83.6	72.1	14.2	23.0
3. Top-crosses; ♂♂ of 2 × ♀♀ of 1........	85.7	85.8	5.8	10.3

* Data from Waters (1938).

bility of the eggs laid by the random-bred Leghorns, whence came the top-cross progeny.)   Mortality to 24 weeks was significantly lower for the top-crosses than for the Leghorns not inbred.   To these important findings should be added the confirmatory evidence of Maw (1942) that top-crossing produces birds characterized by low mortality and comparatively high production, but it is not clear that there were any significant differences between his top-crosses and the random-bred controls.   Results to be expected from such top-crosses will doubtless vary according to the genotype and the degree of homozygosity of the inbred strain used. The results of Waters suggest that the possibilities of top-crossing merit considerable investigation.

Crosses of Strains not Inbred.   Apart from the use of strains deliberately inbred for crossing, a certain amount of hybrid vigor is to be expected in some crosses between flocks, strains, or breeds that may be considered entirely free from inbreeding.   In the broader interpretation of that term, some inbreeding is present in any of those three commonly cited divisions of the poultry population.

A flock of White Leghorns in which inbreeding has been avoided will still be homozygous for certain genes affecting color of the plumage, ear lobes, skin, and eggshells and for others affecting the comb or other characteristics.   To the extent that these genes are included, while those which distinguish Wyandottes, Houdans, or other breeds are excluded, the White Leghorns, as a breed and variety, are somewhat inbred.   The same applies to any other breed.   Furthermore, within any color variety of one breed (e.g., White Leghorns), strains may be differentiated by selection for different objectives on the part of different poultry breeders and by natural selection in different environments. To the extent that uniformity is thus increased within the strain, so is the inbreeding.

The scale in Fig. 140 illustrates the fact that there is really a steady gradation in the different degrees of inbreeding and no sharp boundary between any of them. It is as difficult to specify any point on this scale at which inbreeding begins or stops as it is to mark a spot on the ther-

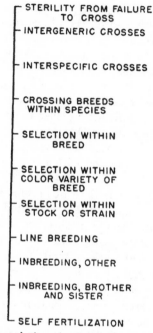

Fig. 140. A scale showing gradations in the degree of inbreeding between the two extremes.

mometer to divide hot from cold. One might expect, therefore, that some measure of hybrid vigor should result from crossing strains, varieties, or breeds. Other things being equal, it should be proportional to the number of pairs of genes by which the crossed groups differ. That difference may be, in some crosses, so slight as to cause no perceptible hybrid vigor, while in others it may be quite pronounced.

Data on the value of various crosses of strains within a breed are scarce, but this lack may be overcome by the numerous interstrain crosses now being made as a result of the recently stimulated interest in the utilization of hybrids of various kinds. Warren (1942) found some hybrid vigor from crosses of two American strains of White Leghorns but less than from crosses of distinct breeds. Older poultrymen will recall some phenomenal records made by a California breeder who crossed American and Australian White Leghorns.

Crosses between Two Breeds. Obviously more hybrid vigor is to be expected from crosses of different breeds than from crosses of strains within a breed merely because breeds differ genetically more than strains do. Reports from different investigators show that, when two breeds are crossed, any stimulation resulting may be conspicuous with respect to some items but entirely lacking so far as others are concerned. There is general agreement that hatchability (of the eggs from which the cross-breds hatch) is raised by 5 to 20 per cent in most crosses (Warren, 1927, 1942; Byerly et al., 1934; Knox and Olsen, 1938; and others). A reminder that neither this result nor any other manifestation of hybrid vigor is to be expected without fail in every cross is found in the data of Dudley (1944) showing no significant increase in hatchability for crosses of White Leghorns and Rhode Island Reds.

Some of the best evidence on this score comes from the few cases in which the same hens have been mated with (1) males of their own breed and (2) males of another (Table 72).

Faster growth of hybrid chicks than of purebreds has been noted by most investigators (Warren, 1927, 1942; Bice and Tower, 1939; Knox et al., 1943). The same thing has been observed in turkeys by Asmundson (1942). As is to be expected, there are exceptions to this rule. Among 11 interbred crosses of various kinds made by Horlacher et al. (1941) to determine the suitability of some of them for the production of broilers, the hybrids at 10 weeks weighed in three cases significantly less than birds of the heavier parent breed. In four crosses, the hybrids did not differ much from the heavier parents, but in four others they were significantly heavier. The cross White Wyandotte ♂ × Rhode Island Red ♀ proved consistently good for 3 years. At 12 weeks of age broilers from this cross weighed 11 per cent more (125 gm.) than the pure Wyandottes, which in turn were 134 gm. heavier than the Rhode Island Reds. Unfortunately, these hybrids apparently sold at a discount because of the Columbian pattern in their plumage.

The hybrid vigor resulting from crosses between suitable breeds is of great value to those raising broilers, but one must not expect the accelerated rate of growth to be maintained much beyond 12 weeks, if any. At maturity, birds of the F_1 generation from parents differing in size are more likely to be intermediate in size than to exceed either parent.

An important point making the hybrid vigor of crossbred broilers of special value is that their more rapid growth does not require proportionately more feed. Evidence that the hybrids utilize their feed more

TABLE 72. HATCHABILITY OF EGGS LAID BY HENS MATED WITH MALES OF THEIR OWN BREED AND WITH OTHERS

Breeds crossed	Hatchability, per cent, for hens mated	
	With males of same breed	With males of other breed as shown
Warren (1942):		
White Leghorn ♀♀ *A* × Barred Plymouth Rock ♂♂.....................	61	80
White Leghorn ♀♀ *B* × Barred Plymouth Rock ♂♂.....................	84	86
White Leghorn ♀♀ *C* × Barred Plymouth Rock ♂♂.....................	71	80
Funk (1934):		
Barred Rock ♀♀ × Rhode Island Red ♂♂................................	57	74
White Leghorn ♀♀ × White Plymouth Rock ♂♂..........................	71	80

efficiently than purebreds during the period of rapid growth has accumulated from Bice and Tower (1939), Hess *et al.* (1941), Horlacher *et al.* (1941), and Mehrhof *et al.* (1945).

The superior viability of hybrid chicks has been pointed out by several investigators (Warren, 1927, 1942; Horlacher *et al.*, 1941; Dudley, 1944). In Horlacher's broilers, the hybrids from 8 different crosses out of 11 suffered less than 10 per cent mortality to 12 weeks of age, but only 2 of 7 lots of purebred birds did as well. Concerning viability of adult hybrids, there is less evidence, and it is not conclusive. Warren (1942) could find no consistent indication that hybrid vigor is reflected in lower mortality of adults, nor were the data of Dudley (1944) conclusive. On the other hand, Knox *et al.* (1943) found the viability of crossbreds after 20 weeks to be better than that of purebreds in 9 out of 10 comparisons. The differences were 6 and 10 per cent in 2 different crosses.

With respect to the egg production of hybrids, it would appear from such data as are available that, if it is increased at all above the level of the two parent breeds, the differences are slight and vary greatly depending on the strains used. Warren (1942) found that in most of such crosses the hybrids laid as well as the higher producing parent breed, or better. Some crosses seemed to yield better results than others. Zorn and Krallinger (1934) crossed Leghorns and Faverolles and found the F_1 generation to be only intermediate between the two parent breeds in laying ability. Knox et al. (1943) made a number of crosses among Rhode Island Reds, White Wyandottes, and Light Sussex but found none of them to surpass the pure Rhode Island Reds in egg production. The hybrids of Dudley (1944) from White Leghorns and Rhode Island Reds had averages of 197 and 204 eggs, against 194 for pure Leghorns and 197 for pure Rhode Island Reds. It would seem that these records of the hybrids might have looked still better if 20 to 25 per cent of the pure Rhode Island Reds had not been culled for late maturity.

From a review of these and other experiments, one is led to conclude that the influence on egg production of hybrid vigor from simple crosses between breeds might perhaps be better revealed by experiments in which the same males and females are mated (in diallel crosses) with birds of their own breed and of others.

Crosses among Three Breeds. Advocates of crossbreeding have usually attempted to soothe the protesting devotees of the pure-breeding cult with the assurance that the F_1 hybrids should never be used for breeding. Nevertheless, swine breeders have found that, when such F_1 animals are crossed with some third breed, the offspring are even better than the parents. If such an accumulation of hybrid vigor can be made in the fowl, it has yet to be demonstrated. Neither Warren (1942) nor Knox et al. (1943) could find any marked superiority of the progeny from three breeds over that from two breeds. It is quite possible that other breeds or strains thus mixed might yield different results.

Interspecific Hybrids. Crosses between related mammalian species are commonly made to produce two very useful domestic animals. One of these is the mule, a familiar example of hybrid vigor. Crossing the zebu (Brahman) cattle with the species more familiar to most readers of this book is sometimes followed by further backcrosses to secure a combination of the productivity of some breeds with the zebu's ability to tolerate heat and to withstand tick-borne diseases. In fowls, no such useful hybrids between species have yet been developed.

The Ceylonese Jungle Fowl, *Gallus lafayettii*, crosses readily with the domestic fowl, according to experiments of the Ceylon Poultry Club reviewed by Lotsy and Kuiper (1924) and others carried out by Ghigi (1934). The hybrids are fertile among themselves and in backcrosses to the domestic fowl.

The Grey Jungle Fowl, *G. sonneratii*, also produces fertile hybrids with the domestic species (Lotsy and Kuiper, 1924; Ghigi, 1922). These are apparently fertile in both sexes and will breed *inter se* and in back-crosses.

The Black Jungle Fowl, *G. varius,* apparently does not cross so readily, but Houwink (1921) reported that he had raised several hybrids between that species and *G. bankiva (gallus),* some fertile and some sterile. Ghigi (1934) found fertility of this hybrid to be limited in the male. His one F_1 female laid eggs, but none were fertile.

Intergeneric Hybrids. To complete the record of all possible types of mating between the limits of self-fertilization and complete incompatibility shown in Fig. 140, a brief reference to crosses of the fowl with birds of other genera is in order.

With Other Pheasants. The most common hybrids of the domestic fowl are those with different geographic races of ring-necked pheasants, which have been designated by ornithologists as *Phasianus colchicus colchicus, P. c. torquatus,* and *P. c. mongolicus.* A number of these were collected by Poll (1912), who reviewed previous records of such hybrids and showed that their invariable sterility results from incomplete gametogenesis in both males and females. In a number of hybrid males studied by Cutler (1918), spermatogenesis went no further than the formation of primary spermatocytes.

Sandnes and Landauer (1938), noting that with a single exception all the recorded hybrids of this type had come from the cross of fowl ♀ × pheasant ♂ and that females were rare among the hybrids, made the reciprocal cross by artificial insemination. Embryonic mortality was 43 per cent, but 58 embryos died late enough to permit identification of sex, and 97 chicks were hatched. Of these, 20 were still alive (and not sexed) some months later. Excluding these last, the sex ratio in this cross and that for recorded hybrids of the reciprocal cross were as follows:

	Hybrid offspring	
	Males	Females
Pheasant ♀ × fowl ♂......	66	69
Fowl ♀ × pheasant ♂.....	23	6

The deficiency of females in the second of these reciprocal crosses conforms to expectation according to Haldane's rule. This holds that, when, in the offspring of an interspecific cross, one sex is missing, rare, or sterile, that sex is the heterogametic one.

The transmission of mutant characters in such crosses was studied by Serebrovsky (1929) in Poll's hybrids. The general rule seemed to be that mutations dominant in the fowl were also dominant in the hybrids, examples being bare neck, extension of black, foot feathering, and dominant white. Sex-linked barring was transmitted by one hen to her hybrid sons but not to her daughter. The manifestation by such hybrids of dominant white from a Leghorn parent has also been reported by Danforth and Sandnes (1939).

With the Guinea Hen. From the classification of the Galliformes given in Chap. 1, it can be seen that the guinea hen, *Numida meleagris*, belongs to an entirely different family from that of the pheasants. Although few offspring from crosses of such widely different species are found in the animal kingdom, a number of hybrids between the domestic fowl and the guinea hen have been recorded. Some of the earlier cases were reviewed by Guyer (1909, 1912), who studied five specimens 3 years old, all males. A hybrid from a guinea ♀ × Rhode Island Red ♂ was described by Viljoen and de Bruin (1935). The four hybrids reported by Funk (1938) from pearl guinea hens and a Rhode Island Red father are particularly interesting because, contrary to the usual predominance of males, some of them were females that even laid eggs. In all these hybrids, the comb is absent or rudimentary.

Attempts to produce this hybrid by artificial insemination have not been successful. Marchlewski (1937) and Owen (1941) found the fertility of eggs to be less than 15 per cent. Most of the embryos died early, but Marchlewski had two chicks that died at 26 days of incubation after starting to hatch.

With the Peafowl. Two adult hybrids from a peacock, *Pavo cristatus*, and a Buff Cochin hen were described by Trouessart (1920), but attempts of Tiniakov (1934) to produce such a hybrid by artificial insemination were only partially successful. From five fertile eggs, one chick hatched (after 25 days of incubation), but it died when 6 days old.

With the Turkey. No authentic records of naturally occurring hybrids between the fowl and *Meleagris gallopavo* are known to the author. Warren and Scott (1935) and Quinn *et al.* (1937) tried to produce them by artificial insemination with little success. In the cross, turkey ♂ × fowl ♀, Quinn *et al.* incubated 656 eggs of which only 5 were fertile, and all of these died early. The reciprocal cross was more successful, the proportion of fertile eggs being about 20 per cent. A similar difference in fertility between the two crosses was noted by Warren and Scott. One of their hybrids lived to 22 days of incubation, and the other investigators had one survive a little longer.

Literature Cited

Asmundson, V. S. 1942. Crossbreeding and heterosis in turkeys. *Poultry Sci.,* 21:311–316.

Bice, C. M., and B. A. Tower. 1939. Crossbreeding poultry for meat production. *Hawaii Agr. Expt. Sta. Bull.* 81.

Bird, S., and J. W. Sinclair. 1938. On the validity of progeny tests of sires obtained on culled populations of daughters. *Sci. Agr.,* 19:1–6.

Byerly, T. C., C. W. Knox, and M. A. Jull. 1934. Some genetic aspects of hatchability. *Poultry Sci.,* 13:230–238.

Cole, L. J., and J. G. Halpin. 1916. Preliminary report of results of an experiment on close inbreeding in fowls. *J. Am. Assoc. Instruct. Invest. Poultry Husbandry,* 3:7–8.

—— and ——. 1922. Results of eight years of inbreeding of Rhode Island Red fowls. *Anat. Record,* 23:97.

Cole, R. K., and F. B. Hutt. 1947. A genetic study of feathered feet in White Leghorns. *Poultry Sci.,* 26:536.

Cutler, D. W. 1918. On the sterility of hybrids between the pheasant and the Gold Campine fowl. *J. Genetics,* 7:155–165.

Danforth, C. H., and G. Sandnes. 1939. Behavior of genes in inter-generic crosses. *J. Heredity,* 30:537–542.

Dryden, J. 1921. Egg-laying characteristics of the hen. *Oregon Agr. Expt. Sta. Bull.* 180.

Dudley, F. J. 1934. Experiments on in-breeding poultry. *Ministry Agr. Fisheries, London, Bull.* 83.

——. 1944. Results of crossing the Rhode Island Red and White Leghorn breeds of poultry. *J. Agr. Sci.,* 34:76–81.

Dumon, A. G. 1930. The effects of inbreeding on hatchability. *Proc. World's Poultry Congr., 4th Congr., London:* 1–5.

——. 1938. La sélection généalogique et consanguine de la poule pondeuse (Leghorn). *Agricultura (Louvain),* 41:11–41.

Dunkerly, J. S. 1930. The effect of inbreeding. *Proc. World's Poultry Congr., 4th Congr., London:* 47–72.

Dunn, L. C. 1923. Experiments on close inbreeding in fowls. *Storrs (Conn.) Agr. Expt. Sta. Bull.* 111.

——. 1928. The effect of inbreeding and crossbreeding on fowls. *Verhandl. V Intern. Kongr. Vererb., Z. ind. Abst. Vererb., Supplementb.* 1:609–617.

——. 1928a. The effect of inbreeding on the bones of the fowl. *Storrs (Conn.) Agr. Expt. Sta. Bull.,* 152:53–112.

Funk, E. M. 1934. Factors influencing hatchability in the domestic fowl. *Missouri Agr. Expt. Sta. Bull.* 341.

——. 1938. The guinhen: hybrid resulting from crossing a guinea hen and a male chicken. *Am. Poultry J.,* 69:16.

Ghigi, A. 1922. L'hybridisme dans la genèse des races domestiques d'oiseaux. *Genetica,* 4:364–374.

——. 1934. Richerche sull'origine delle razze domestiche di polli da forme selvatiche. *Atti congr. mondiale pollicoltura. 5th Congr., Rome,* 2:3–13.

Godfrey, A. B. 1946. Value of the sisters' performance in selecting breeding cockerels. *Poultry Sci.,* 25:148–156.

Guyer, M. F. 1909. Atavism in guinea-chicken hybrids. *J. Exptl. Zoöl.,* 7:723–745.

Guyer, M. F. 1912. Modifications in the testes of hybrids from the guinea and the common fowl. *J. Morphol.*, **23**:45–59.

Hall, G. O. 1934. Breeding a low producing strain of Single Comb White Leghorns. *Poultry Sci.*, **13**:123–127.

―――. 1935. The value of the pedigree in breeding for egg production. *Poultry Sci.*, **14**:323–329.

Hays, F. A. 1934. Effects of inbreeding on fecundity in Rhode Island Reds. *Mass. Agr. Expt. Sta. Bull.* 312.

―――. 1940. Breeding small flocks of domestic fowl for high fecundity. *Poultry Sci.*, **19**:380–384.

Hess, C. W., T. C. Byerly, and M. A. Jull. 1941. The efficiency of feed utilization by Barred Plymouth Rock and crossbred broilers. *Poultry Sci.*, **20**:210–216.

Horlacher, W. R., R. M. Smith, and W. H. Wiley. 1941. Crossbreeding for broiler production. *Arkansas Agr. Expt. Sta. Bull.* 411.

Houwink, R. 1921. Wild fowls, their mutual relationship and their connection with domesticated breeds. *Trans. World's Poultry Congr. 1st Congr., The Hague–Scheveningen,* Appendix: 19–20.

Hutt, F. B., R. K. Cole, M. Ball, J. H. Bruckner, and R. F. Ball. 1944. A relation between environment to two weeks of age and mortality from lymphomatosis in adult fowls. *Poultry Sci.*, **23**:396–404.

Jull, M. A. 1929. Studies in hatchability. II. Hatchability in relation to consanguinity of the breeding stock. *Poultry Sci.*, **8**:219–229.

―――. 1929a. Studies in hatchability. III. Hatchability in relation to coefficients of inbreeding. *Poultry Sci.*, **8**:361–368.

―――. 1930. Studies in hatchability. IV. The effect of intercrossing inbred strains of chickens on fertility and hatchability. *Poultry Sci.*, **9**:149–156.

―――. 1933. Inbreeding and intercrossing in poultry. *J. Heredity*, **24**:93–101.

―――. 1934. Limited value of ancestors' egg production in poultry breeding. *J. Heredity*, **25**:61–64.

Knox, C. W. 1946. The development and use of chicken inbreds. *Poultry Sci.*, **25**:262–272.

――― and M. W. Olsen. 1938. A test of crossbred chickens. Single Comb White Leghorns and Rhode Island Reds. *Poultry Sci.*, **17**:193–199.

―――, J. P. Quinn, and A. B. Godfrey. 1943. Comparison of Rhode Island Reds, White Wyandottes, Light Sussex, and crosses among them to produce F_1 and three-way cross progeny. *Poultry Sci.*, **22**:83–87.

Lamoreux, W. F., F. B. Hutt, and G. O. Hall. 1943. Breeding for low fecundity in the fowl with the aid of the progeny test. *Poultry Sci.*, **22**:161–169.

Lerner, I. M., and L. W. Taylor. 1940. The effect of controlled culling of chickens on the efficiency of progeny tests. *J. Agr. Research*, **60**:755–763.

Lippincott, W. A. 1920. Improving mongrel farm flocks through selected standardbred cockerels. *Kansas Agr. Expt. Sta. Bull.* 223.

Lotsy, J. P., and K. Kuiper. 1924. A preliminary statement of the results of Mr. Houwink's experiments concerning the origin of some domestic animals. V. *Genetica*, **6**:221–277.

Marchlewski, J. 1937. Guinea-fowl (*Numida meleagris* L.) and common fowl (*Gallus domesticus* L.) hybrids obtained by means of artificial insemination. *Bull. intern. acad. polon. sci. Lettres, Classes sci. math. nat. B*, **II**:127–131.

Maw, A. J. G. 1942. Crosses between inbred lines of the domestic fowl. *Poultry Sci.*, **21**:548–553.

Mehrhof, N. R., W. F. Ward, and O. K. Moore. 1945. Comparison of purebred and crossbred cockerels with respect to fattening and dressing qualities. *Florida Agr. Expt. Sta. Bull.* 410.

Mueller, C. D., and F. B. Hutt. 1946. The numbers of daughters necessary for progeny tests in the fowl. *Poultry Sci.* 25:246–255.

Owen, R. D. 1941. Reciprocal crosses between the guinea and the domestic fowl. *J. Exptl. Zoöl.*, 88:187–217.

Pearl, R. 1911. Breeding poultry for egg production. *Maine Agr. Expt. Sta. Bull.*, 192:113–176.

———— and F. M. Surface. 1909. Data on the inheritance of fecundity obtained from the records of egg production of the daughters of "200-egg" hens. *Maine Agr. Expt. Sta. Bull.*, 166:49–84.

Petrov, S. G. 1935. Analysis of the development of high and low lines of Leghorns at Cornell. *Poultry Sci.*, 14:330–339.

Poll, H. 1912. Mischlingsstudien VII. Mischlinge von Phasianus und Gallus. *Sitzber. Akad. Wiss. Berlin*, 38:864–883.

Quinn, J. P., W. H. Burrows, and T. C. Byerly. 1937. Turkey-chicken hybrids. *J. Heredity*, 28:169–173.

Sandnes, G. C., and W. Landauer. 1938. The sex ratio in the cross of *Phasianus torquatus* ♀ × *Gallus domesticus* ♂. *Am. Naturalist*, 72:180–183.

Schmidt, J. 1922. Diallel crossings with the domestic fowl. *J. Genetics*, 12:241–245.

Serebrovsky, A. S. 1929. Observations on interspecific hybrids of the fowl. *J. Genetics*, 21:327–340.

Shoffner, R. N. 1948. The variation within an inbred line of S. C. W. Leghorns. *Poultry Sci.*, 27:235–236.

Tiniakov, G. 1934. Peacock and hen hybrids, and a comparative analysis of the caryotype of their parents (Russian with English summary). *Biol. Zhur.*, 3:41–63.

Trouessart, E. 1920. Hybrides de paon et de poule. *Rev. hist. nat. appliq.* (pt. II) 1:100–102.

Viljoen, N. F., and J. H. de Bruin. 1935. Anatomical studies No. 59. On a false masculine hermaphrodite in an avian hybrid. *Onderstepoort J. Vet. Sci.*, 5:351–356.

Warren, D. C. 1927. Hybrid vigor in poultry. *Poultry Sci.*, 7:1–8.

————. 1942. The crossbreeding of poultry. *Kansas Agr. Expt. Sta. Bull.* 52.

———— and H. M. Scott. 1935. An attempt to produce turkey-chicken hybrids. *J. Heredity*, 26:105–107.

Waters, N. F. 1938. The influence of inbred sires top-crossed on White Leghorn fowl. *Poultry Sci.*, 17:490–497.

————. 1945. The influence of inbreeding on hatchability. *Poultry Sci.*, 24:329–334.

———— and W. V. Lambert. 1936. Inbreeding in the White Leghorn fowl. *Iowa Agr. Expt. Sta. Research Bull.* 202.

———— and ————. 1936a. A ten year inbreeding experiment in the domestic fowl. *Poultry Sci.*, 15:207–218.

Wright, S. 1923. Mendelian analysis of the pure breeds of livestock. I. The measurement of inbreeding and relationship. *J. Heredity*, 14:339–348.

————. 1931. Evolution in Mendelian populations. *Genetics*, 16:97–159.

Zorn, W., and H. F. Krallinger. 1934. Die Legeleistung von Bastarden zwischen weissen, einfachkammigen Leghorns und Lachshühnern. *Arch. Geflügelk.*, 8:233–250.

APPENDIX

SYMBOLS FOR THE GENES OF THE FOWL

The study of many mutations in the past three decades has shed much light on the gene complex of the fowl but has created chaos with respect to the symbols by which the mutations have been designated. This is merely because numerous symbols have been assigned by various workers who were apparently unaware that these same symbols had been previously used for other mutations. The symbols p and s have each been used for no less than four different genes.

In the following list, the usual rules of priority have been followed to the best of the author's knowledge, and the authorities are given by whom the symbols were first used. Complete citations of their papers in which the symbols were introduced will be found in the literature lists of the chapters given in the last column. Symbols assigned for the first time in this book are starred [*]. For some of these, other symbols proposed earlier have had to be discarded merely because they had been used still earlier by someone else. It is hoped that the list will forestall similar troubles in the future.

Symbols have not been assigned to any variations that are not clearly caused by the action of one pair of genes. This excludes some characters apparently unifactorial but showing poor penetrance or much influence of modifying genes. It also excludes quantitative characters, such as egg production, age at first egg, etc.

In devising symbols, the author has been guided by the recommendations of the International Committee on Nomenclature for Genetics of the Mouse [*J. Heredity*, **31** (1940)]. It would be helpful in maintaining uniformity if those proposing new symbols for genes of the fowl would follow suit. The author will be grateful for information about any additions or corrections that should be made in the following list.

Symbol	Character	When introduced and by whom	Description, citation in Chap.
a	Albinism, autosomal	1933. Warren, *J. Heredity*, **24**	7
ab	Barring, autosomal	*	7
al	Albinism, sex-linked	1941. Mueller and Hutt, *J. Heredity*, **32**	7
Ap	Apterylosis	*	5
B	Barring, sex linked	1908. Spillman, *Am. Naturalist*, **42**	7
bd	Breda comb	*	4
Bl	Blue	1933. Hertwig, *Verhandl. deut. zool. Ges.*	7
Br	Brown eye	1933. MacArthur, *Genetics*, **18**	14
By	Brachydactyly	*	3
c	Recessive white	1914. Hadley, *Rhode Island Expt. Sta. Bull.* 161	7
ch	Chondrodystrophy	1942. Lamoreux, *J. Heredity*, **33**	3
Cl	Cornish lethal	*	3
cn	Crooked-neck dwarf	*	8
Cp	Creeper	1933. Hutt, *Genetics*, **18**	3 and 14 †
Cr	Crest	1927. Dunn and Jull, *J. Genetics*, **19**	5
D	Duplex comb	1923. Punnett, "Heredity in Poultry"	4
dp	Diplopodia	*	3
dw	Dwarf	*	9
e	Columbian restriction	1918. Lippincott, *Am. Naturalist*, **52**	7
F	Frizzling	1930. Hutt, *J. Genetics*, **22**	5
Fl	Flightless	1940. Hutt and Lamoreux, *J. Heredity*, **31**	5 and 14 †
fr	Fray	1938. Warren, *J. Heredity*, **29**	5
g	Yellow head	1935. Deakin and Robertson, *Am. Naturalist*, **69**	6
h	Silkiness	1927. Dunn and Jull, *J. Genetics*, **19**	5
Hf	Hen feathering	*	5
I	Dominant white	1913. Hadley, *Rhode Island Expt. Sta. Bull.* 155	7
id	Dermal melanin	1936. Hutt, *Neue Forschung. Tierzucht. u Abstammungsl.*	6
ig	Cream	1932. Taylor, *Proc. Intern. Genetic Congr., 6th Congr.*	7
K	Slow feathering	1929. Hertwig and Rittershaus, *Z. ind. Abst. Vererb.*, **51**	5

* New symbols assigned for the first time in this book.
† When two chapters are cited, the first contains the description of the mutation, and the second cites the report in which the symbol was first used.

SYMBOLS (*Continued*)

Symbol	Character	When introduced and by whom	Description, citation in Chap.
ko	Head streak	1930. Rittershaus, *Züchter.*, **2**	7
l	Recessive white lethal	1923. Dunn, *Am. Naturalist*, **57**	8
la	Lacing	*	7
Li	Light down	1929. Hertwig and Rittershaus, *Z. ind. Abst. Vererb.*, **51**	7
lo	Congenital loco	*	8
M	Multiple spurs	1941. Hutt, *J. Heredity*, **32**	4
ma	Marbling	1933. Hertwig, *Verhandl. deut. zool. Ges.*	7
Mb	Muffs and beard	*	5
md	Missing mandible	*	3
mf	Modified frizzling	1936. Hutt, *J. Genetics*, **32**	5
mi	Microphthalmia	*	8
mo	Mottling	*	7
mx	Amaxilla	*	3
n	Naked	1938. Hutt and Sturkie, *J. Heredity*, **29**	5
Na	Naked neck	1933. Hertwig, *Verhandl. deut. zool. Ges.*	5
O	Blue egg	1940. Hutt and Lamoreux, *J. Heredity*, **31**	11 and 14 †
P	Pea comb	1906. Bateson and Punnett, *Repts. Evol. Comm. Roy. Soc.*, **III**	4
pi	Pied	*	7
pk	Pink eye	*	7
Po	Polydactyly	1927. Dunn and Jull, *J. Genetics*, **19**	3
Po^d	Duplicate	*	3
po	Normal	*	3
R	Rose comb	1906. Bateson and Punnett, *Repts. Evol. Comm. Roy. Soc.*, **III**	4
Rp	Rumplessness	1936. Dunn and Landauer, *J. Genetics*, **33**	3
rp-2	Recessive rumplessness	1945. Landauer, *Genetics*, **30**	3
rs	Red-splashed white	*	7
S	Silver	1917. Goodale, *Science*, **46**	7 and 14 †
Sd	Sex-linked dilution	*	7
sl	Spurless	*	4
sm	Short mandible	*	3
Sp	Spangling	1932. Taylor, *J. Genetics*, **26**	7
st	Unstriped	*	7

SYMBOLS (*Continued*)

Symbol	Character	When introduced and by whom		Description, citation in Chap.
sy	Stickiness	*		8
su	Short upper beak	*		3
{ *T*	Normal (rapid)	1946.	Jones and Hutt, *J. Heredity*, **37**	5
{ *t^s*	Retarded	1946.	Jones and Hutt, *J. Heredity*, **37**	5
{ *t*	Tardy	1946.	Jones and Hutt, *J. Heredity*, **37**	5
ta	Talpid	1942.	Cole, *J. Heredity*, **33**	8
td	Thyrogenous dwarfism	*		9
U	Uropygial	1936.	Hutt, *Neue Forschung. Tierzucht. u. Abstammungsl.*	4
v	Vulture hocks	*		5
W	White skin	1925.	Dunn. *Anat. Record*, **31**	6
wg	Wingless	*		3

* New symbols assigned for the first time in this book.

† When two chapters are cited, the first contains the description of the mutation, and the second cites the report in which the symbol was first used.

GLOSSARY

The Glossary contains definitions of genetical terms used in the book and of a few others that the reader may encounter elsewhere.

Acrosome. The apical body at the anterior tip of the spermatozoon.

Allele. One of two alternative genes that have the same locus in homologous chromosomes or of the two contrasting characters induced by such genes; in multiple alleles, one of several. For example, the gene causing rose comb is the dominant allele of that for single comb.

Allelomorph. Synonymous with allele, and the original term introduced by Bateson in 1902; shortened to allele by some geneticists about 30 years later.

Anaphase. That stage of mitosis following the metaphase and in which the daughter chromosomes move toward the poles of the spindle.

Aneuploid. An adjective, frequently used as a noun, referring to an organism (or to part of one) that has more or less than (1) the complement of chromosomes normal for the species and sex or (2) some multiple of that complement. For examples, see trisomic and monosomic.

Atavism (atavistic). The reappearance of some ancestral character after a lapse of several generations in which it has not been evident.

Autosomal. Pertaining to an autosome or to characters induced by genes in one or more autosomes, in contradistinction to sex-linked characters.

Autosome. Any chromosome other than a sex chromosome.

Backcross. The mating of an F_1 hybrid or of an equivalent heterozygote to one of the two parental varieties, types, or genotypes that produced the hybrid.

Bimodal. An adjective describing a distribution of frequencies that shows two classes as having greater numbers than others.

Binucleate. Having two nuclei.

Bivalent. Applied to homologous chromosomes when united or associated in pairs, especially during synapsis.

Blastoderm. A membrane formed in the blastodisc of the egg by repeated segmentation following fertilization.

Blastodisc. The germinal disc, or circular spot, at which the nucleus of the egg is located and in which segmentation begins after fertilization. By the time of laying (of hens' eggs) the blastodisc of a fertile egg is covered by the blastoderm, while that of an infertile one is disintegrating.

Carrier. An organism heterozygous with respect to some recessive character. While a bird of the genotype Rr is heterozygous for both rose and single combs, it would ordinarily be referred to as a carrier of the gene for single comb, which it does not show, but not as a carrier of the gene for rose comb, because that part of its genotype is revealed by the bird's rose comb.

Character. A convenient term, a shortened form of characteristic, used to designate any structure, trait, or function of an organism, whether it be hereditary or acquired. Genetic characters are said to be the end products of their causative genes, the net result of the interaction among genes and of genes with environmental influences.

Chromatid. One of the two genetically identical strands formed by a chromosome in anticipation of cell division.

Chromatin. The part of a cell's nucleus which forms the most conspicuous part of the nuclear network and of the chromosomes and is deeply stained by basic, or "nuclear," dyes.

Chromomeres. Chromatinic granules arranged in linear order and thus comprising the chromosome.

Chromosome map. A diagram showing what genes are known to belong in specific linkage groups and their positions in relation to one another within those groups.

Chromosomes. Literally, colored bodies. When stained with basic dyes, they are visible under the microscope as rods, loops, or dots in dividing cells that have been properly "fixed." They carry the genes, arranged in linear order.

Cleavage. Division, or segmentation, of the fertilized egg; usually restricted to the earlier divisions when the numbers of cells resulting from the segmentations can still be counted.

Complementary genes. Genes which in combination cause an effect different from that of either gene by itself; for example, the genes *R* and *P,* which separately induce rose and pea combs, respectively, but in combination cause a walnut comb.

Congenital. Present at birth, but not necessarily of genetic orgin.

Coupling phase. That type of association of two linked pairs of genes in which the chromosome carrying them has either both dominant alleles or both recessive alleles; for example, *F I* and *f i. See also* repulsion phase. .

Crossing over. The interchange (during meiosis) of segments of homologous chromosomes and thus of chains of genes in those segments; the term is also applied to the new combinations of characters that result from the interchange.

Crossover. When used as a noun in the geneticist's jargon, this refers to the organism which, because of crossing over during the formation of one (or both) of the gametes from which it arose, carries the alleles of two or more linked genes in a combination different from that in which they were transmitted to one (or both) of its parents. To illustrate, when a dihybrid that received *F* and *I* from one parent and *f* and *i* from the other produces by an *ff ii* mate some chicks that are *F* and *i* or *f* and *I,* these are crossovers, *i.e.,* new combinations in contrast with the parental combinations.

Crossover distance. The distance in a chromosome separating two linked genes, as measured by the amount of crossing over between them, and expressed as the proportion of gametes tested that give rise to crossovers.

Crossover unit. A measure of the distance between linked genes, and synonymous with the proportion of crossovers between them. To illustrate, if the amount of crossing over between *F* and *I* is 17 per cent, these two genes are said to be 17 crossover units apart.

Cryptomere. A genetic character that is present in an organism but rendered invisible by some other character; for example, color patterns in recessive white birds. Presence of the cryptomere can be demonstrated by breeding tests.

Cytology. The study of cells, their structure, properties, and functions.

Cytoplasm. The protoplasm of the cell exclusive of the nucleus.

Diakinesis. A stage of meiosis in which the homologous chromosomes come together in pairs prior to their separation.

Diallel crosses. The mating of two or more animals at different times to the same two or more animals of the opposite sex in order thus to evaluate their genotypes with respect to some quantitative character; one kind of progeny test.

Dihybrid. Heterozygous with respect to two pairs of genes.

Diploid. Having two sets of chromosomes, as in somatic cells of animals, in contradistinction to the haploid state of the germ cells, which have only a single set of chromosomes.

Dominant. Referring to genes or characters that are manifested by organisms heterozygous for them, in contradistinction to recessive genes or characters, which are revealed only in homozygotes.

Duplicate genes. Two pairs of genes with equal effects on one character.

Dysgenic. Conducive to the accumulation of undesirable genes in the germ plasm of a species or population and hence to the weakening of the racial fitness of future generations; the opposite of eugenic.

Egg. A female reproductive cell. Strictly defined, a hen's oöcyte becomes an egg when it extrudes the second polar body. This occurs soon after the egg enters the oviduct, or just before, and hence about 24 to 30 hours before laying.

Epistasis. The masking of the action of one gene (or pair of genes) by another that is not allelomorphic to the first. For example, sex-linked barring is dominant to non-barring, but the barring carried by White Leghorns does not show because the dominant white of that breed prevents the formation of color. Dominant white is thus epistatic to color and to barring.

Epistatic. *See* epistasis.

Equatorial plate. The plate formed by the chromosomes as they lie at the equator of the spindle in the metaphase stage of mitosis.

Estrogen. A feminizing substance that may be produced by the ovary, by other organs, or synthetically, but having in all cases the physiological properties of the normal ovarian hormone.

Eugenic. Conducive to the improvement of "the racial qualities of future generations, either physically or mentally" (Galton).

F_1 generation. The first filial generation; the first generation from some specific mating.

F_2 generation. The second filial generation from some specific mating. It is produced by mating the F_1 generation *inter se* or by its self-fertilization in species in which that is possible.

Factor. Same as gene.

Fecundity. Although in most biological writing this refers to the capacity for reproduction and is often used synonymously with fertility, it has a special connotation when applied to domestic birds. In this narrower sense it refers to the capacity for laying eggs, whether these be fertile or infertile, and whether used for reproduction or not.

Fertilization. Fusion of the male and female pronuclei, following penetration of the egg by the male gamete, thus reestablishing the diploid number of chromosomes and initiating development of the embryo.

Gamete. A reproductive cell, whether an egg or a sperm.

Gametogenesis. The formation of gametes.

Gene. A unit of inheritance, carried in a chromosome and transmitted in the germ cells, which, by interacting with other genes, with the cytoplasm, and with the environment, influences the development of a character and sometimes controls it completely.

Genetics. The science that deals with heredity and variation, seeking to elucidate the principles underlying the former and the causes for the latter.

Genotype. The genetic constitution of an organism, including genes without visible effect as well as those revealed by the phenotype. It may refer to all the genes or to a single pair.

Germ cell. A reproductive cell, or one capable of giving rise to gametes, in contradistinction to somatic, or body, cells, which cannot do so.

Gonad. A reproductive gland; an ovary, testis, or ovotestis.

Gonadotropic. An adjective usually applied to a hormone or hormonal substance that is capable of activating or stimulating the gonad.

Gynandromorph. An animal in which part of the body is genetically female and another part genetically male.

Haploid. Single; referring to the reduced number of chromosomes as found in the gametes. *See also* diploid.

Hemizygous. Referring to the single state of sex-linked genes in individuals of the heterogametic sex. To illustrate, a Barred Rock male may be homozygous or heterozygous for barring, but the female can be neither, as she has only one sex chromosome. She must be hemizygous, if barred.

Hermaphrodite. An organism that produces both eggs and sperms; sometimes erroneously applied to fowls that are hormonal intersexes.

Heterogametic. Producing gametes of two kinds with respect to sex chromosomes, the difference being such that one kind induces (upon fertilization) a male zygote and the other a female.

Heteroploid. Referring to a complement of chromosomes that is not a multiple of the haploid number.

Heterosis. Synonymous with hybrid vigor.

Heterozygote. The noun applied to an organism that is heterozygous for some specific pair or pairs of genes and hence produces gametes of two kinds with respect to the alleles for which it is heterozygous.

Heterozygous. Carrying both the dominant and the recessive genes of a pair of alleles or two different genes of a series of multiple alleles.

Homogametic. Producing gametes that are all of equal potency with respect to the sex of the zygote to which they give rise upon fertilization.

Homologous chromosomes. Those occurring in somatic cells in pairs, both being alike in size and form and differing from each other with respect to genes less than they differ from other pairs. One member of a pair is normally inherited from each parent.

Homozygote. The noun applied to an organism homozygous for some specific pair or pairs of genes and hence producing gametes all alike with respect to the genes concerned.

Homozygous. Carrying two of either the dominant or recessive genes of a pair of alleles, or carrying two identical genes of a series of multiple alleles.

Hormone. The biologically active secretion of a ductless gland.

Hybrid. In general biological usage, this refers to the offspring of a cross between different species or varieties. Geneticists apply it also to organisms heterozygous with respect to one or more pairs of genes. Thus, when Rose-comb and Single-comb Brown Leghorns are crossed, the rose comb is said to be dominant in the *hybrid,* even though these hybrids are phenotypically indistinguishable from pure Rose-comb Brown Leghorns.

Hybrid vigor. The extra vigor, exceeding that of their parent stocks, frequently shown by the hybrids from the crossing of such genetically dissimilar parents as different species, breeds, strains, or inbred lines. It may be expressed as more rapid growth, larger size, greater viability, or otherwise.

Hypostatic. The adjective applied to a character that is masked by some recessive character not an allele of the first. To illustrate, sex-linked barring is hypostatic to recessive white, so that White Plymouth Rocks cannot show the barring that most of them carry. Recessive white is thus epistatic to barring.

Inbreeding. The mating of relatives.

Inbreeding, coefficient of. A measure of the extent to which inbreeding has reduced heterozygosity in comparison with that prevailing in similar animals not inbred.

Inhibitor. A gene or character suppressing some process or function that would proceed if the inhibitor were not present. For example, the gene Id inhibits the deposition of melanin in the dermis and hence induces white or yellow color in shanks that would otherwise be blue, slate, or willow.

Inter se. Among themselves.

Intersex. An organism showing characteristics intermediate between those of normal males and females of its species.

Lethal gene. A gene that at some time between fertilization of the egg and the normal life span of the species causes the premature death of the organism homozygous or hemizygous for it; in a narrower sense, often restricted to genes causing death before birth, at birth, or soon after it.

Line breeding. A form of inbreeding that concentrates the blood (genes) of some specific ancestor, *i.e.,* the mating of later generations back to that ancestor or to its descendants.

Linkage. The association of two or more characters in inheritance because their causative genes are located in the same chromosome.

Linkage group. A group of genetic characters each of which has been shown by suitable tests to be linked with other members of the same group. The number of linkage groups in a species cannot exceed the number of pairs of chromosomes that is normal for that species.

Locus. The position of a gene in a chromosome or in a linkage group, usually stated in terms of its relation to other genes in the same chromosome.

Loose linkage. A term used somewhat loosely in reference to genes that are linked but so far apart on the chromosome that crossing over between them may be of the order of 30 per cent or more.

Mass selection. Selection of breeding stock based on the appearance or performance of individuals, *i.e.,* phenotypic selection.

Matroclinous. Resembling the mother.

Maturation divisions. Same as meiosis.

Meiosis. That process (in the formation of gametes) consisting of two cell divisions by which the number of chromosomes is reduced in the gametes to half the number found in somatic cells.

Metaphase. The stage of cell division at which the chromosomes are arranged in the equatorial plate near the centre of the cell.

Micron (μ). The one-thousandth part of a millimetre; a measure commonly used in the microscopical study of cells and tissues.

Mitosis. The normal type of cell division in somatic cells, during which the chromosomes become condensed, duplicated (by a process usually said to be division), aligned at the centre of the cell, and thence carried to the two daughter cells in such a way that both these receive identical chromosomes.

Modifier, or modifying gene. A gene, usually with lesser effects, that influences the expression of some other gene.

Monohybrid. Heterozygous with respect to a single pair of genes.

Monosomic. Having one chromosome less than the normal diploid number for the species and sex concerned.

Morphological character. A genetic variation in form or structure, in contradistinction to physiological characters, which are variations in function. The distinction is often arbitrary.

Morphology. The study of form and structure.

Mosaic. An organism in which some part of the body has one genotype and the remaining part has another.

Multifactorial. Referring to a character that is dependent for its expression upon the combined action of an undetermined number of genes.

Multiple alleles. A series of three or more genes any one of which may occupy a single locus on a chromosome. All of them influence the same character, but in differing degrees.

Multiple factors. An undetermined number of genes that together influence the expression of some one genetic character.

Mutation. A sudden change in a gene or in the chromosomes, resulting in a new variation that is hereditary. It may refer either to the invisible change in the cells or to the resultant visible change in the chicken.

New combinations. Applied in tests for linkage to the combinations of genes or characters that differ from the parental combinations of the genes concerned. If the genes are linked, the new combinations are also crossovers, but otherwise they result merely from independent assortment.

Non-disjunction. The failure of homologous chromosomes to separate during meiosis, so that one daughter cell gets both, the other one neither.

Normal overlaps. In a population showing continuous intergradation between some mutant character and the normal type, those members which are indistinguishable from normal ones though carrying the genotype which in most individuals causes some expression of the character.

Nucleus. A small body within a cell that stains deeply with basic dyes, contains the chromosomes, and reproduces itself in cell division.

Oöcyte. An egg cell prior to completion of the process of maturation, *i.e.*, prior to extrusion of the second polar body.

Oögenesis. Formation of the egg, referring particularly to the process of meiosis, or maturation, by which the primary oöcyte becomes an egg with the haploid number of chromosomes.

Oögonia. Cells in the ovary which are descended from the primordial germ cells and of which some eventually become oöcytes.

Outcross. The mating of stock that is somewhat inbred or homogeneous to unrelated individuals.

Ovariotomy. Removal of the ovary; synonymous wtih ovariectomy.

Ovotestis. A single gonad of which part resembles an ovary in its histological structure and part resembles a testis.

Ovulation. Escape of the egg from the ovarian follicle; not the laying of the egg, which is termed "oviposition."

Ovum. An egg. Strictly speaking, it refers to an egg at the stage when it is ready for fertilization.

Parental combinations. Applied in tests for linkage to the particular combinations of genes or characters that were present in the two parents that produced the dihybrid (or polyhybrid) individual used for the test; sometimes called "non-crossover" combinations.

Patroclinous. Resembling the father.

Penetrance. The extent to which a character is expressed in a group of individuals homozygous for it; measured as the proportion (per cent) of such individuals that show the character.

Phenotype. The genetic nature of an organism in so far as it is revealed by visible characters or measurable performance, in contradistinction to the genotype, which may not be evident without a breeding test.

Physiological character. A hereditary character affecting function rather than form or structure. *See also* morphological character. To illustrate, frizzling of the feathers might be considered a morphological character, but the rapid growth of feathers induced by the gene *k* is a physiological character.

Polar body. One of two minute cells containing a haploid set of chromosomes that are extruded by the ovum before fusion of the male and female pronuclei.

Polychromatism. Occurring in several different colors.

Polyploid. An organism having three or more complete sets of homologous chromosomes, *i.e.*, at least one set in excess of the normal diploid number.

Polyspermy. Penetration of the egg by more than one sperm, a condition that is normal in the eggs of birds.

Poularde. An ovariotomized female fowl, or one lacking female hormones because the ovary is undeveloped.

Progeny test. Evaluation of the genotype of an animal by the kinds of offspring that it produces.

Pronucleus. The nucleus of an egg or sperm during fertilization.

Prophase. The stage in cell division from the first appearance of the chromosomes up to the metaphase.

Protoplasm. The active or living substance of the cell, including the nucleus and the cytoplasm.

Proven sire. One with enough progeny that have been measured (in appearance or in performance) to reveal the kind of inheritance transmitted to them, whether good or bad, and hence to give some idea of the genotype of the sire.

Pseudogynandromorph. An animal appearing to be male in one part and female in another, but really of one sex throughout.

Quantitative character. An inherited character the expression of which is influenced by multiple factors in such a way that there is continuous intergradation between the extremes of its expression; a multifactorial character; for examples, fecundity, body size.

Recessive. An adjective, frequently used as a noun, referring to a gene or character that is expressed only by homozygotes; that member of a pair of alleles which does not show in heterozygotes.

Reciprocal crosses. Two crosses between two species, breeds, strains, or genotypes, A and B, such that one mating is $\male\ A \times \female\ B$ and the other is $\male\ B \times \female\ A$.

Recombinations. In tests for linkage, the progeny that show a combination of characters different from either of the parental combinations; crossovers; also new combinations that are not crossovers.

Repulsion phase. That type of association of two linked pairs of genes in which the chromosome carrying them has the dominant allele of one pair and the recessive allele of the other; for example, $F\ i$ and $f\ I$. *See also* coupling phase.

Reversion. The appearance of an individual that differs in some respect from both its parents but resembles a grandparent or some ancestor more remote; frequently used with reference to domestic animals that resemble the wild-type ancestor from which the domestic forms have arisen.

Secondary sexual character. A character induced by hormones of the ovary or testis, but not including variations in the reproductive tract, which are sometimes designated as primary sexual characters.

Segregation. The separation, during meiosis, of allelomorphic genes and the random recombination at fertilization of the two kinds of gametes thus produced, with the result that different types appear in the progeny in typical Mendelian ratios.

Semi-lethal. In genetic parlance this term implies that a gene or character is lethal to part of the population having the genotype for its expression, and *not* that it leaves any individuals half dead.

Sex chromosomes. Chromosomes that exert a preponderant influence upon the determination of sex. In animals the homogametic sex has two homologous sex chromosomes, and the heterogametic sex has either one of these alone or one with a dissimilar mate.

Sex dichromatism. Different colors in the two sexes.

Sex dimorphism. A difference between the sexes in size, structure, color, or some other attribute.

Sex limited. Manifested only in one sex, *e.g.*, egg production.

Sex linked. An adjective applied to a gene carried in the kind of sex chromosome that is paired in the homogametic sex or to the character induced by such a gene.

Sex-linked cross. A cross between individuals carrying different alleles of a pair of sex-linked genes in such a way that the character shown by one sex appears among the offspring in the opposite sex only. This occurs when the heterogametic sex carries the dominant allele, as in the cross in the fowl, barred ♀ × non-barred ♂.

Siblings. Brothers and sisters.

Sib-tested. This adjective is applied to an individual for which the genotype with respect to some quantitative character has been estimated from the phenotypes of its brothers or sisters, or both.

Simple. In addition to its usual meaning, this word has a special connotation in the geneticist's vocabulary, being applied to characters dependent for their expression upon the action of a single pair of genes.

Somatic. Referring to all cells and tissues other than germ cells.

Sperm. A shortened form of the word "spermatozoon" or of its plural form.

Spermatid. One of the four cells derived from a primary spermatocyte by the meiotic divisions and which, with some modification in shape but with no further cell divisions, becomes a spermatozoon.

Spermatocyte. A male reproductive cell prior to completion of the maturation divisions. Primary spermatocytes are derived from spermatogonia, and the first division of a primary spermatocyte produces two secondary ones.

Spermatogenesis. The formation of spermatozoa.

Spermatogonia. Male germ cells at stages intermediate between the primordial germ cell and the primary spermatocyte.

Spermatozoon (pl. -zoa). A mature male germ cell.

Spindle. A group of structures which in fixed preparations of dividing cells resemble threads arranged in the form of a spindle.

Sport. A mutation, referring particularly to the visible character and not to the change in the chromosomes.

Symbol. One or two letters, sometimes more, or sometimes a combination of letters and numbers, used to designate a gene or character so that its name need not be written out in full.

Synapsis. The union in pairs of homologous chromosomes (one of maternal and one of paternal origin) to form bivalent chromosomes during one stage of meiosis.

Telophase. The last stage of mitosis, when movement of the chromosomes has ceased.

Tetrad. The quadruple group of chromatids formed during meiosis by the association of two homologous chromosomes each of which consists of two chromatids.

Transgressive inheritance. The appearance in an F_2 generation (or later) of individuals showing a more extreme development of some character than that seen in the original parents that were crossed.

Trisomic. Having one chromosome more than the normal diploid number for the species and sex concerned.

Unifactorial. An adjective applied to a character that is dependent for its expression upon the action of a single pair of genes. Such a character may be dominant, in which case it is expressed in the heterozygote, or recessive, in which case it is revealed only by recessive homozygotes.

Unit character. Same as unifactorial character.

W chromosome. For species having heterogametic females (as in birds and the Lepidoptera) this term is sometimes used to designate the unpaired sex chromosome which occurs only in females. It is the counterpart of the Y chromosome. It is doubtful whether the use of Z and W introduces clarity or confusion. It would probably be simpler to use only X and Y, as one must know in either case whether the species concerned has heterogametic males or females.

Wild type. The normal phenotype of a species as it occurs in nature or (in the case of some domesticated species) as it is presumed to have been prior to domestication. It is a convenient norm by comparison with which mutations may be designated as dominant or recessive to the wild type.

X chromosome. A designation commonly used for the sex chromosome which, in species having heterogametic males (as in mammals), occurs singly in the male but is paired in the female. It can also be applied to the corresponding chromosome in species having the female heterogametic. *See also* Z chromosome.

Xenia. The immediate effect of male gametes (after mating) upon some maternally determined character. It occurs in some plants but has not been demonstrated in animals.

Y chromosome. The sex chromosome that occurs singly in heterogametic males or females and does not occur in the opposite sex of the same species. *See also* W chromosome.

Z chromosome. A designation sometimes used, in referring to species having heterogametic females, for the sex chromosome which occurs singly in such females but is paired in males of the same species. It is thus commonly used in writing of birds, moths, and butterflies by those who prefer to restrict the homologous term, X chromosome, to the type of sex determination in which the male is heterogametic. *See also* W chromosome.

Zygote. The cell formed by union of male and female gametes; the fertilized egg.

AUTHOR INDEX

To avoid unnecessary duplication, this index refers only to citations in the text, and not to the lists of Literature Cited. The title and citation of any paper can be found by referring from this index to the page given and thence to the list of Literature Cited at the end of the chapter. Junior authors are not listed separately.

SUBJECT INDEX

Definitions of genetical terms will be found in the Glossary; symbols for genes are listed in the Appendix.

577

www.ingramcontent.com/pod-product-compliance
Lightning Source LLC
Jackson TN
JSHW021137200325
80917JS00001B/1